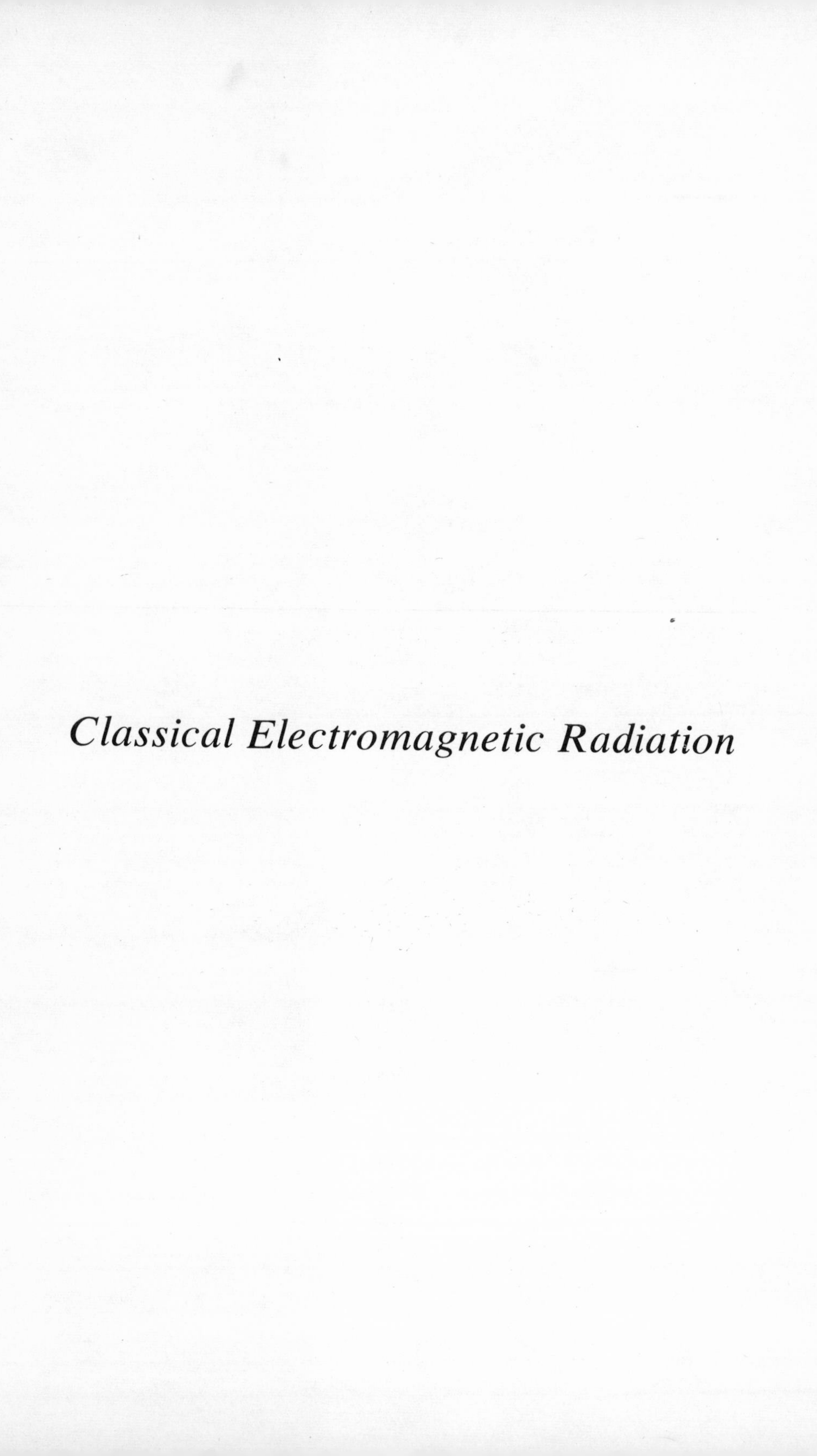

Classical Electromagnetic Radiation

CLASSICAL ELECTROMAGNETIC RADIATION

by Jerry B. Marion

DEPARTMENT OF PHYSICS AND ASTRONOMY
UNIVERSITY OF MARYLAND
COLLEGE PARK, MARYLAND

ACADEMIC PRESS NEW YORK AND LONDON

ACADEMIC PRESS INC.
111 Fifth Avenue, New York, New York 10003

United Kingdom Edition published by
ACADEMIC PRESS INC. (LONDON) LTD.
Berkeley Square House, London W. 1

LIBRARY OF CONGRESS CATALOG CARD NUMBER: 65-18431

First Printing, 1965
Second Printing, 1967

PRINTED IN THE UNITED STATES OF AMERICA.

Preface

This book presents an account of classical electrodynamics with emphasis on radiation problems and the wave aspects of the electromagnetic field. Designed as a text for a one-semester, three- or four-hour course for physics students at the advanced undergraduate level, the book may also be used in the electrodynamics portion of courses in mathematical physics or in theoretical physics.

The objective of the book is to provide a modern and reasonably sophisticated mathematical treatment of classical electrodynamics at the undergraduate level. Since the wave aspects of the electromagnetic field are the topics which are most important in "modern physics," Maxwell's equations are introduced after a minimum of preliminary material, and the remainder of the book develops the various implications of these equations.

It is assumed that the reader has a recent acquaintanceship with the basic principles of electromagnetism, so only a brief survey of the fundamental material is given in Chapter 1. Chapters 2 and 3 include a detailed discussion of Laplace's equation and a treatment of multipole effects, since such material is of considerable importance in the development of radiation theory, but is rarely included in basic courses. The main concern of this book, however, is not electrostatics, so Laplace's equation is treated only as a general boundary-value problem, and the solutions are developed accordingly. Thus, no mention is made of the method of images, not is the connection made between harmonic functions and the Cauchy-Riemann equations of complex analysis.

The electromagnetic field equations are developed in the time-dependent form in Chapter 4, concluding the coverage of introductory material. The subsequent chapters treat the subjects of wave propagation in space and in material media (Chapter 5), reflection and refraction (Chapter 6), the Liénard-Wiechert potentials (Chapter 7), and radiating systems (Chapter 8). In Chapter 9 the discussion turns to the interaction of electromagnetic radiation with microscopic matter, and a brief development of classical electron theory is given. The next two chapters lead up to the discussion of diffraction theory (Chapter 12) by presenting a treatment of spherical waves and by discussing at some length the subject of interference. The concluding chapter is an introduction to relativistic electrodynamics.

Because of the desire to present material upon which modern theories of matter and radiation are based, certain topics must be emphasized at the expense of others. Some aspects of electromagnetic radiation that are usually classified as "physical optics" are discussed in detail, but it was not deemed appropriate to include, for example, the topics of double refraction, optical activity, or anisotropic media. Similarly, only passing mention is made of the application of the theory to optical instruments. The subject of waveguides also lies primarily outside the domain of this book, and therefore only a brief discussion is given in connection with the properties of radiation fields within hollow, perfectly conducting pipes. (The reader may consult engineering texts for further details regarding these interesting devices.

The subject of electrodynamics is intimately connected with the theory of relativity. But, historically, essentially all the classical results had been worked out before the development of special relativity, and indeed, these investigations paved the way for the construction of relativity theory. It is possible to treat electrodynamics by first postulating special relativity and then deriving many of the results which were originally obtained from experiment in the pre-relativity era. The approach adopted here, however, is to present a more-or-less historical development and only at the end to show that relativity provides a beautiful and complete unification of the subject. This procedure places the climax appropriately at the end, and from a pedagogical standpoint seems preferable to attempting a formal deduction of the subject from a grand, all-encompassing principle laid down at the beginning.

Because this book is directed toward applications of electrodynamics in "modern physics," which employs the Gaussian system in discussions of atomic and nuclear physics, this system is used throughout the book in preference to the MKS system. Furthermore, since the velocity of light plays such an important role in electrodynamics, it does not seem pedagogically sound to set up the basic equations (Maxwell's equations) in such a way that the fundamental constant c disappears. Finally, it is comforting (at least to the author) to see a factor of 4π explicitly appear when an integration over the entire solid angle is performed.

The suggestions for further reading are frequently extensive, in order to give a sufficient number of references so that there is a reasonable probability that some source of collateral reading may easily be located.

The author wishes to express his gratitude to the University of Maryland Computer Science Center for extending to him the use of the IBM 7090/1401 computer for calculating many of the curves which appear in the illustrations of this book.

JERRY B. MARION

The gods did not reveal from the beginning
All things to us; but in the course of time
Through seeking, men find that which is better.
But as for certain truth, no man has known it,
Nor will he know it.
—Xenophanes (6th Century B.C.)

Contents

Chapter 3. The Equations of Laplace and Poisson

Chapter 4. The Electromagnetic Field Equations

Chapter 5. Electromagnetic Waves

Chapter 8. Radiating Systems

Chapter 9. Classical Electron Theory

Chapter 10. Spherical Scalar Waves

Chapter 11. Interference Phenomena

Chapter 12. Scalar Diffraction Theory

CHAPTER 1

Fundamentals of Electromagnetics

1.1 Introduction

In this book we shall be concerned mainly with radiation phenomena associated with electromagnetic fields. We shall study the generation of electromagnetic waves, the propagation of these waves in space, and their interaction with matter of various forms. The fundamental equations which govern all of these processes are *Maxwell's equations.* These are a set of partial differential equations which describe the space and time behavior of the electromagnetic field vectors. By way of review,* we shall first examine briefly the *static* and *steady-state* properties of the electromagnetic field. In Chapters 2 and 3 we shall discuss two topics that are usually not considered at great length in introductory accounts of electromagnetism—solutions of *Laplace's equation* and *multipole effects*—since these subjects are of importance in radiation phenomena. In Chapter 4 we shall treat time-varying electromagnetic fields and will arrive at the statement of

* It is assumed that the reader has a recent acquaintanceship with this basic material, so that only a brief survey is given in the present chapter. The reader who is lacking in this background should refer to one of the books listed in the *Suggested References* at the end of this chapter.

Maxwell's equations in their most general form. Then, for the remainder of the book, we shall be concerned entirely with radiation problems.

From time to time, it will be necessary to make reference to background material which is familiar from the study of classical mechanics. Rather than duplicate the details here, references will be given to the appropriate sections or equations in *Classical Dynamics of Particles and Systems.** The reader will find that the texts listed in the Suggested References can be used as alternative sources of such material.

1.2 Units

In discussing electromagnetic phenomena, it is customary to adopt one of the many possible systems of units.† Much effort has been devoted to the defense of one or another system of units as being intrinsically better than any other. However, it is clear that the nature of the physical world can in no way be related to the choice of units. One must therefore seek the system that is most convenient for the types of problems he wishes to consider; it seems futile to attempt a justification of the choice on any other basis. The reader has no doubt been exposed to the MKS system since this system is popular for the discussion of practical or engineering problems. MKS units (volts, amperes, webers/m^2, etc.) are indeed of a convenient magnitude for the treatment of laboratory-scale effects. But in the study of the interaction of electromagnetic radiation with the fundamental constituents of matter (atoms, molecules, electrons, etc.), the arguments in favor of the MKS system lose much of their validity and it becomes more convenient to adopt the Gaussian system of units. Since we wish to emphasize in this book the relationship of electromagnetism to "modern physics," it seems reasonable to adopt a system of units that is widely used in atomic physics and allied areas. We shall therefore use the Gaussian system in which all electric quantities are measured in electrostatic units (esu) and all magnetic quantities are measured in electromagnetic units (emu). The question of units will arise from time to time as we introduce new quantities, so it seems unnecessary to give an extended discussion at this point. A summarizing list will be found in Appendix D which includes the conversion factors for passing between MKS and Gaussian units; Appendix E gives the fundamental electromagnetic equations in both systems.

The remainder of this chapter will therefore serve not only to provide the reader with a review of the fundamentals of electromagnetism but also to accustom him to the use of Gaussian units.

* Marion (Ma65a); see the Bibliography at the end of this book.

† An excellent summary of various systems of units is given by Jackson (Ja62, p. 611 ff).

1.3 The Field Vectors

In order to describe the electromagnetic field we shall use four vectors:

$\mathbf{E} \equiv$ *Electric intensity vector* or *electric field vector* (statvolts/cm)

$\mathbf{D} \equiv$ *Electric displacement vector* or *dielectric displacement vector* or, simply, *displacement vector* (statvolts/cm)

$\mathbf{B} \equiv$ *Magnetic induction vector* or *magnetic field vector* (gauss)†

$\mathbf{H} \equiv$ *Magnetic intensity vector* (oersted)†

We shall consider **E** and **B** to be the fundamental field vectors, and that **D** and **H** can be obtained from these together with the properties of the medium in which the fields occur.

The mathematical relations that the field vectors satisfy cannot be derived—they must be obtained from experiment. In the following sections we shall discuss the laws of electromagnetism that are valid for steady-state conditions. In Chapter 4 time-varying fields will be studied. The results of these considerations may be summarized in four partial differential equations—Maxwell's equations—which appear to be a true and accurate description of the behavior of electromagnetic fields. It must be emphasized that Maxwell's equations cannot be *derived* except by starting with four equally fundamental statements; they are mathematical representations of *empirical* facts.

1.4 Coulomb's Law

The first experimental fact which we wish to invoke is that the force between two point charges at rest is directed along the line connecting the charges, and the magnitude of the force is directly proportional to the magnitude of each charge and inversely proportional to the square of the distance between the charges. This is Coulomb's law* and in Gaussian units assumes the form

$$\boxed{\mathbf{F}_{12} = \frac{q_1 q_2}{r^2}\mathbf{e}_r} \tag{1.1}$$

† The units *oersted* and *gauss* are identical, but historically oersted is applied to **H** and gauss to **B**.

* Named for Charles Augustin Coulomb (1736–1806) who determined by measurements with a torsion balance in 1785 that the inverse power of r which appears in the electrostatic

for the force exerted on q_1 by q_2. (The Gaussian unit of charge is the *statcoulomb*.) The quantity r is the distance between the charges and $\mathbf{e}_r$ is the unit vector in the direction from q_2 to q_1. If the charges carry the same sign, the force is repulsive; if the signs are opposite, the force is attractive. The force on a unit positive test charge in the field of a charge q defines the electric intensity vector according to

$$\mathbf{F} = q\mathbf{E} \tag{1.2}$$

Thus, the field due to a point charge q is

$$\boxed{\mathbf{E} = \frac{q}{r^2}\mathbf{e}_r} \tag{1.3}$$

An important property of the electric field (indeed, of the *electromagnetic* field) is that it is *linear*. That is, the principle of superposition applies and the field due to a number of charges is just the vector sum of the individual fields. Were it not for this property, the analysis of electromagnetic phenomena would be virtually impossible.

We may verify by direct differentiation that any vector which is proportional to $\mathbf{e}_r/r^2$ has an identically vanishing curl. Thus,*

$$\mathbf{curl}\,\mathbf{E} \equiv 0 \tag{1.4}$$

Now, if $\mathbf{E}$ can be represented as the gradient of some scalar function, then Eq. (1.4) will always be valid since **curl grad** is a null operator. Therefore, if we write

$$\boxed{\mathbf{E} = -\mathbf{grad}\,\Phi} \tag{1.5}$$

* In Chapter 4 we shall find that this result requires modification in the case of time-varying fields.

force law was 2 ± 0.02. A result with the same accuracy had previously been obtained (1771) by Henry Cavendish (1731–1810) but remained unknown until Lord Kelvin had the Cavendish manuscripts published in 1879. An even earlier measurement (1769) had been made by John Robison (1739–1805) who obtained 2 ± 0.06. But credit for the discovery of the inverse-square law properly belongs to Joseph Priestley (1733–1804). In 1766, acting on a suggestion from Benjamin Franklin, Priestley found that there was no electric force on a charge placed anywhere within a hollow, charged conductor. He reported in 1767: "May we not infer from this experiment that the attraction of electricity is subject to the same laws with that of gravitation, and is therefore according to the squares of the distances." (See Problem 1-1.) This brilliant deduction went unappreciated and it was not until Coulomb's experiments that the inverse-square law could be considered as established. Maxwell repeated Cavendish's experiment and reduced the uncertainty to 1 part in 21,600. The techniques used by S. J. Plimpton and W. E. Lawton in 1956 (*Phys. Rev.* **50**, 1066) were considerably more refined and they succeeded in achieving an accuracy of 2 parts in 10^9.

this is *sufficient* to insure Eq. (1.4). It is easy to show* that Eq. (1.5) is also a *necessary* condition for the validity of Eq. (1.4). Thus, in general, it is permissible to represent **E** as the gradient of a scalar function Φ (at least in the *static* case). The function Φ (measured in *statvolts*) is known as the *scalar potential* of the electrostatic field.

Since the electric field due to a point charge varies as $1/r^2$, Gauss' law applies.† Thus, if a charge q is contained within a region of space bounded by a surface S, the integral of the normal component of **E** taken over the surface is $4\pi q$:

$$\oint_S \mathbf{E} \cdot d\mathbf{a} = 4\pi q \tag{1.6}$$

where $d\mathbf{a}$ is the *directed* element of area; the direction is that of the outward normal to the surface S. This equation is the integral expression of Gauss' law for the electric field in free space‡ due to a charge q. We may obtain a differential relation by using the divergence theorem§ to transform the left-hand side of Eq. (1.6) and by expressing the charge q as the volume integral of the charge density ρ (statcoulombs/cm^3). If the surface S bounds the volume V in which all of the charge is contained, then

$$\int_V \operatorname{div} \mathbf{E}\, dv = \oint_S \mathbf{E} \cdot d\mathbf{a} \tag{1.7a}$$

and,

$$\int_V \rho\, dv = q \tag{1.7b}$$

Therefore, we have

$$\int_V \operatorname{div} \mathbf{E}\, dv = 4\pi \int_V \rho\, dv$$

This relation must be valid for an arbitrary volume V (if V always contains the entire charge), so the integrands must themselves be equal:

$$\boxed{\operatorname{div} \mathbf{E} = 4\pi\rho} \qquad \text{(in free space)} \tag{1.8}$$

* The proof is given in Marion, *Principles of Vector Analysis* (Ma65b, Section 3.7).

† The derivation is given in Ma65b (Section 3.8); see also Appendix A of this volume.

‡ We use the term *free space* (or *vacuum*) to denote the absence of matter, but we do not preclude the possibility that there may be free charges (or currents) in this space.

§ A review of the essentials of vector analysis is given in Appendix A.

This equation states that the divergence of **E** is nonvanishing in a region of space containing charge and, therefore, that electric field lines must always originate and terminate on electric charges.

Since **E** may be obtained from the scalar potential according to Eq. (1.5), Gauss' law may be expressed as

$$\operatorname{div} \mathbf{grad}\, \Phi = -4\pi\rho$$

or,

$$\boxed{\nabla^2 \Phi = -4\pi\rho} \qquad \text{(in free space)} \tag{1.9}$$

which is *Poisson's equation* for the scalar potential. In the event that there is no free charge in the medium ($\rho = 0$), *Laplace's equation* results:

$$\nabla^2 \Phi = 0 \qquad \text{(no free charge)} \tag{1.10}$$

The solutions of these important equations will be discussed in Chapter 3.

From Eqs. (1.3) and (1.5) we see that

$$\mathbf{grad}\, \Phi = -\frac{q}{r^2}\mathbf{e}_r \tag{1.11}$$

The potential at a distance r from a point charge q may be obtained by integrating this expression:

$$\Phi = \frac{q}{r} \tag{1.12}$$

where the possible constant of integration has been suppressed. The potential due to a volume distribution of charge may be obtained by summing over all the discrete charges and integrating over any continuous charge density distribution. In performing such an operation we must be careful to note that the quantity r which appears in Eq. (1.12) becomes the distance from the element of charge (the *source point*) to the point at which Φ is measured (the *field point*). Thus, if the field point is specified by the vector **r** and if the source point is located at **r**′, then (see Fig. 1-1)

$$\boxed{\Phi(\mathbf{r}) = \int_V \frac{\rho(\mathbf{r}')}{|\mathbf{r} - \mathbf{r}'|}\, dv'} \qquad \text{(in free space)} \tag{1.13}$$

where dv' is the element of volume* at **r**′. If we use Eq. (1.9) then we have

$$\Phi(\mathbf{r}) = -\frac{1}{4\pi}\int_V \frac{\nabla^2\Phi}{|\mathbf{r} - \mathbf{r}'|}\, dv' \tag{1.13a}$$

* dv' is sometimes written $d^3\mathbf{r}'$ or $dx_1'\, dx_2'\, dx_3'$.

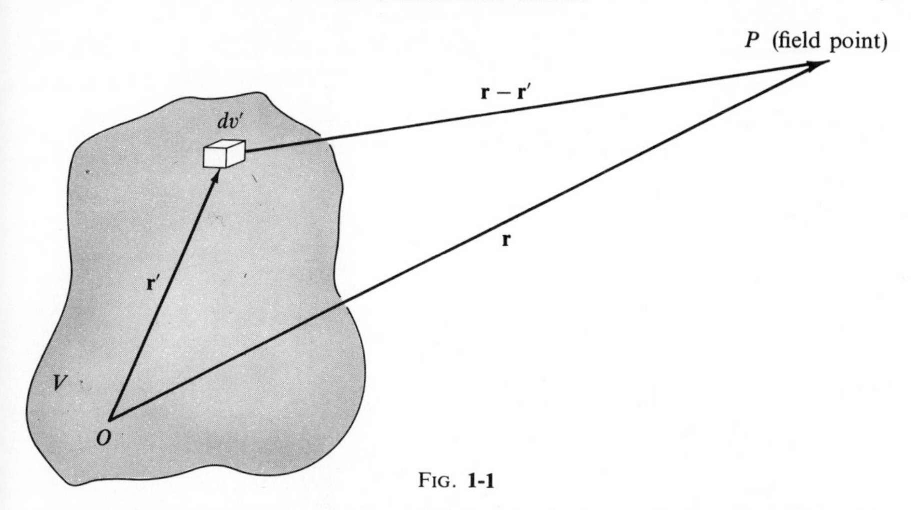

FIG. 1-1

It is important to realize that the potential Φ is defined only to within an additive constant. [This constant was suppressed in Eq. (1.12).] That is, the field vector **E** which is obtained from the gradient of Φ will be unaffected by adding any constant to Φ. It is not a particular value of Φ that is physically meaningful, but only *differences* in potential. It proves convenient in most cases to define the potential to be zero at infinity. Using this convention, the potential of a charge distribution is the amount of work required to bring the charges together from an original configuration in which the charges are dispersed over an infinite sphere.*

1.5 Dielectric Media

The considerations of the consequences of Coulomb's law presented in the preceding section are valid only for the case of isolated charges existing in free space. The presence of matter requires a modification of the equations. Certain materials exhibit the property that their electrons are not free to move about under the influence of an applied electric field. Such materials are called *insulators*; if an insulator can be *polarized* by an applied electric field, it is called a *dielectric*.† Polarization by the field can result from the alignment of molecules which have a natural asymmetry in their charge distribution (the so-called *polar molecules*, e.g., water) or from an induced asymmetry in naturally symmetrical molecules. These two possibilities are illustrated schematically in Fig. 1-2. Of course, not every

* For additional details concerning potentials and fields, see Marion (Ma65a, Chapter 5).

† A thorough study of dielectric materials was begun in 1837 by Michael Faraday. Much work had been done by Henry Cavendish in the 1770's but his manuscripts remained unpublished until 1879.

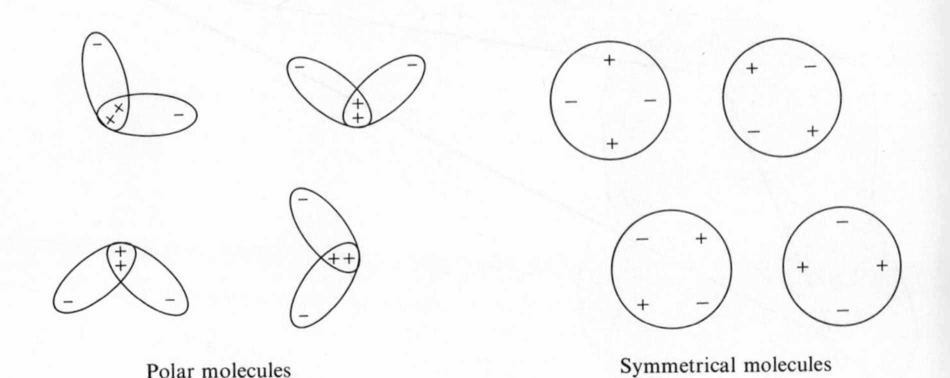

FIG. 1-2a

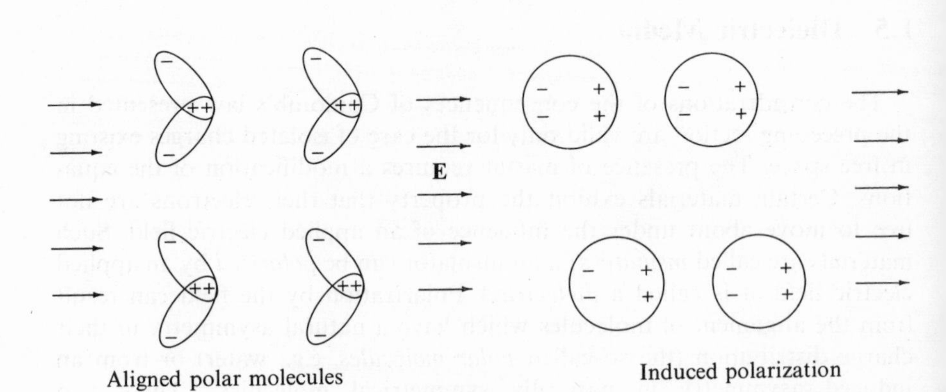

FIG. 1-2b

polar molecule will be precisely aligned by the field since thermal motion will tend to destroy complete polarization, but a time average over the random motion of each molecule will result in a net partial polarization in the direction of the field. Induced polarization, on the other hand, does not suffer from temperature effects. However, the net polarization within any given volume of the medium will fluctuate due to the wandering in and out of the volume by polarized molecules of either type. Therefore, within any small volume the local polarization will be a function of time, and at any given time the polarization will be different from one small region of the material to another. In general, we are interested in the average value of the polarization in the medium, and if we are content to consider averages over regions with characteristic dimensions of 10^{-3} to 10^{-4} cm or greater, then the remnant statistical fluctuations are usually too small to be important. By considering only averages we forego, of course, the possibility of considering any details of the local fields. That is, we are restricted to the considerations of *macroscopic* rather than *microscopic* phenomena. The field equations which are produced by the averaging process are called the *macroscopic field equations*. The equations which relate to discrete charges are sometimes called the *microscopic field equations*.

Within each unit volume of a dielectric placed in an external field we therefore have a certain density of induced dipoles. The electric dipole moment,* $\mathbf{p}$, of a pair of charges $+q$ and $-q$ which are separated by a distance $\boldsymbol{l}$ is

$$\mathbf{p} = q\boldsymbol{l} \tag{1.14}$$

where the direction of $\boldsymbol{l}$ is from $-q$ to $+q$. The net dipole moment per unit volume is called the *polarization* $\mathbf{P}$ of the medium. We may schematically represent each small volume of the dielectric as in Fig. 1-3 in which the external field $\mathbf{E}$ has induced net charges $-q'$ and $+q'$ on opposite faces of the volume and has produced a polarization vector $\mathbf{P}$ within the volume.

If we begin with a material which is unpolarized, then upon placing this material in a uniform field a certain amount of net charge will pass through

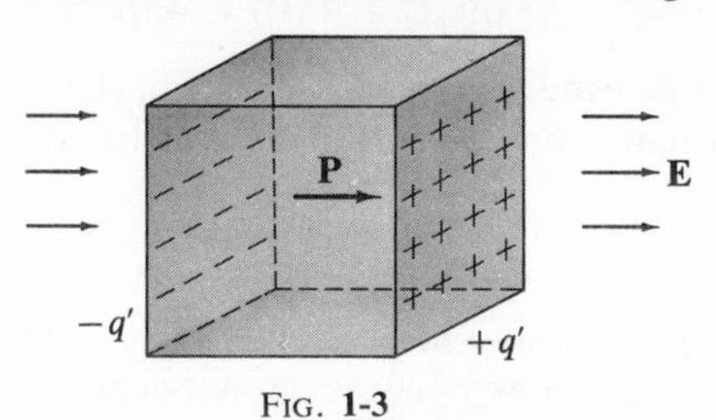

FIG. 1-3

* See Chapter 2 for a detailed discussion of dipole moments.

a given element of area $d\mathbf{a}$ due to the polarization process. The amount of charge will equal the component of $\mathbf{P}$ that is normal to $d\mathbf{a}$, i.e., $\mathbf{P} \cdot d\mathbf{a}$. If we consider a closed surface, then

$$\oint_S \mathbf{P} \cdot d\mathbf{a} = q' \tag{1.15}$$

where q' is the net polarization charge within the volume V bounded by the surface S. Using the divergence theorem we may write

$$\int_V \operatorname{div} \mathbf{P}\, dv = q' \tag{1.15a}$$

Therefore, if $\mathbf{P}$ is a constant vector, its divergence vanishes and $q' = 0$. It follows that there can be no internal charges in a medium for which the polarization is homogeneous. However, surface charges will be present at the boundary surfaces of such a medium.

If the density of polarization charge within V is ρ', then

$$q' = -\int_V \rho'\, dv \tag{1.16}$$

where the minus sign arises since, by definition, the direction of the polarization vector is from negative to positive charges (whereas the electric field is directed from positive to negative charges). Combining Eqs. (1.15) and (1.16) and using the divergence theorem, we find

$$\operatorname{div} \mathbf{P} = -\rho' \tag{1.17}$$

If we now wish to write an equivalent of Eq. (1.8) that will be valid in a dielectric medium, we must take account of the fact that there are in general both free charges and polarization charges present. If we denote the densities of these two types of charge by ρ and ρ', respectively, we must replace our original equation by

$$\operatorname{div} \mathbf{E} = 4\pi(\rho + \rho') \tag{1.18}$$

Using Eq. (1.17), we have

$$\operatorname{div}(\mathbf{E} + 4\pi\mathbf{P}) = 4\pi\rho \tag{1.18a}$$

The quantity appearing in parentheses in Eq. (1.18a) was, for convenience, given the special name *dielectric displacement* by Maxwell*:

$$\boxed{\mathbf{D} \equiv \mathbf{E} + 4\pi\mathbf{P}} \tag{1.19}$$

* The term *displacement* was used by Maxwell at a time (1861) when it was believed that the effects to which it referred were entirely physical displacements. The early mechanical theories have long since been replaced, but some of the terminology still remains, not all of it appropriate.

Therefore, the fundamental equation for dielectric media becomes

$$\boxed{\operatorname{div} \mathbf{D} = 4\pi\rho} \tag{1.20}$$

where ρ is the *free* charge density. In the absence of any polarization this expression reduces to the previous result [Eq. (1.8)].

Experimentally it is found that for a large class of materials $\mathbf{P}$ is proportional to $\mathbf{E}$, at least for field strengths that are not too great. Hence, we may write

$$\mathbf{P} = \chi_e \mathbf{E} \tag{1.21}$$

where χ_e is the *electric susceptibility* of the medium. Then,

$$\mathbf{D} = (1 + 4\pi\chi_e)\mathbf{E} \tag{1.22}$$

The proportionality factor between $\mathbf{D}$ and $\mathbf{E}$ is called the *dielectric constant* of the medium:

$$\varepsilon \equiv 1 + 4\pi\chi_e \tag{1.23}$$

Therefore,

$$\boxed{\mathbf{D} = \varepsilon\mathbf{E}} \tag{1.24}$$

We have written the dielectric constant as simple proportionality factor; however, in some media (certain crystal lattices, for example), it is found that $\mathbf{D}$ and $\mathbf{E}$ are in general not co-linear so that ε is actually a tensor. Since we shall not enter into the discussion of such media, we shall continue to write ε as a scalar. If, in addition to being a scalar, ε is also independent of position within the material, then the material is called a *linear homogeneous isotropic* dielectric; we shall call such a material an *ideal dielectric.* For free space, which cannot be polarized, $\varepsilon = 1$.

1.6 The Laws of Ampère and Biot-Savart

The next experimental result that we wish to use is the fact that electric currents produce magnetic fields.* If a current I (statamperes) flows in a wire,† and if we map by some means the magnetic field so produced in free space and compute the line integral of $\mathbf{B} \cdot d\mathbf{l}$ along any closed path Γ

* Discovered in 1820 by Hans Christian Oersted (1777–1851).

† Under *steady-state* conditions (for which all of the considerations of this chapter apply), all charges are either static or are in uniform motion so that a *steady current* exists. The *fields* produced under such conditions are therefore *static*.

that surrounds the wire, we find that the result is proportional to I independent of the details of the path. This fact is expressed by Ampère's circuital law:*

$$\boxed{\oint_\Gamma \mathbf{B} \cdot d\mathbf{l} = \frac{4\pi}{c} I} \tag{1.25}$$

The constant of proportionality, $4\pi/c$, is a consequence of our decision to use Gaussian units. The quantity c is the velocity of light in free space and the reason for its appearance in Ampère's law will become apparent only after we have begun our examination of the wave properties of the electromagnetic field (Section 5.2).

The integral statement of Ampère's law, Eq. (1.25), may be expressed in differential form by using Stokes' theorem to transform the left-hand side and by writing the total current I as the integral of the current density $\mathbf{J}$ (statamp/cm^2):

$$\int_S \mathbf{curl\,B} \cdot d\mathbf{a} = \oint_\Gamma \mathbf{B} \cdot d\mathbf{l} \tag{1.26a}$$

$$\int_S \mathbf{J} \cdot d\mathbf{a} = I \tag{1.26b}$$

Therefore, Eq. (1.25) becomes

$$\int_S \mathbf{curl\,B} \cdot d\mathbf{a} = \frac{4\pi}{c} \int_S \mathbf{J} \cdot d\mathbf{a}$$

where S denotes any open surface that is bounded by the curve Γ around which the line integral of $\mathbf{B} \cdot d\mathbf{l}$ is calculated (see Fig. 1-4). Since the surface S is arbitrary, the integrands must themselves be equal. Thus,

$$\boxed{\mathbf{curl\,B} = \frac{4\pi}{c} \mathbf{J}} \tag{1.27}$$

* André-Marie Ampère (1775–1836). The investigations of Ampère and of Biot and Savart into the magnetic effects of electric currents were begun soon after the announcement of Oersted's fundamental discovery. Ampère's first paper on the subject was in fact delivered only one week after the arrival of the news of Oersted's finding. Ampère's collected results were published in 1825 and constitute one of the most important memoirs in physics.

Since Ampère and Biot and Savart expressed their results in terms of the forces experienced by current-carrying wires rather than in the integral or differential forms which are customarily used today, there tends to be some ambiguity in the attachment of names to statements of the laws. We shall adopt one of the common practices and call Eq. (1.25) *Ampère's circuital law*; Eq. (1.28) was formulated by Laplace from the experiments of Biot and Savart and will be called the *Biot-Savart* law. Ampère's law of magnetic force is given by Eq. (1.38).

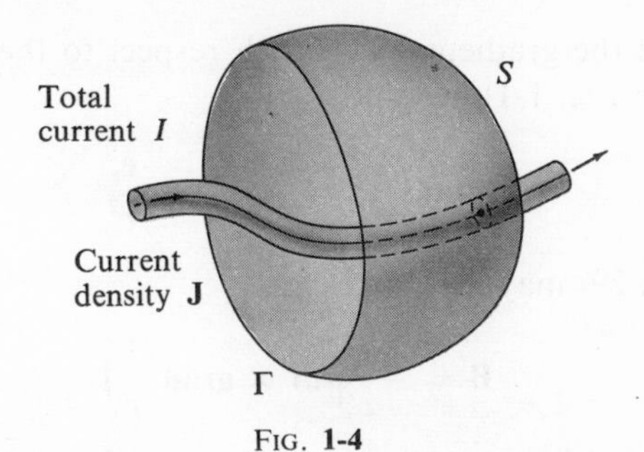

FIG. 1-4

which is the differential expression of Ampère's law. We shall note in Section 4.4 that this result is valid only for steady-state conditions and requires modification in the event that the currents vary with time.

The law of Biot and Savart relates to the magnetic field produced by an element of a circuit in which a current flows. The differential statement is* (see Fig. 1-5)

$$\boxed{d\mathbf{B} = \frac{I}{c}\frac{d\mathbf{l} \times \mathbf{e}_r}{r^2}} \tag{1.28}$$

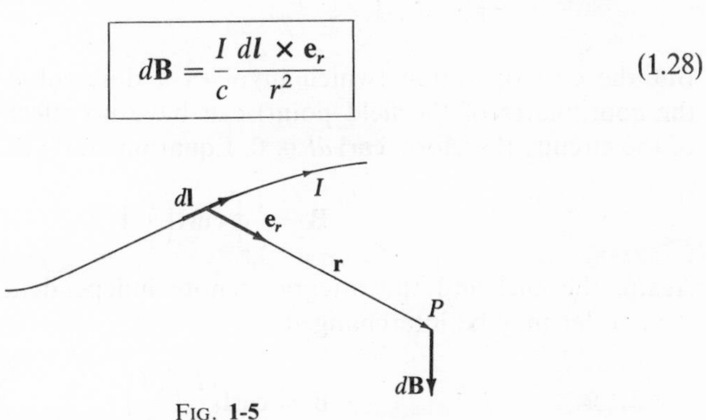

FIG. 1-5

We cannot, of course, isolate a portion of a circuit and treat alone the effects of such an element; a circuit must form a complete loop in order that a steady current may flow. Therefore, by integrating Eq. (1.28) completely around the circuit, we obtain

$$\mathbf{B} = \frac{I}{c}\oint \frac{d\mathbf{l} \times \mathbf{e}_r}{r^2} \tag{1.29}$$

where the path of integration must coincide exactly with the circuit loop. It is easy to see that the field produced at a certain distance from an infinitely long straight wire may be obtained from either Eq. (1.29) or Eq. (1.25) (see Problem 1-11).

* Laplace formulated the law in this manner, based on the experiments performed in 1820 by Jean-Baptiste Biot (1774–1862) and Félix Savart (1791–1841).

If we compute the gradient of $1/r$ with respect to the coordinates of the field point P (see Fig. 1-1), we find

$$\mathbf{grad}\left(\frac{1}{r}\right) = -\frac{\mathbf{r}}{r^3} = -\frac{\mathbf{e}_r}{r^2} \tag{1.30}$$

Therefore, Eq. (1.29) may be written as

$$\mathbf{B} = -\frac{I}{c}\oint d\mathbf{l} \times \mathbf{grad}\left(\frac{1}{r}\right) \tag{1.31}$$

The integrand of this expression may be transformed by making use of the vector identity

$$\mathbf{curl}(\varphi\mathbf{G}) = \varphi\,\mathbf{curl}\,\mathbf{G} - \mathbf{G} \times \mathbf{grad}\,\varphi$$

or, identifying φ and $\mathbf{G}$ as $1/r$ and $d\mathbf{l}$, respectively,

$$\mathbf{curl}\left(\frac{d\mathbf{l}}{r}\right) = \frac{1}{r}\,\mathbf{curl}\,d\mathbf{l} - d\mathbf{l} \times \mathbf{grad}\left(\frac{1}{r}\right)$$

But the curl operation (which involves a differentiation with respect to the coordinates of the field point) can have no effect on the coordinates of the circuit; therefore, $\mathbf{curl}\,d\mathbf{l} \equiv 0$. Equation (1.31) then becomes

$$\mathbf{B} = \frac{I}{c}\oint \mathbf{curl}\left(\frac{d\mathbf{l}}{r}\right)$$

Again, the curl and the integral denote independent operations; hence, their order may be interchanged:

$$\mathbf{B} = \mathbf{curl}\left(\frac{I}{c}\oint\frac{d\mathbf{l}}{r}\right) \tag{1.32}$$

If we define

$$\mathbf{A} \equiv \frac{I}{c}\oint\frac{d\mathbf{l}}{r} \tag{1.33}$$

then,

$$\boxed{\mathbf{B} = \mathbf{curl}\,\mathbf{A}} \tag{1.34}$$

This equation expresses the magnetic field in terms of the auxiliary function $\mathbf{A}$ which is called the *vector potential* of the electromagnetic field. The relationship of $\mathbf{A}$ to the magnetic field is similar to that of Φ to the electric field. Just as a constant can be added to Φ without affecting the calculation of the electric field vector, the gradient of a scalar function can be added to $\mathbf{A}$ without affecting the calculation of the magnetic induction vector. (This follows from the fact that the curl of the gradient of a function vanishes identically.) We shall return to this point in Section 4.6 when we discuss the *gauge* of the potentials.

Since the divergence of the curl of any vector vanishes identically, Eq. (1.32) gives

$$\boxed{\operatorname{div} \mathbf{B} = 0} \tag{1.35}$$

No isolated magnetic poles have ever been found in Nature, so magnetic field lines have neither beginning nor end; the relation $\operatorname{div} \mathbf{B} = 0$ expresses this fact. In an ideal situation, the lines of $\mathbf{B}$ are closed curves, in contrast to the lines of $\mathbf{E}$ which must originate and terminate on charges. In a real situation, however, the lines of $\mathbf{B}$ are in general not closed, even though they have no end and no beginning. For example, consider a current flowing in a ring-shaped conductor. If the ring is ideal (perfectly homogeneous and of uniform cross section), then the magnetic field lines will be closed loops encircling the ring. On the other hand, if the ring is a *real* conductor (with slight inhomogeneities and nonuniformities), the field lines will in general be spirals about the ring and will not connect after any finite number of turns around the ring.*

If the current I in Eq. (1.32) is distributed within an extended conductor of volume V so that we may refer to a current density $\mathbf{J}$, then

$$\mathbf{B}(\mathbf{r}) = \mathbf{curl}\left(\frac{1}{c}\int_V \frac{\mathbf{J}(\mathbf{r}')}{|\mathbf{r} - \mathbf{r}'|}\, dv'\right) \tag{1.36}$$

[Compare Eq. (1.13) and Fig. 1-1.]

The vector potential therefore is

$$\boxed{\mathbf{A}(\mathbf{r}) = \frac{1}{c}\int_V \frac{\mathbf{J}(\mathbf{r}')}{|\mathbf{r} - \mathbf{r}'|}\, dv'} \tag{1.37}$$

1.7 The Lorentz Force

The results of the previous section were expressed in terms of currents flowing in circuits. For many of the topics which we wish to discuss it is

* For a discussion of the topological properties of field lines, see K. L. McDonald, *Am. J. Phys.* **22**, 586 (1954).

necessary to consider the effects of isolated charges in motion. In order to obtain the expression for the force on a moving charge, we use Ampère's statement of the force on an element dl of a circuit carrying a current I when in the presence of a magnetic field $\mathbf{B}$:

$$d\mathbf{F} = \frac{I}{c}\,d\boldsymbol{l} \times \mathbf{B} \tag{1.38}$$

The current element $I\,dl$ may be considered to be the equivalent of $q\mathbf{u}$, the product of a particle's electric charge and its velocity. Therefore, the magnetic force on a moving charge is

$$\mathbf{F}_{\text{mag}} = \frac{q}{c}\mathbf{u} \times \mathbf{B} \tag{1.39}$$

If the charge is also subject to an electric force [Eq. (1.10)], then the total force is

$$\boxed{\mathbf{F} = q\left(\mathbf{E} + \frac{1}{c}\mathbf{u} \times \mathbf{B}\right)} \tag{1.40}$$

This result is known as the Lorentz force* on a moving charge and is valid for steady-state as well as for time-varying fields.

We also note that if $I\,dl \to q\mathbf{u}$, then the vector potential [Eq. (1.33)] for a moving charge may be expressed as

$$\mathbf{A} = \frac{q}{c}\frac{\mathbf{u}}{r} \tag{1.41}$$

which is therefore just $\mathbf{u}/c$ times the scalar potential [Eq. (1.12)]:

$$\Phi = \frac{q}{r} \tag{1.42}$$

We will find extensive use for both of these potential functions in many of the discussions of electromagnetic phenomena.

1.8 Magnetic Materials

Just as the electric field in matter is altered by the presence of aligned electric dipoles, so is the magnetic field affected by the presence of aligned magnetic dipoles. Following the view of Ampère, we regard *current* rather

* After Hendrik Antoon Lorentz (1853–1928), who began a comprehensive development of the theory of electrons in 1892, but the result was first derived in 1889 by Oliver Heaviside (1850–1925). The magnetic portion of the force [Eq. (1.39)] is sometimes referred to alone as the Lorentz force.

than *magnetism* to be the fundamental quantity. Thus, an elementary picture would have the orbital motion of the electrons within atoms and molecules as providing the currents which give rise to magnetism. Every atom or molecule is then a tiny magnetic dipole and the material is said to be *magnetized* if there is some net alignment of these dipoles. In detail, such a simple description is inadequate, but it is qualitatively correct and since we shall not inquire into the atomic theory of magnetism, it will be sufficient for our purposes. We may therefore represent every magnetic dipole as a small current loop, with the magnitude of the dipole given by the product of the current and the area enclosed by the loop and with the direction of the moment given by the right-hand rule as in Fig. 1-6.* The Ampèrian current of the loop is I', the directed area of the loop is **S**, and the dipole moment is

$$\mathbf{m} \equiv \frac{I'}{c} \mathbf{S} \tag{1.43}$$

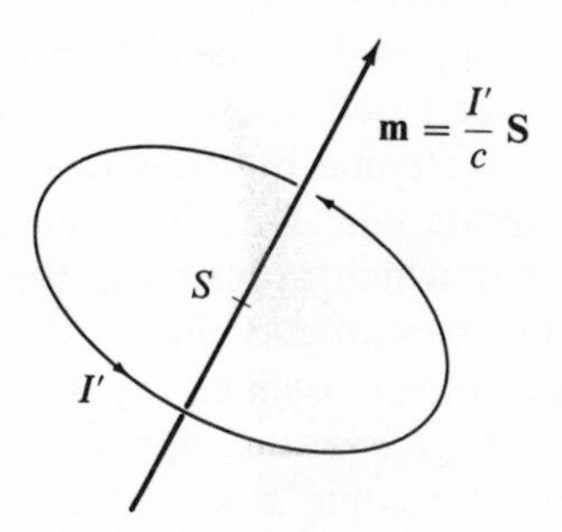

FIG. 1-6

This definition of the magnetic dipole moment is then consistent with that for the electric dipole moment [see Eq. (1.14)] in the sense that the torque on an electric dipole in a uniform electric field and the torque on a magnetic dipole in a uniform magnetic field are both given by similar expressions (see Problem 1-23):

$$\left.\begin{aligned} \boldsymbol{\tau}_e &= \mathbf{p} \times \mathbf{E} \\ \boldsymbol{\tau}_m &= \mathbf{m} \times \mathbf{B} \end{aligned}\right\} \tag{1.44}$$

In nonmagnetized matter there is a random distribution of the elementary magnetic dipoles, but if the material is placed in a magnetic field a partial alignment occurs (see Fig. 1-7). The degree of alignment is dependent upon

* We consider here only a *planar* current loop. If the loop is not planar, then it is necessary to deal with projections onto the three mutually perpendicular planes defined by the coordinate axes. See, for example, Marion (Ma65b, Section 3.6).

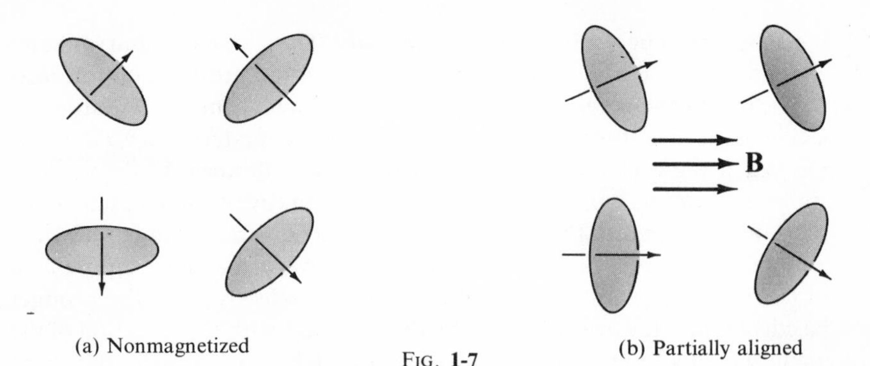

FIG. 1-7

the nature of the material. There are three general classes of matter: *paramagnetic* materials, in which the alignment is in the direction of the field but is weak; *ferromagnetic* materials, in which the alignment is in the direction of the field and is strong; and *diamagnetic* materials, in which the alignment is weak but is opposed to the direction of the external field so that the internal field is decreased. All matter is intrinsically diamagnetic, but the diamagnetism is overcome by the para- and ferromagnetic effects that take place in some materials. This diamagnetic property of matter is to be contrasted with that which applies for the electric field case since electric dipoles (induced or permanent) always align with the applied field.*

The magnetic dipole moment defined by Eq. (1.43) is a microscopic quantity. If we take an average over an appropriate volume of the material, then we may define a macroscopic quantity, the *magnetization* **M**, which is the net magnetic dipole moment per unit volume:

$$\mathbf{M} = \frac{d\mathbf{m}}{dv} \tag{1.45}$$

In general, $d\mathbf{m}$ and $\mathbf{M}$ will vary from one of the unit volumes to another. That is, the Ampèrian currents which give rise to the equivalent dipoles will vary from place to place within the material, and therefore across any surface constructed within the material there will in general be a net flow of Ampèrian current. We may consider each Ampèrian current loop to be decomposed into three mutually perpendicular current loops. Then, only the current loops whose planes are *normal* to the surface will contribute to the net flow of Ampèrian current *through* the surface. Therefore, the components of the magnetic moments associated with the contributing loops all lie *parallel* to the surface. Furthermore, only those current loops which encircle the bounding edge of the surface will be able to contribute to the net flow of current through the surface.

* The alignment may not be co-linear if the dielectric "constant" is actually a tensor.

Let us consider the net flow of the Ampèrian current in the z-direction through a small area $dx\,dy$ which is normal to the z-axis (see Fig. 1-8). This current is the z-component of $\mathbf{I}'$ and is equal to the product of the z-component of the Ampèrian current density $\mathbf{J}'$ and the area:

$$I'_z = J'_z\,dx\,dy \tag{1.46}$$

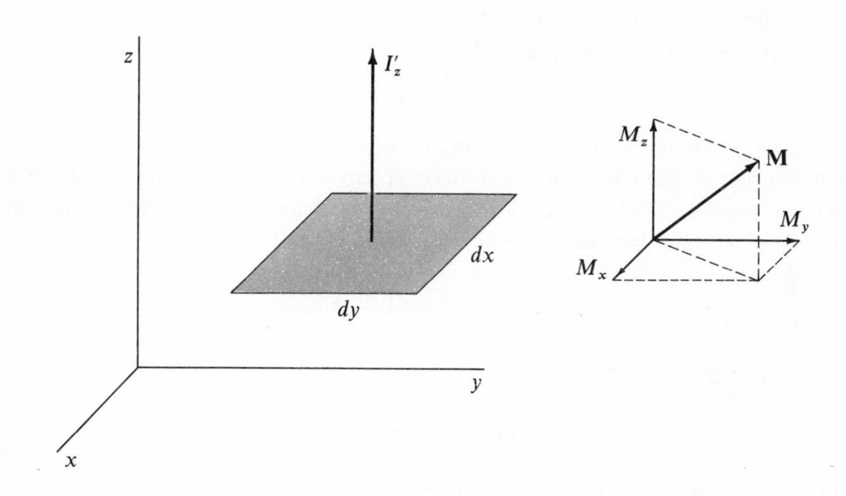

FIG. 1-8

Now, the z-component of the magnetic moment is

$$dm_z = \frac{1}{c} I'_z\,dx\,dy$$

so that upon dividing by $dv/dz = dx\,dy$, we have

$$\frac{dm_z}{dv}\,dz = M_z\,dz = \frac{1}{c} I'_z \tag{1.47}$$

Combining Eqs. (1.46) and (1.47) we may write

$$\frac{1}{c} J'_z\,dx\,dy = M_z\,dz \tag{1.48}$$

Integrating over a surface S bounded by a curve Γ,

$$\frac{1}{c}\int_S J'_z\,dx\,dy = \oint_\Gamma M_z\,dz \tag{1.49}$$

For an arbitrary surface, this equation must be expressed vectorially:

$$\frac{1}{c}\int_S \mathbf{J}' \cdot d\mathbf{a} = \oint_\Gamma \mathbf{M} \cdot dl$$

$$= \int_S \mathbf{curl\,M} \cdot d\mathbf{a} \tag{1.49a}$$

where the last equality results from the application of Stokes' theorem. Therefore, we have in general,

$$\mathbf{J}' = c\,\mathbf{curl\,M} \tag{1.50}$$

If we now wish to write an equivalent of Eq. (1.27) that will be valid in a magnetic material, we must take account of the fact that in general there is present both a true current density **J** and an Ampèrian current density **J**′. Hence, we must replace our original equation by

$$\mathbf{curl\,B} = \frac{4\pi}{c}(\mathbf{J} + \mathbf{J}') \tag{1.51}$$

and using Eq. (1.50), this becomes

$$\mathbf{curl}(\mathbf{B} - 4\pi\mathbf{M}) = \frac{4\pi}{c}\mathbf{J} \tag{1.52}$$

For convenience, we define a quantity called the *magnetic intensity vector*,

$$\boxed{\mathbf{H} \equiv \mathbf{B} - 4\pi\mathbf{M}} \tag{1.53}$$

so that

$$\boxed{\mathbf{curl\,H} = \frac{4\pi}{c}\mathbf{J}} \tag{1.54}$$

Now, in para- and diamagnetic materials, it is found experimentally that **M** is closely proportional to **H**; i.e.,

$$\mathbf{M} = \chi_m\mathbf{H} \tag{1.55}$$

where χ_m is called the *magnetic susceptibility*. Thus,

$$\mathbf{B} = (1 + 4\pi\chi_m)\mathbf{H} \equiv \mu\mathbf{H} \tag{1.56}$$

where μ is the *permability* of the material.* For free space, $\mu = 1$. The simple proportionality between **B** and **H** does not hold for ferromagnetic

* Properly, μ and χ_m are tensors.

materials except for small fields; for large fields we must use the experimentally determined relationship $\chi_m = \chi_m(\mathrm{H})$. Magnetic materials may therefore be categorized according to the magnitudes of their permeabilities:

Diamagnetic: $\mu < 1$

Paramagnetic: $\mu > 1$

Ferromagnetic: $\mu \gg 1$

1.9 Summary of Equations for Static Fields

We have now established all of the fundamental field equations that are valid for steady-state conditions, i.e., for static fields. In Chapter 4 we shall find that some modifications are necessary for time-varying fields, but for the static-field case we may summarize our results as follows:

Field equations:

$$\operatorname{div} \mathbf{D} = 4\pi\rho \qquad \text{[Coulomb's law]} \tag{1.57a}$$

$$\textbf{curl}\, \mathbf{E} = 0 \qquad \text{[Conservative nature of electrostatic forces]} \tag{1.57b}$$

$$\operatorname{div} \mathbf{B} = 0 \qquad \text{[Absence of free magnetic poles]} \tag{1.57c}$$

$$\textbf{curl}\, \mathbf{H} = \frac{4\pi}{c}\mathbf{J} \qquad \text{[Ampère's law]} \tag{1.57d}$$

Force on a moving charge:

$$\mathbf{F} = q\left(\mathbf{E} + \frac{1}{c}\mathbf{u} \times \mathbf{B}\right) \qquad \text{[Lorentz force law]} \tag{1.58}$$

The *additive* constituentive relations are

$$\mathbf{D} = \mathbf{E} + 4\pi\mathbf{P} \tag{1.59a}$$

$$\mathbf{H} = \mathbf{B} - 4\pi\mathbf{M} \tag{1.59b}$$

The *multiplicative* constituentive relations are

$$\mathbf{D} = \varepsilon\mathbf{E} \tag{1.60a}$$

$$\mathbf{H} = \frac{1}{\mu}\mathbf{B} \tag{1.60b}$$

For steady-state conditions, all current loops must be closed. (We note, however, that a loop may be "closed" at infinity.) Therefore,

$$\boxed{\operatorname{div} \mathbf{J} = 0} \tag{1.61}$$

[Note that this relation follows from Eq. (1.57d) by taking the divergence of both sides; div **curl** $\equiv 0$.]

To these equations we may add one further result. For many materials it is found experimentally that the current density **J** is directly proportional to the electric field **E**. This is Ohm's law,* which may be stated as

$$\boxed{\mathbf{J} = \sigma \mathbf{E}} \tag{1.62}$$

where σ (measured in sec^{-1}) is called the *conductivity* of the material.

The equations which require a modification for time-varying fields (by the addition of a term involving a time derivative) are: (1.57b), (1.57d), and (1.61).

1.10 Boundary Conditions on the Field Vectors

Electromagnetic fields within matter, as we have seen, are influenced by polarization and magnetization effects that are characteristic of the particular material. We may then expect that the field vectors will undergo some change at a bounding surface that separates two different materials. We wish, therefore, to derive the relations that must be satisfied by each of the field vectors at such a boundary.

First, we consider the condition on the displacement vector **D** at the interface between two media. As in Fig. 1-9, we let **D** be directed from a medium with dielectric constant ε_1 into a medium with dielectric constant ε_2. At the boundary we construct a "Gaussian pillbox" of cross-sectional area S and thickness Δt (Fig. 1-9). We let **n** be the unit normal to the surface S. The pillbox is of volume $V = S\,\Delta t$ and is assumed to contain a certain amount of free charge whose density is ρ. If we integrate $\operatorname{div} \mathbf{D} = 4\pi\rho$ over the volume V, we have

$$\int_V \operatorname{div} \mathbf{D}\, dv = 4\pi \int_V \rho\, dv \tag{1.63}$$

* Discovered in 1826 by Georg Simon Ohm (1787–1854). Ohm's fundamental researches in electricity were little appreciated until quite late in his life when recognition was finally accorded him, shortly before his death.

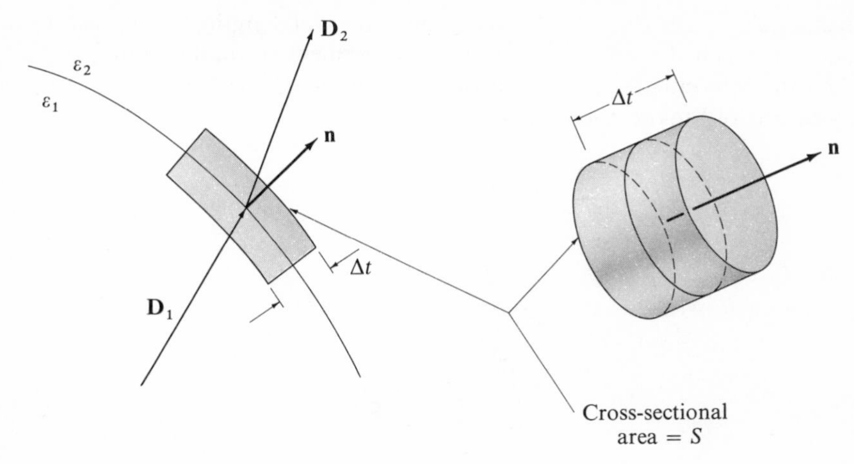

FIG. **1-9**

or, using the divergence theorem,

$$\oint_S \mathbf{D} \cdot \mathbf{n}\, da = 4\pi \int_V \rho\, dv \tag{1.63a}$$

The left-hand side may be integrated by noting that since the normal component of **D** is involved there is no contribution from the sides of the pillbox. The right-hand side may be integrated if the volume V is sufficiently small so that ρ is essentially constant. Thus,

$$(\mathbf{D}_2 \cdot \mathbf{n} - \mathbf{D}_1 \cdot \mathbf{n})S = 4\pi \cdot \rho \cdot S \cdot \Delta t \tag{1.64}$$

Since free charge may exist on the interface, the product $\rho \cdot \Delta t$ must remain finite as Δt approaches zero. In the limit,

$$\lim_{\Delta t \to 0} (\rho \cdot \Delta t) = \rho_s \tag{1.65}$$

where ρ_s is the surface density of free charge. Therefore, we have the result

$$\boxed{(\mathbf{D}_2 - \mathbf{D}_1) \cdot \mathbf{n} = 4\pi\rho_s} \tag{1.66}$$

which relates the change in the *normal* component of **D** across a boundary to the surface density of charge on that boundary. If $\rho_s = 0$, then the normal component of **D** is continuous across the boundary. We may, of course, also write Eq. (1.66) as

$$(\varepsilon_2 \mathbf{E}_2 - \varepsilon_1 \mathbf{E}_1) \cdot \mathbf{n} = 4\pi\rho_s \tag{1.66a}$$

The next condition that must be fulfilled at the boundary between two media may be obtained from $\mathbf{curl}\, \mathbf{E} = 0$. If we construct at the boundary a rectangular path (Fig. 1-10) which has sides of length Δl and width Δt and for which the sides are parallel to a segment of the bounding surface, then the line integral of $\mathbf{E} \cdot d\mathbf{l}$ around the path $ABCDA$ may be expressed by means of Stokes' theorem as

$$\oint_{ABCDA} \mathbf{E} \cdot d\mathbf{l} = \int_S \mathbf{curl}\, \mathbf{E} \cdot \mathbf{n}_0 \, da = 0 \tag{1.67}$$

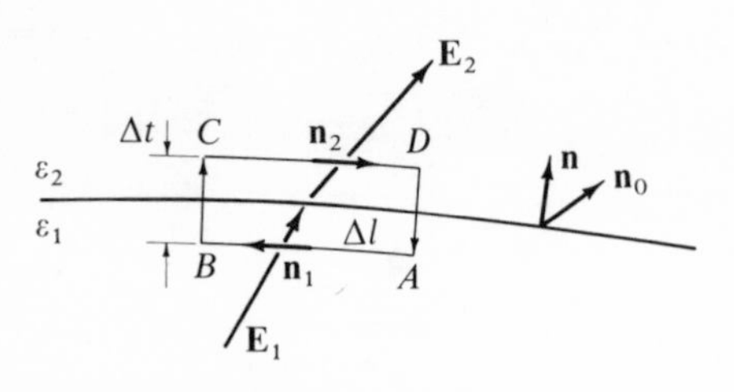

FIG. **1-10**

where S is the rectangular area $\Delta l \cdot \Delta t$ and where $\mathbf{n}_0$ is the unit vector normal to this rectangle and lies along the boundary surface. Performing the line integral, there results

$$\oint \mathbf{E} \cdot d\mathbf{l} = (\mathbf{E}_1 \cdot \mathbf{n}_1)\Delta l + (\mathbf{E}_2 \cdot \mathbf{n}_2)\Delta l + \text{(contribution from the ends)} = 0 \tag{1.68}$$

where $\mathbf{n}_1$ and $\mathbf{n}_2$ are the unit vectors along the portions of the path lying in medium 1 and 2, respectively, Now $\mathbf{n}_1 = -\mathbf{n}_2$, so that we have

$$(\mathbf{E}_2 - \mathbf{E}_1) \cdot \mathbf{n}_2 \, \Delta l + \text{(ends)} = 0$$

Since the contribution from the ends is proportional to Δt, the second term vanishes in the limit $\Delta t \to 0$. Also, $\mathbf{n}_2 = \mathbf{n}_0 \times \mathbf{n}$, so that we have

$$(\mathbf{E}_2 - \mathbf{E}_1) \cdot (\mathbf{n}_0 \times \mathbf{n}) = 0 \tag{1.69}$$

Re-arranging the order of the triple scalar product, we obtain

$$\mathbf{n}_0 \cdot [(\mathbf{E}_2 - \mathbf{E}_1) \times \mathbf{n}] = 0$$

But the orientation of the rectangle, and hence of $\mathbf{n}_0$, is arbitrary; thus, the term in the brackets must vanish identically;

$$\boxed{(\mathbf{E}_2 - \mathbf{E}_1) \times \mathbf{n} = 0} \tag{1.70}$$

This relation states that the *tangential* component of $\mathbf{E}$ must be continuous across the boundary between two media.

We may obtain the boundary condition on the magnetic induction vector **B** in a manner entirely analogous to that used for **D**. Since div **B** = 0, we have immediately

$$\boxed{(\mathbf{B}_2 - \mathbf{B}_1)\cdot\mathbf{n} = 0} \tag{1.71}$$

or, the *normal* component of **B** is continuous across the boundary.

The condition on the magnetic intensity vector **H** may be obtained by using a construction identical to that in Fig. 1-10. However, since **curl H** does not vanish, but is equal to $(4\pi/c)\mathbf{J}$, if $\mathbf{J} \to \infty$ as $\Delta t \to 0$, then the tangential component of **H** will not be continuous across the boundary. We may define a *surface current density* **K** according to

$$\mathbf{K} \equiv \lim_{\substack{\Delta t \to 0 \\ \mathbf{J} \to \infty}} \mathbf{J}\,\Delta t \tag{1.72}$$

so that the expression analogous to Eq. (1.70) is

$$\boxed{(\mathbf{H}_2 - \mathbf{H}_1) \times \mathbf{n} = \frac{4\pi}{c}\mathbf{K}} \tag{1.73}$$

Thus, the *tangential* component of **H** is in general continuous only if there are no surface currents at the interface.

1.11 Point Charges and the Delta Function

The discussion of phenomena on a macroscopic scale allows the treatment of charge and current distributions as if they were truly continuous. That is, we average over sufficiently large regions of space so that the actual discrete nature of the static and moving charges does not influence the results. On the other hand, we shall frequently wish to discuss effects which relate to individual charges. For simplicity, these charges will usually be considered to be without spatial extent, i.e., they will be *point charges.* Of course, the point-charge representation is an idealization of the actual situation, but for many purposes the distinction is not important.

In order to express the fact that a charge is located at a given point, it is convenient to introduce a generalization of the Kronecker delta which is called the *Dirac delta function.** This function has the properties that it vanishes unless its argument vanishes.

$$\delta(x - x') = 0, \qquad x \neq x' \tag{1.74}$$

* After the English theorist, P. A. M. Dirac (1902–) who introduced the function into quantum theory. Dirac was the 1933 Nobel Laureate in physics.

and that the integral over all x is unity:

$$\int_{-\infty}^{+\infty} \delta(x - x')\,dx = 1 \tag{1.75}$$

It is clear that no ordinary function can actually possess both of these properties since they require $\delta(x - x')$ to be zero everywhere except at $x = x'$, at which point it is infinite. However, it is possible to define the delta function as the limit of an ordinary function* so that it remains integrable and approaches infinity in the limit.

If we assume that we have made a proper definition of the delta function, consistent with all of the above requirements, we have

$$\int_{-\infty}^{+\infty} f(x)\delta(x - x')\,dx = f(x') \tag{1.76}$$

In three dimensions we may write

$$\begin{aligned} \delta(\mathbf{r} - \mathbf{r}') &\equiv \delta(x - x')\delta(y - y')\delta(z - z') \\ &= 0, \qquad \mathbf{r} \neq \mathbf{r}' \end{aligned} \tag{1.77}$$

Therefore, the equivalents of Eqs. (1.75) and (1.76) are

$$\int_{\text{all space}} \delta(\mathbf{r} - \mathbf{r}')\,dv = 1 \tag{1.78}$$

$$\int_{\text{all space}} f(\mathbf{r})\delta(\mathbf{r} - \mathbf{r}')\,dv = f(\mathbf{r}') \tag{1.79}$$

Now, we may verify by direct differentiation that $1/r$ is a solution of Laplace's equation for $r > 0$:

$$\nabla^2\left(\frac{1}{r}\right) = 0, \qquad r > 0 \tag{1.80}$$

Since the potential Φ of a point charge is

$$\Phi = \frac{q}{r}, \qquad r > 0 \tag{1.81}$$

we may write the integral of Eq. (1.9) as

$$\int_{\text{all space}} \nabla^2\Phi\,dv = q\int_{\text{all space}} \nabla^2\left(\frac{1}{r}\right)dv = -4\pi\int_{\text{all space}} \rho\,dv \tag{1.82}$$

If q is indeed a point charge, the density ρ is a delta function:

$$\int_{\text{all space}} \rho\,dv = \int_{\text{all space}} q\delta(\mathbf{r})\,dv = q \tag{1.83}$$

* There are many methods of definition; see, for example, Problem 1-30

Combining Eqs. (1.82) and (1.83), we have

$$\int_{\text{all space}} \nabla^2\left(\frac{1}{r}\right) dv = -4\pi \tag{1.84}$$

Since $\nabla^2(1/r)$ vanishes for $r > 0$ and has an integral over all space of -4π, we may then write

$$\nabla^2\left(\frac{1}{r}\right) = -4\pi\delta(\mathbf{r}) \tag{1.85}$$

In terms of the potential Φ, we have

$$\nabla^2\Phi = -4\pi q\delta(\mathbf{r}) \tag{1.86}$$

Equation (1.85) may be expressed more generally as

$$\boxed{\nabla^2\left(\frac{1}{|\mathbf{r} - \mathbf{r}'|}\right) = -4\pi\delta(\mathbf{r} - \mathbf{r}')} \tag{1.87}$$

Applied in this manner, the delta function is of considerable value in the formal development of solutions to Poisson's equation by the method of Green's functions. We shall not, however, pursue this particular application of delta functions in this book.

Suggested References*

There exists a vast literature of general works on electricity and magnetism. Some of the more useful of the recent books at the intermediate level are:

Corson and Lorrain (Co62)
Kip (Ki62)
Owen (Ow63)
Peck (Pe53)
Pugh and Pugh (Pu60)
Reitz and Milford (Re60)
Schwarz (Sc64)
Scott (Sc59)
Slater and Frank (Sl47)
Whitmer (Wh62)

A few of the texts at the advanced level are:

Jackson (Ja62)
Panofsky and Phillips (Pa60)
Sommerfeld (So52)
Stratton (St41)
Tralli (Tr63)
Van Bladel (Va64)

Some of the intermediate texts which were written primarily for students of engineering but which are still quite useful for physics students are:

Fano, Chu and Adler (Fa60)
Langmuir (La61)
Plonsey and Collin (Pl61)
Skilling (Sk48)

* A complete bibliography will be found at the end of the book.

Among the more general textbooks which contain good sections on electromagnetism are:

Blass (Bl62)	Kompaneyets (Ko62)
Constant (Co58)	Page (Pa52)
Houston (Ho48)	Wangsness (Wa63)
Joos and Freeman (Jo50)	

Two of the older works which are of excellent quality and are still quite useful are:

Jeans (Je25)	Abraham and Becker (Ab50; see also Be64)

A very readable and enjoyable account of the development of the classical theory of electricity and magnetism is given by Whittaker (Wh51); this masterful work is highly recommended to every student of physics. Some of the original papers which describe fundamental experiments in electricity and magnetism have been collected (and commented on) by Shamos (Sh59).

Problems

1-1. Prove that if the electric field is everywhere zero inside a uniformly charged spherical shell, then the law of electrostatic force must vary as the inverse square of the distance. Devise a proof using differential equations (method of Laplace) and one using a geometrical construction (method of Poynting).

1-2. Show that the average value of the potential Φ taken over the surface of a spherical region of space that contains no charge is equal to the value of the potential at the center of the sphere, independent of the distribution of charge exterior to the sphere.

1-3. Show that the electric field inside a uniformly polarized sphere is constant and is given by $\mathbf{E} = -(4\pi/3)\mathbf{P}$. Use this result to show that the electric field $\mathbf{E}_s$ which exists in a spherical cavity cut in a uniformly polarized dielectric medium is related to the field $\mathbf{E}$ in the medium by

$$\mathbf{E}_s = \frac{2 + \varepsilon}{3}\mathbf{E}$$

1-4. Within a dielectric sphere of radius a the polarization vector $\mathbf{P}$ is radial outward and its magnitude is proportional to the distance from the center of the sphere: $P = P_0 r$. Find ρ', $\mathbf{D}$, and $\mathbf{E}$ as functions of r.

1-5. The space between two long coaxial cylinders is filled with a dielectric. Show that the electric field intensity can be made independent of position between the cylinders by an appropriate choice for the radial variation of the dielectric constant.

1-6. An electret is an object which has a permanent electric dipole moment. Consider a disk electret of radius a and thickness d in which the polarization vector $\mathbf{P}$ is constant and parallel to the axis of the disk. Calculate the electric potential, Φ, exterior to the disk and show that Φ depends only on the product Pd and on the solid angle subtended by the disk at the field point. (The potential is therefore independent of the exact *shape* of the electret.) Show also that insofar as edge effects can be neglected, $\mathbf{D} = 0$ within the electret.

1-7. Show by a direct calculation that the force on an electric dipole in a nonuniform electric field is $\mathbf{F} = (\mathbf{p} \cdot \mathbf{grad})\,\mathbf{E}$. Show also that the same result may be obtained by expanding $\mathbf{p} \times \mathbf{curl}\,\mathbf{E} = 0$.

1-8. The *capacitance* C of a conductor is defined to be the quantity of charge which must be placed on the conductor in order to produce a potential change of one unit; i.e., $C = q/\Phi$. Calculate the capacitance of the following objects: (a) an isolated sphere of radius a; (b) two concentric spheres of radii a and $b > a$, if the outer sphere carries a charge $+q$ and the inner one a charge $-q$; (c) two coaxial cylinders of radii a and $b > a$, if the outer cylinder carries a charge density $+\rho_l$ (charge per unit length) and the inner one a charge density $-\rho_l$. What are the units of the capacitance calculated in case (c)?

1-9. Consider a condenser whose dielectric is air and is formed by two square, parallel plates of area S which are separated by a distance d. Show that the capacitance is $C = S/4\pi d$. If the alignment of the plates is disturbed so that on one edge the separation is $d + \delta$ and on the opposite edge is $d - \delta$, where $\delta \ll d$, show that the capacitance becomes approximately

$$C = \frac{S}{4\pi d}\left(1 + \frac{\delta^2}{3d^2}\right)$$

1-10. Use Gauss' law to calculate the electric field $\mathbf{E}$ and the potential Φ due to an infinitely long cylindrical conductor of radius a which carries a charge density per unit length ρ_l. Can the potential be referred to the value at infinity in this case? How might one define the "zero" of potential?

1-11. Calculate the magnetic field at a distance a from an infinitely long straight wire in which flows a current I. Show that the same result may be obtained by using either Ampère's law [Eq. (1.25)] or the Biot-Savart law [Eq. (1.29)].

1-12. Two infinitely long wires lie parallel to the z-axis and pass through the points $x = 1, y = 0$ and $x = -1, y = 0$, respectively. A current I flows in each wire, but in opposite directions. Calculate the magnetic field, $\mathbf{B}$, in space. What is the force per unit length experienced by the wires?

1-13. Calculate the magnetic field **B** along the axis of a solenoid which is of radius a and length $L \gg a$ if there are N turns of wire per unit length in which flows a current I.

1-14. Find the magnetic induction vector at the center of a loop of wire formed into a regular hexagon of side a and in which flows a current I. Generalize the result to a regular polygon of N sides. Compare the result for $N \to \infty$ with that for a circular current loop.

1-15. A long, straight conductor of radius a carries a current of uniform density. Find **B** for any point within the conductor.

1-16. A sphere of radius a is uniformly charged with a density ρ. If the sphere rotates with a constant angular velocity $\boldsymbol{\omega}$, show that the magnetic induction, **B**, at the center of the sphere is $(4\pi/3c)\rho a^2\boldsymbol{\omega}$.

1-17. Specify a design for the winding of a wire on a spherical form, so that when a current flows in the wire, a uniform magnetic field will be produced within the sphere.

1-18. The magnetic field of the Earth is approximately that of a magnetic dipole. Calculate the magnetic dipole moment using the fact that the horizontal component of the Earth's field at the surface of the Earth is approximately 0.23 G at a magnetic latitude of 45°.

1-19. Consider two current elements $I_1\,dl_1$ and $I_2\,dl_2$ of two different circuits. Use Ampère's force law [Eq. (1.38)] together with the Biot-Savart law [Eq. (1.28)] to compute the force $d\mathbf{F}_{12}$ on the first current element due to the second. Show that in general $d\mathbf{F}_{12} \neq -d\mathbf{F}_{21}$, so that Newton's third law is not obeyed by the current elements. Finally, show that the third law is satisfied if the force of one *entire* circuit on the other is considered (i.e., perform an integration over both circuits).

1-20. A current I_1 flows in a square wire loop, each side of which has a length a. A current I_2 flows in an infinitely long wire which lies in the plane of the square loop and is at a distance b from and is parallel to one side of the square. Find the total force on the square loop.

1-21. Consider a wire of length $8a$ formed in a square which lies in the x-y plane with center at the origin. If a current I flows in the wire, calculate the vector potential **A** and the magnetic field **B** at an arbitrary point in space defined by the vector **r**, where $|\mathbf{r}| \gg a$.

1-22. Consider two coaxial cylinders of length L and with radii a and b $(a < b)$, the regions between whose ends are closed by two plates. A uniform current I flows along one cylinder, through an end plate, back along the other cylinder, and then into the original cylinder through the other end plate, thus completing the circuit. Find the magnetic induction vector, $\mathbf{B}$, at an arbitrary point in the vacuum between the cylinders. What is the field for $r < a$ and $r > b$?

1-23. Show that the torque on an electric dipole placed in a uniform electric field is given by $\boldsymbol{\tau}_e = \mathbf{p} \times \mathbf{E}$ and that the torque on a magnetic dipole placed in a uniform magnetic field is given by $\boldsymbol{\tau}_m = \mathbf{m} \times \mathbf{B}$. Show also that there is no net force on the dipole in either case.

1-24. A particle with mass m and charge q moves in a constant magnetic field $\mathbf{B}$. Show that, if the initial velocity is perpendicular to $\mathbf{B}$, the path is circular and the angular velocity is

$$\boldsymbol{\omega} = -\frac{q}{mc}\mathbf{B}$$

If the linear velocity of the particle is $\mathbf{u}$, show that the radius of the orbit is

$$R = \left|\frac{mcu}{qB}\right|$$

1-25. A particle with mass m and charge q moves in a crossed field (i.e., $\mathbf{E}$ is perpendicular to $\mathbf{B}$). Write the equation of motion of the particle. Next, transform to a set of coordinates that are moving with a velocity

$$\mathbf{v} = c\frac{\mathbf{E} \times \mathbf{B}}{B^2}$$

relative to the original inertial system, and show that the equation of motion in this coordinate system is independent of $\mathbf{E}$. Explain the significance of this result. Indicate how it would be possible to use crossed electric and magnetic fields to produce a *velocity selector*; i.e., show that charged particles (with arbitrary mass and charge) moving in such a device will proceed undeflected only if they have a velocity given by the expression above.

1-26. Obtain the integrated equations of motion for a particle with mass m and charge q which moves in combined electric and magnetic fields, with $\mathbf{E}$ in the x-direction and $\mathbf{B}$ in the y-direction. Let the initial velocity be $\mathbf{u}_0$, and calculate the average velocity in the x-, y-, and z-directions. Sketch the projection of the trajectory on the x-z plane. Distinguish three possible cases, depending on the magnitude of the initial velocity.

1-27. Show that the relation $\mathbf{J} = \sigma\mathbf{E}$ is equivalent to the usual statement of Ohm's law, viz., $V = IR$, or (voltage) = (current) $\times$ (resistance). Note that $\mathbf{J}$ is a current *density*.

1-28. At the interface between two dielectric media, the electric vector in the first medium makes an angle θ_1 with the normal to the boundary plane. Show that the angle which the electric vector makes with the normal in the second medium may be obtained by Snell's law:

$$|\mathbf{E}_1| \sin \theta_1 = |\mathbf{E}_2| \sin \theta_2$$

Could a dielectric lens be made to "focus" an electric field?

1-29. Consider an ideal dielectric medium which is placed in a uniform electric field **E**. The polarization within the dielectric is **P**. A needlelike cavity is formed in the medium with the long dimension in the direction of **E**; the transverse dimensions of the cavity are small. Similarly, a disk-shaped cavity is formed with the large dimension perpendicular to the field; the longitudinal dimensions of the cavity are small. Calculate the fields within each of these cavities. If the force on a test charge, δq, is measured in each of these cavities, what properties of the fields can be determined?

1-30. Consider the function

$$F(x, a) = \frac{1}{\sqrt{2\pi}} \frac{\exp[-(x^2/2a^2)]}{a}$$

Plot $F(x, a)$ for $a = 1$, 0.4, and 0.1. What is the area under the curve as a function of a? Show that if we define

$$\Delta(x - x_0) \equiv \lim_{a \to 0} F(x - x_0, a)$$

then,

$$G(\xi) = \int_{-\infty}^{+\infty} \Delta(\xi - x) G(x)\, dx$$

where G is an arbitrary function. Identify the function $\Delta(\xi - x)$.

CHAPTER 2

Multipole Fields

2.1 Introduction

In this chapter we continue the discussion of electromagnetic effects under steady-state conditions. We first consider a static collection of charges and calculate the scalar potential by a power series expansion. The various terms in such an expansion may be identified with the *multipole moments* of the system; the monopole, dipole, and quadrupole terms are treated in detail. If the charges are allowed to move, then currents are produced and magnetic effects are introduced. In the event that the currents are *steady* (i.e., not time dependent), the vector potential may be written in a magnetic multipole expansion that is analogous to the electric multipole expansion for static charges. We shall find a close similarity between the electric and magnetic effects for steady-state conditions. If we remove the requirement of steady-state conditions, then the fields are no longer static and *radiation* can occur; this subject will be treated beginning in Chapter 7.

2.2 The Electric Dipole

Let us first consider an elementary example of a static system of charges. Our system will consist (see Fig. 2-1) of two charges of equal magnitude,

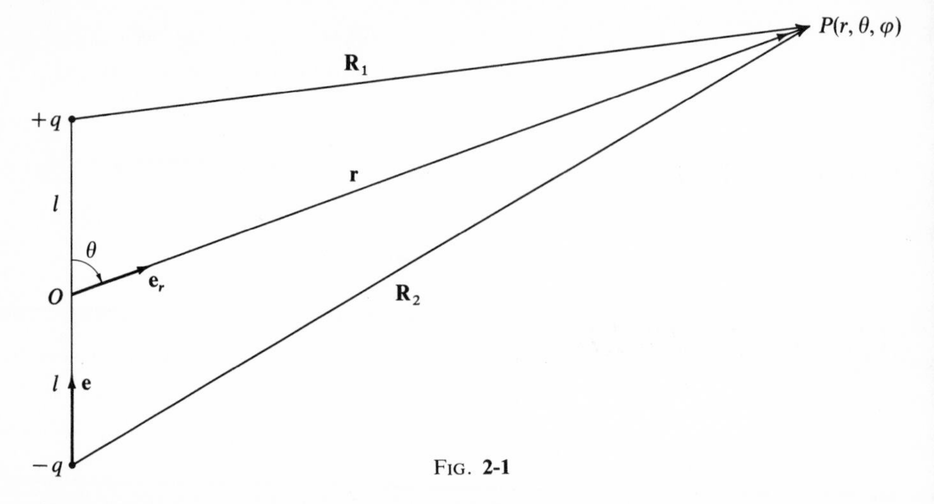

FIG. 2-1

but of opposite sign, each situated a distance l from the origin O which is taken to lie on the line connecting the charges. Such a system of charges is the simplest example of an *electric dipole*. The potential at the point $P(r, \theta, \varphi)$ is given by

$$\Phi(r, \theta, \varphi) = q\left(\frac{1}{R_1} - \frac{1}{R_2}\right) \tag{2.1}$$

where $R_\alpha = |\mathbf{R}_\alpha|$. We wish, however, to express the potential in terms of the magnitude of the vector $\mathbf{r}$ ($|\mathbf{r}| = r$) and the angles θ and φ. (Since the charge distribution is axially symmetric, clearly the potential must be independent of the azimuthal angle, φ.) In order to do this, we first express R_1 and R_2 as functions of r and θ. Using the cosine law, we may write

$$\begin{aligned} R_1^2 &= r^2 + l^2 - 2rl\cos\theta \\ &= r^2\left[1 + \left(\frac{l}{r}\right)^2 - 2\left(\frac{l}{r}\right)\cos\theta\right] \end{aligned} \tag{2.2}$$

Thus,

$$\begin{aligned} \frac{1}{R_1} &= \frac{1}{r}\left[1 + \left(\frac{l}{r}\right)^2 - 2\left(\frac{l}{r}\right)\cos\theta\right]^{-\frac{1}{2}} \\ &= \frac{1}{r}\left[1 + \left(\frac{l}{r}\right)\cos\theta + \frac{1}{2}\left(\frac{l}{r}\right)^2(3\cos^2\theta - 1)\right. \\ &\qquad \left. + \frac{1}{2}\left(\frac{l}{r}\right)^3(5\cos^3\theta - 3\cos\theta) + \cdots\right] \end{aligned} \tag{2.3}$$

where we have assumed $l \ll r$ in order to expand the radical. We shall restrict our attention to field points P that are at distances large compared with the dimensions of the dipole. Therefore, we have approximately

$$\frac{1}{R_1} = \frac{1}{r} + \frac{l}{r^2}\cos\theta + \frac{1}{2}\frac{l^2}{r^3}(3\cos^2\theta - 1)$$
$$\frac{1}{R_2} = \frac{1}{r} - \frac{l}{r^2}\cos\theta + \frac{1}{2}\frac{l^2}{r^3}(3\cos^2\theta - 1) \tag{2.4}$$

where the minus sign in the expression for $1/R_2$ arises from $\cos(\pi - \theta) = -\cos\theta$. Thus, the potential becomes approximately

$$\Phi(r, \theta) = q\left(\frac{1}{R_1} - \frac{1}{R_2}\right)$$
$$= 2ql\frac{\cos\theta}{r^2} \tag{2.5}$$

The potential due to a dipole therefore decreases with distance as $1/r^2$, whereas the potential due to a single charge decreases as $1/r$. It is reasonable that the potential due to a dipole should decrease with distance more rapidly than the potential due to a single charge since, as the observation point P is moved farther and farther away, the dipole charge distribution appears more and more to be simply a small unit with zero charge.

We define the *electric dipole moment* of the pair of equal charges as the product of q and the separation $2l$:

$$\mathbf{p} \equiv 2ql\mathbf{e} \tag{2.6}$$

The dipole moment is a vector whose direction is defined as the direction from the negative to the positive charge; $\mathbf{e}$ is the unit vector in this direction (see Fig. 2-1).

If $\mathbf{e}_r$ is the unit vector in the direction of the field point P, then the dipole potential may be expressed as

$$\boxed{\Phi = \frac{\mathbf{p}\cdot\mathbf{e}_r}{r^2}} \tag{2.7}$$

The electric field vector $\mathbf{E}$ for the dipole is given by the negative of the gradient of Φ:

$$\mathbf{E} = -\mathbf{grad}\,\Phi \tag{2.8}$$

The spherical components of **E** may be calculated most easily by referring to Eq. (2.5). Writing $p = 2ql$, we have

$$\left.\begin{aligned} E_r &= -\frac{\partial \Phi}{\partial r} = 2p\frac{\cos\theta}{r^3} \\ E_\theta &= -\frac{1}{r}\frac{\partial \Phi}{\partial \theta} = p\frac{\sin\theta}{r^3} \\ E_\varphi &= -\frac{1}{r\sin\theta}\frac{\partial \Phi}{\partial \varphi} = 0 \end{aligned}\right\} \tag{2.9}$$

Figure 2-2 shows some lines of equal potential and some electric field lines. Both sets of curves are symmetric about the polar axis so that the

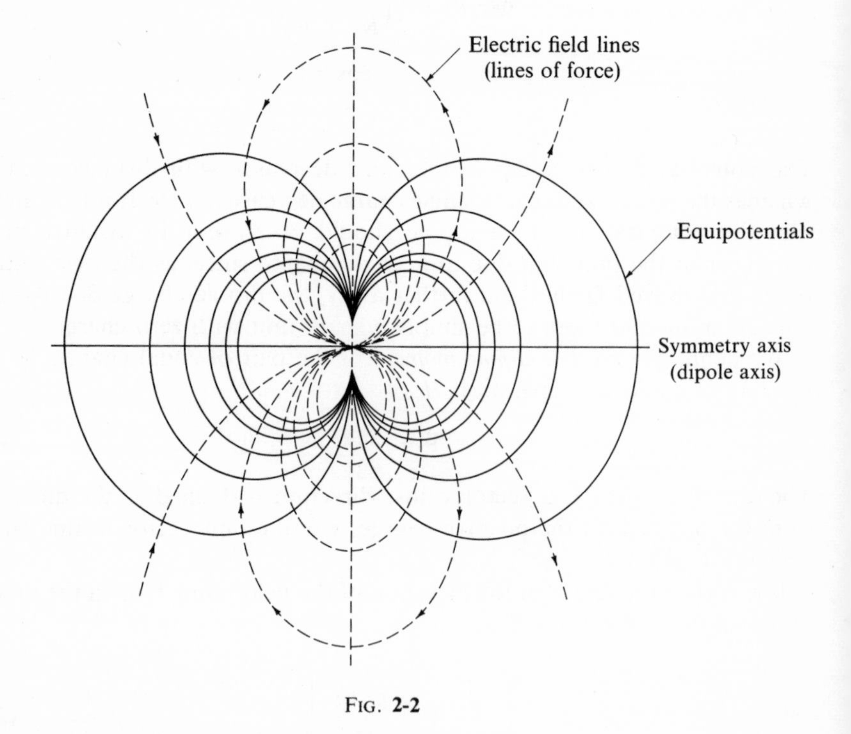

FIG. **2-2**

equipotential surfaces may be obtained by rotating the curves of Fig. 2-2 about the symmetry axis. (The direction of the dipole moment in Fig. 2-2 is horizontally from left to right.)

We have considered our dipole to be of finite size. But we may also define a *point dipole* as the limit in which the separation vanishes and the magnitude of the charge becomes infinite in such a way that the product remains finite. Thus, for a point dipole of moment p,

$$p \equiv \lim_{\substack{l \to 0 \\ q \to \infty}} 2ql \tag{2.10}$$

2.3 Multipole Expansion of the Potential

Next, we consider the general situation in which we have a static collection of charges* q_α arbitrarily located (but in the vicinity of the origin). We let $\mathbf{r}'_\alpha = \mathbf{r}'_\alpha(x'_{\alpha,i})$ be the vector which designates the position of the αth charge at the point $(x'_{\alpha,1}, x'_{\alpha,2}, x'_{\alpha,3})$. The vectors to the field point $P = P(x_i)$ from the charge q_α and from the origin are denoted by $\mathbf{R}_\alpha = \mathbf{r} - \mathbf{r}'_\alpha$ and $\mathbf{r}$, respectively (see Fig. 2-3). The field point P is considered fixed, so that the vector $\mathbf{R}_\alpha$ is a function of the coordinates $x'_{\alpha,i}$ of the charges q_α.

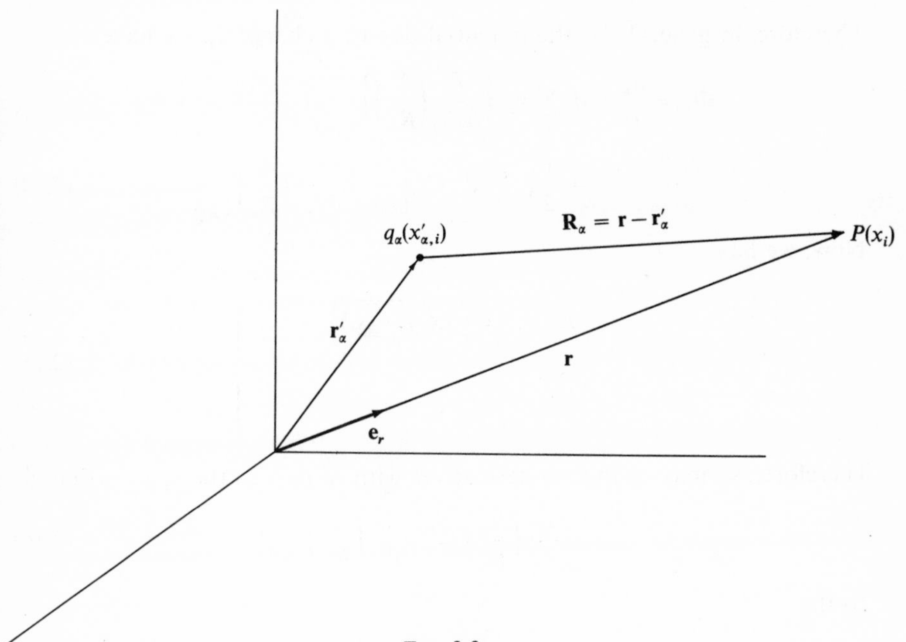

FIG. 2-3

* We use the convention throughout (except in the concluding chapter) that Greek subscripts refer to individual charges or particles, whereas Roman indices refer to coordinate axes. The notation x_i, or (x_1, x_2, x_3), is used for coordinates when summations are necessary in the discussion; otherwise, the more familiar (x, y, z) is used.

The potential at P due to q_α is

$$\Phi_\alpha = \frac{q_\alpha}{R_\alpha} \tag{2.11}$$

Again, we wish to express the potential in terms of $\mathbf{r}$. We have

$$\mathbf{R}_\alpha = \mathbf{r} - \mathbf{r}'_\alpha \tag{2.12}$$

where $\mathbf{r}$ is a function of the coordinates x_i of the point P. Now, any function of $\mathbf{R}_\alpha$, $f(\mathbf{R}_\alpha)$, may be expanded in a Taylor series about $\mathbf{R}_\alpha = \mathbf{r}$ (i.e., about the origin). Using the Taylor series that represents a function of three variables, $x'_{\alpha,1}, x'_{\alpha,2}, x'_{\alpha,3}$, we have

$$\begin{aligned} f(\mathbf{R}_\alpha) = f(\mathbf{r}) &+ \sum_i x'_{\alpha,i}\left[\frac{\partial f(\mathbf{R}_\alpha)}{\partial x'_{\alpha,i}}\right]_{\mathbf{R}_\alpha=\mathbf{r}} \\ &+ \frac{1}{2}\sum_{i,j} x'_{\alpha,i}x'_{\alpha,j}\left[\frac{\partial^2 f(\mathbf{R}_\alpha)}{\partial x'_{\alpha,i}\,\partial x'_{\alpha,j}}\right]_{\mathbf{R}_\alpha=\mathbf{r}} + \cdots \end{aligned} \tag{2.13}$$

Therefore, in general, for the potential due to a charge q_α, we have

$$\begin{aligned} \Phi_\alpha = \frac{q_\alpha}{r} &+ q_\alpha \sum_i x'_{\alpha,i}\left[\frac{\partial}{\partial x'_{\alpha,i}}\left(\frac{1}{R_\alpha}\right)\right]_{R_\alpha=r} \\ &+ \frac{1}{2}q_\alpha \sum_{i,j} x'_{\alpha,i}x'_{\alpha,j}\left[\frac{\partial^2}{\partial x'_{\alpha,i}\,\partial x'_{\alpha,j}}\left(\frac{1}{R_\alpha}\right)\right]_{R_\alpha=r} + \cdots \end{aligned} \tag{2.14}$$

Now, we have

$$\left.\begin{aligned} R_\alpha &= \sqrt{\sum_i (x'_{\alpha,i} - x_i)^2} \\ r &= \sqrt{\sum_i x_i^2} \end{aligned}\right\} \tag{2.15}$$

Therefore, we may change to derivatives with respect to the x_i according to

$$\frac{\partial}{\partial x'_{\alpha,i}}\left(\frac{1}{R_\alpha}\right) = -\frac{\partial}{\partial x_i}\left(\frac{1}{R_\alpha}\right) \tag{2.16}$$

so that

$$\begin{aligned} \left[\frac{\partial}{\partial x'_{\alpha,i}}\left(\frac{1}{R_\alpha}\right)\right]_{R_\alpha=r} &= -\left[\frac{\partial}{\partial x_i}\left(\frac{1}{R_\alpha}\right)\right]_{R_\alpha=r} \\ &= -\frac{\partial}{\partial x_i}\left(\frac{1}{r}\right) \end{aligned} \tag{2.17}$$

Consequently, the potential may be written as

$$\Phi_\alpha = \frac{q_\alpha}{r} - q_\alpha \sum_i x'_{\alpha,i} \frac{\partial}{\partial x_i}\left(\frac{1}{r}\right) + \frac{1}{2} q_\alpha \sum_{i,j} x'_{\alpha,i} x'_{\alpha,j} \frac{\partial^2}{\partial x_i \, \partial x_j}\left(\frac{1}{r}\right) - \cdots \tag{2.18}$$

The potential due to a collection of charges may then be written as

$$\Phi = \sum_\alpha \Phi_\alpha = \Phi^{(0)} + \Phi^{(2)} + \Phi^{(4)} + \cdots + \Phi^{(2l)} + \cdots \tag{2.19}$$

where

$$\Phi^{(0)} \equiv \sum_\alpha \frac{q_\alpha}{r} = \frac{q}{r} \tag{2.20a}$$

$$\Phi^{(2)} \equiv - \sum_\alpha q_\alpha \sum_i x'_{\alpha,i} \frac{\partial}{\partial x_i}\left(\frac{1}{r}\right) \tag{2.20b}$$

$$\Phi^{(4)} \equiv \frac{1}{2} \sum_\alpha q_\alpha \sum_{i,j} x'_{\alpha,i} x'_{\alpha,j} \frac{\partial^2}{\partial x_i \, \partial x_j}\left(\frac{1}{r}\right) \tag{2.20c}$$

$$\Phi^{(2l)} \equiv \frac{(-1)^l}{l!} \sum_\alpha q_\alpha \sum_{i,j,\ldots,l} x'_{\alpha,i} x'_{\alpha,j} \cdots x'_{\alpha,l} \frac{\partial^l}{\partial x_i \, \partial x_j \cdots \partial x_l}\left(\frac{1}{r}\right) \tag{2.20d}$$

The first term, $\Phi^{(0)}$, is just the potential that would result if the total charge $q = \Sigma_\alpha q_\alpha$ were located at the origin; it is called the *monopole potential.* The *monopole moment* is just the total charge q. The term $\Phi^{(2)}$ is called the *dipole potential*, and as we shall see, is equivalent to the potential discussed in the preceding section. The term $\Phi^{(4)}$ is called the *quadrupole potential*, and, in general, the term $\Phi^{(2l)}$ is called the $2l$th multipole potential.

In the following sections we shall investigate the potentials $\Phi^{(2)}$ and $\Phi^{(4)}$ in detail.

2.4 The Dipole Potential

We first direct our attention to the term $\Phi^{(2)}$, given by Eq. (2.20b):

$$\begin{aligned} \Phi^{(2)} &= - \sum_\alpha q_\alpha \sum_i x'_{\alpha,i} \frac{\partial}{\partial x_i}\left(\frac{1}{r}\right) \\ &= - \sum_\alpha q_\alpha \mathbf{r}'_\alpha \cdot \mathbf{grad}\left(\frac{1}{r}\right) \end{aligned} \tag{2.21}$$

But the sum over the $q_\alpha \mathbf{r}'_\alpha$, in analogy with Eq. (2.6), is just the *dipole moment* of the system:

$$\mathbf{p} = \sum_\alpha q_\alpha \mathbf{r}'_\alpha \tag{2.22}$$

Thus,

$$\begin{aligned}\Phi^{(2)} &= -\mathbf{p} \cdot \mathbf{grad}\left(\frac{1}{r}\right) \\ &= -\mathbf{p} \cdot \left(-\frac{\mathbf{r}}{r^3}\right) \\ &= \frac{\mathbf{p} \cdot \mathbf{e}_r}{r^2}\end{aligned} \tag{2.23}$$

as before [see Eq. (2.7)]. Notice that the gradient operation in the above expressions is carried out with respect to the coordinates of the *field point* (the x_i). Therefore, the second term in the general expansion for the potential corresponds exactly to the approximate potential for the simple dipole that was computed in Section 2.2. (The monopole term is, of course, zero for the simple dipole.)

The electric dipole field vector $\mathbf{E}^{(2)}$ may be calculated by taking the gradient of $\Phi^{(2)}$:

$$\begin{aligned}\mathbf{E}^{(2)} &= -\mathbf{grad}\, \Phi^{(2)} \\ &= -\mathbf{grad}\left(\frac{\mathbf{p} \cdot \mathbf{r}}{r^3}\right)\end{aligned} \tag{2.24}$$

Expanding the gradient of the product of two scalar functions ($\mathbf{p} \cdot \mathbf{r}$ and $1/r^3$), we find

$$\mathbf{E}^{(2)} = -\frac{1}{r^3}\, \mathbf{grad}(\mathbf{p} \cdot \mathbf{r}) - (\mathbf{p} \cdot \mathbf{r})\, \mathbf{grad}\left(\frac{1}{r^3}\right) \tag{2.25}$$

Now,

$$\mathbf{grad}(\mathbf{p} \cdot \mathbf{r}) = \sum_i p_i \mathbf{e}_i = \mathbf{p} \tag{2.26}$$

and

$$\mathbf{grad}\left(\frac{1}{r^3}\right) = -\frac{3\mathbf{r}}{r^5} \tag{2.27}$$

Therefore,

$$\begin{aligned}\mathbf{E}^{(2)} &= -\frac{\mathbf{p}}{r^3} + (\mathbf{p} \cdot \mathbf{r})\frac{3\mathbf{r}}{r^5} \\ &= \frac{1}{r^5}[3(\mathbf{p} \cdot \mathbf{r})\mathbf{r} - \mathbf{p}r^2]\end{aligned} \tag{2.28}$$

We see, as before, that the dipole potential varies as $1/r^2$ and the electric dipole field varies as $1/r^3$.

2.5 The Quadrupole Potential and The Quadrupole Moment

The third term in the general expansion for the potential due to an arbitrary, static distribution of charges is

$$\Phi^{(4)} = \tfrac{1}{2}\sum_{\alpha} q_\alpha \sum_{i,j} x'_{\alpha,i}x'_{\alpha,j}\,\frac{\partial^2}{\partial x_i\,\partial x_j}\left(\frac{1}{r}\right) \tag{2.29}$$

Although this expression may be used directly for the calculation of quadrupole potentials, it is frequently more convenient to make a modification which transforms the expression into a form that is familiar from a study of the inertia tensor in rigid-body dynamics. We may proceed in the following manner.

As mentioned in Section 1.11, $1/r$ is a solution of Laplace's equation, except at $r = 0$; thus,

$$\sum_i \frac{\partial^2}{\partial x_i^2}\left(\frac{1}{r}\right) = 0, \qquad r > 0 \tag{2.30}$$

This expression may be rewritten as

$$\sum_{i,j} \frac{\partial^2}{\partial x_i\,\partial x_j}\left(\frac{1}{r}\right)\delta_{ij} = 0, \qquad r > 0 \tag{2.30a}$$

Since this is a null quantity, any constant times this quantity may be added to $\Phi^{(4)}$ without altering the value. If we choose this constant to be $-\frac{1}{6}\Sigma_\alpha q_\alpha r'^2_\alpha$, where $r'^2_\alpha = |\mathbf{r}'_\alpha|^2$, then we have

$$\Phi^{(4)} = \tfrac{1}{6}\sum_{\alpha} q_\alpha \sum_{i,j} (3x'_{\alpha,i}x'_{\alpha,j} - r'^2_\alpha\delta_{ij})\frac{\partial^2}{\partial x_i\,\partial x_j}\left(\frac{1}{r}\right) \tag{2.31}$$

We may write this expression as

$$\boxed{\Phi^{(4)} = \tfrac{1}{6}\sum_{i,j} Q_{ij}\,\frac{\partial^2}{\partial x_i\,\partial x_j}\left(\frac{1}{r}\right)} \tag{2.31a}$$

The nine quantities

$$\boxed{Q_{ij} \equiv \sum_{\alpha} q_\alpha(3x'_{\alpha,i}x'_{\alpha,j} - r'^2_\alpha\delta_{ij})} \tag{2.32}$$

form a 3×3 array which is a tensor* and is called the *quadrupole tensor*:

$$\{\mathbf{Q}\} = \begin{Bmatrix} Q_{11} & Q_{12} & Q_{13} \\ Q_{21} & Q_{22} & Q_{23} \\ Q_{31} & Q_{32} & Q_{33} \end{Bmatrix} \tag{2.33}$$

It is clear that this tensor is symmetric, i.e., $Q_{ij} = Q_{ji}$, so that $\{\mathbf{Q}\}$ can contain at most *six* independent elements. In fact, there exists one additional relation among the Q_{ij}, which reduces the number of independent elements to *five*. In order to show this, we write

$$Q_{kk} = \sum_{\alpha} q_\alpha(3x'^2_{\alpha,k} - r'^2_\alpha \delta_{kk}) \tag{2.34}$$

Summing over k, we find

$$\sum_k Q_{kk} = \sum_\alpha q_\alpha\left[3\left(\sum_k x'^2_{\alpha,k}\right) - r'^2_\alpha\left(\sum_k \delta_{kk}\right)\right] \tag{2.35}$$

But,

$$\sum_k x'^2_{\alpha,k} = |\mathbf{r}'_\alpha|^2 = r'^2_\alpha \tag{2.36a}$$

and,

$$\sum_k \delta_{kk} = 3 \tag{2.36b}$$

Therefore, Eq. (2.35) reduces to

$$\sum_k Q_{kk} = 0 \tag{2.37}$$

Thus, the sum of the diagonal elements of $\{\mathbf{Q}\}$ (called the *trace* of $\{\mathbf{Q}\}$) vanishes, and at most *five* of the Q_{ij} are independent.

If the quadrupole tensor is referred to principal axes, then all the off-diagonal elements vanish. This simplification, together with the vanishing of the trace, reduces the number of independent elements to *two*. In many important situations the charge distribution possesses an axis of symmetry. If we choose the x_3-axis, say, to correspond to the symmetry axis (which is, of course, a principal axis), then $Q_{11} = Q_{22}$. Hence, there is only *one* independent element of $\{\mathbf{Q}\}$:

$$Q_{33} = -(Q_{11} + Q_{22}) = -2Q_{11} = -2Q_{22} \tag{2.38}$$

as required by Eq. (2.37). The quantity Q_{33} is often abbreviated to Q and

* See Marion (Ma65a, Chapter 12) for a discussion of tensors; in particular, compare Eq. (2.32) with Eq. (13.10) of Ma65a for the elements of the inertia tensor. A brief summary of tensor analysis is given in Appendix A.

referred to as the *quadrupole moment** of a symmetrical charge distribution (athough, of course, the quadrupole moment is properly a tensor, the only independent element of which is Q_{33} in this particular case).

We may summarize the reduction in the number of independent elements of $\{\mathbf{Q}\}$ in the following manner:

Q_{ij}: 9 elements

↓ $\{\mathbf{Q}\}$ symmetric

at most 6 independent elements

↓ trace of $\{\mathbf{Q}\}$ vanishes

at most 5 independent elements

↓ $\{\mathbf{Q}\}$ referred to principal axes

at most 2 independent elements

↓ symmetrical charge distribution

1 independent element $= Q$

The quadrupole tensor defined by Eq. (2.32) exhibits these properties, and for this reason quadrupole potential calculations using this tensor are usually more convenient than the direct application of Eq. (2.29).

If the x_3'-axis is the symmetry axis of the charge distribution, and if the distribution is continuous rather than discrete, then

$$Q = \int_V \rho(\mathbf{r}')(3x_3'^2 - r'^2)\, dx_1'\, dx_2'\, dx_3' \tag{2.39}$$

where $\rho(\mathbf{r}')$ is the charge density at the point defined by the vector $\mathbf{r}'$ and where the integration extends over the volume V of the charge density distribution. In the event that the distribution consists entirely of *positive* charge (as for atomic nuclei), and if there is a preponderance of charge along the x_3'-axis (i.e., if the distribution is *prolate*), then $Q > 0$; on the other hand, $Q < 0$ for an *oblate* distribution of positive charge.

▶ **Example 2.5.** Consider the charge distribution in Fig 2-4. This distribution may be considered to be two identical dipoles with moments $p = 2q\delta$ separated by a distance $2l$ (or, alternatively, as two dipoles with $p = 2lq$ separated by a distance 2δ). We have

$$\left.\begin{array}{lll} +q & \text{at} & x_3' = l + \delta \\ -q & \text{at} & l - \delta \\ -q & \text{at} & -l + \delta \\ +q & \text{at} & -l - \delta \end{array}\right\}$$

* Some authors call this quantity the *quadrupole strength*. This is perhaps a better term, but popular usage is *moment*.

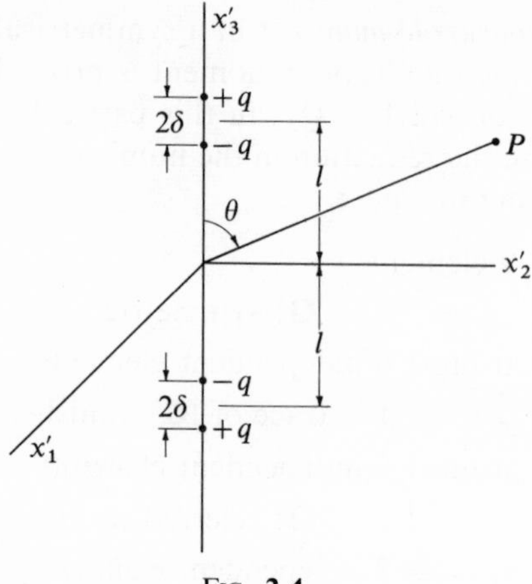

FIG. 2-4

We note first that both the monopole and dipole moments vanish identically, so that the quadrupole term is the lowest-order contribution to the potential. Since the distribution is symmetric about the x_3'-axis, we have only the single independent quadrupole tensor element Q_{33}:

$$\begin{aligned} Q = Q_{33} &= 2\sum_{\alpha} q_\alpha x_{\alpha,3}'^2 \\ &= 2[q(l+\delta)^2 - q(l-\delta)^2 - q(-l+\delta)^2 + q(-l-\delta)^2] \\ &= 16ql\delta = 8pl \end{aligned} \tag{1}$$

Also,

$$Q_{11} = Q_{22} = -\tfrac{1}{2}Q_{33} = -4pl \tag{2}$$

Then, using Eq. (2.31a), we have

$$\begin{aligned} \Phi^{(4)} &= \tfrac{1}{6}\sum_{i,j} Q_{ij}\frac{\partial^2}{\partial x_i\,\partial x_j}\left(\frac{1}{r}\right) \\ &= \tfrac{1}{3}\sum_{k} Q_{kk}\frac{\partial^2}{\partial x_k^2}\left(\frac{1}{r}\right) \\ &= \frac{4pl}{3}\cdot\frac{1}{r^5}(-x_1^2 - x_2^2 + 2x_3^2) \\ &= \frac{4pl}{3}\,\frac{(3x_3^2 - r^2)}{r^5} \end{aligned} \tag{3}$$

Since $x_3 = r\cos\theta$, we may write Eq. (3) as

$$\Phi^{(4)} = \frac{4pl}{3}\,\frac{(3\cos^2\theta - 1)}{r^3} \tag{4}$$

This potential as a function of the polar angle θ is shown in Fig. 2-5. Notice that there are *positive* and *negative* regions of the potential. The two negative charges lie closer to the x_2-axis than do the two positive charges; therefore, near $\theta = 90°$ their influence on the potential is greater, and the potential becomes negative in this region. The potential vanishes along the direction $\theta_0 = \cos^{-1}(1/\sqrt{3}) \cong 54.7°$.

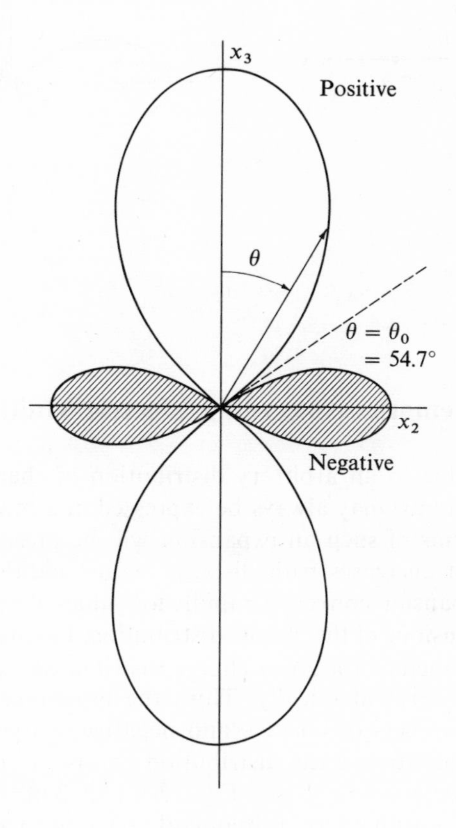

FIG. 2-5

If the charge distribution is a square array, as in Fig. 2-6, then the potential is no longer independent of the azimuthal angle φ. In this case the quadrupole potential is given by (see Problem 2-11)

$$\Phi^{(4)} = \tfrac{1}{2}ql^2\frac{(\cos^2\theta - \sin^2\theta\sin^2\varphi)}{r^3} \tag{5}$$

where $\varphi = 0$ along the positive x_1-axis. The potential in the x_2-x_3 plane ($\varphi = \pi/2$) is shown in Fig. 2-7; again there are both positive and negative portions of the potential.

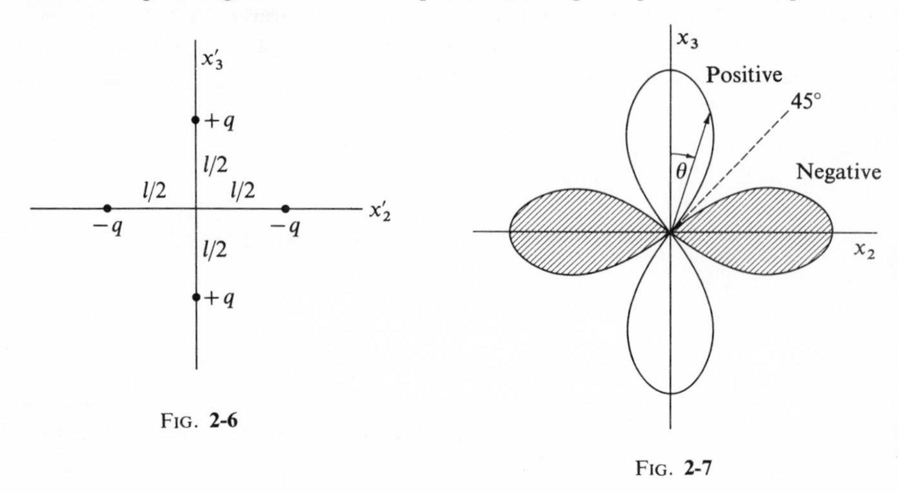

FIG. 2-6

FIG. 2-7

2.6 Further Remarks concerning Electric Multipoles*

The potential due to an arbitrary distribution of charge (whether it be discrete or continuous) may always be expressed in a multipole expansion. In general, all terms of such an expansion will be present, although each higher-order term decreases with distance by an additional factor of $1/r$. Therefore, the expansion converges rapidly for values of r that are large compared to the dimensions of the charge distribution. Furthermore, because of the particular geometry of a given charge distribution, some of the multipole terms may vanish identically. Thus, the monopole term vanishes if there are equal numbers of positive and negative charges, and the dipole term vanishes in addition if the distribution consists of equivalent dipoles which are oppositely oriented (see Figs. 2-4 and 2-6). In such cases, the lowest-order nonvanishing term is frequently referred to as a *pure multipole.* Thus, Fig. 2-1 shows a *pure dipole* and Fig. 2-6 shows a *pure quadrupole.* It must be remembered, however, that in these cases the dipole or quadrupole term is only the *leading* term in an expansion and that, in general, all higher-order terms are also present.

The simplest example of a *pure multipole* of a given order may be generated by superimposing, with a slight displacement, two multipoles of the next lowest order which have opposite signs. Thus, a *pure dipole* is formed by

* These comments, with obvious modifications of nomenclature, apply to magnetic multipoles as well; see Section 2.7.

charges $+q$ and $-q$ separated by a distance l; a *pure quadrupole* is formed by dipoles of moments $\mathbf{p}$ and $-\mathbf{p}$ separated by a distance l, etc. Such a series of multipoles is shown in Fig. 2-8.

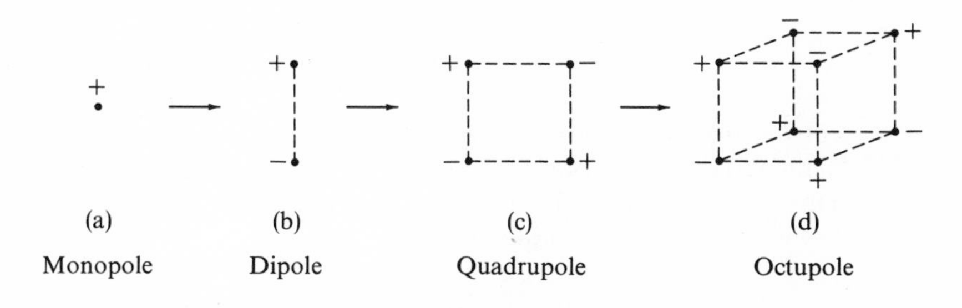

FIG. **2-8**

Multipole moments are in general dependent upon the choice of origin for their calculation. For example, the potential due to a single charge is q/R, where R is the distance from the charge to the field point. But if a multipole expansion is made with the origin located at a point other than that occupied by the charge, then no term in the expansion will vanish identically even for this simple case. [This is exactly the situation of Fig. 2-3 and Eq. (2.18)]. On the other hand, the dipole moment is independent of the choice of origin if the distribution has zero net charge (see Problem 2-2). In addition to the general dependence on the choice of origin, the quadrupole and higher-order moments also depend on the *orientation* of the axes. (But recall that principal axes can always be found which diagonalize a tensor.)

2.7 Magnetic Multipoles

We now turn our attention to the representation by a multipole expansion of the magnetic effects of steady currents. We begin by writing the expression for the vector potential [Eq. (1.37)]:

$$\mathbf{A}(\mathbf{r}) = \frac{1}{c}\int_V \frac{\mathbf{J}(\mathbf{r}')}{|\mathbf{r}-\mathbf{r}'|}\,dv' = \frac{1}{c}\int_V \frac{\mathbf{J}(\mathbf{r}')}{R}\,dv' \tag{2.40}$$

As in the electrostatic case, we may expand the term $1/R = 1/|\mathbf{r}-\mathbf{r}'|$. Thus, retaining only the monopole and dipole terms, we may write, as in Eqs. (2.20) and (2.21),

$$\mathbf{A}(\mathbf{r}) = \frac{1}{cr}\int_V \mathbf{J}(\mathbf{r}')\,dv' - \frac{1}{c}\int_V \mathbf{J}(\mathbf{r}')\left[\mathbf{r}\cdot\mathbf{grad}\left(\frac{1}{r}\right)\right]dv' \tag{2.41}$$

[The quadrupole and higher-order terms may be treated in a manner analogous to that used in the electrostatic case; for simplicity, we omit these terms (see Problem 2-16).]

Let us first examine the monopole term:

$$\mathbf{A}^{(0)} = \frac{1}{cr} \int_V \mathbf{J}(\mathbf{r}')\, dv' \tag{2.42}$$

The current density in the system may be considered to arise from many closed* filamentary current loops. Therefore, the volume integral of $\mathbf{J}$ may be represented as the sum over all of the line integrals of the filamentary currents around the individual loops (see Fig. 2-9):

$$\int_V \mathbf{J}(\mathbf{r}')\, dv' = \sum_\beta \oint_{\Gamma_\beta} I'_\beta\, d\mathbf{s}'_\beta \tag{2.43}$$

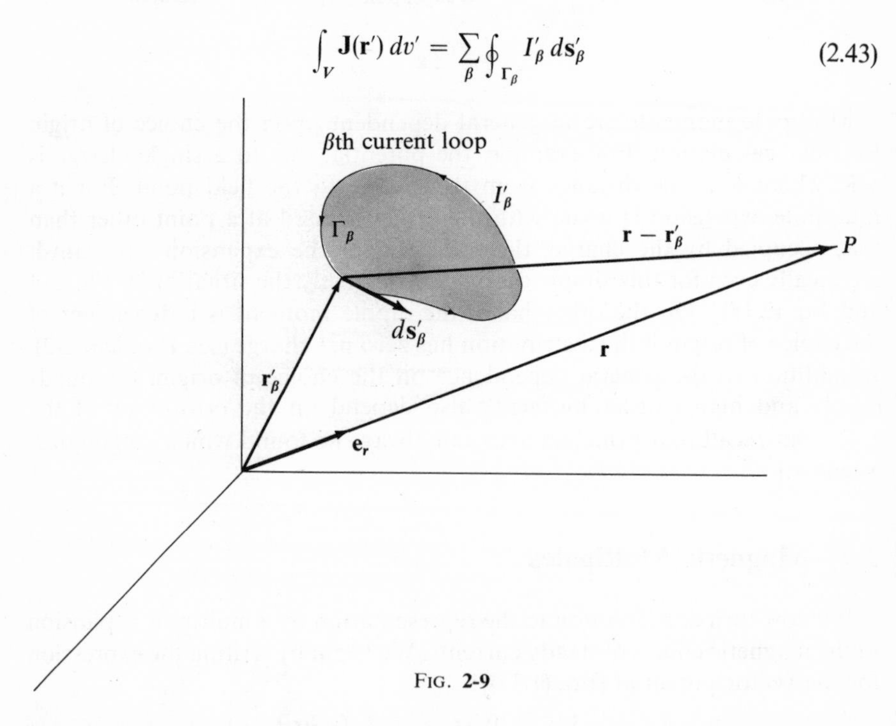

FIG. 2-9

But since I'_β is constant for any given loop, the right-hand side of this expression becomes

$$\sum_\beta I'_\beta \oint_{\Gamma_\beta} d\mathbf{s}'_\beta$$

which vanishes since the integrand is an exact differential. Thus,

$$\mathbf{A}^{(0)} \equiv 0 \tag{2.44}$$

* "Closed" since the current density is by hypothesis *steady*.

This important result states that there is no monopole term in a magnetic multipole expansion. This conclusion agrees with that based on the interpretation of div $\mathbf{B} = 0$ given in Section 1.5, viz., that free magnetic poles do not exist.

The second term in Eq. (2.41) may be transformed in a similar manner with the result

$$\mathbf{A}^{(2)} = -\frac{1}{c}\sum_{\beta} I'_{\beta} \oint_{\Gamma_{\beta}} \mathbf{r}'_{\beta} \cdot \mathbf{grad}\left(\frac{1}{r}\right) d\mathbf{s}'_{\beta} \tag{2.45}$$

(Recall that the gradient operation is carried out with respect to the coordinates of the *field point.*) Now,

$$\begin{aligned} \mathbf{r}'_{\beta} \cdot \mathbf{grad}\left(\frac{1}{r}\right) d\mathbf{s}'_{\beta} \\ &= \frac{1}{2} d\left(\mathbf{r}'_{\beta}\left[\mathbf{r}'_{\beta} \cdot \mathbf{grad}\left(\frac{1}{r}\right)\right]\right) \\ &\quad + \frac{1}{2}\left(d\mathbf{s}'_{\beta}\left[\mathbf{r}_{\beta} \cdot \mathbf{grad}\left(\frac{1}{r}\right)\right] - \mathbf{r}'_{\beta}\left[d\mathbf{s}'_{\beta} \cdot \mathbf{grad}\left(\frac{1}{r}\right)\right]\right) \\ &= \frac{1}{2} d\left(\mathbf{r}'_{\beta}\left[\mathbf{r}'_{\beta} \cdot \mathbf{grad}\left(\frac{1}{r}\right)\right]\right) - \frac{1}{2}\mathbf{grad}\left(\frac{1}{r}\right) \times (\mathbf{r}'_{\beta} \times d\mathbf{s}'_{\beta}) \end{aligned} \tag{2.46}$$

Substituting this last expression into Eq. (2.45), the integral of the first term vanishes since it is an exact differential and there remains

$$\mathbf{A}^{(2)} = \frac{1}{2}\mathbf{grad}\left(\frac{1}{r}\right) \times \left(\frac{1}{c}\sum_{\beta} I'_{\beta} \oint_{\Gamma_{\beta}} \mathbf{r}'_{\beta} \times d\mathbf{s}'_{\beta}\right) \tag{2.47}$$

where $\mathbf{grad}(1/r)$ has been removed from the integral since the integration is over the coordinates of the current loop and is therefore independent of the coordinates of the field point.

Now, if a surface, S, is bounded by a closed curve, Γ, as in Fig. 2-10, then (see Problem 2-15)

$$\oint_{\Gamma} \mathbf{r} \times d\mathbf{s} = 2\int_{S} d\mathbf{a} \tag{2.48}$$

Therefore, Eq. (2.47) may be expressed as

$$\mathbf{A}^{(2)} = \mathbf{grad}\left(\frac{1}{r}\right) \times \left(\frac{1}{c}\sum_{\beta} I'_{\beta} \int_{S_{\beta}} d\mathbf{a}'_{\beta}\right) \tag{2.49}$$

where S_{β} is a surface bounded by the βth current loop.

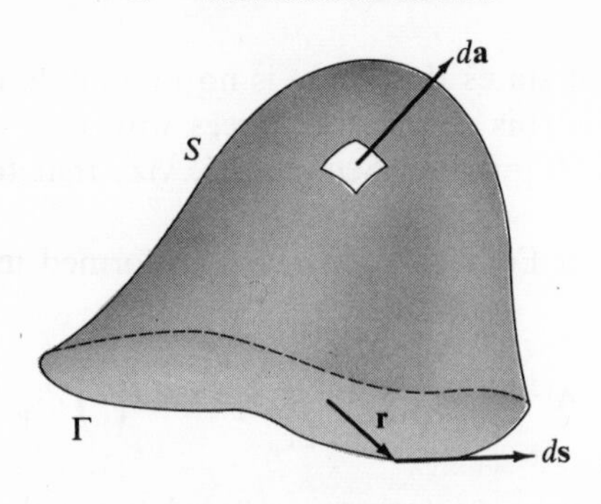

FIG. 2-10

In Section 1.8 we defined the magnetic moment of a current I' flowing in a plane loop which encloses an area **S** to be [Eq. (1.43)]:

$$\mathbf{m} = \frac{I'}{c}\mathbf{S} \tag{2.50}$$

We may generalize this to read

$$\mathbf{m} = \frac{I'}{c}\int_S d\mathbf{a} \tag{2.50a}$$

where S is a surface such as that in Fig. 2-10; the current I' flows in the loop, Γ, which bounds S. Therefore, the term in parentheses in Eq. (2.49) is just the sum of all of the elementary dipole moments $\mathbf{m}_\beta$:

$$\begin{aligned}\mathbf{A}^{(2)} &= \mathbf{grad}\left(\frac{1}{r}\right) \times \sum_\beta \mathbf{m}_\beta \\ &= \mathbf{grad}\left(\frac{1}{r}\right) \times \mathbf{m}_{\text{total}}\end{aligned} \tag{2.51}$$

where $\mathbf{m}_{\text{total}}$ is the magnetic dipole moment of the entire system of currents. We may expand **grad**$(1/r)$ and write this result as

$$\mathbf{A}^{(2)} = \frac{\mathbf{m}_{\text{total}} \times \mathbf{e}_r}{r^2} \tag{2.51a}$$

This expression for the dipole portion of the vector potential is analogous to Eq. (2.23) for the electrostatic case.

Since $\mathbf{A}^{(0)} \equiv 0$, the lowest order contribution to the magnetic field will be obtained by taking the curl of the dipole term in the vector potential expansion:

$$\mathbf{B}^{(2)} = \mathbf{curl}\,\mathbf{A}^{(2)} \tag{2.52}$$

Abbreviating $\mathbf{m}_{\text{total}}$ by $\mathbf{m}$, we may write

$$\mathbf{B}^{(2)} = \mathbf{curl}\left(\frac{\mathbf{m} \times \mathbf{r}}{r^3}\right) \tag{2.53}$$

Using the vector identity,

$$\mathbf{curl}(\mathbf{a} \times \mathbf{b}) = (\mathbf{b} \cdot \mathbf{grad})\mathbf{a} - (\mathbf{a} \cdot \mathbf{grad})\mathbf{b} + \mathbf{a}\,\mathrm{div}\,\mathbf{b} - \mathbf{b}\,\mathrm{div}\,\mathbf{a}$$

we have

$$\mathbf{B}^{(2)} = \left(\frac{\mathbf{r}}{r^3} \cdot \mathbf{grad}\right)\mathbf{m} - \left(\mathbf{m} \cdot \mathbf{grad}\right)\frac{\mathbf{r}}{r^3} + \mathbf{m}\,\mathrm{div}\left(\frac{\mathbf{r}}{r^3}\right) - \frac{\mathbf{r}}{r^3}\,\mathrm{div}\,\mathbf{m} \tag{2.54}$$

Now, all of the differential operations are performed with respect to the coordinates of the field point. Since such operations have no influence on the magnetic moment, the first and last terms in Eq. (2.54) vanish. Furthermore, $\mathrm{div}(\mathbf{r}/r^3) \equiv 0$, so that $\mathbf{B}^{(2)}$ becomes

$$\begin{aligned} \mathbf{B}^{(2)} &= -(\mathbf{m} \cdot \mathbf{grad})\frac{\mathbf{r}}{r^3} \\ &= -\frac{1}{r^3}(\mathbf{m} \cdot \mathbf{grad})\mathbf{r} - \mathbf{r}(\mathbf{m} \cdot \mathbf{grad})\,\frac{1}{r^3} \end{aligned} \tag{2.55}$$

Evaluating the first term in rectangular coordinates we find [see Eq. (A.26b)]

$$\begin{aligned} (\mathbf{m} \cdot \mathbf{grad})\mathbf{r} &= \left(\sum_i m_i \frac{\partial x_1}{\partial x_i},\quad \sum_i m_i \frac{\partial x_2}{\partial x_i},\quad \sum_i m_i \frac{\partial x_3}{\partial x_i}\right) \\ &= (m_1, m_2, m_3) \\ &= \mathbf{m} \end{aligned} \tag{2.56a}$$

The second term is [see Eq. (A.26a)]

$$\begin{aligned} (\mathbf{m} \cdot \mathbf{grad})\frac{1}{r^3} &= \mathbf{m} \cdot \mathbf{grad}\left(\frac{1}{r^3}\right) \\ &= -\frac{3\mathbf{m} \cdot \mathbf{r}}{r^5} \end{aligned} \tag{2.56b}$$

Thus,

$$\begin{aligned} \mathbf{B}^{(2)} &= -\frac{\mathbf{m}}{r^3} + (\mathbf{m} \cdot \mathbf{r})\frac{3\mathbf{r}}{r^5} \\ &= \frac{1}{r^5}[3(\mathbf{m} \cdot \mathbf{r})\mathbf{r} - \mathbf{m}r^2] \end{aligned} \tag{2.57}$$

Hence, the magnetic dipole field is of exactly the same form as the electric dipole field [see Eq. (2.28)].

Suggested References

A more-or-less introductory account of multipole fields is given by Owen (Ow63, Chapter 2).

A brief (and formal) discussion will be found in Band (Ba59, Chapter 4).

More advanced treatments are given by Landau and Lifshitz (La62, Chapter 5), Panofsky and Phillips (Pa60, Chapter 1), and Stratton (St41, Chapters 3 and 4).

Problems

2-1. An electric dipole and a fixed electric charge are located as in the figure. Compute the force and the torque acting on the dipole.

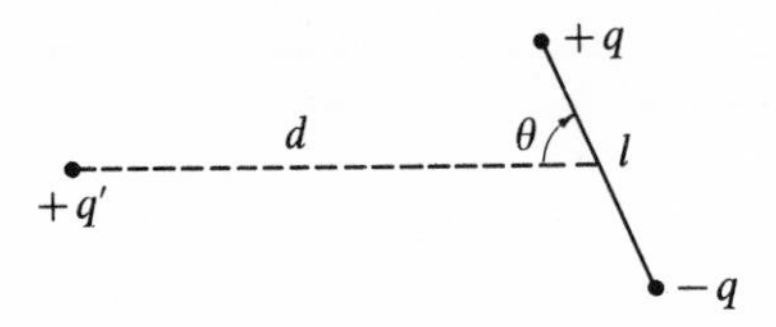

2-2. Show that the electric dipole moment of a system of charges is independent of the choice of origin if the system has zero net charge.

2-3. A charge $q_1 = +2e$ is located at the origin and a charge $q_2 = -e$ is located at the point $(x, y) = (1, 0)$. Calculate the potential at the points $(0, 5)$ and $(5, 0)$ in the following ways: (a) by a direct calculation of q/R for each charge, (b) by considering one term of a multipole expansion, (c) two terms, and (d) three terms. Discuss the difference in the rates of convergence toward the exact values for the two different field points.

2-4. Compute the quadrupole tensor for the following distribution of charges:

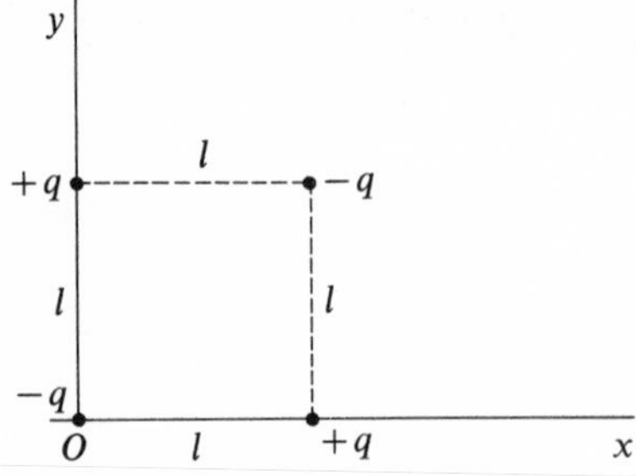

Diagonalize the tensor by a coordinate rotation and find the quadrupole moment.

2-5. A charge q is distributed uniformly along the line from $z = -h$ to $z = h$. Calculate the multipole moments of this charge distribution.

2-6. Calculate the dipole and quadrupole moments of a uniformly charged ring of radius a which has total charge $+q$. Add a charge $-q$ at the center of the ring and recompute the moments.

2-7. The linear charge density on a ring of radius a is given by

$$\rho_l = \frac{q}{a}(\cos\theta - \sin 2\theta)$$

Find the monopole, dipole, and quadrupole moments of the system and calculate the potential at an arbitrary point in space, accurate to terms in $1/r^3$.

2-8. Calculate the dipole moment for the following charge distribution:

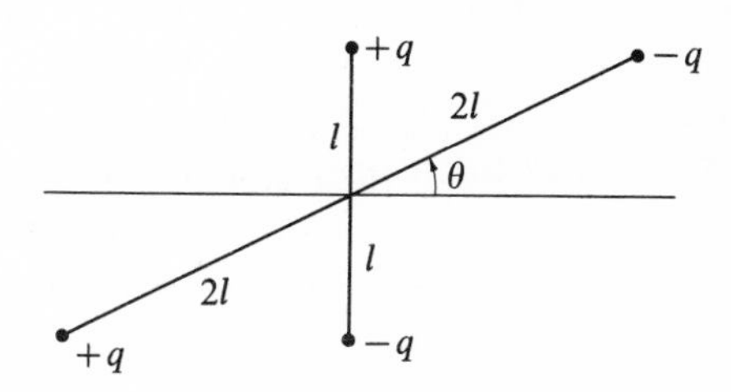

Plot the dipole moment as a function of θ and comment on the result.

2-9. Calculate the quadrupole tensor for the charge distribution of the previous problem for the general angle θ. Find the values of θ for which the tensor becomes diagonal. (Choose the x_3-axis to coincide with the axis of the dipole whose moment is $2lq$.)

2-10. Find the expression for the electric field vector for the linear quadrupole in Fig. 2-4. Sketch some of the field lines.

2-11. Derive the quadrupole potential for the charge distribution shown in Fig. 2-6. Find the expression for the corresponding electric field vector and sketch some of the field lines for the plane $\varphi = \pi/2$.

2-12. Consider a collection of electric charges q_α that are in arbitrary motion within a certain specified finite region of space. Write the first term of the multipole expansion for the vector potential [Eq. (2.41)] as

$$\mathbf{A}^{(0)} = \frac{1}{cr} \sum_{\alpha} q_{\alpha} \mathbf{u}_{\alpha}$$

where $\mathbf{u}_{\alpha}$ is the velocity of the αth charge, $\mathbf{u}_{\alpha} = \dot{\mathbf{r}}_{\alpha}$. Calculate the average value of $\mathbf{A}^{(0)}$ taken over the interval of time τ:

$$\langle \mathbf{A}^{(0)} \rangle = \frac{1}{\tau} \int_0^{\tau} \mathbf{A}^{(0)} \, dt$$

Show that $\langle \mathbf{A}^{(0)} \rangle$ approaches zero as τ becomes very large, in agreement with Eq. (2.44).

2-13. Continue the development begun in Problem 2-12 and apply it to the second term in the expansion for **A**. Construct an appropriate definition for the magnetic dipole moment $\mathbf{m}_{\text{total}}$ of a collection of moving charges by modifying Eq. (2.50a) for the case of discrete charges. Show that

$$\langle \mathbf{A}^{(2)} \rangle = \frac{\langle \mathbf{m}_{\text{total}} \rangle \times \mathbf{e}_r}{r^2}$$

in analogy with Eq. (2.51a). If all of the charges have the same ratio of charge to mass, q/m, and if all of the velocities are $\ll c$, then show that $\langle \mathbf{m}_{\text{total}} \rangle$ is proportional to the total angular momentum **L** of the system. The proportionality constant, $g \equiv q/2mc$, is called the *gyromagnetic ratio* of the system.

2-14. Show that the gyromagnetic ratio (see Problem 2-13) for a system of two charges, q_1 and q_2, whose masses are m_1 and m_2 is

$$g = \frac{\mu}{2c}\left(\frac{q_1}{m_1^2} + \frac{q_2}{m_2^2}\right)$$

where $\mu = m_1 m_2/(m_1 + m_2)$ is the reduced mass and where the velocities are assumed to be small compared with the velocity of light.

2-15. Prove Eq. (2.48) by applying Stokes' theorem to the quantity $\mathbf{r} \times \mathbf{k}$ where **k** is an arbitrary constant vector. Verify the result explicitly for the case of a plane area bounded by a circle; let the origin of **r** be located (a) at the center of the circle and (b) at some point outside the circle but in the plane of the circle.

2-16. Calculate the quadrupole term $\mathbf{A}^{(4)}$ in the expansion of the vector potential.

CHAPTER 3

The Equations of Laplace and Poisson

3.1 Introduction

In Chapter 1 we found that the general problem of the electrostatic field is described by Poisson's equation:

$$\nabla^2 \Phi = -\frac{4\pi}{\varepsilon}\rho \tag{3.1a}$$

In free space this equation reduces to Laplace's equation:

$$\nabla^2 \Phi = 0 \tag{3.1b}$$

The Laplacian operator occurs in many different types of physical problems,* probably the most important of which is that of wave propagation. Although we are interested in this book primarily in electromagnetic wave phenomena rather than in electrostatics, some of the mathematical functions which arise in the solution of wave equation are the same as those that result from the solution of Laplace's equation. It is somewhat easier to introduce these harmonic functions (Legendre functions, spherical harmonics, and Bessel functions) in connection with electrostatic problems.

* For example, gravitational attraction, fluid flow, heat flow, chemical diffusion, etc.

We shall study such problems in some detail in order to become familiar with the functions that will be of use later in discussions of radiation phenomena. This will be the extent of the treatment of electrostatics; we will not discuss the method of images nor the use of conjugate functions in the solution of problems in electrostatics. The interested reader is referred to the list of Suggested References for sources of such material.

3.2 General Properties of Harmonic Functions

We first discuss some of the important properties of *harmonic functions*, i.e., functions that satisfy Laplace's equation:

Property 1. If Φ is a solution of Laplace's equation in a region V of space which is bounded by a surface S, then Φ can attain neither a maximum nor minimum within V.

To prove Property 1, we note first that for a maximum to exist we must have

$$\frac{\partial^2 \Phi}{\partial x_i^2} < 0, \qquad \text{for} \qquad i = 1, 2, 3 \tag{3.2}$$

and for a minimum to exist we must have

$$\frac{\partial^2 \Phi}{\partial x_i^2} > 0, \qquad \text{for} \qquad i = 1, 2, 3 \tag{3.3}$$

But Φ satisfies the equation

$$\nabla^2 \Phi = \sum_i \frac{\partial^2 \Phi}{\partial x_i^2} = 0 \tag{3.4}$$

Thus, neither Eq. (3.2) nor Eq. (3.3) can be satisfied. Since Φ obeys Laplace's equation throughout V and on the surface S, both the maximum and the minimum values of Φ must be attained throughout V so that Φ is *constant*. For example, if S is a conducting surface placed in an electric field, the potential Φ must be a constant throughout V. As a result, we conclude that $\mathbf{E} = -\,\mathbf{grad}\,\Phi$ must vanish within the surface S.

Property 2. If Φ is a solution of Laplace's equation in a region of space V which is bounded by a surface S, then this solution is unique if *either* of the following boundary conditions apply:* (a) the value of Φ is specified on the surface S; or (b) the normal derivative of Φ is specified on the surface S.

In order to prove Property 2, let us assume that the solution is not unique

* (a) is called the *Dirichlet condition* and (b) is called the *Neumann condition*, after P. G. L. Dirichlet and K. G. Neumann who made extensive investigations of boundary-value problems during the middle of the nineteenth century.

and seek a contradiction. Let two solutions to Laplace's equation be Φ_1 and Φ_2, and let the difference between these be $\bar{\Phi}$:

$$\bar{\Phi} \equiv \Phi_1 - \Phi_2 \tag{3.5}$$

The property will be proven if we show that $\bar{\Phi}$ vanishes throughout V. The proof can be carried out by making use of Green's theorem:*

$$\oint_S \psi \frac{\partial \varphi}{\partial n} da = \int_V [\psi \nabla^2 \varphi + (\mathbf{grad}\, \varphi) \cdot (\mathbf{grad}\, \psi)] \, dv \tag{3.6}$$

where φ and ψ are arbitrary scalar functions and where $\partial\varphi/\partial n$ is the normal derivative of φ on the surface S. If we identify both ψ and φ with $\bar{\Phi}$, we have

$$\oint_S \bar{\Phi} \frac{\partial \bar{\Phi}}{\partial n} da = \int_V [\bar{\Phi}\, \nabla^2 \bar{\Phi} + |\mathbf{grad}\, \bar{\Phi}|^2] \, dv \tag{3.7}$$

Now, if both Φ_1 and Φ_2 are solutions to Laplace's equation, then so is $\bar{\Phi}$. Therefore, Eq. (3.7) becomes

$$\int_V |\mathbf{grad}\, \bar{\Phi}|^2 \, dv = \oint_S \bar{\Phi} \frac{\partial \bar{\Phi}}{\partial n} da \tag{3.8}$$

From this equation we see that if we have either (a) $\bar{\Phi} = 0$ or (*b*) $\partial\bar{\Phi}/\partial n = 0$ on the surface S, then

$$\int_V |\mathbf{grad}\, \bar{\Phi}|^2 \, dv = 0 \tag{3.9}$$

Since $|\mathbf{grad}\, \bar{\Phi}|^2$ is a positive-definite quantity, Eq. (3.9) can be satisfied only if

$$\mathbf{grad}\, \bar{\Phi} = 0 \tag{3.10}$$

Thus, $\bar{\Phi}$ is constant throughout the volume V. If we have condition (*a*) above, viz., that Φ_1 and Φ_2 are equal on S and, hence that $\bar{\Phi} = 0$ on S, then we must also have $\bar{\Phi} = 0$, and $\Phi_1 = \Phi_2$ throughout V, so that the solution is unique. For condition (*b*) above, viz., that the normal derivatives of Φ_1 and Φ_2 are equal on S and hence that $\partial\bar{\Phi}/\partial n = 0$ on S, then Eq. (3.10) implies that $\bar{\Phi}$ is equal to an arbitrary (and trivial) constant throughout V. Thus, $\Phi_1 = \Phi_2$ (to within a trivial additive constant), and the solution is again unique.

Therefore, we conclude that we need only to specify Φ or $\mathbf{grad}\, \Phi = -\mathbf{E}$ on a given surface† in order to calculate a *unique* solution for Φ throughout the volume enclosed by the surface.

* See Eq. (A.55), Appendix A, or Marion (Ma65b, Section 3.5).

† Such a surface can, for example, be at infinity.

3.3. Solutions of Laplace's Equation in Rectangular Coordinates

In rectangular coordinates, Laplace's equation becomes

$$\frac{\partial^2 \Phi}{\partial x^2} + \frac{\partial^2 \Phi}{\partial y^2} + \frac{\partial^2 \Phi}{\partial z^2} = 0 \tag{3.11}$$

We attempt a solution by the method of *separation of variables** and assume that $\Phi(x, y, z)$ can be written as the product of three functions, each of which depends only on a single variable:

$$\Phi(x, y, z) = X(x)Y(y)Z(z) \tag{3.12}$$

Then, upon substituting into Eq. (3.11) and dividing by $\Phi = XYZ$, we find

$$\frac{1}{X}\frac{d^2X}{dx^2} + \frac{1}{Y}\frac{d^2Y}{dy^2} + \frac{1}{Z}\frac{d^2Z}{dz^2} = 0 \tag{3.13}$$

This equation can be valid only if we have

$$\left.\begin{aligned} \frac{1}{X}\frac{d^2X}{dx^2} &= \alpha'^2 \\ \frac{1}{Y}\frac{d^2Y}{dy^2} &= \beta'^2 \\ \frac{1}{Z}\frac{d^2Z}{dz^2} &= \gamma'^2 \end{aligned}\right\} \tag{3.14}$$

where

$$\alpha'^2 + \beta'^2 + \gamma'^2 = 0 \tag{3.15}$$

Equation (3.15) is called the *auxiliary condition* on the Eqs. (3.14).

It is apparent from Eq. (3.15) that the separation constants α', β', γ' cannot all be real, nor can they all be imaginary. If two of these constants are real, then the remaining one must be imaginary. Similarly, if two are imaginary, the third is real. If one constant vanishes, then one of the remaining two must be real and the other imaginary.

From Eqs. (3.14) we see that an imaginary separation constant implies an oscillatory solution, whereas a real constant leads to an exponential solution. If we arbitrarily let α' and β' be imaginary and let γ' be real, and

* This technique is also discussed by Marion (Ma65a, Chapter 15), where it is applied to the one-dimensional wave equation.

if we then define a new set of constants α, β, γ such that $\alpha'^2 \equiv -\alpha^2$, $\beta'^2 \equiv -\beta^2$, and $\gamma'^2 \equiv \gamma^2$, then we have $\alpha^2 > 0$, $\beta^2 > 0$, $\gamma^2 > 0$ (i.e., α, β, γ are all real). Equations (3.14) then become

$$\left.\begin{aligned} \frac{d^2X}{dx^2} + \alpha^2 X = 0 \\ \frac{d^2Y}{dy^2} + \beta^2 Y = 0 \\ \frac{d^2Z}{dz^2} - \gamma^2 Z = 0 \end{aligned}\right\} \tag{3.16}$$

where

$$\gamma^2 = \alpha^2 + \beta^2 \tag{3.17}$$

Thus, X and Y have oscillatory solutions, and Z has an exponential solution:

$$\left.\begin{aligned} X(x) &= Ae^{i\alpha x} + Be^{-i\alpha x} \\ Y(y) &= Ce^{i\beta y} + De^{-i\beta y} \\ Z(z) &= Ee^{\gamma z} + Fe^{-\gamma z} \end{aligned}\right\} \tag{3.18}$$

The solution for Φ is then the product of these three functions. But this is only a *particular* solution. In general, there will be a set of values of α, β, and γ that will serve equally well as separation constants; we denote these as

$$\left.\begin{aligned} \alpha_r &= \alpha_1, \alpha_2, \alpha_3, \ldots \\ \beta_s &= \beta_1, \beta_2, \beta_3, \ldots \\ \gamma_{rs} &= \sqrt{\alpha_r^2 + \beta_s^2} \end{aligned}\right\} \tag{3.19}$$

where the allowed values of γ are found from the auxiliary condition, Eq. (3.17).

Thus, the complete solution for $\Phi(x, y, z)$ is in general an extremely complicated function:

$$\begin{aligned} \Phi(x, y, z) &= X(x)Y(y)Z(z) \\ &= \sum_{r,s=1}^{\infty} (A_r e^{i\alpha_r x} + B_r e^{-i\alpha_r x})(C_s e^{i\beta_s y} + D_s e^{-i\beta_s y}) \\ &\qquad \cdot (E_{rs} e^{\gamma_{rs} z} + F_{rs} e^{-\gamma_{rs} z}) \end{aligned} \tag{3.20}$$

In shorthand notation, we write this as

$$\boxed{\Phi(x, y, z) \sim e^{\pm i\alpha x}\, e^{\pm i\beta y}\, e^{\pm \gamma z}} \tag{3.21}$$

We note that, in general, the selection of which separation constants are real and which are imaginary is arbitrary. (Of course, in a particular problem the physical situation will dictate the choice.) Thus, if the auxiliary condition were

$$\alpha^2 = \beta^2 + \gamma^2 > 0 \tag{3.22}$$

with

$$\left.\begin{aligned} \frac{d^2X}{dx^2} + \alpha^2 X &= 0 \\ \frac{d^2Y}{dy^2} - \beta^2 Y &= 0 \\ \frac{d^2Z}{dz^2} - \gamma^2 Z &= 0 \end{aligned}\right\} \tag{3.23}$$

then the solution would be

$$\Phi(x, y, z) \sim e^{\pm i\alpha x}\, e^{\pm \beta y}\, e^{\pm \gamma z} \tag{3.24}$$

The constants which appear in the general solution [Eq. (3.20)] viz., $\alpha_r, \beta_s, \gamma_{rs}, A_r, B_r, C_s, D_s, E_{rs}, F_{rs}$, will all be determined by the boundary conditions for the problem.

▶ **Example 3.3(a).** Let us compute for all points in space the potential Φ which arises from the configuration of Fig. 3-1. The planes $x = na$, $n = 0, \pm 1, \pm 2, \ldots$ are held at ground potential ($\Phi = 0$), while the planes lying between these and along $y = 0$

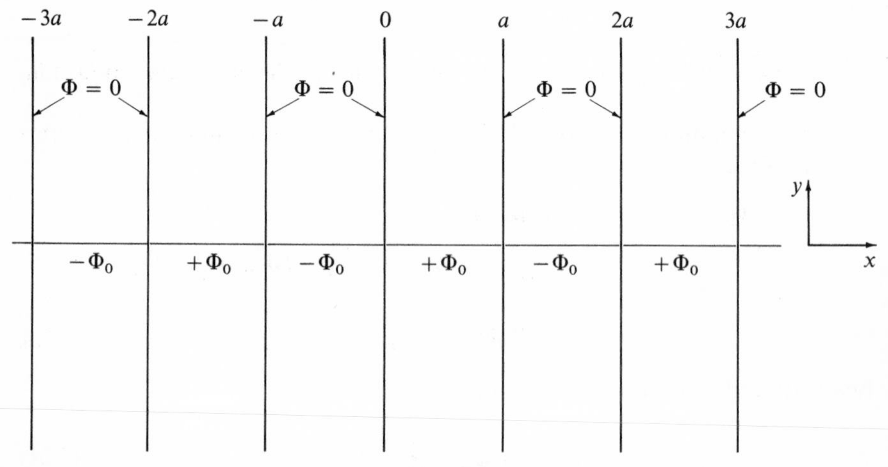

FIG. 3-1

alternately have $\Phi = \Phi_0$ and $\Phi = -\Phi_0$. The solution will be of the form given in Eq. (3.24), but since the potential in this problem is clearly independent of z, we have $\gamma = 0$ and $Z = \text{const}$. Similarly, the potential must obviously be oscillatory in x. These choices for X and Z then require that the solution for Y be exponential. Therefore, we have

$$\Phi(x, y, z) = \Phi(x, y) \sim e^{\pm i\alpha x} e^{\pm \beta y} \tag{1}$$

where

$$\alpha^2 = \beta^2 \tag{2}$$

We know that along the line $y = 0$, the potential is given by a series of step functions, as shown in Fig. 3-2. Thus, $\Phi(x, 0)$ can be represented by a Fourier series,* and since

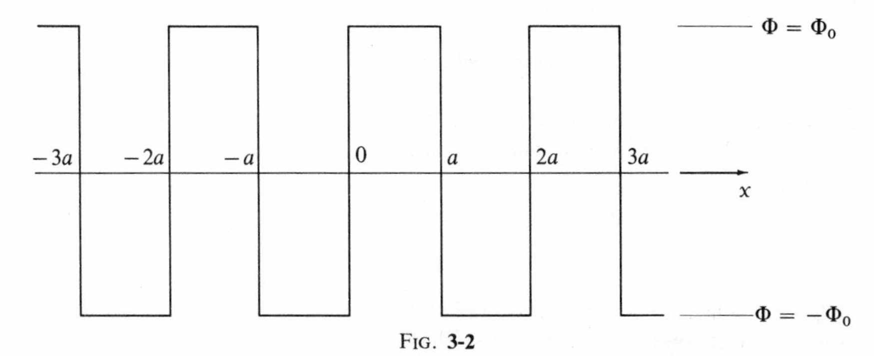

FIG. 3-2

the potential is an odd function of x, by a Fourier *sine* series. According to Eqs. (B.1) and (B.2), we may write a Fourier sine series for an arbitrary function $f(x)$ defined in the interval $-\pi < x < \pi$ as

$$f(x) = \frac{1}{\pi} \sum_{r=1}^{\infty} \sin rx \int_{-\pi}^{+\pi} f(\xi) \sin r\xi \, d\xi$$

The interval may be altered from $\pm\pi$ to $\pm a$ by making the change of variable $\xi \to \pi x'/a$. And since $f(x) = \Phi(x, 0)$ is *odd* in this case, we need integrate only from $x' = 0$ to $x' = a$ and double the result. Thus,

$$\Phi(x, 0) = \frac{2}{a} \sum_{r=1}^{\infty} \sin \frac{r\pi x}{a} \int_0^a \Phi(x', 0) \sin \frac{r\pi x'}{a} \, dx' \tag{3}$$

Now,

$$\int_0^a \Phi(x', 0) \sin \frac{r\pi x'}{a} \, dx' = \Phi_0 \int_0^a \sin \frac{r\pi x'}{a} \, dx' = \frac{2a}{r\pi} \Phi_0 \tag{4}$$

for $r = 1, 3, 5, \ldots$; the integral vanishes for even values of r. We have, therefore,

$$X(x) = \Phi(x, 0) = \frac{4\Phi_0}{\pi} \sum_{\substack{r \\ \text{odd}}} \frac{1}{r} \sin \frac{r\pi x}{a} \tag{5}$$

* See Appendix B for a brief summary of Fourier series.

We may now identify α as the coefficient of x in the sine terms. There is a particular value of α, say α_r, for each value of r:

$$\alpha_r = \frac{r\pi}{a} \tag{6}$$

But we also have $\alpha^2 = \beta^2$, so that

$$\beta_r = \pm\frac{r\pi}{a} \tag{7}$$

and

$$Y(y) = \Phi(0, y) \sim e^{\pm r\pi y/a} \tag{8}$$

We must choose only the solution which varies as $\exp(-r\pi|y|/a)$ in order that the potential not diverge at $|y| = \infty$. Therefore, the complete solution is

$$\Phi(x, y, z) = \frac{4\Phi_0}{\pi} \sum_{\substack{r \\ \text{odd}}} \frac{1}{r} e^{-r\pi|y|/a} \sin\frac{r\pi x}{a} \tag{9}$$

If we examine the potential at values of y such that $\pi|y|/a \gg 1$, then only the term with $r = 1$ will contribute significantly. Then,

$$\Phi \cong \frac{4\Phi_0}{\pi} e^{-\pi|y|/a} \sin\frac{\pi x}{a} \tag{10}$$

and we see clearly both the exponential damping with y and the oscillatory nature of the potential as a function of x.

Note that we have nowhere explicitly used the fact that the planes at $x = 0, \pm a, \pm 2a, \ldots$, are held at ground potential. Thus, we can be assured that if we were to remove these planes, the solution would be unaffected, and we would automatically have $\Phi = 0$ on the planes $x = \pm na$. Reference to Fig. 3-1 shows that this must indeed be true due to the symmetry about any point on any plane $x = \pm na$ of the distribution of planes with potential $\pm\Phi_0$.

▶ **Example 3.3(b).** Let us next consider the calculation of the potential within a conducting box for which all of the sides except one are grounded and the remaining side is at a potential Φ_0. Let the lengths of the sides in the x-, y-, and z-directions be, respectively, a, b, and c, as in Fig. 3-3.

By the symmetry of the problem, we must have oscillatory solutions in the x- and y- directions and an exponential solution in the z direction. Therefore,

$$\Phi(x, y, z) \sim e^{\pm i\alpha x} e^{\pm i\beta y} e^{\pm \gamma z} \tag{1}$$

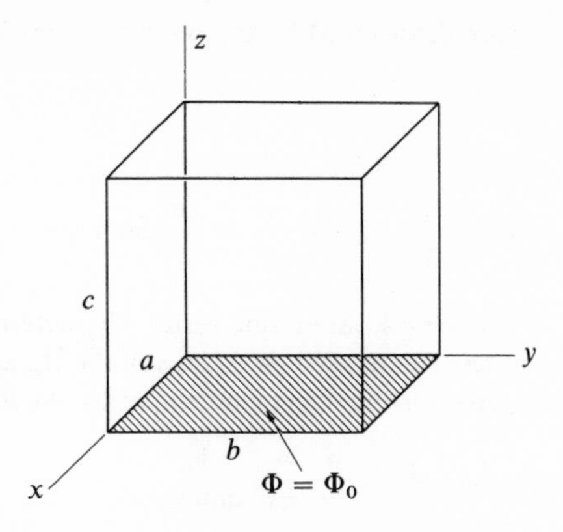

FIG. 3-3

where $\gamma = \sqrt{\alpha^2 + \beta^2}$. In order that the potential vanish at $x = 0$, a and at $y = 0$, b, it is clear that we must have

$$\left.\begin{aligned} X(x) &= \sin\frac{r\pi x}{a} \\ Y(y) &= \sin\frac{s\pi y}{b} \end{aligned}\right\} \tag{2}$$

Hence, we identify

$$\alpha_r = \frac{r\pi}{a}; \qquad \beta_s = \frac{s\pi}{b} \tag{3}$$

so that there must be a γ for each pair of values for r, s:

$$\gamma_{rs} = \pi\sqrt{\frac{r^2}{a^2} + \frac{s^2}{b^2}} \tag{4}$$

Consequently, there will be particular potential functions which satisfy the conditions of the problem and which have the form

$$\Phi_{rs} = \sin\frac{r\pi x}{a}\sin\frac{s\pi y}{b}\sinh\gamma_{rs}(c - z) \tag{5}$$

where we have chosen to write the exponential factor in terms of the hyperbolic sine function, and where we have placed $(c - z)$ in the argument in order to insure that the boundary condition $\Phi(x, y, c) = 0$ is met. The general solution to the problem will be

$$\Phi(x, y, z) = \sum_{r,s} A_{rs}\Phi_{rs} \tag{6}$$

where the coefficients A_{rs} are determined by the boundary condition at $z = 0$:

$$\Phi(x, y, 0) = \Phi_0 \tag{7}$$

Thus,

$$\Phi_0 = \sum_{r,s=1}^{\infty} A_{rs} \sin\frac{r\pi x}{a} \sin\frac{s\pi y}{b} \sinh \gamma_{rs} c \tag{8}$$

Here, Φ_0 is expressed as a *double* Fourier sine series, characteristic of the expansion of an odd function in two dimensions, and the values of the A_{rs} are found in a manner entirely analogous to that used for the single Fourier series. We find

$$A_{rs} = \frac{4}{\pi r} \cdot \frac{4}{\pi s} \cdot \frac{\Phi_0}{\sinh \gamma_{rs} c} \tag{9}$$

from which we have, in general,

$$\Phi(x, y, z) = \frac{16\Phi_0}{\pi^2} \sum_{\substack{r,s \\ \text{odd}}} \frac{1}{rs} \frac{\sinh \gamma_{rs}(c - z)}{\sinh \gamma_{rs} c} \sin\frac{r\pi x}{a} \sin\frac{s\pi y}{b} \tag{10}$$

where, as in the previous example, the sums over r and s run only over odd values.

Notice that the solutions to more complicated problems may be obtained by *superposition*. For example, if it is required to find the potential within a conducting box with one side at a potential Φ_1, another side at a potential Φ_2, and the remaining sides grounded, we may proceed as follows. First, we construct a solution for all sides grounded except the one at Φ_1. Next, the solution is found for all sides grounded except the one at Φ_2. The sum of these two solutions is then the desired solution for the complete problem.

3.4 Solutions of Laplace's Equation in Spherical Coordinates

In spherical coordinates, Laplace's equation may be written as [see Eq. (A.52), Appendix A]

$$\nabla^2\Phi = \frac{1}{r^2}\frac{\partial}{\partial r}\left(r^2 \frac{\partial \Phi}{\partial r}\right) + \frac{1}{r^2 \sin\theta}\frac{\partial}{\partial \theta}\left(\sin\theta \frac{\partial \Phi}{\partial \theta}\right) + \frac{1}{r^2 \sin^2\theta}\frac{\partial^2 \Phi}{\partial \varphi^2} = 0 \tag{3.25}$$

The Laplacian can be separated in spherical coordinates, so we write

$$\Phi(r, \theta, \varphi) = R(r)P(\theta)Q(\varphi) \tag{3.26}$$

Upon substituting this expression for Φ into Eq. (3.25) and dividing by $\Phi = RPQ$, we find

$$\frac{1}{r^2 R}\frac{d}{dr}\left(r^2 \frac{dR}{dr}\right) + \frac{1}{r^2 P \sin\theta}\frac{d}{d\theta}\left(\sin\theta \frac{dP}{d\theta}\right) + \frac{1}{r^2 Q \sin^2\theta}\frac{d^2 Q}{d\varphi^2} = 0 \tag{3.27}$$

We next multiply this equation by $r^2 \sin^2\theta$ to obtain

$$\frac{\sin^2\theta}{R}\frac{d}{dr}\left(r^2 \frac{dR}{dr}\right) + \frac{\sin\theta}{P}\frac{d}{d\theta}\left(\sin\theta \frac{dP}{d\theta}\right) = -\frac{1}{Q}\frac{d^2 Q}{d\varphi^2} \tag{3.28}$$

Now, the left-hand side of this equation is a function only of r, θ, while the right-hand side is a function of φ only. Thus, both sides must be equal to the same constant, which we shall write as m^2. Then,

$$\frac{d^2 Q}{d\varphi^2} + m^2 Q = 0 \tag{3.29}$$

which has the solution

$$Q(\varphi) \sim e^{\pm im\varphi} \tag{3.30}$$

But, the potential must be a single-valued function of φ; i.e., $Q(\varphi) = Q(\varphi + 2n\pi)$. Therefore, the constant m must be an integer (or zero).

Setting the left-hand side of Eq. (3.28) equal to m^2 and dividing by $\sin^2\theta$, we have

$$\frac{1}{R}\frac{d}{dr}\left(r^2 \frac{dR}{dr}\right) = -\frac{1}{P \sin\theta}\frac{d}{d\theta}\left(\sin\theta \frac{dP}{d\theta}\right) + \frac{m^2}{\sin^2\theta} \tag{3.31}$$

Again, the variables are separated, and if we equate each side of this equation to the constant term $l(l+1)$, we find

$$\frac{d}{dr}\left(r^2 \frac{dR}{dr}\right) - l(l+1)R = 0 \tag{3.32}$$

and

$$\frac{1}{\sin\theta}\frac{d}{d\theta}\left(\sin\theta \frac{dP}{d\theta}\right) + \left[l(l+1) - \frac{m^2}{\sin^2\theta}\right]P = 0 \tag{3.33}$$

It is customary to define $x \equiv \cos\theta$, and then since

$$\frac{d}{d\theta} = -\sin\theta \frac{d}{dx}$$

Eq. (3.33) becomes

$$\frac{d}{dx}\left[(1 - x^2)\frac{dP}{dx}\right] + \left[l(l + 1) - \frac{m^2}{1 - x^2}\right]P = 0 \tag{3.34}$$

Let us first consider the case $m = 0$; then,

$$\frac{d}{dx}\left[(1 - x^2)\frac{dP}{dx}\right] + l(l + 1)P = 0 \tag{3.35}$$

This equation will apply for any problem which has azimuthal symmetry, i.e., the potential Φ does not depend on φ, so that $Q = 1$ and $m = 0$.

Equation (3.35) may be written as

$$\boxed{(1 - x^2)\frac{d^2P}{dx^2} - 2x\frac{dP}{dx} + l(l + 1)P = 0} \tag{3.36}$$

which is the familiar form of Legendre's equation as encountered in the study of ordinary differential equations. Solutions to this equation may be found by expressing P as an infinite power series in x. The requirement that the series converge forces an upper limit on the allowable powers of x so that the series breaks off and becomes a polynomial of degree l. There are actually two forms of the series, one which converges for $x \to \pm 1$ and one which diverges at these limits. The convergent series is almost invariably the meaningful solution for physical problems, and for a given value of l the series is known as the *Legendre polynomial* of order l, denoted by $P_l(\cos\theta)$. The portion of the complete solution of Laplace's equation which contains the dependence on θ may therefore be expressed as

$$\sum_{l=0}^{\infty} a_l P_l(\cos\theta)$$

Although the Legendre polynomials may be generated by means of the series expansion referred to above, they may also be obtained in the following way. First, we make the expansion [cf. Eq. (2.3)]:

$$(1 - 2\mu x + \mu^2)^{-\frac{1}{2}} = U_0(x) + \mu U_1(x) + \mu^2 U_2(x) + \cdots \tag{3.37}$$

where the $U_n(x)$ are polynomials of degree n (which may be explicitly obtained by writing out the expansion in detail). The series, which is just a binomial expansion, is valid if $|2\mu x - \mu^2| < 1$.

Next, we make a similar expansion for the *derivative* of Eq. (3.37):

$$\frac{d}{dx}(1 - 2\mu x + \mu^2)^{-\frac{1}{2}} = \mu(1 - 2\mu x + \mu^2)^{-\frac{3}{2}}$$

$$= V_0(x) + \mu V_1(x) + \mu^2 V_2(x) + \cdots \tag{3.38}$$

This series is uniformly convergent for $-1 \leqslant x \leqslant 1$, and may therefore be integrated term by term with respect to x for any interval in this range. In particular, we may write

$$\int_0^x \frac{d}{dx}(1 - 2\mu x + \mu^2)^{-\frac{1}{2}}\, dx = \int_0^x [V_0(x) + \mu V_1(x) + \cdots]\, dx \tag{3.39}$$

Now,

$$\begin{aligned}\int_0^x \frac{d}{dx}(1 - 2\mu x + \mu^2)^{-\frac{1}{2}}\, dx &= (1 - 2\mu x + \mu^2)^{-\frac{1}{2}} - (1 + \mu^2)^{-\frac{1}{2}} \\ &= \sum_{n=0}^{\infty} \mu^n U_n(x) - \sum_{n=0}^{\infty} \mu^n U_n(0)\end{aligned} \tag{3.40}$$

Equating the right-hand sides of Eqs. (3.39) and (3.40), we find

$$\sum_{n=0}^{\infty} [U_n(x) - U_n(0)]\mu^n = \sum_{n=0}^{\infty} \mu^n \int_0^x V_n(x)\, dx$$

Since the coefficients of each power of μ must be equal we obtain

$$\int_0^x V_n(x)\, dx = U_n(x) - U_n(0)$$

Hence, the functions $V_n(x)$ are just the derivatives of the $U_n(x)$:

$$V_n(x) \equiv \frac{d}{dx} U_n(x) \tag{3.41}$$

Therefore, our two series expansions may be written as

$$(1 - 2\mu x + \mu^2)^{-\frac{1}{2}} = \sum_{n=0}^{\infty} \mu^n U_n(x) \tag{3.42}$$

$$\mu(1 - 2\mu x + \mu^2)^{-\frac{3}{2}} = \sum_{n=0}^{\infty} \mu^n \frac{d}{dx} U_n(x) \tag{3.43}$$

Next, we differentiate Eq. (3.42) with respect to μ:

$$(x - \mu)(1 - 2\mu x + \mu^2)^{-\frac{3}{2}} = \sum_n n\mu^{n-1} U_n(x) \tag{3.44}$$

Using the series expansion of $(1 - 2\mu x + \mu^2)^{-\frac{3}{2}}$, we obtain

$$(x - \mu) \cdot \frac{1}{\mu} \sum_n \mu^n \frac{d}{dx} U_n(x) = \sum_n n\mu^{n-1} U_n(x)$$

or,

$$(x - \mu) \sum_n \mu^n U_n'(x) = \sum_n n\mu^n U_n(x) \tag{3.45}$$

where

$$U_n'(x) \equiv \frac{d}{dx} U_n(x)$$

Equating the coefficients of μ^n on the two sides of Eq. (3.45), we find

$$xU_n'(x) - U_{n-1}'(x) = nU_n(x) \tag{3.46}$$

An equation of this type which involves functions of different orders, is called a *recursion relation.* We need to find one more such relation; in order to do so, we rewrite Eq. (3.44) as

$$(x - \mu)(1 - 2\mu x + \mu^2)^{-\frac{1}{2}} = (1 - 2\mu x + \mu^2) \sum_n n\mu^{n-1} U_n(x)$$

Substitution of Eq. (3.42) into the left-hand side of this equation yields

$$(x - \mu) \sum_n \mu^n U_n(x) = (1 - 2\mu x + \mu^2) \sum_n n\mu^{n-1} U_n(x) \tag{3.47}$$

Equating the coefficients of μ^n on the two sides of Eq. (3.47) and combining terms, we obtain the second recursion relation:

$$(n + 1)U_{n+1}(x) - (2n + 1)xU_n(x) + nU_{n-1}(x) = 0 \tag{3.48}$$

Next, we differentiate this last equation with respect to x:

$$(n + 1)U_{n+1}'(x) - (2n + 1)U_n(x) - (2n + 1)xU_n'(x) + nU_{n-1}'(x) = 0$$

If we substitute for $U_{n-1}'(x)$ in this expression from Eq. (3.46), we find

$$(n + 1)U_{n+1}'(x) - (n^2 + 2n + 1)U_n(x) - (n + 1)xU_n'(x) = 0$$

Canceling one factor of $(n + 1)$ and substituting l for $(n + 1)$, we have

$$U_l'(x) - lU_{l-1}(x) - xU_{l-1}'(x) = 0 \tag{3.49}$$

and using Eq. (3.46) again,

$$(1 - x^2)U_l'(x) - lU_{l-1}(x) + xlU_l(x) = 0 \tag{3.50}$$

Differentiating this expression with respect to x, we obtain

$$\frac{d}{dx}[(1 - x^2)U_l'(x)] - lU_{l-1}'(x) + lU_l(x) + xlU_l'(x) = 0$$

or, finally,

$$\frac{d}{dx}\left[(1 - x^2)\frac{d}{dx} U_l(x)\right] + l(l + 1)U_l(x) = 0 \tag{3.51}$$

where Eq. (3.46) has been used to substitute for $U_{l-1}'(x)$. Equation (3.51) is identical with Eq. (3.35); therefore, we may identify the functions $U_l(x)$

with the Legendre polynomials of order l. Thus, we have shown that the polynomials which result from the expansion of $(1 - 2\mu x + \mu^2)^{-\frac{1}{2}}$ are *Legendre polynomials**† and are solutions of Laplace's equation. The first few of these polynomials are

$$\left.\begin{aligned} P_0(x) &= 1 \\ P_1(x) &= x \\ P_2(x) &= \tfrac{1}{2}(3x^2 - 1) \\ P_3(x) &= \tfrac{1}{2}(5x^3 - 3x) \\ P_4(x) &= \tfrac{1}{8}(35x^4 - 30x^2 + 3) \\ P_5(x) &= \tfrac{1}{8}(63x^5 - 70x^3 + 15x) \end{aligned}\right\} \tag{3.52}$$

The Legendre polynomials are all normalized to unity at $x = 1$. Figures 3-4a and 3-4b show the first few of these functions plotted versus x and θ.

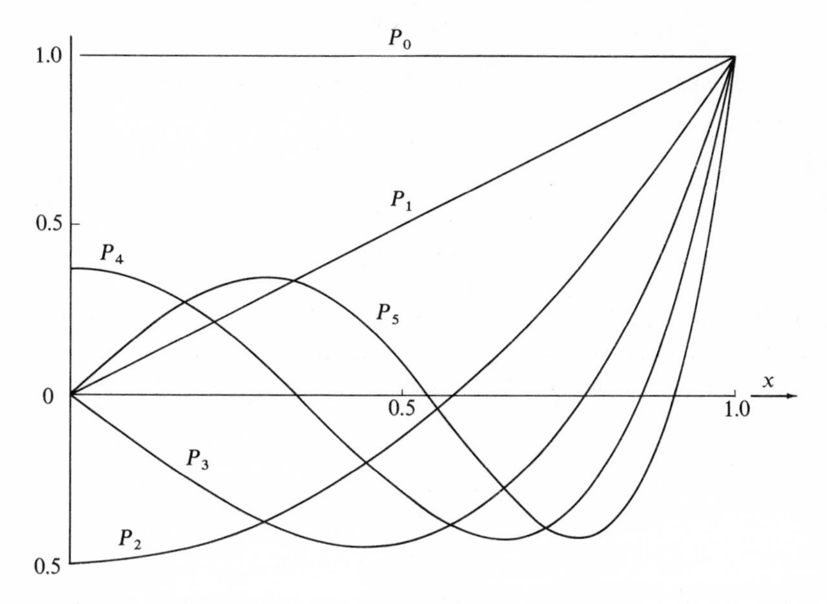

FIG. 3-4a

* These functions were discovered in 1784 by Adrien Marie Legendre (1752–1833) in connection with his study of the gravitational attraction of spheroids.

† The function $(1 - 2\mu x + \mu^2)^{-\frac{1}{2}}$ is called the *generating function* for the Legendre polynomials.

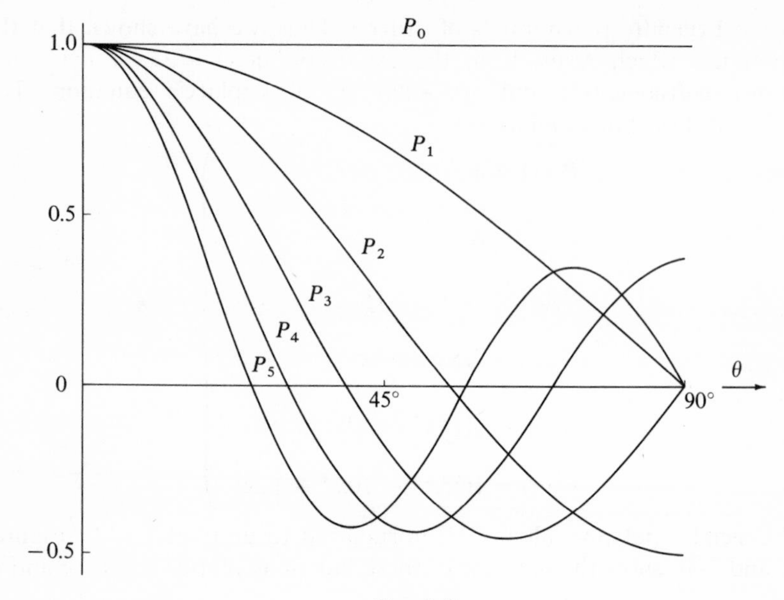

FIG. 3-4b

A convenient expression for the Legendre polynomials is *Rodriquez' formula*:

$$P_l(x) = \frac{1}{2^l l!} \frac{d^l}{dx^l} (x^2 - 1)^l \tag{3.53}$$

It is easy to verify by direct calculation that this expression does indeed yield the polynomials listed above. Rodriguez' formula may be used to prove the orthogonality of the Legendre polynomials (see Problem 3-14):

$$\int_{-1}^{+1} P_{l'}(x) P_l(x)\, dx = \frac{2}{2l+1} \delta_{ll'} \tag{3.54}$$

The Legendre polynomials form a *complete orthogonal set* of functions with respect to the variable x. We may therefore write for an arbitrary function $f(x)$,

$$f(x) = \sum_{l=0}^{\infty} A_l P_l(x), \qquad -1 \leqslant x \leqslant 1 \tag{3.55}$$

If we multiply both sides of this equation by $P_{l'}(x)$ and integrate, then using Eq. (3.54) we find

$$A_l = \frac{2l+1}{2} \int_{-1}^{+1} f(x) P_l(x)\, dx \tag{3.56}$$

In order to complete our specification of the general solution of Laplace's equation in spherical coordinates, we must solve the radial equation

$$\frac{d}{dr}\left(r^2 \frac{dR}{dr}\right) - l(l+1)R = 0 \tag{3.57}$$

If we write

$$R(r) \equiv \frac{\mathscr{R}(r)}{r} \tag{3.58}$$

then we obtain

$$\frac{d^2\mathscr{R}}{dr^2} - \frac{l(l+1)}{r^2}\mathscr{R} = 0 \tag{3.59}$$

It is not necessary to expand $\mathscr{R}(r)$ as a power series; it is readily verified that the solution to Eq. (3.59) is, for a particular l,

$$\mathscr{R}_l(r) = A_l r^{l+1} + B_l r^{-l} \tag{3.60}$$

and, hence,

$$R_l(r) = A_l r^l + B_l r^{-(l+1)} \tag{3.61}$$

We may therefore write the general solution, for the case $m = 0$, as

$$\boxed{\Phi(r, \theta) = \sum_{l=0}^{\infty} \left[A_l r^l + B_l r^{-(l+1)}\right] P_l(\cos\theta)} \tag{3.62}$$

Example 3.4(a). Let us compute the potential at all points in space exterior to a conducting sphere of radius a placed in a uniform electric field $\mathbf{E}_0$. If we choose our axis such that $\mathbf{E}_0$ lies along the polar axis (i.e., the line represented by $\theta = 0$), then the problem has azimuthal symmetry and we may use Eq. (3.62).

Now, in rectangular coordinates a uniform field in the z-direction is given by

$$\mathbf{E}_0 = E_0 \mathbf{e}_z = -\,\mathbf{grad}\,\Phi_0 \tag{1}$$

so that

$$\Phi_0 = -E_0 z \tag{2}$$

or, in spherical coordinates

$$\Phi_0 = -E_0 r \cos\theta = -E_0 r P_1(\cos\theta) \tag{3}$$

Note that Φ_0 does not obey our usual condition that $\Phi(r \to \infty) = 0$. This is because we have assumed a uniform field of infinite extent, and thus the sources of such a field must lie at infinity; Φ_0 may not then vanish as $r \to \infty$.

Since our sphere is of finite extent, clearly the field at large r must be equal to $\mathbf{E}_0$ and the potential there is given by Eq. (2) or Eq. (3).

The *total* potential $\Phi(r, \theta)$ must be the sum of Φ_0 and the potential due to the charge distribution induced in the conducting sphere. Since the sphere is a *conductor*, the induced charge must generate an electric field which just cancels the external field and therefore gives exactly zero field within the sphere. At large values of r, Eq. (3.62) reduces to*

$$\Phi(r, \theta) \sim \sum_{l=0}^{\infty} A_l r^l P_l(\cos\theta), \qquad r \to \infty \tag{4}$$

and since this must agree with Φ_0, we conclude that all of the A_l vanish except A_1, and, in fact, $A_1 = -E_0$. Therefore, in general we have

$$\Phi(r, \theta) = -E_0 r P_1(\cos\theta) + \sum_{l=0}^{\infty} B_l r^{-(l+1)} P_l(\cos\theta) \tag{5}$$

which must reduce to $\Phi = 0$ at $r = a$. That is,

$$\Phi(a, \theta) = -E_0 a P_1 + \sum_{l=0}^{\infty} B_l a^{-(l+1)} P_l = 0 \tag{6}$$

Multiplying this equation by $P_{l'}(x)$ and integrating, we have

$$E_0 a \int_{-1}^{+1} P_1(x) P_{l'}(x)\, dx = \sum_{l=0}^{\infty} B_l a^{-(l+1)} \int_{-1}^{+1} P_l(x) P_{l'}(x)\, dx \tag{7}$$

Using the orthogonality relation [Eq. (3.54)], we find

$$E_0 a \cdot \frac{2}{2l'+1} \delta_{1l'} = B_{l'} a^{-(l'+1)} \cdot \frac{2}{2l'+1} \tag{8}$$

We may write this expression as

$$B_l = E_0 a^{(l+2)} \delta_{1l} \tag{9}$$

from which

$$B_1 = E_0 a^3 \tag{10}$$

Therefore, the solution is

$$\begin{aligned} \Phi(r, \theta) &= -E_0 r P_1(\cos\theta) + \frac{B_1}{r^2} P_1(\cos\theta) \\ &= -E_0 \left(1 - \frac{a^3}{r^3}\right) r \cos\theta \end{aligned} \tag{11}$$

* The symbol $\sim$ here means "approaches asymptotically."

The components of the electric field vector **E** can now be easily calculated from Φ:

$$\left.\begin{aligned} E_r &= -\frac{\partial\Phi}{\partial r} = E_0\left(1 + \frac{2a^3}{r^3}\right)\cos\theta \\ E_\theta &= -\frac{1}{r}\frac{\partial\Phi}{\partial\theta} = -E_0\left(1 - \frac{a^3}{r^3}\right)\sin\theta \end{aligned}\right\} \tag{12}$$

The surface density of induced charge ρ_s may be computed from Gauss' law. Since there can be no electric field within the conducting sphere, the normal (or *radial*) component of **E** at the surface must equal $4\pi\rho_s$ [see Eq. (1.66a)]:

$$E_r\big|_{r=a} = 4\pi\rho_s \tag{13}$$

Using Eq. (12) for E_r, we find

$$\rho_s = \frac{3}{4\pi}E_0\cos\theta \tag{14}$$

The total charge on the sphere is the integral of this quantity over the sphere, which vanishes, as it must.

From Eq. (11) we see that we may write

$$\Phi(r,\theta) = \Phi_0 + E_0a^3\frac{\cos\theta}{r^2} \tag{15}$$

If we define

$$\mathbf{p} = E_0a^3\mathbf{e}_z \tag{16}$$

where $\mathbf{e}_z$ is the unit vector in the direction of the field **E**, then Φ may be expressed as

$$\Phi(r,\theta) = \Phi_0 + \frac{\mathbf{p}\cdot\mathbf{e}_r}{r^2} \tag{17}$$

The second term is just the potential due to a dipole [see Eq. (2.7)]. Thus, a conducting sphere of radius a in a uniform field E_0 acts as a dipole of moment $p = E_0a^3$ due to the distribution of charge induced on its surface.

The electric field lines for this example are shown in Fig. 3-5. Recall that electric field lines must originate and terminate on electric charges; in this case these charges are just those that are induced on the surface of the sphere and which give rise to the dipole character of the sphere.

▶ **Example 3.4(b).** Let us next consider the calculation of the potential at any point for the case in which a dielectric sphere of radius a and dielectric constant ε is placed in a uniform electric field $\mathbf{E}_0$ which exists in a medium with dielectric constant ε_0. Again, we have for the potential of the applied field,

$$\Phi_0 = -E_0z = -E_0r\cos\theta = -E_0rP_1(\cos\theta) \tag{1}$$

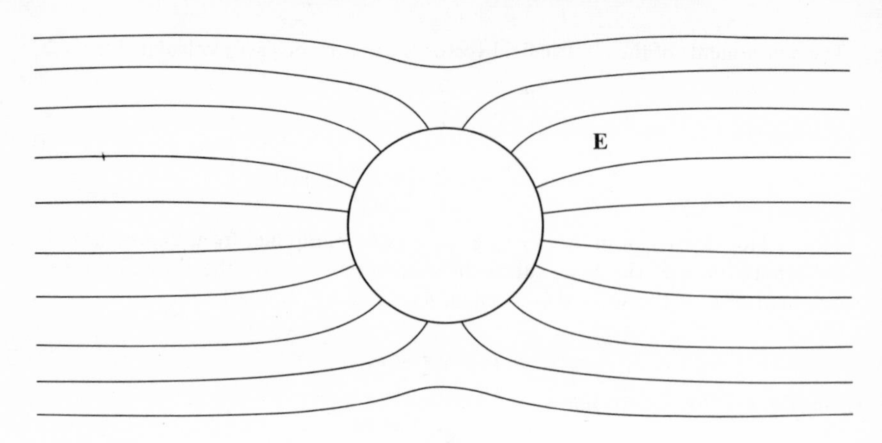

FIG. 3-5

The total potential $\Phi(r, \theta)$ must satisfy the following conditions:

(1) $\Phi(r, \theta) \to \Phi_0$ for $r \to \infty$.

(2) $\Phi(r, \theta)$ must be continuous at $r = a$.

(3) $\Phi(r, \theta)$ must be finite at $r = 0$.

(4) The normal component of the electric displacement vector **D** must be continuous at $r = a$.

In order to satisfy Condition (1), the solution exterior to the sphere ($r \geqslant a$) must be of the form

$$\Phi_{\text{ext}}(r, \theta) = \Phi_0 + \sum_{l=0}^{\infty} B_l r^{-(l+1)} P_l(\cos\theta) \tag{2}$$

while the solution interior to the sphere ($r \leqslant a$) must be [Condition (3)]

$$\Phi_{\text{int}}(r, \theta) = \Phi_0 + \sum_{l=0}^{\infty} A_l r^l P_l(\cos\theta) \tag{3}$$

According to Condition (2), these solutions must be equal at $r = a$. Thus,

$$\Phi_{\text{ext}}(a, \theta) = \Phi_{\text{int}}(a, \theta) \tag{4}$$

or,

$$\sum_l B_l a^{-(l+1)} P_l(\cos\theta) = \sum_l A_l a^l P_l(\cos\theta) \tag{4a}$$

Since the Legendre polynomials are linearly independent, the coefficients of the $P_l(\cos\theta)$ must be equal; therefore,

$$A_l = B_l a^{-(2l+1)} \tag{5}$$

By differentiating Eqs. (2) and (3) with respect to r, we obtain the radial components of the internal and external fields:

$$E_{\text{ext},r} = -\frac{\partial\Phi_{\text{ext}}}{\partial r} = E_0 P_1(\cos\theta) + \sum_l (l+1) B_l r^{-(l+2)} P_l(\cos\theta) \tag{6}$$

$$E_{\text{int},r} = -\frac{\partial \Phi_{\text{int}}}{\partial r} = E_0 P_1(\cos\theta) - \sum_l l A_l r^{l-1} P_l(\cos\theta) \tag{7}$$

In order to satisfy Condition (4), we must have

$$\varepsilon_0 E_{\text{ext},r}|_{r=a} = \varepsilon_1 E_{\text{int},r}|_{r=a} \tag{8}$$

Thus,

$$\varepsilon_0[E_0 P_1(\cos\theta) + \sum_l (l+1) B_l a^{-(l+2)} P_l(\cos\theta)] = \varepsilon_1[E_0 P_1(\cos\theta) - \sum_l l A_l a^{l-1} P_l(\cos\theta)]$$

Equating the coefficients of corresponding orders of the Legendre polynomials, we obtain

$$B_0 a^{-2} = 0, \qquad l = 0 \tag{10a}$$

$$\varepsilon_0[E_0 + 2B_1 a^{-3}] = \varepsilon_1[E_0 - A_1], \qquad l = 1 \tag{10b}$$

$$\varepsilon_0[(l+1)B_l a^{-(l+2)}] = \varepsilon_1[-l A_l a^{l-1}], \qquad l > 1 \tag{10c}$$

From Eq. (10a), $B_0 = 0$, and hence, from Eq. (5), $A_0 = 0$. And substituting Eq. (5) into Eq. (10b), we find

$$A_1 = \frac{\varepsilon_1 - \varepsilon_0}{\varepsilon_1 + 2\varepsilon_0} E_0 \tag{11a}$$

Equations (5) and (11a) then give

$$B_1 = \frac{\varepsilon_1 - \varepsilon_0}{\varepsilon_1 + 2\varepsilon_0} a^3 E_0 \tag{11b}$$

Substituting Eq. (5) into Eq. (10c) shows that all of the A_l and B_l vanish for $l > 1$. Therefore, the complete solutions for the potentials are

$$\Phi_{\text{ext}}(r, \theta) = \Phi_0 + \frac{\varepsilon_1 - \varepsilon_0}{\varepsilon_1 + 2\varepsilon_0} E_0 a^3 \frac{\cos\theta}{r^2} \tag{12a}$$

$$\Phi_{\text{int}}(r, \theta) = \Phi_0 + \frac{\varepsilon_1 - \varepsilon_0}{\varepsilon_1 + 2\varepsilon_0} E_0 r \cos\theta \tag{12b}$$

Since $E_0 r \cos\theta = E_0 z = -\Phi_0$, Eq. (12b) becomes

$$\Phi_{\text{int}}(r, \theta) = \frac{3\varepsilon_0}{\varepsilon_1 + 2\varepsilon_0} \Phi_0 = -\frac{3\varepsilon_0}{\varepsilon_1 + 2\varepsilon_0} E_0 z \tag{12c}$$

Notice that the internal field is constant and uniform:

$$E_{\text{int},z} = -\frac{\partial \Phi_{\text{int}}}{\partial z}$$

$$= \frac{3\varepsilon_0}{\varepsilon_1 + 2\varepsilon_0} E_0 \tag{13}$$

If $\varepsilon_1 > \varepsilon_0$, then $E_{\text{int}} < E_0$; on the other hand, $D_{\text{int}} > D_0 = \varepsilon_0 E_0$.

If the medium in which the dielectric sphere is placed is vacuum, then $\varepsilon_1 > \varepsilon_0 = 1$. Therefore,

$$E_{\text{int},z} = \frac{3}{\varepsilon_1 + 2} E_0 < E_0 \tag{14}$$

Thus, the electric field within the dielectric sphere is smaller than the applied field. This results from the fact that there is an induced surface polarization charge which gives rise to an opposing electric field within the sphere. The internal **D** field is

$$D_{\text{int},z} = \frac{3\varepsilon_1}{\varepsilon_1 + 2} E_0 > D_0 = \varepsilon_0 E_0 \tag{15}$$

That is, the electric displacement is greater within the sphere than outside. This results from the fact that the lines of **D** converge on the sphere; and, since these lines are continuous, the density within the sphere must be greater than outside. Figure 3-6 shows some of the lines of electric displacement in the vicinity of the sphere.

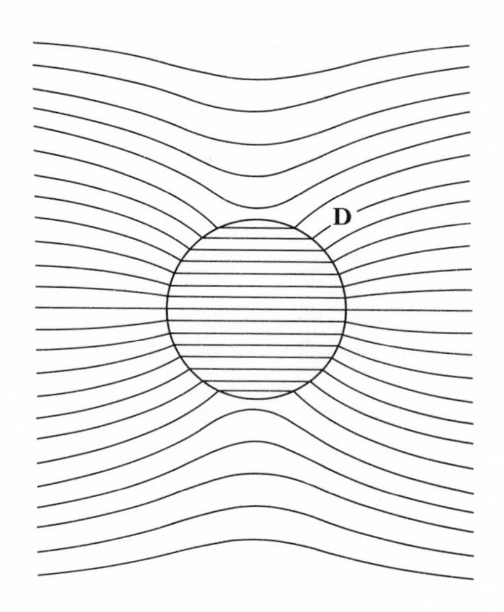

FIG. 3-6

We note that the external electric field [which may be obtained from Eq. (12a)] is equal to E_0 plus a dipole field of moment

$$p = \frac{\varepsilon_1 - 1}{\varepsilon_1 + 2} a^3 E_0, \qquad (\varepsilon_0 = 1)$$

Thus, the dielectric sphere in a uniform field in free space acts as a simple dipole. Similarly, a spherical cavity in a dielectric medium in which there is a uniform field may also be represented by a dipole.

3.5 Spherical Harmonics

Thus far we have considered only the case of problems which involve a symmetry about the polar axis and whose solutions therefore are independent of the azimuthal angle φ. Consequently, we have been able to set the separation constant m in Eqs. (3.29) and (3.33) equal to zero. If the problem does not possess azimuthal symmetry, then the solutions in terms of the normal Legendre functions will no longer be adequate. Indeed, for convergent solutions to exist for such problems, we find that both of the constants l and m are limited to zero or integral numbers and, further, that m is limited, for any given value of l, to the $2l + 1$ values $m = 0, \pm 1, \pm 2, \ldots, \pm l$. The solutions of the equation for θ [Eq. (3.33)] are then written as $P_l^m(\cos\theta)$ and are called the *associated Legendre polynomials.* These functions may be defined by the more general Rodriguez formula:

$$P_l^m(x) = \frac{(-1)^m}{2^l l!}(1 - x^2)^{m/2}\frac{d^{l+m}}{dx^{l+m}}(x^2 - 1)^l \tag{3.63}$$

The relationship between $P_l^m(x)$ and $P_l^{-m}(x)$ is

$$P_l^{-m}(x) = (-1)^m\frac{(l - m)!}{(l + m)!}P_l^m(x) \tag{3.64}$$

For a given value of m, the functions $P_l^m(x)$ and $P_{l'}^m(x)$ are orthogonal; that is,

$$\int_{-1}^{+1} P_l^m(x)P_{l'}^m(x)\,dx = \frac{2}{2l + 1}\frac{(l + m)!}{(l - m)!}\delta_{ll'} \tag{3.65}$$

Just as the $P_l(x)$ form a complete orthogonal set for the expansion of functions of the variable x, the product of the $P_l^m(x)$ and $\exp(im\varphi)$ form such a set for the expansion of an arbitrary function on the surface of a sphere. Such functions are called *spherical harmonics* (or *surface zonal harmonics* or *tesseral harmonics*) and are customarily written in a normalized way as

$$\boxed{Y_l^m(\theta, \varphi) = \sqrt{\frac{2l + 1}{4\pi}\frac{(l - m)!}{(l + m)!}}\,P_l^m(\cos\theta)e^{im\varphi}} \tag{3.66}$$

These functions obey the orthogonality relation

$$\int_{4\pi} Y_l^m(\theta, \varphi)Y_{l'}^{m'*}(\theta, \varphi)\,d\Omega$$

$$= \int_0^{2\pi} d\varphi \int_0^{\pi} \sin\theta\,d\theta\,Y_l^m(\theta, \varphi)Y_{l'}^{m'*}(\theta, \varphi) = \delta_{ll'}\delta_{mm'} \tag{3.67}$$

where $d\Omega = \sin\theta\, d\theta\, d\varphi$ is the element of solid angle, and where $Y_{l'}^{m'*}$ denotes the complex conjugate of $Y_{l'}^{m'}$.

The first few spherical harmonics are

$$Y_0^0(\theta, \varphi) = \sqrt{\frac{1}{4\pi}} \qquad \Big\} \quad l = 0 \tag{3.68a}$$

$$\left.\begin{aligned} Y_1^0(\theta, \varphi) &= \sqrt{\frac{3}{4\pi}} \cos\theta \\ Y_1^{\pm 1}(\theta, \varphi) &= \mp \sqrt{\frac{3}{8\pi}} \sin\theta\, e^{\pm i\varphi} \end{aligned}\right\} \quad l = 1 \tag{3.68b}$$

$$\left.\begin{aligned} Y_2^0(\theta, \varphi) &= \sqrt{\frac{5}{16\pi}} (2\cos^2\theta - \sin^2\theta) \\ Y_2^{\pm 1}(\theta, \varphi) &= \mp \sqrt{\frac{15}{8\pi}} \cos\theta \sin\theta\, e^{\pm i\varphi} \\ Y_2^{\pm 2}(\theta, \varphi) &= \sqrt{\frac{15}{32\pi}} \sin^2\theta\, e^{\pm 2i\varphi} \end{aligned}\right\} \quad l = 2 \tag{3.68c}$$

$$\left.\begin{aligned} Y_3^0(\theta, \varphi) &= \sqrt{\frac{7}{16\pi}} (2\cos^3\theta - 3\cos\theta \sin^2\theta) \\ Y_3^{\pm 1}(\theta, \varphi) &= \mp \sqrt{\frac{21}{64\pi}} (4\cos^2\theta \sin\theta - \sin^3\theta) e^{\pm i\varphi} \\ Y_3^{\pm 2}(\theta, \varphi) &= \sqrt{\frac{105}{32\pi}} \cos\theta \sin^2\theta\, e^{\pm 2i\varphi} \\ Y_3^{\pm 3}(\theta, \varphi) &= \mp \sqrt{\frac{35}{64\pi}} \sin^3\theta\, e^{\pm 3i\varphi} \end{aligned}\right\} \quad l = 3 \tag{3.68d}$$

For the case $m = 0$, the spherical harmonics are related to the normal Legendre functions according to

$$Y_l^0(\theta, \varphi) = \sqrt{\frac{2l+1}{4\pi}}\, P_l(\cos\theta) \tag{3.69}$$

If we expand the function $f(\theta, \varphi)$ in terms of the $Y_l^m(\theta, \varphi)$,

$$f(\theta, \varphi) = \sum_{l=0}^{\infty} \sum_{m=-l}^{l} C_l^m Y_l^m(\theta, \varphi) \tag{3.70}$$

then the coefficients C_l^m are given by

$$C_l^m = \int_{4\pi} f(\theta, \varphi) Y_l^{m*}(\theta, \varphi)\, d\Omega \tag{3.71}$$

The general solution of Laplace's equation can be written in terms of spherical harmonics as

$$\boxed{\Phi(r, \theta, \varphi) = \sum_{l=0}^{\infty} \sum_{m=-l}^{l} \left[A_l^m r^l + B_l^m r^{-(l+1)}\right] Y_l^m(\theta, \varphi)} \tag{3.72}$$

3.6. Solutions of Laplace's Equation in Cylindrical Coordinates

Written in cylindrical coordinates, Laplace's equation becomes [see Eq. (A.47)]

$$\nabla^2\Phi = \frac{1}{r}\frac{\partial}{\partial r}\left(r\frac{\partial \Phi}{\partial r}\right) + \frac{1}{r^2}\frac{\partial^2 \Phi}{\partial \theta^2} + \frac{\partial^2 \Phi}{\partial z^2} = 0 \tag{3.73}$$

If we write

$$\Phi(r, \theta, z) = R(r)Q(\theta)Z(z) \tag{3.74}$$

then, upon substituting this expression into Eq. (3.73) and multiplying by r^2/Φ, we have

$$\frac{r}{R}\frac{d}{dr}\left(r\frac{dR}{dr}\right) + \frac{r^2}{Z}\frac{d^2 Z}{dz^2} = -\frac{1}{Q}\frac{d^2 Q}{d\theta^2} \tag{3.75}$$

We have separated the term depending on the coordinate θ from the terms depending on r and z. Therefore, we may equate both sides of Eq. (3.75) to a constant, n^2, and obtain

$$\frac{d^2 Q}{d\theta^2} + n^2 Q = 0 \tag{3.76}$$

Just as for the solution of Eq. (3.29), we now have

$$Q(\theta) \sim e^{\pm in\theta} \tag{3.77}$$

where, again, n must be an integer (or zero) in order to insure the single-valuedness of $Q(\theta)$.

The left-hand side of Eq. (3.75) may now be written as

$$\frac{1}{rR}\frac{d}{dr}\left(r\frac{dR}{dr}\right) - \frac{n^2}{r^2} = -\frac{1}{Z}\frac{d^2Z}{dz^2} \tag{3.78}$$

where we have divided through by r^2. The variables are again separated, and we equate both sides of Eq. (3.78) to $-k^2$:

$$\frac{d^2Z}{dz^2} - k^2Z = 0 \tag{3.79}$$

$$r\frac{d}{dr}\left(r\frac{dR}{dr}\right) + (k^2r^2 - n^2)R = 0 \tag{3.80}$$

The solution for $Z(z)$ is

$$Z(z) \sim e^{\pm kz} \tag{3.81}$$

Equation (3.80) may be put into familiar form by making the substitution

$$\left.\begin{aligned} u &= kr \\ \frac{d}{dr} &= k\frac{d}{du} \end{aligned}\right\} \tag{3.82}$$

We obtain

$$\frac{1}{u}\frac{d}{du}\left(u\frac{dR}{du}\right) + \left(1 - \frac{n^2}{u^2}\right)R = 0 \tag{3.83}$$

or,

$$\boxed{u^2\frac{d^2R}{du^2} + u\frac{dR}{du} + (u^2 - n^2)R = 0} \tag{3.84}$$

which will be recognized as Bessel's equation.* Now, $u = 0$ is a regular singular point of this equation, and we may attempt a solution by expanding $R(u)$ about this point; we write

$$R(u) = u^b \sum_{k=0}^{\infty} a_k u^k = \sum_k a_k u^{k+b} \tag{3.85a}$$

Then,

$$\frac{dR}{du} = \sum_k (k + b)a_k u^{k+b-1} \tag{3.85b}$$

$$\frac{d^2R}{du^2} = \sum_k (k + b)(k + b - 1)a_k u^{k+b-2} \tag{3.85c}$$

* Named for Friedrich Wilhelm Bessel (1784–1846), Prussian astronomer and mathematician.

Substituting Eqs. (3.85) into the differential equation, we have

$$\sum_k (k+b)(k+b-1)a_k u^{k+b} + \sum_k (k+b)a_k u^{k+b} + \sum_k a_k u^{k+b+2} - n^2 \sum_k a_k u^{k+b} = 0 \tag{3.86}$$

Since the various powers of u are linearly independent, the coefficient of each power must separately vanish. Therefore, setting equal to zero the coefficient of u^{k+b}, we find

$$[(k+b)(k+b-1) + (k+b) - n^2]a_k + a_{k-2} = 0$$

or,

$$[(k+b)^2 - n^2]a_k + a_{k-2} = 0 \tag{3.87}$$

For the case $k = 0$ (note that $a_{-2} \equiv 0$) we obtain the *indicial equation,*

$$b^2 - n^2 = 0 \tag{3.88}$$

with roots

$$\left.\begin{aligned} b_1 &= n \geq 0 \\ b_2 &= -n \end{aligned}\right\} \tag{3.89}$$

For the case $k = 1$, we have

$$[(b+1)^2 - n^2]a_1 = 0 \tag{3.90}$$

Hence, $a_1 = 0$ for both of the roots b_1 and b_2.

If we use $b_1 = n$ in Eq. (3.87), there results

$$a_k = -\frac{a_{k-2}}{(n+k)^2 - n^2} = -\frac{a_{k-2}}{k(2n+k)} \tag{3.91}$$

which is the recursion relation for Bessel's equation. Since we have found $a_1 = 0$, Eq. (3.91) requires that all a_k with k odd also vanish. Thus, k is restricted to even values. If we substitute 2λ for k in Eq. (3.91), then we may allow λ to assume the values 0, 1, 2, . . . :

$$a_{2\lambda} = -\frac{a_{2\lambda-2}}{2^2\lambda(n+\lambda)} \tag{3.92}$$

Therefore,

$$\lambda = 1: \qquad a_2 = -\frac{a_0}{2^2 \cdot 1(n+1)}$$

$$\lambda = 2: \qquad a_4 = -\frac{a_2}{2^2 \cdot 2(n+2)} = \frac{a_0}{(2^2)^2 \cdot 1 \cdot 2(n+1)(n+2)}$$

and, in general,

$$a_{2\lambda} = \frac{(-1)^{\lambda} a_0}{2^{2\lambda} \lambda!(n+1)(n+2)\cdots(n+\lambda)} \tag{3.93}$$

Thus, for the case $b_1 = n$, the solution is

$$R_1(u) = u^n \sum_{\lambda=0}^{\infty} \frac{(-1)^{\lambda} a_0}{2^{2\lambda} \lambda!(n+1)(n+2)\cdots(n+\lambda)} u^{2\lambda} \tag{3.94}$$

Except for some special values of n, this is not an elementary function. It is customary to define $a_0 \equiv 1/(2^n n!)$; in this case, $R_1(u)$ becomes a *Bessel function** of order n:

$$J_n(u) = \frac{u^n}{2^n n!} \sum_{\lambda=0}^{\infty} \frac{(-1)^{\lambda}}{2^{2\lambda} \lambda!(n+1)(n+2)\cdots(n+\lambda)} u^{2\lambda} \tag{3.95a}$$

$$= \left(\frac{u}{2}\right)^n \sum_{\lambda=0}^{\infty} \frac{(-1)^{\lambda}}{\lambda!\Gamma(\lambda+n+1)} \left(\frac{u}{2}\right)^{2\lambda} \tag{3.95b}$$

$$= \left(\frac{u}{2}\right)^n \left[\frac{1}{n!} - \frac{(u/2)^2}{1!(n+1)!} + \frac{(u/2)^4}{2!(n+2)!} - \frac{(u/2)^6}{3!(n+3)!} + \cdots\right] \tag{3.95c}$$

Therefore, the functions $J_0(u)$ and $J_1(u)$ may be written as

$$J_0(u) = 1 - \frac{(u/2)^2}{(1!)^2} + \frac{(u/2)^4}{(2!)^2} - \frac{(u/2)^6}{(3!)^2} + \cdots \tag{3.96a}$$

$$J_1(u) = \frac{u}{2} - \frac{(u/2)^3}{1!2!} + \frac{(u/2)^5}{2!3!} - \frac{(u/2)^7}{3!4!} + \cdots \tag{3.96b}$$

The Bessel functions of the first two orders are shown in Fig. 3-7. These functions are all oscillatory with a constantly decreasing amplitude. Thus, there are an infinite number of roots for the Bessel function of any order.† The first few of these are given in Table 3.1. As n becomes very large, the νth root is approximately‡ $\nu\pi + (n - \frac{1}{2})(\pi/2)$. A comparison of this formula with the values in Table 3.1 reveals that the approximation is accurate to better than 10% even for $n = 2$.

* These functions were first studied by Euler (1764) in connection with his investigation of the vibration of circular membranes, but the first systematic treatment was given by Bessel (1824). Jacob Bernoulli was probably the first to investigate a special case (1703), and Daniel Bernoulli also used a special case in his study of the oscillations of heavy chains (1732).

† Roots of Bessel functions are tabulated, for example, in Jahnke and Emde (Ja45, pp. 166–168).

‡ This result is due to G. G. Stokes, 1850.

Table 3.1

SOME ROOTS OF J_0, J_1, AND J_2

Bessel function	1st root	2nd root	3rd root	4th root
J_0	2.405	5.520	8.654	11.792
J_1	3.832	7.016	10.173	13.324
J_2	5.136	8.417	11.620	14.796

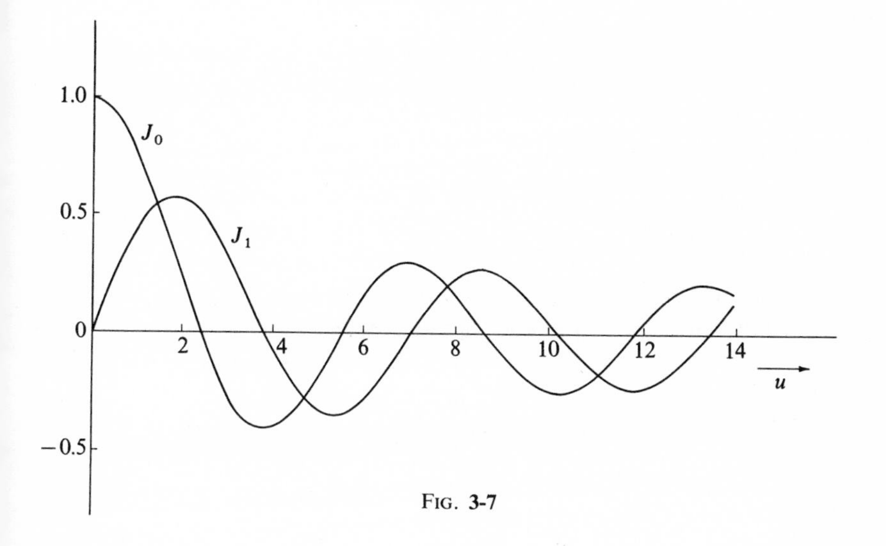

FIG. 3-7

The solution for the root $b_2 = -n$ is

$$J_{-n}(u) = \left(\frac{u}{2}\right)^{-n} \sum_{\lambda=0}^{\infty} \frac{(-1)^\lambda}{\lambda!\Gamma(\lambda - n + 1)} \left(\frac{u}{2}\right)^{2\lambda} \tag{3.97}$$

If n is not an integer, then $J_n(u)$ and $J_{-n}(u)$ are linearly independent solutions. However, if n is an integer, the solutions are linearly dependent, and, in fact,

$$J_{-m}(u) = (-1)^m J_m(u), \qquad m = \text{integer} \tag{3.98}$$

In the event that n is an integer (and even if n is not an integer), the general solution of Bessel's equation is usually written in terms of the linearly independent functions $J_n(u)$ and $N_n(u)$, where the latter is the *Neumann* *function** (or *Bessel function of the second kind*) of order n which is given by†

$$N_n(u) = \frac{J_n(u)\cos n\pi - J_{-n}(u)}{\sin n\pi} \tag{3.99}$$

Therefore, a particular solution $R_n(u) = R_n(kr)$ of Bessel's equation may be expressed as

$$R_n(kr) = A_n J_n(kr) + B_n N_n(kr) \tag{3.100}$$

The Bessel functions $J_n(kr)$ are regular at the origin and, for small kr, vary as

$$J_n(kr) \sim \frac{1}{\Gamma(n+1)}\left(\frac{kr}{2}\right)^n, \qquad kr \ll 1 \tag{3.101}$$

The asymptotic forms are‡

$$J_n(kr) \sim \sqrt{\frac{2}{\pi kr}}\cos\left(kr - \frac{n\pi}{2} - \frac{\pi}{4}\right), \qquad kr \gg 1 \tag{3.102}$$

The Bessel functions therefore exhibit an asymptotic sinusoidal variation with kr, but with an amplitude that decreases with increasing kr. The region of transition between the two forms given in Eqs. (3.101) and (3.102) is near $kr \approx n$.

The first two orders of the Neumann functions are shown in Fig. 3-8; these functions are irregular at the origin (becoming $-\infty$ at $r = 0$) and, for small kr, vary as

$$N_n(kr) \sim \begin{cases} \dfrac{2}{\pi}\left[ln\left(\dfrac{kr}{2}\right) + 0.5772\ldots\right] & (n = 0), \\ & \qquad kr \ll 1 \\ -\dfrac{\Gamma(n)}{\pi}\left(\dfrac{2}{kr}\right)^n & (n \neq 0), \end{cases} \tag{3.103}$$

The asymptotic forms are

$$N_n(kr) \sim \sqrt{\frac{2}{\pi kr}}\sin\left(kr - \frac{n\pi}{2} - \frac{\pi}{4}\right), \qquad kr \gg 1 \tag{3.104}$$

* Introduced by Karl G. Neumann, 1867.

† For details regarding the form of $N_n(u)$ when n becomes an integer (and for a succinct discussion of Bessel functions in general), see Whittaker and Watson (Wh52, Chapter 17).

‡ The asymptotic expression for J_0 was given by Poisson in 1817; Jacobi obtained the general result for integral n.

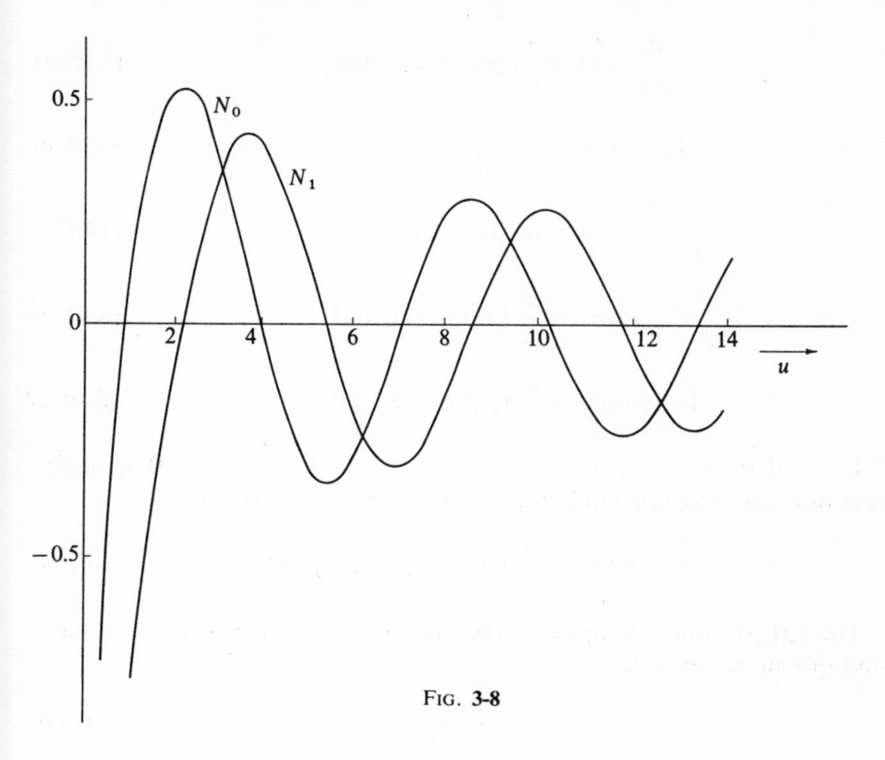

FIG. 3-8

Because of the irregularity of the $N_n(kr)$, we choose only the $J_n(kr)$ to treat problems which involve the origin.

The complete solution in cylindrical coordinates becomes

$$\Phi(r, \theta, z) \sim \sum_{n=0}^{\infty} [A_n J_n(kr) + B_n N_n(kr)] e^{\pm in\theta} e^{\pm kz} \tag{3.105}$$

But, we must take account of the fact that various values of k may yield equally acceptable solutions. Calling these values k_m, we have

$$\boxed{\Phi(r, \theta, z) \sim \sum_{m,n} [A_{mn} J_n(k_m r) + B_{mn} N_n(k_m r)] e^{\pm in\theta} e^{\pm k_m z}} \tag{3.106}$$

Some properties of the Bessel functions which will prove useful are listed below, where $Z_n(u)$ stands for either $J_n(u)$ or $N_n(u)$:

$$\frac{d}{du} J_0(u) = -J_1(u) \tag{3.107a}$$

$$\frac{d}{du} Z_n(u) = \frac{n}{u} Z_n(u) - Z_{n+1}(u) \tag{3.107b}$$

$$\int Z_1(u)\, du = -Z_0(u) \tag{3.107c}$$

$$\int uZ_0(u)\, du = uZ_1(u) \tag{3.107d}$$

$$\int u^2 Z_0^2(u)\, du = \frac{u^2}{2} [Z_0^2(u) + Z_1^2(u)] \tag{3.107e}$$

$$\int uZ_n^2(u)\, du = \frac{u^2}{2} [Z_n^2(u) - Z_{n-1}(u)Z_{n+1}(u)] \tag{3.107f}$$

If $k_m\rho$ is the mth root of $J_n(kr)$, i.e., $J_n(k_m\rho) = 0$, then the orthogonality condition on these functions states that, in the interval $0 \le r \le \rho$,

$$\int_0^\rho J_n(k_m r)J_n(k_{m'} r) r\, dr = \frac{\rho^2}{2} J_{n+1}^2(k_{m'}\rho)\delta_{mm'} \tag{3.108}$$

The $J_n(k_m r)$ form a complete orthogonal set for the expansion of a function of r in the interval $0 \le r \le \rho$:

$$f(r) = \sum_{m=1}^{\infty} D_{mn} J_n(k_m r) \tag{3.109}$$

If we multiply both sides of this equation by $rJ_n(k_{m'} r)$ and integrate over the range $0 \le r \le \rho$, then

$$\int_0^\rho f(r)J_n(k_{m'} r) r\, dr = \sum_m D_{mn} \int_0^\rho J_n(k_m r)J_n(k_{m'} r) r\, dr$$

The right-hand side may be evaluated by using the orthogonality relation [Eq. (3.108)]:

$$\int_0^\rho f(r)J_n(k_{m'} r) r\, dr = \sum_m D_{mn} \cdot \frac{\rho^2}{2} J_{n+1}^2(k_{m'}\rho)\delta_{mm'}$$

$$= D_{m'n} \frac{\rho^2}{2} J_{n+1}^2(k_{m'}\rho)$$

Therefore,

$$D_{mn} = \frac{2}{\rho^2 J_{n+1}^2(k_m\rho)} \int_0^\rho f(r)J_n(k_m r) r\, dr \tag{3.110}$$

The series generated by such an expansion is called a Fourier-Bessel series.

▶**Example 3.6.** Consider a long, grounded, conducting cylinder of radius a whose axis is the z-axis and which extends from $z = 0$ to $z = \infty$. At $z = 0$ the cylinder is closed by a plate (which does not touch the cylinder wall) which is held at a potential Φ_0. Compute the potential at all points interior to the cylinder.

The solution must clearly be independent of the angle θ, so we must have $n = 0$. Also, since the origin is involved and Φ must not be infinite there, $B_n = 0$. At large values of z, Φ must vanish, so the term $\exp(kz)$ is not allowed. Therefore, we have

$$\Phi(r, \theta, z) = \sum_m A_{m0} J_0(k_m r) e^{-k_m|z|}, \qquad r < a \tag{1}$$

Now,

$$\Phi(a, \theta, z) = 0 \tag{2}$$

Therefore,

$$\sum_m A_{m0} J_0(k_m a) e^{-k_m|z|} = 0 \tag{3}$$

Thus, the k_m are such that the quantities $k_m a$ are the zeroes of $J_0(kr)$.

The other boundary condition is

$$\Phi(r, \theta, 0) = \Phi_0 \tag{4}$$

or,

$$\Phi_0 = \sum_{m=1}^{\infty} A_{m0} J_0(k_m r) \tag{5}$$

We may use Eq. (3.110) to evaluate the coefficients A_{m0}:

$$A_{m0} = \frac{2\Phi_0}{a^2 J_1^2(k_m a)} \int_0^a r J_0(k_m r)\, dr \tag{6}$$

and using Eq. (3.107d), we find

$$A_{m0} = \frac{2\Phi_0}{a^2 J_1^2(k_m a)} \cdot \frac{a}{k_m} J_1(k_m a) \tag{7}$$

$$= \frac{2\Phi_0}{k_m a J_1(k_m a)}$$

Thus, the complete solution is

$$\Phi(r, \theta, z) = 2\Phi_0 \sum_m \frac{e^{-k_m|z|}}{k_m a} \frac{J_0(k_m r)}{J_1(k_m a)} \tag{8}$$

The expansion of functions in Fourier-Bessel series is of sufficient importance to warrant a detailed examination of the solution to this particular boundary-value problem. First, if a numerical or a graphical representation of the solution is desired, it is necessary to evaluate the sum in Eq. (8) for the particular parameters of the problem. (We may generalize such a representation by measuring the potential in units of Φ_0 and by measuring the distances r and z in units of the cylinder radius a.) The numerical values of J_0 and J_1 may be obtained from the series expansions in Eqs. (3.96) and the values k_m may be obtained from the extensive tabulations similar to Table 3.1 which may be found, for example, in Jahnke and Emde (Ja45, pp. 166–168).

If we begin such a procedure with the view toward obtaining reasonable accuracy in the final result, then we immediately encounter a formidable practical difficulty. This difficulty is a result of the fact that each term of the Fourier-Bessel series is itself the quotient of two series for the Bessel functions. We therefore have series within a series and we must take care to examine each series for the point at which it has converged to the predetermined accuracy. For example, consider the evaluation of $J_1(k_m a)$ for $m = 3$. Since a is the unit of length, we have, using Eq. (3.96b),

$$\begin{aligned} J_1(k_3 a) &= J_1(10.173) \\ &\cong 5.1 - 68 + 298 - 660 + 875 \\ &\qquad -773 + 487 + 231 + 85 - 25 + \cdots \end{aligned}$$

(with only slide-rule accuracy). We see that the series first diverges and after five terms the factorials in the denominator become sufficiently large to force the series to begin to converge. But even after ten terms, the inaccuracy in the result is greater than k_3 itself! Clearly, several more terms would be necessary in order to obtain a value which is accurate in, say, the third decimal place. For larger values of m, this procedure becomes completely unmanageable. The series for $J_0(k_{10} a)$ is still diverging after 20 terms. But more important is the fact that the value of the numerator is approximately 10^{46}. Such numbers exceed the nominal capacity of most electronic computers and special procedures are necessary to permit their calculation. We must therefore conclude that the use of the series expansions of the Bessel functions is of little practical value for arguments that are much in excess of unity.

The difficulty of large numbers in the series expansions may be circumvented by using instead the *integral representations* of the Bessel functions (see Problem 3-29):

$$J_0(u) = \frac{2}{\pi}\int_0^{\pi/2} \cos(u \cos \xi)\, d\xi \tag{3.111a}$$

$$J_1(u) = \frac{2u}{\pi}\int_0^{\pi/2} \sin^2 \xi \cos(u \cos \xi)\, d\xi \tag{3.111b}$$

By using a numerical integration procedure with a grid of, say, 300 points, the values of J_0 and J_1 can be evaluated to quite sufficient accuracy by means of an electronic computer. Then, by using a Fourier–Bessel series of *integrals* the values of Φ can be obtained. Figures 3-9 and 3-10 show Φ/Φ_0 as functions of z/a for various radii and of r/a for various values of z. It is apparent, for example, that the potential decreases very rapidly for points some distance away from the end-plate; for z equal to twice the cylinder radius, Φ is no larger than 1.5% of Φ_0 at any radius.

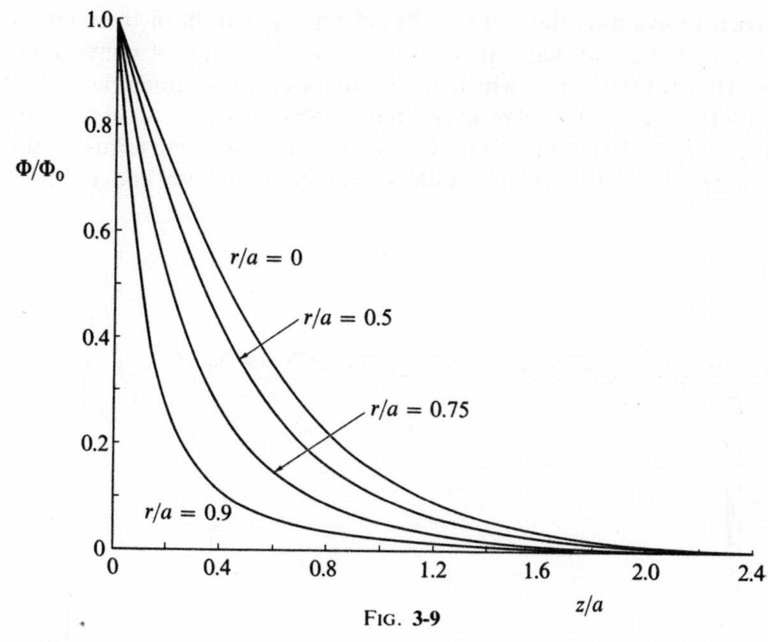

FIG. 3-9

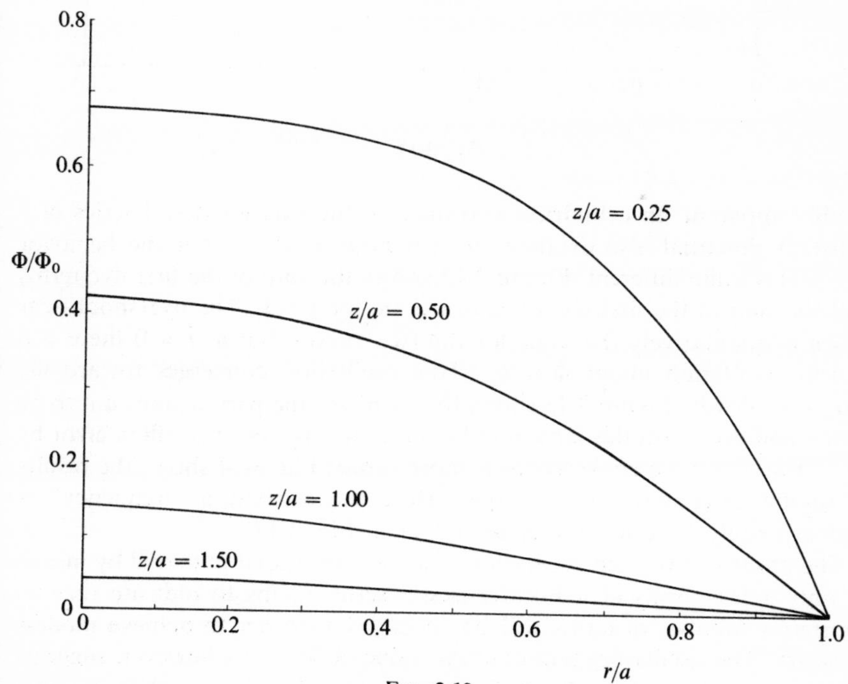

FIG. 3-10

If we wish to examine the Fourier–Bessel representation of the constant potential Φ_0 of the end-plate, then we find another type of convergence difficulty. The Fourier series which represents a constant potential over a certain interval in *rectangular* coordinates, $\Phi(x) = \Phi_0$, $0 < x < a$, was given in Eq. (5) of Example 3.3(a). The sum of the first ten terms of this series is shown in Fig. 3-11. The Gibbs overshoot at both end points is

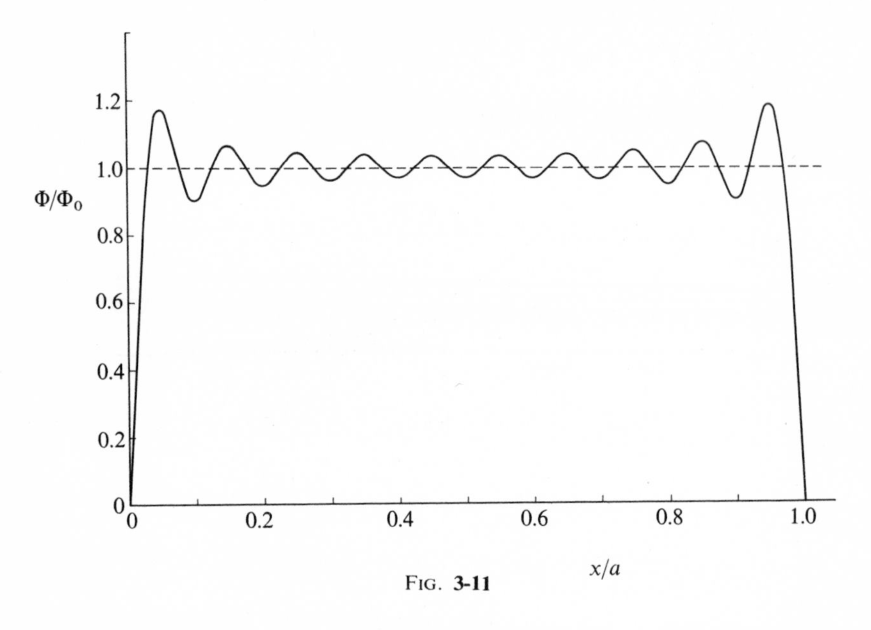

FIG. **3-11**

readily apparent. In cylindrical coordinates, the Fourier-Bessel series of a constant potential also exhibits an overshoot at $r = a$, but the behavior at $r = 0$ is quite different. Figure 3-12 shows the sum of the first five terms and the sum of the first six terms of Eq. (8) for $z = 0$. The overshoot near $r = a$ is qualitatively the same for the two curves, but at $r = 0$ there is a violent oscillation about $\Phi = \Phi_0$. This oscillation converges toward Φ_0 only very slowly. Figure 3-13 shows the values of the partial sums out to 50 terms, and even with this large number of terms, the result is still in error by 10%. For $r > 0$ the convergence is more rapid; Fig. 3-14 shows the results of similar calculations for $r = 0.9a$. Here the oscillation "frequency" is approximately 20 terms, rather than 2, as in Fig. 3-13.

The unsatisfactory representation of a constant radial potential by means of only a few terms of a Fourier-Bessel series seems to indicate that an enormous number of terms will be necessary in order to achieve modest accuracy. The oscillatory nature of the value of $\Phi(r = 0)$, however, suggests an alternative procedure. Figure 3-13 shows that the values of Φ for n terms

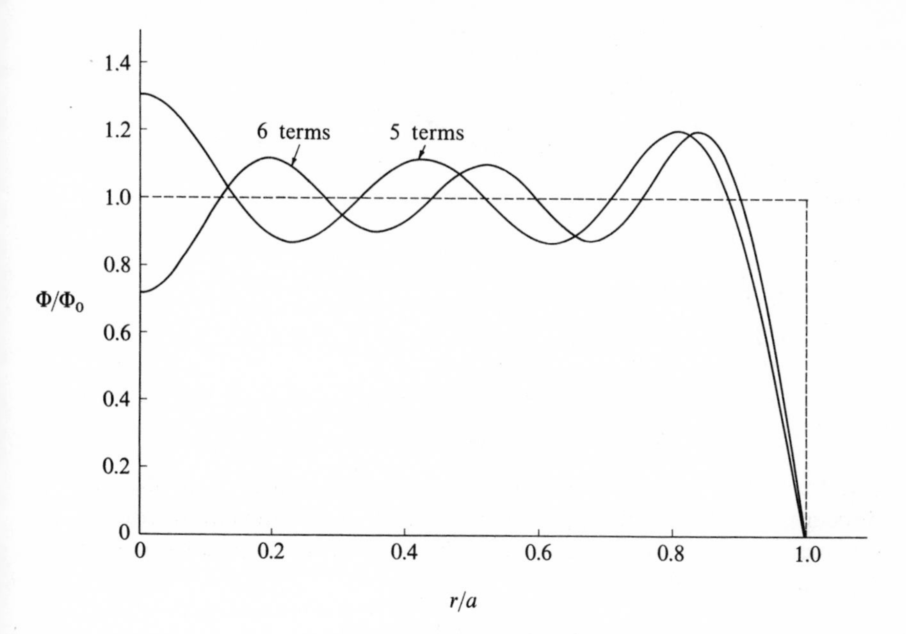

FIG. **3-12**

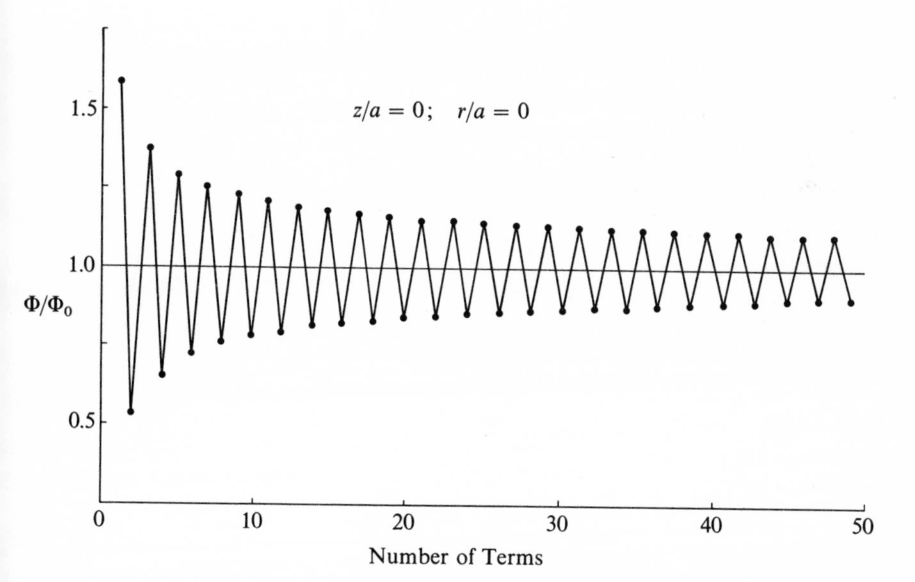

FIG. **3-13**

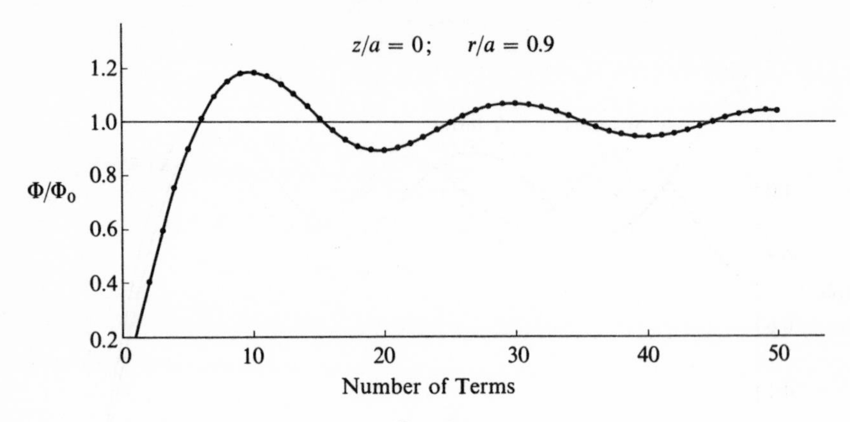

FIG. 3-14

and for $n + 2$ terms average to a value which differs from Φ_0 in one direction by an amount approximately equal to the deviation from Φ_0 in the opposite direction of the value of Φ for $n + 1$ terms. Therefore, we may define an average Φ according to

$$\Phi_{av} = \tfrac{1}{4}(\Phi_n + 2\Phi_{n+1} + \Phi_{n+2})$$

The results of this averaging procedure are shown in Fig. 3-15 for n = 6.

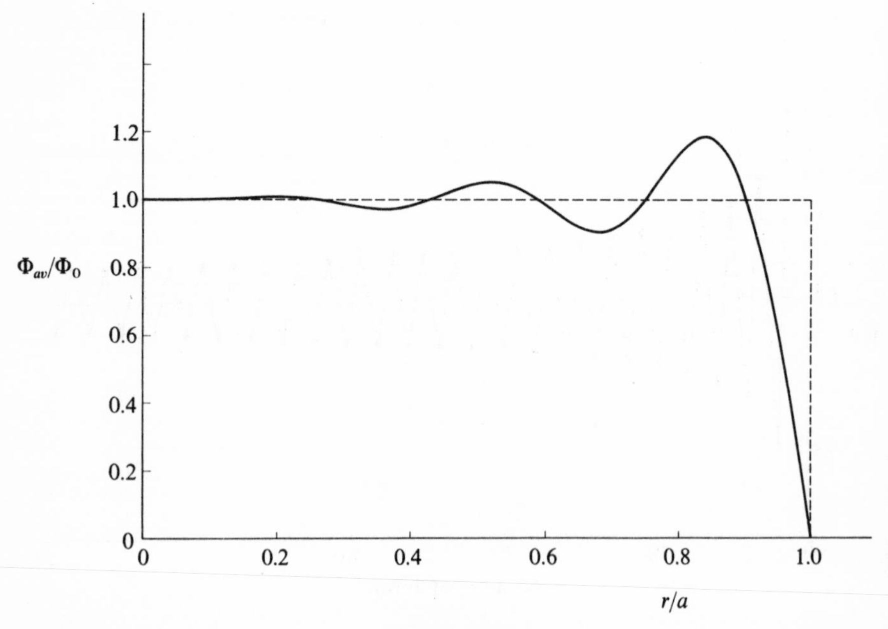

FIG. 3-15

Thus, by appropriately averaging the sixth, seventh, and eighth partial sums, we obtain a representation of the potential which is a considerable improvement over any single curve. For example, a value very close to Φ_0 is now found for $r = 0$. An even better approximation could, of course, be obtained if more partial sums were included in the average; for example,

$$\Phi_{av} = \tfrac{1}{8}(\Phi_n + 2\Phi_{n+1} + 2\Phi_{n+2} + 2\Phi_{n+3} + \Phi_{n+4})$$

The detailed numerical investigation of this problem serves to emphasize the fact that although the series representation of a solution is usually relatively easy to obtain, the actual calculation of a numerical result may be a nontrivial operation. This is particularly true if a discontinuous function must be represented with some degree of accuracy.

3.7. A Simple Example of Poisson's Equation—The Parallel-Plate Diode

The development of a general solution of Poisson's equation,

$$\nabla^2\Phi = -\frac{4\pi}{\varepsilon}\rho \tag{3.112}$$

in which $\rho = \rho(\mathbf{r})$, is a formidable problem. An elegant method makes use of *Green's functions* (see Suggested References). A discussion of this powerful technique, however, would carry us too far afield from the purposes of this volume. As far as Poisson's equation is concerned, we will therefore confine our treatment to the discussion of a simple example, one which has important practical applications—the space-charge-limited current flow in a parallel-plate diode.

Consider the idealized parallel-plate diode illustrated in Fig. 3-16. A constant potential difference $\Phi_0 > 0$ is maintained between the cathode and the anode which are separated by a distance d. Electrons are assumed

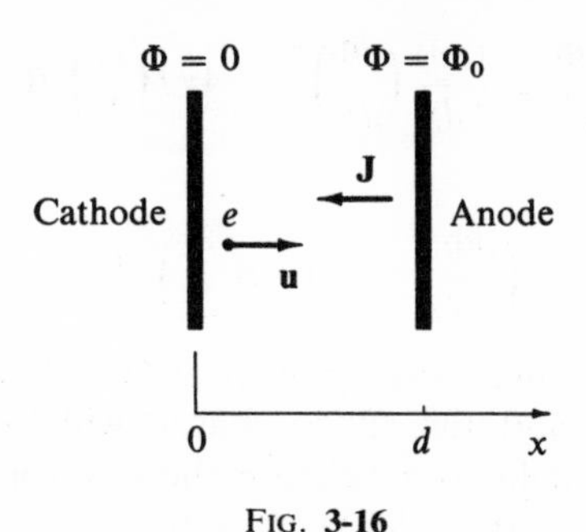

FIG. 3-16

to be liberated in unlimited quantity at the cathode and are accelerated to the anode. At any position x, where the potential is $\Phi(x)$, the electron velocity $u(x)$ may be obtained from

$$\tfrac{1}{2}mu^2 = e\Phi \tag{3.113}$$

This equation is valid only if the electrons are released at $x = 0$ with $u = 0$. This is, of course, always a small emission velocity, but the approximation of zero velocity is sufficiently accurate for our purposes.

Since the region between the plates is vacuum, Poisson's equation becomes

$$\frac{d^2\Phi}{dx^2} = -4\pi\rho \tag{3.114}$$

where the charge density is a function of x: $\rho = \rho(x)$, the so-called *space charge* density.

Now, charge is conserved so that under equilibrium conditions the current density is independent of position and is given by

$$J = -\rho u \tag{3.115}$$

The minus sign for electron current signifies that the direction of *positive* current is taken to be in the $+x$-direction.

Because the supply of electrons is unlimited, they will tend to collect in the space near the cathode. These electrons constitute a space charge, and they depress the field in the region of the cathode to the point that equilibrium conditions are attained.

Substituting Eqs. (3.113) and (3.115) into Eq. (3.114), we have

$$\frac{d^2\Phi}{dx^2} = 4\pi\frac{J}{u} = 4\pi J\left(\frac{m}{2e\Phi}\right)^{\frac{1}{2}}$$

This equation may be integrated by multiplying both sides by $d\Phi/dx$. Thus,

$$\frac{d\Phi}{dx}\frac{d^2\Phi}{dx^2} = \frac{1}{2}\frac{d}{dx}\left(\frac{d\Phi}{dx}\right)^2 = 4\pi J\left(\frac{m}{2e}\right)^{\frac{1}{2}}\Phi^{-\frac{1}{2}}\frac{d\Phi}{dx}$$

or,

$$\left(\frac{d\Phi}{dx}\right)^2 = 16\pi J\left(\frac{m}{2e}\right)^{\frac{1}{2}}\Phi^{\frac{1}{2}} \tag{3.116}$$

where the constant of integration vanishes since the electrons are liberated at the surface $x = 0$ and the space charge will build up until there is no longer an electric field to accelerate the electrons away. Therefore, at $x = 0$, we have $d\Phi/dx = 0$ as well as $\Phi = 0$.

Equation (3.116) may be integrated and the same boundary conditions applied to yield

$$\Phi^{\frac{3}{4}} = 3(\pi J)^{\frac{1}{2}}\left(\frac{m}{2e}\right)^{\frac{1}{4}} x \tag{3.117}$$

We may now solve for J, using the fact that $\Phi(x = d) = \Phi_0$:

$$J = \frac{1}{9\pi d^2}\left(\frac{2e}{m}\right)^{\frac{1}{2}} \Phi_0^{\frac{3}{2}} \tag{3.118}$$

The proportionality of the current density to $\Phi_0^{\frac{3}{2}}$ is known as the *Child-Langmuir law.** The variation with distance of the potential, the field, and the charge density may be summarized as follows:

$$\left.\begin{aligned} \Phi(x) &\propto x^{\frac{4}{3}} \\ E(x) &\propto x^{\frac{1}{3}} \\ \rho(x) &\propto x^{-\frac{2}{3}} \end{aligned}\right\} \tag{3.119}$$

These results are illustrated in Fig. 3-17. The diode is evidently a non-linear device and does not obey Ohm's law.

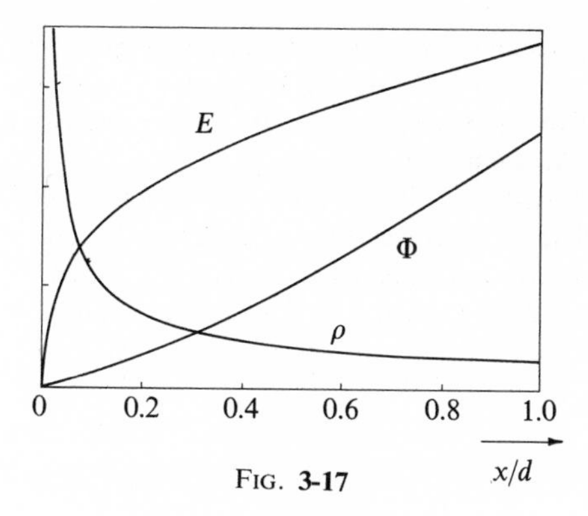

FIG. **3-17**

Suggested References

Laplace's equation is intimately connected with the general theory of potentials. The standard work on this subject is Kellogg (Ke29). Jeffreys and Jeffreys (Je46, Chapter 6) give a brief treatment; other chapters (14, 21, 24) are devoted to the mathematics associated with solutions of Laplace's equation; the quotations at

* The result was first published by C. D. Child [*Phys. Rev.* **32**, 492 (1911)], but Irving Langmuir made an independent derivation [*Phys. Rev.* **2**, 450 (1913)]. The important case of cylindrical electrodes was investigated by Langmuir and K. B. Blodgett [*Phys. Rev.* **22**, 347 (1923)]; the $\frac{3}{2}$ power still obtains for this case (and, indeed, for *any* symmetrical geometry).

the beginning of each chapter are delightful. A short account of potential theory will also be found in Menzel (Me53, Sections 11–19).

In addition to the books listed above, some sources at the intermediate level for material on Legendre functions, Bessel functions, and spherical harmonics are: Byerly (By93); Churchill (Ch41, Chapters 8, 9); Davis (Da63, Chapter 4); Hochstadt (Ho61, Chapters 2, 3); Margenau and Murphy (Ma43, Chapters 2, 3); and Pipes (Pi46, Chapters 13, 14). Advanced and authoritative references are Morse and Feshbach (Mo53, Chapter 5) and Whittaker and Watson (Wh52, Chapters 15, 17). An extensive tabulation of properties of special functions is given by Van Bladel (Va64, Appendix 4).

Treatments of Laplace's equation from the standpoint of electrostatics will be found in numerous books. At the intermediate level, see, for example: Corson and Lorrain (Co62, Chapter 4); Jeans (Je25, Chapter 8); Langmuir (La61, Chapter 2); Plonsey and Collins (Pl61, Chapter 4), an excellent survey; and Slater and Frank (Sl47, Chapter 3), a brief treatment.

Advanced accounts of electrostatic problems include: Jackson (Ja62, Chapters 2, 3); Morse and Feshbach (Mo53, Chapter 11); Panofsky and Phillips (Pa60, Chapters 3–5); Smythe (Sm50, Chapters 4, 5), a comprehensive treatment; Stratton (St41, Chapter 3); Tralli (Tr63, Chapter 6); and Van Bladel (Va64, Chapters 3–5).

The method of images is discussed in detail by Jeans (Je25, Chapter 8) and by Maxwell (Ma04, Vol. I, Chapter 11). A brief account will be found, for example, in Scott (Sc59, Chapter 4).

Conformal mapping techniques for two-dimensional problems are treated by: Jeans (Je25, Chapter 8); Maxwell (Ma04, Vol. I, Chapter 12); Morse and Feshbach (Mo53, Chapter 4); and Smythe (Sm50, Chapter 4). A short discussion is given, for example, by Owen (Ow63, Appendix D).

Green's function methods for the solution of Poisson's equation are discussed by: Jackson (Ja62, Chapter 3); Owen (Ow63, Appendix E); and Tralli (Tr63, Chapter 6).

Laplace's equation is also fundamental to the subject of hydrodynamics. An extensive treatment from this standpoint will be found, for example, in Lamb (La32).

Problems

3-1. Consider two infinitely long coaxial cylinders, the inner one of radius a and the outer one of radius b. The cylinders are perfect conductors and the outer one is held at a potential Φ_0 while the inner one is grounded ($\Phi = 0$). Integrate directly Laplace's equation (in cylindrical coordinates) to obtain

$$\Phi = \Phi_0 \frac{\ln(r/a)}{\ln(b/a)}$$

for the potential as a function of r between the cylinders (i.e., for $a < r < b$).

3-2. Integrate directly Laplace's equation (in spherical coordinates) to obtain the potential in the region between two concentric conducting spheres, the outer one being held at a potential Φ_0 and the inner one being grounded.

3-3. A potential in the x-z plane is independent of z and given by a repeating step function of magnitude $2\Phi_0$ and period $2a$ (as in Fig. 3-2). In addition,

y

$\Phi = 0$

$y = y_0$

x

$-\Phi_0 \quad \Phi_0 \quad -\Phi_0 \quad \Phi_0 \quad -\Phi_0 \quad \Phi_0$

$-3a \quad -2a \quad -a \quad 0 \quad a \quad 2a \quad 3a$

the plane defined by $y = y_0$ is held at ground potential. Find the potential for all points of space in the region $0 < y < y_0$.

3-4. Refer to Fig. 3-3. Allow the surfaces $z = 0$ and $z = c$ to be at the potential Φ_0; all other surfaces have $\Phi = 0$. Find the potential at any point within the box. If the box is a cube (i.e., if $a = b = c$), compare the potential at the center with the average potential on the walls. (A numerical calculation will be necessary.)

3-5. A hollow, rectangular pipe is defined by the planes $x = \pm a$ and $y = \pm b$; the pipe is infinitely long in the $\pm z$-directions. The surface at $y = b$ is held at a potential given by $\Phi(x, b) = \Phi_0 \exp(-|x|/l)$; the other three surfaces are grounded. Find the potential $\Phi(x, y)$ for points interior to the pipe.

3-6. Obtain the potential for any point within the two-dimensional "box," subject to the boundary conditions given in the figure. Sketch the field lines and the equipotentials within the box.

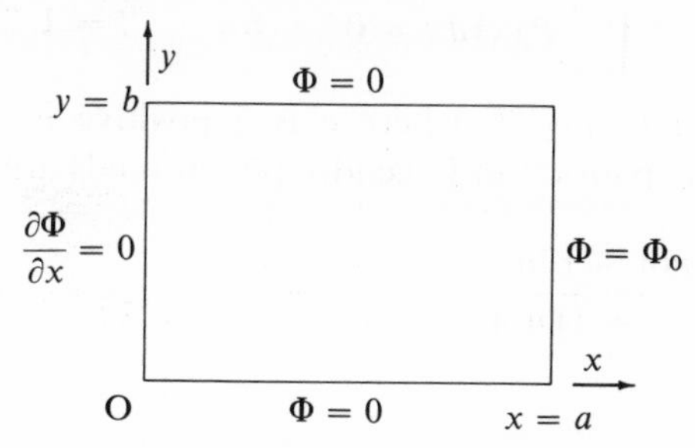

3-7. In the preceding problem replace $\Phi = \Phi_0$ by $\Phi = \Phi(y)$ along $x = a$ and let $\partial\Phi/\partial x = \xi(y)$ along $x = 0$. Find the potential at any point within the box.

3-8. If the function $f(x)$ has continuous derivatives of all orders in the interval $-1 \leqslant x \leqslant 1$, show that

$$\int_{-1}^{+1} f(x)P_l(x)\,dx = \frac{(-1)^l}{2^l l!}\int_{-1}^{+1}(x^2-1)^l \frac{d^l f(x)}{dx^l}\,dx$$

[Use Rodriquez' formula and integrate by parts l times.] Evaluate the integral for $f(x) = x^m$ where m is an integer, $0 \leqslant m < l$. Use this result to show that the Legendre polynomials are orthogonal functions.

3-9. Show that the function

$$Q_l(x) = \frac{1}{2l+1}\int_{-1}^{+1}\frac{(1-\xi^2)^l}{(x-\xi)^{l+1}}\,d\xi$$

is a solution of the Legendre equation. This function is known as the *Legendre function of the second kind* and is the solution that is irregular at $x = \pm 1$.

3-10. Show that if $f(x)$ is continuous in the range $-1 \leqslant x \leqslant 1$, then the polynomial $F(x)$, of degree n, that is the best least-squares approximation to $f(x)$, is given by

$$F(x) = \sum_{l=0}^{n} A_l P_l(x)$$

where the coefficients A_l are given by Eq. (3.46). By the "best least-squares approximation" it is meant that the integral

$$\int_{-1}^{+1}[f(x)-F(x)]^2\,dx$$

is a minimum.

3-11. Use Rodriguez' formula to show that $P_l(x)$ has l real and distinct roots in the interval $-1 < x < 1$.

3-12. Show that

$$\int_{-1}^{+1} P_l(x)\,dx = 0 \qquad \text{for} \qquad l = 1, 2, 3, \ldots$$

3-13. Show that if $f(x) = x^n$, where n is a positive integer, then the coefficients A_l of an expansion in Legendre polynomials are given by

$$A_l = \begin{cases} (2l+1)\dfrac{n(n-1)(n-2)\cdots(n-l+2)}{(n+l+1)(n+l-1)\cdots(n-l+3)}, & n-l \geq 0, \quad \text{even} \\[2ex] 0, & \text{otherwise} \end{cases}$$

Write out explicitly the series that represent x^2, x^3, x^4, and x^5.

3-14. Prove the orthogonality of the $P_l(x)$ by starting with the equation

$$\int_{-1}^{+1} P'_l(x)\left\{\frac{d}{dx}\left[(1-x^2)\frac{dP_l}{dx}\right] + l(l+1)P_l(x)\right\} dx = 0$$

which is clearly valid in view of Eq. (3.35). Integrate the first term by parts and then write down a comparable equation with l and l' interchanged. Subtract these two equations and then use Rodriguez' formula to evaluate the resulting integral by an l-fold integration by parts. Next, use the fact that

$$\frac{d^{2l}}{dx^{2l}}(x^2-1)^l = (2l)!$$

Evaluate the integral which then remains in terms of Γ functions in order to complete the proof.

3-15. Show that

$$\int_{-1}^{+1} (1 - 2\mu x + \mu^2)^{-\frac{1}{2}}(1 - 2\lambda x + \lambda^2)^{-\frac{1}{2}}\, dx$$

$$= (\lambda\mu)^{-\frac{1}{2}}\ln\left(\frac{1+\sqrt{\lambda\mu}}{1-\sqrt{\lambda\mu}}\right)$$

Use this result to prove the orthogonality of the Legendre polynomials.

3-16. A conducting sphere of radius a on whose surface resides a total charge Q is placed in a uniform electric field $\mathbf{E}_0$. Find the potential at all points in space exterior to the sphere.

3-17. A conducting sphere of radius a is covered with a dielectric (dielectric constant ε) in the form of a spherical shell; the radius of the entire object is b. If the covered sphere is placed in a uniform electric field $\mathbf{E}_0$ in free space, find the potential and the field components for all interior and exterior points.

3-18. A dielectric spherical shell (dielectric constant ε) has inner and outer radii of a and $2a$. If the shell is placed in a uniform electric field $\mathbf{E}_0$, find the field in the interior of the shell.

3-19. A point charge q is located a distance l from the center of a grounded, conducting sphere of radius a $(a < l)$. Find the potential at any point exterior to the sphere (exclude the point at which the charge is located). Calculate also the charge distribution on the surface of the sphere.

3-20. Consider a ring of radius R which is charged uniformly with a total charge Q. Take the origin at the center of the ring and let the polar axis be the axis of the ring. Show that the potential at a point in space specified by (r, θ) is given by

$$\Phi(r, \theta) = \frac{Q}{r}\left[1 - \frac{1}{2}\frac{R^2}{r^2}P_2(\cos\theta) + \cdots\right]$$

Sketch the equipotential lines in a plane that contains the axis of the ring.

3-21. Consider a hemisphere of radius a which is charged uniformly with a total charge Q. If (r, θ) describe the coordinates of a point relative to the center of the base of the hemisphere, show that for $r \gg a$ the potential is approximately given by

$$\Phi(r, \theta) = \frac{Q}{r}\left[1 + \frac{3a}{8r}\cos\theta\right]$$

3-22. A spherical conducting shell of radius a with center at the origin is cut in two along the plane $\theta = \pi/2$. The two halves are then insulated and the upper half $(0 \leqslant \theta < \pi/2)$ is given a potential Φ_0 while the lower half $(\pi/2 < \theta \leqslant \pi)$ is given a potential $-\Phi_0$. Calculate the potential at all points in space. Consider two cases: $r > a$ and $r < a$. Use the explicit expressions for the $P_l(\cos\theta)$ and calculate the first three terms in the expansion for each case.

3-23. In the previous problem, take the polar axis $(\theta = 0)$ to lie in the plane which divides the two hemispheres. Calculate the potential at all points in space exterior to the sphere in terms of spherical harmonics.

3-24. Two concentric spheres have radii of a and b, with $a < b$. If the potential on the inner sphere is given by $\Phi_a P_3(\cos\theta)$ and the potential on the outer sphere is given by $\Phi_b P_5(\cos\theta)$, find the potential for all points between the spheres, i.e., for $a < r < b$.

3-25. A potential field is given by $\Phi_0(r, \theta, \varphi) = r^2 \sin 2\theta \exp(i\varphi)$. Find the potential exterior to a grounded, conducting sphere of radius a placed in this field at the origin.

3-26. A sphere of radius a has a surface distribution of charge which is proportional to $\cos 2\theta$. Find the potential at all points in space exterior to the sphere. Represent the charge distribution by the appropriate multipole.

3-27. A spherical surface of radius a has a potential distribution proportional to $\sin 3\theta \cos\varphi$. Find the potential at all points interior and exterior to the surface.

3-28. Prove Eq. (3.107b) by differentiating the series expression for $J_n(u)$.

3-29. Show that

$$\frac{1}{u}\frac{d}{du}\frac{J_n(u)}{u^n} = -\frac{J_{n+1}(u)}{u^{n+1}}$$

is equivalent to Eq. (3.107b). Use this result together with the integral representation [Eq. (3.111a)],

$$J_0(u) = \frac{2}{\pi}\int_0^{\pi/2} \cos(u \cos \xi)\, d\xi,$$

to prove that

$$J_1(u) = \frac{2u}{\pi}\int_0^{\pi/2} \sin^2 \xi \cos(u \cos \xi)\, d\xi$$

and, in general,

$$J_m(u) = \frac{2}{\pi}\frac{u^m}{1 \cdot 3 \cdot 5 \cdot \cdots \cdot (2m-1)}\int_0^{\pi/2} \sin^{2m} \xi \cos(u \cos \xi)\, d\xi$$

3-30. Show that

$$J_{\frac{1}{2}}(u) = \sqrt{\frac{2}{\pi u}} \sin u$$

$$J_{-\frac{1}{2}}(u) = \sqrt{\frac{2}{\pi u}} \cos u$$

3-31. Use the results of the previous problem and show that

$$J_{\frac{3}{2}}(u) = \sqrt{\frac{2}{\pi u}}\left(\frac{\sin u}{u} - \cos u\right)$$

3-32. An infinitely long cylinder of radius a with dielectric constant ε is placed in a uniform electric field $\mathbf{E}_0$ which is directed perpendicular to the axis of the cylinder. Find the potential at all points exterior to the cylinder.

3-33. Find the potential distribution inside a hollow conducting cylinder of radius a if the cylinder has a length L and the two ends are closed by plates which are held at the potentials $\Phi = \Phi_0$ and $\Phi = 0$, respectively. Also, find the charge distribution on the surface of the cylinder.

3-34. Prove Eq. (3.98).

3-35. Find the density of induced charge on the surface of the cylinder in Example 3.6.

3-36. Consider the x-y plane to be a grounded, conducting plane. A simple dipole of moment $\mathbf{p}$ is located a distance h above this plane. Calculate the potential at any point; also calculate the surface distribution of charge on the conducting plane in the event that (a) $\mathbf{p}$ is parallel to the x-y plane and (b) $\mathbf{p}$ is perpendicular to the x-y plane. (Use cylindrical coordinates.)

3-37. Use Laplace's equation to show that a charged body placed in an electric field cannot be maintained in a position of stable equilibrium by the application of electrostatic forces alone. (This is known as *Earnshaw's theorem.*)

CHAPTER 4

The Electromagnetic Field Equations

4.1 Introduction

In the preceding chapters we have discussed the mathematical description of static electric and magnetic fields. The basic equations which relate to such fields were summarized in Section 1.9. We now wish to consider the more general situation in which the field quantities may depend upon the time. Under such conditions there is an interdependence of the field quantities and it is no longer possible to discuss separately the electric and magnetic fields—we are forced to consider the generalized concept of an *electromagnetic field.* It was James Clerk Maxwell, using the results of Michael Faraday's researches, who succeeded in constructing a unified theory of electromagnetic phenomena* and in his honor the general, time-dependent electromagnetic field equations are called *Maxwell's equations.* These equations, it must be emphasized, are mathematical abstractions of experimental results, but it is found that the description of an extremely wide range of phenomena can be made by means of Maxwell's equations

* J. C. Maxwell, *Treatise on Electricity and Magnetism* (Ma04). The first edition of the *Treatise* was published in 1873, but the basis for Maxwell's theory of electromagnetism had been presented in a paper of 1864 (published, 1865).

without contradiction. Thus, they appear to be a true representation of the classical electromagnetic field. Indeed, their validity goes beyond classical phenomena and they find applicability in discussions of relativistic and quantum effects. We shall, however, confine our attention here to classical problems.

In this chapter we seek to establish the formulation of the field equations, to show that their solutions are unique, to discuss the scalar and vector potentials of the field, and to consider what is meant by the energy density of the field. We shall investigate the wave character of the electromagnetic field in the following chapters and discuss radiation sources and the interaction of electromagnetic radiation with various types of matter.

4.2 The Conservation of Charge and the Equation of Continuity

Under steady-state conditions the charge density in any given region will remain constant. We now relax the requirement of steady-state conditions and allow the charge density to become a function of the time. It is experimentally verified that the net amount of electric charge in a closed system is constant; this is one of the fundamental conservation laws of physics.* Therefore, if the net charge within a certain region decreases with time, this implies that a like amount of charge must appear in some other region. This transport of charge constitutes a current. The net amount of charge which crosses a unit area of a surface in unit time is defined as the *current density*, $\mathbf{J}$ (statamperes/cm^2). The total current flowing through a surface S therefore is

$$I = \oint_S \mathbf{J} \cdot d\mathbf{a} = \oint_S \mathbf{J} \cdot \mathbf{n}\, da \tag{4.1}$$

where $\mathbf{n}$ is the unit vector describing the outward normal to the surface. We define I to be positive for the *outward* flow of *positive* charge.

If there is a net *outward* flow of current through a closed surface, then the charge that is contained within the volume which is bounded by the surface must decrease. Therefore,

$$\oint_S \mathbf{J} \cdot \mathbf{n}\, da = -\frac{dq}{dt} = -\frac{d}{dt} \int_V \rho\, dv \tag{4.2}$$

* The conservation of electric charge, based on experiments with electrified bodies and the transferal of electrification, was put forward by William Watson (1746) and by Benjamin Franklin (1747). The first really satisfactory proof was given by Faraday (1843).

If we hold the surface S fixed in space, the time variation of the volume integral must be due solely to the time variation of ρ. Thus,

$$\oint_S \mathbf{J} \cdot \mathbf{n} \, da = -\int_V \frac{\partial \rho}{\partial t} \, dv \tag{4.3}$$

Transforming the integral of $\mathbf{J} \cdot \mathbf{n}$ by means of the divergence theorem, we obtain

$$\int_V \operatorname{div} \mathbf{J} \, dv = -\int_V \frac{\partial \rho}{\partial t} \, dv$$

Since the volume V is arbitrary, we have finally

$$\boxed{\operatorname{div} \mathbf{J} + \frac{\partial \rho}{\partial t} = 0} \tag{4.4}$$

This is the *equation of continuity* and is an expression of the experimental fact that electric charge is conserved.

Let us next investigate the prediction of the equation of continuity in a particular situation. We consider a volume of material which obeys Ohm's law and which has a conductivity σ. We place a certain amount of charge within a small volume of the material, so that at time $t = 0$ there is a charge density ρ_0 in this volume, and inquire as to the charge density at subsequent times. Using Ohm's law in the equation of continuity, we have

$$\begin{aligned} -\frac{\partial \rho}{\partial t} &= \operatorname{div} \mathbf{J} \\ &= \operatorname{div} \sigma \mathbf{E} \\ &= \frac{4\pi\sigma\rho}{\varepsilon} \end{aligned} \tag{4.5}$$

where we have used Coulomb's law [Eq. (1.20)] in order to obtain the last equality. Equation (4.5) is therefore a differential equation for $\rho(t)$ which we may write as

$$\rho + \tau \frac{\partial \rho}{\partial t} = 0 \tag{4.6}$$

where

$$\tau \equiv \frac{\varepsilon}{4\pi\sigma} \tag{4.7}$$

is the so-called *relaxation time*. (In MKS units, $\tau = \varepsilon/\sigma$.) The solution of Eq. (4.6) is

$$\rho(t) = \rho_0 e^{-t/\tau} \tag{4.8}$$

so that the charge density in the volume decreases exponentially with time; ρ reaches $1/e$ of its original value ρ_0 after a time τ.

The relaxation time τ varies inversely with the conductivity and is therefore subject to strong variations from material to material. Some typical values are: copper, $\sim 1.5 \times 10^{-19}$ sec; distilled water, $\sim 3.5 \times 10^{-6}$ sec; fused quartz, $\gtrsim 2 \times 10^{6}$ sec. Thus, the charge will almost instantaneously disappear from the interior of a good conductor such as copper, but will remain for an extremely long time within fused quartz, a material which is one of the best electrical insulators.

4.3 Electromagnetic Induction

In 1831 Faraday* announced the results of experiments which provided the key link between electric and magnetic phenomena. Faraday showed that a current is induced in a circuit when there is a change in the current flowing in an adjacent circuit, or when a magnet is moved in the vicinity of the circuit, or when the circuit itself is moved in the presence of another current-carrying circuit or magnet.† *Faraday's law*, which is the fundamental relation of *electrodynamics*, states that the emf produced in a circuit is proportional to the time rate of change of the magnetic flux F which links the circuit:

$$\text{emf} = -\frac{1}{c}\frac{dF}{dt} \tag{4.9}$$

where the proportionality constant $1/c$ is a result of the use of Gaussian units, and where

$$\text{emf} \equiv \oint_{\Gamma} \mathbf{E} \cdot d\mathbf{l} \tag{4.10}$$

$$F \equiv \int_S \mathbf{B} \cdot \mathbf{n}\, da \tag{4.11}$$

* Michael Faraday (1791–1867), a gifted physicist (and bookbinder) and a careful and clever technician, is generally acknowledged to be the foremost experimenter of any field of science.

† Electromagnetic induction seems actually to have been discovered first by the American physicist Joseph Henry (1797–1878). However, his results, obtained in 1830 or perhaps as early as 1829, were not published until after Faraday's announcement in 1831. Henry's failure to publish his findings also resulted in the acknowledgment of Heinrich Hertz as the discoverer of electromagnetic waves, although Henry's experiments with the propagation of electromagnetic impulses preceded those of Hertz by more than 40 years.

Since the flux F must link the circuit in which the emf is produced, the surface S over which the integral in Eq. (4.11) is carried out must be *open* and bounded by the curve Γ that represents the circuit and around which the line integral is taken in Eq. (4.10). The minus sign in Eq. (4.9) indicates that the current induced in the circuit (and, hence, the associated magnetic field) is in a direction which opposes the change of flux through the circuit; this is known as *Lenz's law*.*

Now, the time rate of change of F can result from the movement of the circuit in which the emf is induced or from a time variation of **B**. In the latter case, we may write

$$\oint_\Gamma \mathbf{E} \cdot dl = -\frac{1}{c}\int_S \frac{\partial \mathbf{B}}{\partial t} \cdot \mathbf{n}\, da \tag{4.12}$$

Stokes' theorem may be used to transform the line integral:

$$\int_S \mathbf{curl}\,\mathbf{E} \cdot \mathbf{n}\, da = -\frac{1}{c}\int_S \frac{\partial \mathbf{B}}{\partial t} \cdot \mathbf{n}\, da$$

Since the surface S is arbitrary, we must have

$$\boxed{\mathbf{curl}\,\mathbf{E} = -\frac{1}{c}\frac{\partial \mathbf{B}}{\partial t}} \tag{4.13}$$

which is the differential form of Faraday's law.

Notice that in the derivation of Eq. (4.13) from Eq. (4.9) we have made no use of the properties of the circuit in which the emf is produced except its shape. In fact, since the tangential component of **E** is continuous across the boundary between any two media [see Eq. (1.70)], Eq. (4.13) must be valid immediately outside the circuit wire. Thus, it seems reasonable to assume that Faraday's law is correct whether or not a circuit is actually present. This assumption of general validity of the law leads to the prediction of a number of physical effects, none of which has ever been contradicted by experiment. We may therefore conclude that Faraday's law, as stated in Eq. (4.13), is valid for general, time-dependent electromagnetic fields.

4.4 Maxwell's Modification of Ampère's Law

We have previously found that under steady-state conditions Ampère's law may be expressed as [see Eq. (1.54)]

$$\mathbf{curl}\,\mathbf{H} = \frac{4\pi}{c}\,\mathbf{J} \tag{4.14}$$

* Formulated in 1834 by the German physicist Heinrich Friedrich Emil Lenz (1804–1865).

Let us now examine the validity of this equation in the event that the fields are allowed to vary with time. If we take the divergence of both sides of Eq. (4.14), then since the divergence of the curl of any vector vanishes identically, we have

$$\operatorname{div} \mathbf{J} = 0$$

Now, the continuity equation [Eq. (4.4)] states that in general div $\mathbf{J}$ equals $-\partial\rho/\partial t$ and will therefore vanish only in the special case that the charge density is static. Consequently, we must conclude that Ampère's law as stated in Eq. (4.14) is valid only for steady-state conditions and is insufficient for the case of time-dependent fields. It was Maxwell who sought to modify Ampère's law so that it would apply under time-varying conditions as well. His solution to the problem was to make the substitution*

$$\mathbf{J} \to \mathbf{J} + \frac{1}{4\pi}\frac{\partial \mathbf{D}}{\partial t}$$

so that the modified form of Ampère's law becomes

$$\boxed{\mathbf{curl}\,\mathbf{H} = \frac{4\pi}{c}\mathbf{J} + \frac{1}{c}\frac{\partial \mathbf{D}}{\partial t}} \tag{4.15}$$

If we now take the divergence of both sides of this equation, we obtain

$$0 = \frac{4\pi}{c}\operatorname{div}\mathbf{J} + \frac{1}{c}\operatorname{div}\left(\frac{\partial \mathbf{D}}{\partial t}\right)$$

Interchanging the space and time derivatives of $\mathbf{D}$, we find

$$\operatorname{div}\mathbf{J} + \frac{1}{4\pi}\frac{\partial}{\partial t}\operatorname{div}\mathbf{D} = 0$$

Using Coulomb's law [Eq. (1.20)] to substitute $4\pi\rho$ for div $\mathbf{D}$, we have finally

$$\operatorname{div}\mathbf{J} + \frac{\partial \rho}{\partial t} = 0$$

and the continuity equation is recovered intact. That is, Maxwell's modification of Ampère's law is compatible with conservation of charge, whereas Eq. (4.14) is not.

* James Clerk Maxwell (1831-1879) realized this important fact in 1861; his ideas were contained in a letter to Sir William Thomson (Lord Kelvin), but the full development was not published until 1865.

The term which Maxwell added to Ampère's law, viz., $(1/4\pi)\,\partial\mathbf{D}/\partial t$, is called the *displacement current*, and corresponds, for example, to the "current" which must flow in the space (even a vacuum) between a pair of condenser plates when the charged plates are connected by an external circuit. There is a displacement current even though no charge moves across the space. In order to illustrate this, consider the circuit in Fig. 4-1 which consists of a source of alternating current and a capacitor. The circuit is looped by the line Γ which bounds the surface S. If a current I flows in the circuit, Ampère's law states that

$$\oint_{\Gamma} \mathbf{H} \cdot dl = \frac{4\pi}{c} \int_{S} \mathbf{J} \cdot \mathbf{n}\, da = \frac{4\pi}{c} I$$

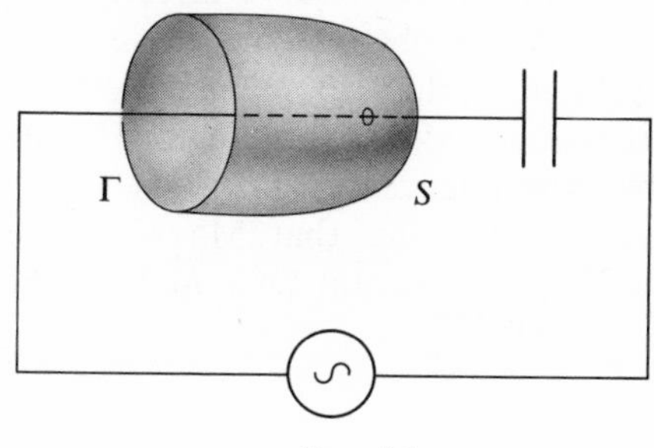

FIG. 4-1

Clearly, this result must be independent of the particular manner in which we construct the surface S. But consider the construction shown in Fig. 4-2. Now, the conduction current I does not flow through the surface and we are forced to conclude that

$$\oint_{\Gamma} \mathbf{H} \cdot dl = 0$$

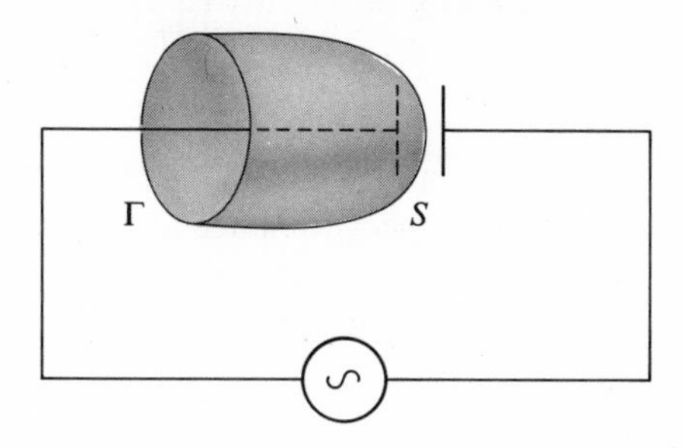

FIG. 4-2

The two situations can be made to yield the same result if we include the displacement current, since then

$$\oint_\Gamma \mathbf{H} \cdot d\mathbf{l} = \frac{4\pi}{c} \int_S \mathbf{J} \cdot \mathbf{n}\, da + \frac{1}{c} \frac{\partial}{\partial t} \int_S \mathbf{D} \cdot \mathbf{n}\, da = \frac{4\pi}{c} I$$

For a perfectly conducting wire and a vacuum between the plates of the capacitor, the integral of $\mathbf{J} \cdot \mathbf{n}$ contributes only in the event that the surface S cuts the circuit and the integral of $\mathbf{D} \cdot \mathbf{n}$ contributes only in the event that the surface passes between the capacitor plates; the value of the integral in either instance is $4\pi I/c$ (see Problem 4-7).

It must be emphasized that the ultimate justification for Maxwell's assumption is in the experimental verification. Indeed, the effects of the displacement current are difficult to observe directly except at very high frequencies. In some microwave phenomena, however, the displacement currents are sufficiently large so that the magnetic effects can actually be measured. Indirect verification is afforded by the prediction of many effects which are confirmed by experiment; we shall treat some of these in later chapters. We may therefore consider that Maxwell's form of Ampère's law has been subjected to experimental tests and has been found to be generally valid.

4.5 Maxwell's Equations

It has been established that Faraday's law for $\mathbf{E}$ [Eq. (4.13)] and the Maxwell–Ampère law for $\mathbf{H}$ [Eq. (4.15)] are valid for time-dependent fields. It still remains to investigate the other two fundamental field equations for $\mathbf{D}$ and $\mathbf{B}$ for time-varying conditions. Taking the divergence of Eq. (4.13), we have

$$\begin{aligned} \operatorname{div} \mathbf{curl}\, \mathbf{E} &= -\frac{1}{c} \operatorname{div} \left(\frac{\partial \mathbf{B}}{\partial t} \right) \\ &\equiv 0 \end{aligned}$$

If we assume that all of the derivatives of $\mathbf{B}$ are continuous, we may interchange the differentiation with respect to space and time:

$$\frac{\partial}{\partial t} \operatorname{div} \mathbf{B} = 0$$

or,

$$\operatorname{div} \mathbf{B} = \text{constant in time}$$

Now, if at any instant in time $\mathbf{B} = 0$, then the constant of integration vanishes. If we assume that the field originated at some time in the past, then

$$\operatorname{div} \mathbf{B} = 0 \tag{4.16}$$

even for the time-varying case. Physically, we may argue that there are no magnetic monopoles in the steady-state situation so that $\operatorname{div} \mathbf{B} = 0$; and since the addition of time-varying fields cannot generate such monopoles, $\operatorname{div} \mathbf{B} = 0$ must be generally valid.

Finally, we may work backwards from the Maxwell–Ampère law (which we assume has been experimentally verified) by taking the divergence of Eq. (4.15). We find

$$\operatorname{div}\left(4\pi\mathbf{J} + \frac{\partial \mathbf{D}}{\partial t}\right) = 0$$

or, using the continuity equation,

$$\frac{\partial}{\partial t}(\operatorname{div} \mathbf{D} - 4\pi\rho) = 0 \tag{4.17}$$

Again, if the field originated at some time in the past, then $\operatorname{div} \mathbf{D} = 4\pi\rho$. Note that the assumption $\rho = 0$ at some past time does not require $\rho = 0$ for all times (conservation of charge), since $\mathbf{D}$ is a *macroscopic* quantity. That is, a medium may be electrically neutral if an average over small volumes is carried out, but this does not prevent the *microscopic* charges from eventually being separated to produce an electric field.

The argument of the vanishing of the fields at some time in the past, used to obtain $\operatorname{div} \mathbf{B} = 0$ and $\operatorname{div} \mathbf{D} = 4\pi\rho$ from the Faraday law and the Maxwell–Ampère law,* may not appeal to some because it appears to suppose an act of *creation*. The argument is not necessary, of course, since the equations are subject to independent experimental verification, but the analysis given above at least indicates the internal consistency of the four field equations.

We therefore conclude that the following four equations are valid descriptions of time-dependent electromagnetic fields:

$$\operatorname{div} \mathbf{D} = 4\pi\rho \tag{4.18a}$$

$$\operatorname{div} \mathbf{B} = 0 \tag{4.18b}$$

$$\mathbf{curl\, E} + \frac{1}{c}\frac{\partial \mathbf{B}}{\partial t} = 0 \tag{4.18c}$$

$$\mathbf{curl\, H} - \frac{1}{c}\frac{\partial \mathbf{D}}{\partial t} = \frac{4\pi}{c}\mathbf{J} \tag{4.18d}$$

* This argument is used by Stratton (St41, p. 6) to "derive" the divergence equations.

These equations are known as *Maxwell's equations* and will form the basis for our discussion of the electromagnetic field.

4.6 The Potential Functions of the Electromagnetic Field*

We have seen in Chapter 1 that the relation $\mathbf{curl}\,\mathbf{E} = 0$ is satisfied for static electric fields and that as a result we may represent such a field in terms of the scalar potential Φ:

$$\mathbf{E} = -\mathbf{grad}\,\Phi \qquad \text{(static fields)} \tag{4.19}$$

Similarly, the fact that $\mathbf{B}$ always satisfies the relation $\operatorname{div}\mathbf{B} = 0$ allows us to express $\mathbf{B}$ as the curl of the vector potential $\mathbf{A}$:

$$\mathbf{B} = \mathbf{curl}\,\mathbf{A} \tag{4.20}$$

But for the time-dependent case we no longer have $\mathbf{curl}\,\mathbf{E} = 0$; however, in view of Eq. (4.20), we may write the third Maxwell equation (4.18c) as

$$\mathbf{curl}\left(\mathbf{E} + \frac{1}{c}\frac{\partial \mathbf{A}}{\partial t}\right) = 0 \tag{4.21}$$

Thus, for the time-dependent case, it is no longer $\mathbf{E}$ that must equal the gradient of the scalar potential, but now it is the quantity in Eq. (4.21) the curl of which vanishes. Therefore,

$$\boxed{\mathbf{E} = -\mathbf{grad}\,\Phi - \frac{1}{c}\frac{\partial \mathbf{A}}{\partial t}} \tag{4.22}$$

For the static case this equation reduces to Eq. (4.19).

Although the specification of $\mathbf{A}$ completely determines $\mathbf{B}$ according to Eq. (4.20), the converse is not true since the curl of the gradient of any scalar vanishes identically, so that we may add to $\mathbf{A}$ the gradient of a scalar ξ without affecting $\mathbf{B}$. That is, $\mathbf{A}$ may be replaced by

$$\mathbf{A}' = \mathbf{A} + \varepsilon\mu\,\mathbf{grad}\,\xi \tag{4.23}$$

But if this is done, Eq. (4.22) becomes

$$\mathbf{E} = -\mathbf{grad}\,\Phi - \frac{1}{c}\frac{\partial}{\partial t}(\mathbf{A} + \varepsilon\mu\,\mathbf{grad}\,\xi) \tag{4.24}$$

* George Green introduced the concept of the potential function into the theory of electricity and magnetism in 1828. His paper was generally unnoticed until Lord Kelvin had it reprinted in 1846. Franz Neumann (father of the eminent mathematician, Karl Neumann) was the first to use the vector potential, 1845.

r,

$$\mathbf{E} = -\mathbf{grad}\left(\Phi + \frac{\varepsilon\mu}{c}\frac{\partial\xi}{\partial t}\right) - \frac{1}{c}\frac{\partial\mathbf{A}}{\partial t} \tag{4.24a}$$

Therefore, if we make the transformation (4.23), we must also replace Φ by

$$\Phi' = \Phi - \frac{\varepsilon\mu}{c}\frac{\partial\xi}{\partial t} \tag{4.25}$$

in order that the expression for **E** remain unchanged. The transformations (4.23) and (4.25) are called *gauge transformations.* Even though we add the gradient of a scalar function to the vector potential and add the time derivative of this function to the scalar potential, the field vectors remain unchanged. Now, it is the *field quantities* and not the *potentials* that possess physical meaningfulness. We therefore say that the field vectors are invariant to gauge transformations; that is, they are *gauge invariant.*

Because of the arbitrariness in the choice of gauge, we are free to impose an additional condition on **A**. We may state this in other terms: a vector is not completely specified by giving only its curl, but if *both* the curl *and* the divergence of a vector are specified, then the vector is uniquely determined. Clearly, it is to our advantage to make a choice for div **A** that will provide a simplification for the particular problem under consideration. One possibility of frequent usefulness is

$$\operatorname{div}\mathbf{A} = -\frac{\varepsilon\mu}{c}\frac{\partial\Phi}{\partial t} \tag{4.26}$$

This equation is the *Lorentz condition* and specifies the *Lorentz gauge* of the potentials. In order to determine the requirement that this condition places on ξ, we take the divergence of Eq. (4.23) and add to it $\varepsilon\mu/c$ times the partial time derivative of Eq. (4.25):

$$\operatorname{div}\mathbf{A}' + \frac{\varepsilon\mu}{c}\frac{\partial\Phi'}{\partial t} = \operatorname{div}\mathbf{A} + \frac{\varepsilon\mu}{c}\frac{\partial\Phi}{\partial t} + \varepsilon\mu\left(\nabla^2\xi - \frac{\varepsilon\mu}{c^2}\frac{\partial^2\xi}{\partial t^2}\right) \tag{4.27}$$

Thus, if the potentials **A**, Φ and **A**$'$, Φ' are to obey the Lorentz condition, we must require that ξ satisfy the wave equation

$$\nabla^2\xi - \frac{\varepsilon\mu}{c^2}\frac{\partial^2\xi}{\partial t^2} = 0 \tag{4.28}$$

Let us now examine the effect of the Lorentz condition on the field equations expressed in terms of the potentials **A** and Φ. For an ideal dielectric medium, the first Maxwell equation (4.18a) may be written as

$$\operatorname{div}\mathbf{E} = \frac{4\pi\rho}{\varepsilon} \tag{4.29}$$

and substituting for **E** from Eq. (4.22), we obtain

$$\nabla^2\Phi + \frac{1}{c}\frac{\partial}{\partial t}\operatorname{div}\mathbf{A} = -\frac{4\pi\rho}{\varepsilon} \tag{4.30}$$

For the fourth Maxwell equation (4.18d) we may write

$$\mathbf{curl}\,\mathbf{B} - \frac{\varepsilon\mu}{c}\frac{\partial\mathbf{E}}{\partial t} = \frac{4\pi\mu}{c}\mathbf{J} \tag{4.31}$$

and substituting for **E** and **B** from Eqs. (4.22) and (4.20), we have

$$\mathbf{curl}\,\mathbf{curl}\,\mathbf{A} + \frac{\varepsilon\mu}{c}\,\mathbf{grad}\,\frac{\partial\Phi}{\partial t} + \frac{\varepsilon\mu}{c^2}\frac{\partial^2\mathbf{A}}{\partial t^2} = \frac{4\pi\mu}{c}\mathbf{J} \tag{4.32}$$

We may use the vector identity

$$\mathbf{curl}\,\mathbf{curl}\,\mathbf{A} = \mathbf{grad}\operatorname{div}\mathbf{A} - \nabla^2\mathbf{A}$$

to write Eq. (4.32) as

$$\nabla^2\mathbf{A} - \frac{\varepsilon\mu}{c^2}\frac{\partial^2\mathbf{A}}{\partial t^2} - \mathbf{grad}\left(\operatorname{div}\mathbf{A} + \frac{\varepsilon\mu}{c}\frac{\partial\Phi}{\partial t}\right) = -\frac{4\pi\mu}{c}\mathbf{J} \tag{4.33}$$

Thus, in Eqs. (4.30) and (4.33) we have a representation of Maxwell's four equations using only two equations for the potentials **A** and Φ. But these two equations are coupled (just as were the Maxwell equations), i.e., both equations involve both potentials. The application of the Lorentz condition [Eq. (4.26)] produces the desired uncoupling:

$$\boxed{\nabla^2\Phi - \frac{\varepsilon\mu}{c^2}\frac{\partial^2\Phi}{\partial t^2} = -\frac{4\pi\rho}{\varepsilon}} \tag{4.34}$$

$$\boxed{\nabla^2\mathbf{A} - \frac{\varepsilon\mu}{c^2}\frac{\partial^2\mathbf{A}}{\partial t^2} = -\frac{4\pi\mu}{c}\mathbf{J}} \tag{4.35}$$

We find, therefore, that in the Lorentz gauge the field potentials satisfy inhomogeneous wave equations. In the event that there are no charges or currents present in the medium, the two wave equations are identical. And if we further restrict the medium to be vacuum, we have

$$\left.\begin{aligned} \nabla^2\Phi - \frac{1}{c^2}\frac{\partial^2\Phi}{\partial t^2} &= 0 \\ \nabla^2\mathbf{A} - \frac{1}{c^2}\frac{\partial^2\mathbf{A}}{\partial t^2} &= 0 \end{aligned}\right\}\quad \text{(vacuum; no charges, no currents)} \tag{4.36}$$

For the case of steady-state conditions (i.e., static fields), the time derivatives in Eqs. (4.34) and (4.35) vanish and we have

$$\left.\begin{aligned} \nabla^2\Phi &= -\frac{4\pi\rho}{\varepsilon} \\ \nabla^2\mathbf{A} &= -\frac{4\pi\mu}{c}\mathbf{J} \end{aligned}\right\} \quad \text{(static fields)} \tag{4.37}$$

Thus, both Φ and each rectangular component of $\mathbf{A}$ satisfy Poisson's equation. We know from the results of Sections 1.4 and 1.6 that the solutions are

$$\left.\begin{aligned} \Phi(\mathbf{r}) &= \int_V \frac{1}{\varepsilon}\frac{\rho(\mathbf{r}')}{|\mathbf{r}-\mathbf{r}'|}\,dv' \\ &= -\frac{1}{4\pi}\int_V \frac{\nabla^2\Phi}{|\mathbf{r}-\mathbf{r}'|}\,dv' \end{aligned}\right\} \quad \text{(static fields)} \tag{4.38}$$

$$\left.\begin{aligned} \mathbf{A}(\mathbf{r}) &= \frac{1}{c}\int_V \mu\frac{\mathbf{J}(\mathbf{r}')}{|\mathbf{r}-\mathbf{r}'|}\,dv' \\ &= -\frac{1}{4\pi}\int_V \frac{\nabla^2\mathbf{A}}{|\mathbf{r}-\mathbf{r}'|}\,dv' \end{aligned}\right\} \quad \text{(static fields)} \tag{4.39}$$

where $\mathbf{r}'$ is the vector connecting the origin with the variable point of integration at which ρ and $\mathbf{J}$ are evaluated, and where $\mathbf{r}$ is the vector to the point (the *field point*) at which Φ and $\mathbf{A}$ are to be calculated; dv' is the volume element at $\mathbf{r}'$ (see Fig. 1-1).

Another interesting gauge is the so-called *Coulomb gauge*, $\operatorname{div}\mathbf{A} = 0$, which is useful in the event that there are no charges present in the field (see Problem 4-9).

4.7 Energy in the Electromagnetic Field

Let us begin by writing the last two of Maxwell's equations for a vacuum, but in which we allow the possibility of moving charges (and, therefore, currents):

$$\frac{1}{c}\frac{\partial\mathbf{B}}{\partial t} = -\,\mathbf{curl}\,\mathbf{E} \tag{4.40a}$$

$$\frac{1}{c}\frac{\partial\mathbf{E}}{\partial t} = \mathbf{curl}\,\mathbf{B} - \frac{4\pi}{c}\mathbf{J} \tag{4.40b}$$

If we take the scalar product of **B** with the first of these equations and the scalar product of **E** with the second and add, we obtain

$$\frac{1}{c}\left(\mathbf{B}\cdot\frac{\partial \mathbf{B}}{\partial t} + \mathbf{E}\cdot\frac{\partial \mathbf{E}}{\partial t}\right) = -\frac{4\pi}{c}\mathbf{J}\cdot\mathbf{E} - (\mathbf{B}\cdot\mathbf{curl}\,\mathbf{E} - \mathbf{E}\cdot\mathbf{curl}\,\mathbf{B}) \tag{4.41}$$

Using the vector identity

$$\mathrm{div}(\mathbf{E}\times\mathbf{B}) = \mathbf{B}\cdot\mathbf{curl}\,\mathbf{E} - \mathbf{E}\cdot\mathbf{curl}\,\mathbf{B}$$

and transforming the term involving the time derivatives, we have

$$\frac{1}{2c}\frac{\partial}{\partial t}(|\mathbf{E}|^2 + |\mathbf{B}|^2) = -\frac{4\pi}{c}\mathbf{J}\cdot\mathbf{E} - \mathrm{div}(\mathbf{E}\times\mathbf{B}) \tag{4.42}$$

We define

$$\boxed{\mathbf{S} \equiv \frac{c}{4\pi}\mathbf{E}\times\mathbf{H}} \tag{4.43}$$

which, for free space, becomes

$$\mathbf{S} = \frac{c}{4\pi}\mathbf{E}\times\mathbf{B} \qquad \text{(free space)} \tag{4.43a}$$

The quantity **S** is called *Poynting's vector.** Then, writing $|\mathbf{E}|^2 = E^2$ and $|\mathbf{B}|^2 = B^2$, we have

$$\frac{1}{8\pi}\frac{\partial}{\partial t}(E^2 + B^2) = -\mathbf{J}\cdot\mathbf{E} - \mathrm{div}\,\mathbf{S} \tag{4.44}$$

We now integrate this equation over a volume V, and obtain

$$\frac{\partial}{\partial t}\int_V \frac{1}{8\pi}(E^2 + B^2)\,dv = -\int_V \mathbf{J}\cdot\mathbf{E}\,dv - \int_V \mathrm{div}\,\mathbf{S}\,dv \tag{4.45}$$

The last term can be transformed to a surface integral by means of the divergence theorem.†

$$\int_V \mathrm{div}\,\mathbf{S}\,dv = \oint_S \mathbf{S}\cdot\mathbf{n}\,da \tag{4.46}$$

If we allow the volume V to be arbitrarily large, then the surface integral can be made to vanish by placing the surface S sufficiently far away so that the field cannot propagate to this distance in any finite time.

* After the English physicist John Henry Poynting (1852–1914).

† The symbol for the surface, S, is not to be confused with the magnitude of the vector **S**.

Now, the current distribution represented by the vector **J** can be considered as made up of various charges q_α moving with velocities $\mathbf{u}_\alpha$. Therefore, the volume integral of $\mathbf{J}\cdot\mathbf{E}$ may be replaced by

$$\int_V \mathbf{J}\cdot\mathbf{E}\,dv \rightarrow \sum_\alpha q_\alpha \mathbf{u}_\alpha \cdot \mathbf{E}_\alpha$$

where $\mathbf{E}_\alpha$ denotes the electric field at the position of the charge q_α.

The electromagnetic force on the αth charged particle is given by the Lorentz expression [Eq. (1.40)]

$$\mathbf{F}_\alpha = q_\alpha\left(\mathbf{E}_\alpha + \frac{1}{c}\mathbf{u}_\alpha \times \mathbf{B}_\alpha\right) \tag{4.47}$$

The work done per unit time on the charge q_α by the electromagnetic field is

$$\frac{\partial T_\alpha}{\partial t} = \mathbf{F}_\alpha \cdot \mathbf{u}_\alpha \tag{4.48}$$

where T_α is the kinetic energy of the αth charged particle. Combining Eqs. (4.47) and (4.48), we may write

$$\frac{\partial T_\alpha}{\partial t} = q_\alpha \mathbf{u}_\alpha \cdot \left(\mathbf{E}_\alpha + \frac{1}{c}\mathbf{u}_\alpha \times \mathbf{B}_\alpha\right)$$

But,

$$\mathbf{u}_\alpha \cdot (\mathbf{u}_\alpha \times \mathbf{B}_\alpha) = (\mathbf{u}_\alpha \times \mathbf{u}_\alpha)\cdot \mathbf{B}_\alpha \equiv 0$$

so that the time derivative reduces to

$$\frac{\partial T_\alpha}{\partial t} = q_\alpha \mathbf{u}_\alpha \cdot \mathbf{E}_\alpha \tag{4.49}$$

(That is, the magnetic part of the Lorentz force is always perpendicular to the velocity and therefore can do no work on a charged particle.)

Equation (4.45) may now be written as

$$\frac{\partial}{\partial t}\left[\int_{\text{all space}} \frac{1}{8\pi}(E^2 + B^2)\,dv + \sum_\alpha T_\alpha\right] = 0 \tag{4.50}$$

Thus, the quantity in the square brackets is conserved. Now, we are considering a closed system in which the total energy is assumed to be constant. The "system" consists of the electromagnetic field and all of the charged particles present in the field. The term $\Sigma_\alpha T_\alpha$ represents the total kinetic energy of the *particles*. We are therefore led to associate the remaining energy term

$$\int_{\text{all space}} \frac{1}{8\pi}(E^2 + B^2)\,dv$$

with the energy of the *electromagnetic field.* This association turns out to be extremely useful, and it is permitted as long as it leads to no contradictions (none are known). The integrand in the expression above may therefore be identified as the *energy density* of the field:

$$\mathscr{E} = \frac{1}{8\pi}(E^2 + B^2) \tag{4.51}$$

The quantity $\int \mathscr{E}\, dv$ may be considered to be a kind of potential energy. One need not ascribe this potential energy to the charged particles, and we will find that, more often than not, it is more convenient to consider this term as a *field energy.* A concept such as energy stored in the field itself rather than residing with the particles is a basic concept of the theory of the electromagnetic field.

It must also be remarked that the conservation law (or, more accurately, the conservation *theorem*) expressed by Eq. (4.50) is a *result* of the Maxwell field equations, not a conclusion based on experiment. That is, the field energy concept cannot be formulated in a consistent way independent of Maxwell's equations. Indeed, to observe that the quantity called the field energy is in fact constant is to provide a measure of confirmation of Maxwell's equations.

Instead of taking the volume integrals in Eq. (4.45) over all space, let us now consider a finite volume. In this case, the surface integral of $\mathbf{S}\cdot\mathbf{n}$ will not, in general, vanish and so this term must be retained. Let us construct the surface S in such a way that in the interval of time under consideration none of the charged particles will cross this surface. Then,

$$\frac{\partial}{\partial t}\left(\int_V \mathscr{E}\, dv + \sum_\alpha T_\alpha\right) = -\oint_S \mathbf{S}\cdot\mathbf{n}\, da \tag{4.52}$$

where the sum over α includes only those particles lying within S. In Eq. (4.52) the left-hand side is the time rate of change of the energy of the field and of the particles contained within the volume V. Thus, the surface integral of $\mathbf{S}\cdot\mathbf{n}$ must be considered as the energy flux flowing out of the volume bounded by the surface S. But, by hypothesis, no particles are crossing the surface, so the Poynting vector $\mathbf{S}$ is therefore to be interpreted as the flux of energy of the *electromagnetic field*, and gives the amount of field energy passing through unit area of the surface per unit time. This result is known as *Poynting's theorem.**

* Discovered by Poynting in 1884, and also independently by Oliver Heaviside (published in January, 1885).

If we consider, instead of a vacuum, a medium which has a dielectric constant ε and a permeability μ (both of which may be functions of position but which are assumed to be isotropic), then the equation equivalent to Eq. (4.45) is (see Problem 4-14)

$$\frac{\partial}{\partial t}\int_V \frac{1}{8\pi}(\mathbf{E}\cdot\mathbf{D}+\mathbf{B}\cdot\mathbf{H})\,dv = -\int_V \mathbf{J}\cdot\mathbf{E}\,dv - \oint_S \mathbf{S}\cdot\mathbf{n}\,da \tag{4.53}$$

and the energy density in the field is given by

$$\boxed{\mathscr{E} = \frac{1}{8\pi}(\mathbf{E}\cdot\mathbf{D}+\mathbf{B}\cdot\mathbf{H}) = \frac{1}{8\pi}\left(\varepsilon E^2 + \frac{1}{\mu}B^2\right)} \tag{4.54}$$

Notice that Eq. (4.44) [or Eq. (4.53)] may also be written in differential form as

$$\frac{\partial\mathscr{E}}{\partial t} + \operatorname{div}\mathbf{S} = -\mathbf{J}\cdot\mathbf{E} \tag{4.55}$$

In the event that the medium has zero conductivity, then $\mathbf{J} = \sigma\mathbf{E} = 0$, and the equation has exactly the same form as the continuity equation (4.4) which expresses charge conservation. The "current density" is now $\mathbf{S}$, and the volume density of the conserved quantity is $\mathscr{E}$. We are therefore led by this analogy to the same conclusion as before regarding the conservation of electromagnetic energy and to the same identification of the flux of electromagnetic energy.

The term on the right-hand side of Eq. (4.55) represents a "leakage" of energy out of the field. ("Out" because of the minus sign.) This term has the dimensions of power per unit volume and is identified as the ohmic loss or Joule heating of the system. This amount of energy per unit time per unit volume is therefore lost as electromagnetic energy and appears as dynamic or heat energy (i.e., in the *motion* of the charged particles).

4.8 Uniqueness of Solution of the Field Equations

We now inquire as to the conditions that must be fulfilled by the field vectors which are obtained as solutions to the field equations in order that these solutions be unique. We consider a region of space V bounded by a surface S. We assume that there are two solutions $\mathbf{E}_1$, $\mathbf{B}_1$ and $\mathbf{E}_2$, $\mathbf{B}_2$ which describe the electromagnetic field within V and which are equal at time $t = 0$. We are required, therefore, to find the conditions on these solutions so that they remain equal for all times $t > 0$.

If $\mathbf{E}_1$, $\mathbf{B}_1$ and $\mathbf{E}_2$, $\mathbf{B}_2$ are solutions to the field equations, then so are $\mathbf{E}$, $\mathbf{B}$, where

$$\left.\begin{aligned} \mathbf{E} &\equiv \mathbf{E}_1 - \mathbf{E}_2 \\ \mathbf{B} &\equiv \mathbf{B}_1 - \mathbf{B}_2 \end{aligned}\right\} \tag{4.56}$$

The vectors $\mathbf{E}$, $\mathbf{B}$ therefore satisfy Eq. (4.53). Now, if we have *either* $\mathbf{n} \times \mathbf{E} = 0$ or $\mathbf{n} \times \mathbf{B} = 0$ on S for $t > 0$ (i.e., if either the tangential components of $\mathbf{E}_1$ and $\mathbf{E}_2$ are equal or if the tangential components of $\mathbf{B}_1$ and $\mathbf{B}_2$ are equal on the bounding surface), then since $(\mathbf{E} \times \mathbf{B}) \cdot \mathbf{n}$ can be permuted to contain either $\mathbf{n} \times \mathbf{E}$ or $\mathbf{n} \times \mathbf{B}$, the surface integral in Eq. (4.53) must vanish for all times $t \geq 0$. Then, if $\mathbf{J} = \sigma\mathbf{E}$, Eq. (4.53) reduces to

$$\frac{\partial}{\partial t}\int_V \frac{1}{8\pi}\left(\varepsilon E^2 + \frac{1}{\mu}B^2\right) dv = -\int_V \sigma E^2\, dv \tag{4.57}$$

The integral on the left is *positive definite* and vanishes at $t = 0$. But the right-hand side of the equation is *negative definite*. Thus, the only solution for $t \geq 0$ is $\mathbf{E} = 0$, $\mathbf{B} = 0$; in other words, $\mathbf{E}_1 = \mathbf{E}_2$, $\mathbf{B}_1 = \mathbf{B}_2$. The uniqueness is therefore established for the condition that the initial ($t = 0$) values of the electric and magnetic field vectors be specified and that the tangential components of one of the vectors on the boundary be specified for $t \geq 0$.

4.9 Electrostatic Energy of a System of Charges—The "Self-Energy" of an Electron

Let us consider an electromagnetic field which arises from the charged particles contained within a certain volume V of space. If all of the particles are at rest, then there are no currents, and since a magnetic field depends upon currents for its existence, the field in this case must be a pure electrostatic field. The energy density is therefore given by $|\mathbf{E}|^2/8\pi$, where $\mathbf{E}$ is the electric field intensity produced by the charges. Thus, the total energy in the field is the potential energy

$$U = \frac{1}{8\pi}\int_V \mathbf{E} \cdot \mathbf{E}\, dv \tag{4.58}$$

Since the field is static, we may use $\mathbf{E} = -\mathbf{grad}\,\Phi$ and write

$$U = -\frac{1}{8\pi}\int_V \mathbf{E} \cdot \mathbf{grad}\,\Phi\, dv \tag{4.58a}$$

This integral may be transformed by using the identity

$$\mathbf{E} \cdot \mathbf{grad}\,\Phi = \operatorname{div}(\Phi\mathbf{E}) - \Phi \operatorname{div} \mathbf{E}$$

Thus,

$$U = \frac{1}{8\pi}\int_V \Phi \operatorname{div} \mathbf{E}\, dv - \frac{1}{8\pi}\int_V \operatorname{div}(\Phi\mathbf{E})\, dv \tag{4.59}$$

By using the divergence theorem, the second integral may be transformed to

$$\int_V \operatorname{div}(\Phi\mathbf{E})\, dv = \oint_S \Phi\mathbf{E}\cdot\mathbf{n}\, da \tag{4.60}$$

Now, $da = r^2 \sin\theta\, d\theta\, d\varphi$ and $E \propto 1/r^2$, $\Phi \propto 1/r$; therefore, the integral vanishes as $1/r$ as r becomes very large. If we allow the volume V to be all space, then Eq. (4.59) for the energy reduces to

$$U = \frac{1}{8\pi}\int_{\text{all space}} \Phi \operatorname{div} \mathbf{E}\, dv \tag{4.61}$$

Using $\operatorname{div} \mathbf{E} = 4\pi\rho$, we obtain finally,

$$\boxed{U = \tfrac{1}{2}\int_{\text{all space}} \rho\Phi\, dv} \tag{4.62}$$

If, instead of a continuous distribution of charge density ρ, we have a collection of discrete point charges q_α, then the integral in Eq. (4.62) is replaced by a summation:

$$U = \tfrac{1}{2}\sum_\alpha q_\alpha\Phi_\alpha \tag{4.63}$$

We can understand this result in the following way. The potential energy of a given charge distribution can be obtained by computing the amount of work necessary to assemble the charges, each charge being moved from infinity (where the potential is zero) to its final position. The value of the potential at the position of the αth charge due to all of the other charges is Φ_α. The total potential energy is then the sum of the product $q_\alpha\Phi_\alpha$ taken over all pairs of charged particles in the distribution:

$$U = \sum_{\substack{\text{all pairs}\\ \text{of particles}}} q_\alpha\Phi_\alpha \tag{4.64}$$

If the sum over pairs is replaced by a sum over particles, then each pair will actually be counted twice; therefore, in Eq. (4.63), a factor $\frac{1}{2}$ is required.

If we consider a single electron in space, then at the position of the electron there is a "self potential energy" given by $e\Phi$, where e is the electronic charge. Now, the potential Φ for a single electron is e/r, and if the electron is considered as a point charge (and, indeed, we have assumed point charges in all of our development of electrodynamics), then the potential at the position of the electron (i.e., $r = 0$) is infinite. Thus, on the point-charge picture, the self-energy of a charged particle is infinite. (That is, to place a finite amount of charge in a region of zero volume requires an infinite amount of work.) This result indicates that the point-charge concept is actually meaningless; charge cannot be considered to be confined to a region with dimensions smaller than a certain value. The magnitude of this distance must be of the order of the "radius" of the electron, which we may estimate as follows.

If we consider the charge of an electron to be uniformly distributed over the surface of a sphere with a radius R, then the charge density is a surface charge density $\rho_s = e/4\pi R^2$. The potential is $\Phi = e/R$, and integrating $\frac{1}{2}\rho_s\Phi$ over the surface of the sphere yields an electrostatic self-energy $e^2/2R$. If we use the Einstein mass-energy relation and equate this electrostatic energy to the rest energy of the electron, $m_e c^2$, we find

$$R = \frac{e^2}{2m_e c^2} \cong 1.41 \times 10^{-13} \text{ cm} \tag{4.65}$$

This result for R is called the *classical radius of the electron*, although we have no reason to expect that the "radius" of an electron (whatever that means) is actually related to this quantity. It should be noted, however, that values of the order of R are found for the radii of nuclei. In fact, the radius R_A of the nucleus of an atom whose mass is A atomic mass units* is given to a good approximation by

$$R_A = \frac{e^2}{2m_e c^2} A^{\frac{1}{3}} \cong 1.4A^{\frac{1}{3}} \times 10^{-13} \text{ cm} \tag{4.66}$$

Although little physical significance can be attached to the value of R given in Eq. (4.65), the combination of physical constants $e^2/m_e c^2$ occurs frequently in the description of atomic and nuclear phenomena.†

4.10 The Lagrange Function for a Charged Particle in an Electromagnetic Field

The Lagrangian method of classical mechanics‡ can be applied to the motion of a charged particle in an electromagnetic field if a suitable Lagrange function can be devised. We shall now simply assert a particular

* One *atomic mass unit* (1 amu) is $\frac{1}{12}$ of the mass of the C^{12} atom, the dominant isotope of carbon.

† The combination $e^2/m_e c^2$, rather than $e^2/2m_e c^2$, is frequently referred to as the *classical radius of the electron*.

‡ See Marion (Ma65a, Chapter 9).

form for the Lagrange function, but in Chapter 13 we will give a more general approach to the Lagrangian method in electrodynamics.

If a charged particle were moving in a static electric field, then we would expect that the Lagrangian could be expressed in the standard manner as the difference between the kinetic and potential energies:

$$L = T - U = \tfrac{1}{2}mu^2 - q\Phi$$

In the event that a magnetic field (possibly time-dependent) is also present, then the above Lagrangian must be modified. Now, magnetic fields interact with *currents* (i.e., moving charges), so we expect that the necessary modification of the Lagrangian entails the addition of a term that depends on $\mathbf{u}$ as well as on the magnetic field. Moreover, the Lagrangian is a *scalar* function; therefore, we anticipate that the term to be added involves the *scalar product* of $\mathbf{u}$ and a vector that describes the magnetic field. The simplest such function is $\mathbf{u} \cdot \mathbf{A}$, and we assert that the correct form of the Lagrangian is

$$\boxed{L = \tfrac{1}{2}mu^2 + \frac{q}{c}\mathbf{u} \cdot \mathbf{A} - q\Phi} \tag{4.67}$$

This expression appears to be plausible, and it will now be demonstrated that the resulting equations of motion are identical with the Lorentz force equation.

The Lagrange equations of motion in rectangular coordinates are

$$\frac{d}{dt}\frac{\partial L}{\partial u_i} = \frac{\partial L}{\partial x_i}, \qquad i = 1, 2, 3 \tag{4.68}$$

where $u_i = \dot{x}_i$. Now,

$$\frac{\partial L}{\partial u_i} = mu_i + \frac{q}{c}A_i \tag{4.69}$$

since the potential Φ is independent of u_i. Vectorially, this equation may be written as

$$\sum_i \mathbf{e}_i \frac{\partial L}{\partial u_i} = \mathbf{p} + \frac{q}{c}\mathbf{A} \tag{4.70}$$

where $\mathbf{p} = m\mathbf{u}$ is the linear momentum of the particle. The *generalized momentum* is $\mathbf{p} + (q/c)\mathbf{A}$ and therefore includes the effect of the field through the vector potential.

Next, we calculate

$$\frac{\partial L}{\partial x_i} = \frac{q}{c}\frac{\partial}{\partial x_i}(\mathbf{u}\cdot\mathbf{A}) - q\frac{\partial \Phi}{\partial x_i} \tag{4.71}$$

This equation may also be expressed vectorially by multiplying by $\mathbf{e}_i$ and summing over i:

$$\begin{aligned}\sum_i \mathbf{e}_i\frac{\partial L}{\partial x_i} &= \frac{q}{c}\sum_i \mathbf{e}_i\frac{\partial}{\partial x_i}(\mathbf{u}\cdot\mathbf{A}) - q\sum_i \mathbf{e}_i\frac{\partial \Phi}{\partial x_i}\\ &= \frac{q}{c}\,\mathbf{grad}(\mathbf{u}\cdot\mathbf{A}) - q\,\mathbf{grad}\,\Phi\end{aligned} \tag{4.72}$$

According to Eq. (A.37), Appendix A, we may write

$$\begin{aligned}\mathbf{grad}(\mathbf{u}\cdot\mathbf{A}) = (\mathbf{u}\cdot\mathbf{grad})\mathbf{A} + (\mathbf{A}\cdot\mathbf{grad})\mathbf{u}\\ + \mathbf{A}\times\mathbf{curl}\,\mathbf{u} + \mathbf{u}\times\mathbf{curl}\,\mathbf{A}\end{aligned} \tag{4.73}$$

Now, the differentiations with respect to the coordinates in this equation are to be carried out for a definite (i.e., constant) velocity. Consequently, the second and third terms on the right-hand side of Eq. (4.73) vanish, and there remains

$$\sum_i \mathbf{e}_i\frac{\partial L}{\partial x_i} = \frac{q}{c}(\mathbf{u}\cdot\mathbf{grad})\mathbf{A} + \frac{q}{c}\mathbf{u}\times\mathbf{curl}\,\mathbf{A} - q\,\mathbf{grad}\,\Phi \tag{4.74}$$

Equating the time derivative of Eq. (4.70) to Eq. (4.74), we have

$$\frac{d}{dt}\left(\mathbf{p} + \frac{q}{c}\mathbf{A}\right) = \frac{q}{c}(\mathbf{u}\cdot\mathbf{grad})\mathbf{A} + \frac{q}{c}\mathbf{u}\times\mathbf{curl}\,\mathbf{A} - q\,\mathbf{grad}\,\Phi \tag{4.75}$$

Next, we must consider the time derivative of $\mathbf{A}$:

$$\begin{aligned}\frac{d\mathbf{A}}{dt} &= \frac{\partial \mathbf{A}}{\partial t} + \sum_i \frac{\partial \mathbf{A}}{\partial x_i}\frac{dx_i}{dt}\\ &= \frac{\partial \mathbf{A}}{\partial t} + \left(\sum_i \mathbf{u}_i\frac{\partial}{\partial x_i}\right)\mathbf{A}\\ &= \frac{\partial \mathbf{A}}{\partial t} + (\mathbf{u}\cdot\mathbf{grad})\mathbf{A}\end{aligned} \tag{4.76}$$

Therefore, Eq. (4.75) becomes

$$\frac{d\mathbf{p}}{dt} = -q\,\mathbf{grad}\,\Phi - \frac{q}{c}\frac{\partial \mathbf{A}}{\partial t} + \frac{q}{c}\mathbf{u} \times \mathbf{curl}\,\mathbf{A} \tag{4.77}$$

If we use the relations

$$\left.\begin{aligned} \frac{d\mathbf{p}}{dt} &= \mathbf{F} \\ -\mathbf{grad}\,\Phi - \frac{1}{c}\frac{\partial \mathbf{A}}{\partial t} &= \mathbf{E} \\ \mathbf{curl}\,\mathbf{A} &= \mathbf{B} \end{aligned}\right\} \tag{4.78}$$

then Eq. (4.77) becomes

$$\mathbf{F} = q\mathbf{E} + \frac{q}{c}\mathbf{u} \times \mathbf{B} \tag{4.79}$$

which is just the Lorentz force equation.

Suggested References

Faraday's law of induction is treated in a particularly clear fashion by Jackson (Ja62, Chapter 6). A nice account is also given by Plonsey and Collin (Pl61, Chapter 8). A detailed discussion of induction in moving systems may be found in Corson and Lorrain (Co62, Appendix E).

Whittaker (Wh51, Chapter 8) gives an interesting description of Maxwell's development of the concept of displacement current.

One of the better treatments of Poynting's theorem and energy flow is that of Stratton (St41, Chapter 2). The interpretation of the significance of Poynting's theorem given by Mason and Weaver is different from that usually stated and is interesting to consider (Ma29, p. 266 ff.; but see the comments by Stratton, p. 110).

The expression for the energy of the field is sometimes derived from considerations of the work necessary to charge condensers and to move current-carrying wires; see, for example, Harnwell (Ha49, Chapters 2, 9).

The electromagnetic potentials and gauge are discussed in a succinct manner by Blass (Bl62, Chapter 24) and by Jackson (Ja62, Chapter 6).

Problems

4-1. A current I flows in opposite directions in each of two (infinitely) long straight wires which are separated by a distance d in vacuum. If the time rate of change of the current is dI/dt, find the electric field vector $\mathbf{E}$ at an arbitrary point in the plane between the wires.

4-2. Consider an infinitely long, straight, resistanceless conductor of circular cross section in which a current flows. Let the current density J be a function of the time and of the radial distance from the center of the conductor, $J = J(r, t)$, and show that

$$J = \frac{c}{4\pi}\frac{1}{r}\frac{\partial}{\partial r}(rB), \qquad \text{and} \qquad \frac{\partial E}{\partial r} = \frac{1}{c}\frac{\partial B}{\partial t}$$

4-3. Consider a charge q which is moving with a uniform velocity $\mathbf{u} = u\mathbf{e}_z$. Construct a circle in the x-y plane centered at the origin and calculate the displacement current that flows through the circle. Next, use the Biot-Savart law in the form

$$\mathbf{B} = \frac{q}{c}\frac{\mathbf{u} \times \mathbf{r}}{r^3}, \qquad (u \ll c)$$

where $\mathbf{r}$ is the vector from the charge to the field point. Calculate the conduction current through the circle, and show that the two results are identical.

4-4. Consider a magnetic field which is everywhere given by $\mathbf{B}(t) = B_0 t\mathbf{e}_3$, where B_0 is a constant. Calculate the vector potential $\mathbf{A}$ and find the induced electric field by assuming $\Phi = 0$. Use a direct integration method to prove that Faraday's law is satisfied.

4-5. A spherical shell of radius a and conductivity σ rotates with an angular velocity $\boldsymbol{\omega} = \omega\mathbf{e}_3$ in a uniform magnetic field described by $\mathbf{B} = B\mathbf{e}_3$. Calculate the emf developed between one pole and a point on the equatorial circle.

4-6. A conducting disk of radius a, thickness d, and conductivity σ, is placed in a magnetic field which is parallel to its axis. If $\mathbf{B}(t) = \mathbf{B}_0 \sin \omega t$, find the induced current density at any point within the disk.

4-7. Show that the capacitance C of a parallel-plate capacitor is given by $C = \varepsilon A/4\pi l$, where ε is the dielectric constant of the material between the plates, A is the area of each plate, and l is the separation of the plates. (Neglect fringing effects.) Use this result to show that the time derivative of the surface integral of $\mathbf{D} \cdot \mathbf{n}\, da$ over the surface S' in Fig. 4-2 is exactly the current I flowing into the capacitor. Thus, justify Maxwell's introduction of the displacement current into Ampère's law.

4-8. Prove the assertion made in Section 4.3 that a vector is completely specified by stating both its curl and its divergence. [It may be assumed that the vector vanishes as $1/r^2$ at infinity. What is the physical meaning of such an assumption?]

4-9. A gauge for the electromagnetic field that is frequently useful in the event that there are no charges is the *Coulomb* or *solenoid* gauge, div $\mathbf{A} = 0$. Show that in this gauge the scalar potential satisfies Poisson's equation. Find also the differential equation satisfied by the vector potential. This latter equation will contain Φ as well as $\mathbf{A}$. Try to eliminate the term containing Φ by separating $\mathbf{J}$ into two terms $\mathbf{J} = \mathbf{J}_1 + \mathbf{J}_2$, where $\mathbf{curl}\,\mathbf{J}_1 = 0$ and div $\mathbf{J}_2 = 0$. Then show that $\mathbf{grad}(\partial\Phi/\partial t) = 4\pi\mathbf{J}_1$ so that the dependence on Φ is eliminated and the equation for $\mathbf{A}$ contains only $\mathbf{J}_2$. The current densities $\mathbf{J}_1$ and $\mathbf{J}_2$ are the *longitudinal* and *transverse* components, respectively, of $\mathbf{J}$. Thus, $\mathbf{A}$ depends only on the transverse current $\mathbf{J}_2$ and the gauge is sometimes called the *transverse gauge*.

4-10. Show that the potentials at the position defined by the vector $\mathbf{r}$ in uniform electric and magnetic fields may be written as $\Phi = -\mathbf{E}\cdot\mathbf{r}$ and $\mathbf{A} = \frac{1}{2}(\mathbf{B} \times \mathbf{r})$.

4-11. Consider a medium in which there are no free charges and in which the current density is given by Ohm's law. Find a gauge for the potentials such that the differential equations for $\mathbf{A}$ and Φ are wave equations which include a damping term. Why is damping to be expected for such a case?

4-12. Consider a conductor of arbitrary shape which is placed in a vacuum. If the conductor is charged, show that the charge will distribute itself so that the electrostatic energy is a minimum. (This is a restricted form of *Thomson's theorem*.)

4-13. A current I flows through a resistor whose resistance is R. Show that the *inward* component of the Poynting vector gives rise to the Joule heating I^2R. (Note that the surface of the resistor is not an equipotential surface so that there may be a parallel component of the electric field at the surface.)

4-14. Show that the energy density of the electromagnetic field in a medium (not vacuum) is given by

$$\mathscr{E} = \frac{1}{8\pi}(\mathbf{E}\cdot\mathbf{D} + \mathbf{B}\cdot\mathbf{H})$$

4-15. It is possible to define a Poynting vector for combined static electric and static magnetic fields even though there is no energy flow in such a case. Show that the surface integral of $\mathbf{S}\cdot\mathbf{n}$ vanishes for any surface within the field.

4-16. A parallel plate capacitor consists of two circular plates of radius a separated by a distance l. The material between the plates has a dielectric constant ε. The capacitor is charged by being placed in a circuit which contains a source of potential V (a battery) and a series resistor R. If the circuit is completed at time $t = 0$, find the following quantities as functions of the time: (a) the electric field between the plates, (b) the magnetic field, (c) Poynting's vector, (d) the field energy, (e) the scalar potential, and (f) the vector potential. Edge effects may be neglected. Are the potentials unique? Demonstrate your answer with an example.

4-17. In the preceding problem replace the dielectric material by a conducting material whose conductivity is σ and remove the resistor from the circuit. Calculate the indicated quantities.

4-18. Calculate the electric energy density in a dielectric medium in the following way. Consider the dielectric to be between the plates of a capacitor whose capacitance is C. Calculate the work W required to charge the capacitor so that a potential difference $\Delta\Phi$ exists between the plates. Then show that the ratio of W to the volume of the dielectric is just $\mathbf{E}\cdot\mathbf{D}/8\pi$.

4-19. A current $I = I(t)$ flows in a circuit which contains resistive (R), capacitive (C), and inductive (L) elements, and across which a potential V is impressed. The differential equation for $I(t)$ is

$$L\frac{dI}{dt} + IR + \frac{Q}{c} = V$$

where Q is the charge on the capacitor; $I = dQ/dt$. If this equation is multiplied by I, it may be written as

$$\frac{d}{dt}\left(\frac{1}{2}LI^2 + \frac{1}{2}\frac{Q^2}{c}\right) = VI - I^2R$$

Interpret the various terms in this expression.

CHAPTER 5

Electromagnetic Waves

5.1 Introduction

In this chapter we will show that Maxwell's equations predict the existence of electromagnetic waves. In free space (i.e., a vacuum) the field vectors satisfy a simple wave equation, but in conducting media there is a pronounced damping or attenuation effect. For either case we find the important result that in a plane electromagnetic wave the field vectors **E** and **B** which relate to the propagation of the wave both lie in a plane that is perpendicular to the direction of propagation. Thus, electromagnetic waves, in contrast to mechanical waves, are entirely *transverse* in character. We shall investigate the polarization properties of these waves as well as the energy flow associated with their propagation. We shall also find that the phase relationship of **E** and **B** depends on the conduction properties of the medium. Having established in this chapter the fundamentals of electromagnetic waves and radiation, we shall investigate in the following chapters some of the specific physical effects associated with the generation of electromagnetic waves and the interaction of these waves with matter.

5.2 Plane Electromagnetic Waves in Free Space

In an infinite vacuum (no charges or currents), the electromagnetic field equations may be written as [cf. Eqs. (4.18)]

$$\operatorname{div} \mathbf{E} = 0 \tag{5.1a}$$

$$\operatorname{div} \mathbf{B} = 0 \tag{5.1b}$$

$$\mathbf{curl}\,\mathbf{E} + \frac{1}{c}\frac{\partial \mathbf{B}}{\partial t} = 0 \tag{5.1c}$$

$$\mathbf{curl}\,\mathbf{B} - \frac{1}{c}\frac{\partial \mathbf{E}}{\partial t} = 0 \tag{5.1d}$$

If we take the curl of Eq. (5.1c), we obtain

$$\mathbf{curl}\,\mathbf{curl}\,\mathbf{E} + \frac{1}{c}\frac{\partial}{\partial t}\mathbf{curl}\,\mathbf{B} = 0$$

where we have interchanged the order of space and time differentiation of the magnetic induction vector. Using the vector operator identity

$$\mathbf{curl}\,\mathbf{curl} = \mathbf{grad}\operatorname{div} - \nabla^2$$

and substituting for **curl B** from Eq. (5.1d), we have

$$\mathbf{grad}\operatorname{div}\mathbf{E} - \nabla^2\mathbf{E} + \frac{1}{c}\frac{\partial}{\partial t}\left(\frac{1}{c}\frac{\partial \mathbf{E}}{\partial t}\right) = 0$$

But, $\operatorname{div}\mathbf{E} = 0$, so that

$$\boxed{\nabla^2\mathbf{E} - \frac{1}{c^2}\frac{\partial^2 \mathbf{E}}{\partial t^2} = 0} \tag{5.2a}$$

We may perform the same operations on Eq. (5.1d) with the result

$$\boxed{\nabla^2\mathbf{B} - \frac{1}{c^2}\frac{\partial^2 \mathbf{B}}{\partial t^2} = 0} \tag{5.2b}$$

Equations (5.2a) and (5.2b) represent wave equations of the familiar type which are satisfied by the electric and magnetic field vectors in free space. The equations indicate that the propagation velocity is c†. In Section

† In 1857 Wilhelm Weber (1804–1890) and Rudolph Kohlrausch (1809–1858) measured the constant c which appears when a combined system of electrostatic and electromagnetic units (esu and emu) are used. They found a value of approximately 3×10^{10} cm/sec. The importance of the fact that this figure is close to that obtained for the velocity of light was first appreciated by Gustav Kirchhoff (1824–1887). Maxwell incorporated this fact into his theory and asserted the equivalence of electromagnetic and light waves (1864).

1.6 it was remarked that the velocity of light c was being introduced in order to use Gaussian units in a consistent way throughout. We now see the origin of this factor; it is known experimentally that electric and magnetic fields propagate with the velocity of light, and in a vacuum this velocity is $c = 3 \times 10^{10}$ cm/sec (more accurately, $c = 2.99793 \times 10^{10}$ cm/sec). Indeed, light waves are just one form of electromagnetic radiation.† We shall make use of this connection later in discussing optical phenomena.

It should be noted that Eqs. (5.2) are *vector* wave equations. That is, they are valid for each rectangular component of **E** and **B**. Therefore, the *scalar* wave equation

$$\nabla^2\Psi - \frac{1}{c^2}\frac{\partial^2\Psi}{\partial t^2} = 0 \tag{5.3}$$

is satisfied for $\Psi = E_x, E_y, E_z, B_x, B_y,$ or B_z.

We are interested now in the *plane wave* solutions to the wave equations; i.e., we seek solutions in which the field vector components that lie in a given plane are functions only of the perpendicular distance of that plane from the origin (and are also, of course, functions of the time). The normal to this plane is the direction of propagation of the wave, and we may choose to orient the coordinate axes so that this direction is, say, the positive x-direction. Since there is then no dependence of Ψ on y or z, the wave equation is *one-dimensional* in form:

$$\frac{\partial^2\Psi}{\partial x^2} - \frac{1}{c^2}\frac{\partial^2\Psi}{\partial t^2} = 0 \tag{5.3a}$$

The general solution of the one-dimensional wave equation‡ is a combination of arbitrary functions of the variables $x + ct$ and $x - ct$:

$$\Psi(x, t) = f(x + ct) + g(x - ct) \tag{5.4}$$

The function $f(x + ct)$ represents a waveform propagating in the negative x-direction, whereas $g(x - ct)$ corresponds to propagation in the direction

† This was the inescapable conclusion drawn from the experiments of Heinrich Hertz (1857–1894) who, in 1887, succeeded in generating by electrical means waves which possessed all of the properties of light waves (except, of course, that the wavelength was much greater). Electrical oscillations, and perhaps even the propagation of electromagnetic impulses, had been observed by Joseph Henry as early as 1842.

‡ These solutions are discussed by Marion (Ma65a, Chapter 15).

of positive x. We confine our attention to the latter case and write the solution as a complex Fourier series:

$$\Psi(x, t) = \sum_s \Psi_s(x, t) \tag{5.5a}$$

where the sth Fourier component has the variation†

$$\Psi_s(x, t) \sim e^{ik_s(x-ct)} = e^{-i(\omega_s t - k_s x)} \tag{5.5b}$$

In general there will be an infinite set of possible frequencies ω_s, and these are related to the *wave numbers* (or *propagation constants*) k_s according to

$$\omega_s = k_s c \tag{5.6}$$

For the idealized case in which the wave is monochromatic‡ (i.e., only a single frequency is present), the subscript s may be deleted. For the moment we shall limit our considerations to waves of this type and write

$$\Psi(x, t) \sim e^{-i(\omega t - kx)} \tag{5.7}$$

In general, the direction of propagation of the wave will not be in the x-direction, but we may preserve the notation of Eq. (5.7) if we define a vector $\mathbf{k}$ whose direction is that of the normal to the wave front and whose magnitude is $|\mathbf{k}| = k$. Then, for propagation in an arbitrary direction we have

$$\boxed{\Psi(\mathbf{r}, t) \sim e^{-i(\omega t - \mathbf{k}\cdot\mathbf{r})}} \tag{5.7a}$$

The vector $\mathbf{k}$ is called the *propagation vector* for the wave.

We note that $\mathbf{k}/k$ defines a unit vector normal to the wave front, and if ζ is the distance from the origin to the plane of interest, then (see Fig. 5-1),

$$\frac{1}{k}(\mathbf{k}\cdot\mathbf{r}) = \zeta \tag{5.8}$$

The grandient operator can then be written as§

$$\mathbf{grad} = \mathbf{e}_x\frac{\partial}{\partial x} + \mathbf{e}_y\frac{\partial}{\partial y} + \mathbf{e}_z\frac{\partial}{\partial z} = \frac{\mathbf{k}}{k}\frac{\partial}{\partial \zeta} \tag{5.9}$$

† We chose arbitrarily to represent the time variation of a plane wave as $\exp(-i\omega t)$. Thus, for a wave propagating in the positive x-direction, the space variation is $\exp(ikx)$; the positive sign in the argument of the space varying term has some minor advantages. In engineering texts it is customary to use $\exp(i\omega t)$ and $\exp(-ikx)$ instead. See also Marion (Ma65a, Chapter 15).

‡ See Chapter 11 for a further discussion of monochromatic and quasi-monochromatic waves.

§ Notice that the gradient operator can be separated in a simple form as in Eq. (5.9) only in rectangular coordinates.

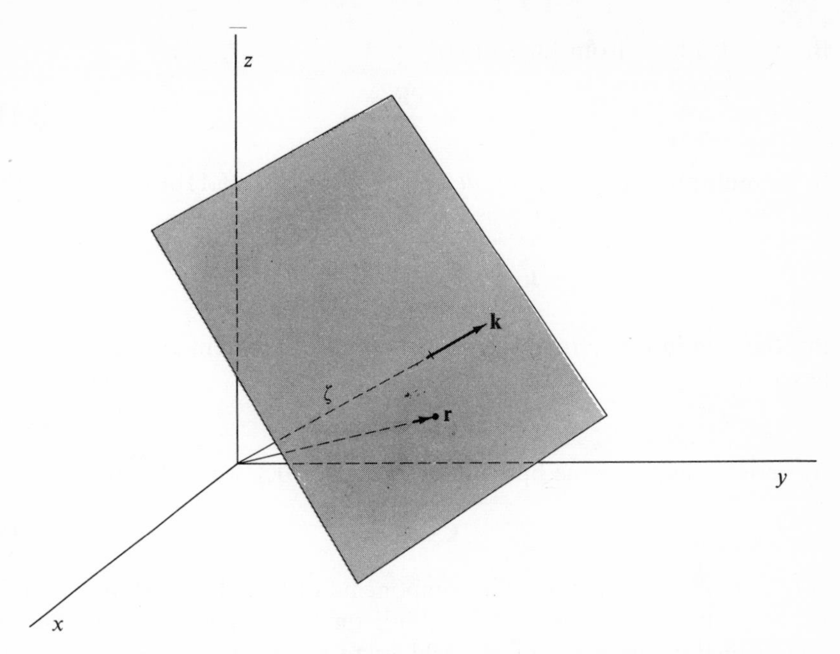

FIG. 5-1

With this notation the field equations can be expressed as

$$\operatorname{div} \mathbf{E} = 0 \quad \to \quad \mathbf{k} \cdot \frac{\partial \mathbf{E}}{\partial \zeta} = 0 \tag{5.10a}$$

$$\operatorname{div} \mathbf{B} = 0 \quad \to \quad \mathbf{k} \cdot \frac{\partial \mathbf{B}}{\partial \zeta} = 0 \tag{5.10b}$$

$$\mathbf{curl}\, \mathbf{E} + \frac{1}{c}\frac{\partial \mathbf{B}}{\partial t} = 0 \quad \to \quad \mathbf{k} \times \frac{\partial \mathbf{E}}{\partial \zeta} + \frac{k}{c}\frac{\partial \mathbf{B}}{\partial t} = 0 \tag{5.10c}$$

$$\mathbf{curl}\, \mathbf{B} - \frac{1}{c}\frac{\partial \mathbf{E}}{\partial t} = 0 \quad \to \quad \mathbf{k} \times \frac{\partial \mathbf{B}}{\partial \zeta} - \frac{k}{c}\frac{\partial \mathbf{E}}{\partial t} = 0 \tag{5.10d}$$

If we take the scalar product of $\mathbf{k}$ with Eq. (5.10d), we have

$$\mathbf{k} \cdot \left(\mathbf{k} \times \frac{\partial \mathbf{B}}{\partial \zeta}\right) - \frac{k}{c}\left(\frac{\partial \mathbf{E}}{\partial t} \cdot \mathbf{k}\right) = 0$$

The vectors in the first term may be permuted to yield $\mathbf{k} \times \mathbf{k}$ which vanishes, so that

$$\mathbf{k} \cdot \frac{\partial \mathbf{E}}{\partial t} = 0 \tag{5.11a}$$

But we also have from Eq. (5.10a),

$$\mathbf{k}\cdot\frac{\partial\mathbf{E}}{\partial\zeta}=0 \tag{5.11b}$$

If we multiply Eq. (5.11a) by dt and multiply Eq. (5.11b) by $d\zeta$ and then add, we find

$$\mathbf{k}\cdot\left(\frac{\partial\mathbf{E}}{\partial\zeta}\,d\zeta+\frac{\partial\mathbf{E}}{\partial t}\,dt\right)=0$$

But the sum in the parentheses is just the total differential of **E**, so that we have

$$\mathbf{k}\cdot d\mathbf{E}=0 \tag{5.12a}$$

By performing the same operations on Eq. (5.10c), we find that

$$\mathbf{k}\cdot d\mathbf{B}=0 \tag{5.12b}$$

Equations (5.12) require the components of **E** and **B** that are *normal* to the wave front to be constant in both time and space. That is, the only *longitudinal* components of the field vectors that are allowed as solutions to the field equations are *static* components. Since such fields do not contribute to the propagation of waves, we shall set them equal to zero for the purpose of discussing the wave properties of the field:

$$\mathbf{E}_l\equiv 0,\qquad \mathbf{B}_l\equiv 0 \tag{5.13}$$

Thus, we have the result that the only components of **E** and **B** that describe wave motion for the case of a plane wave are those components *perpendicular* to the direction of propagation of the wave front. Electromagnetic plane waves are therefore *transverse waves.* Since we have set the longitudinal components equal to zero, we have for the vectors **E** and **B**,

$$\left.\begin{aligned}\mathbf{E}&\equiv\mathbf{E}_{\text{transverse}}\\ \mathbf{B}&\equiv\mathbf{B}_{\text{transverse}}\end{aligned}\right\} \tag{5.14}$$

The wave equations satisfied by the field vectors may be written as

$$\left.\begin{aligned}\frac{\partial^2\mathbf{E}}{\partial\zeta^2}-\frac{1}{c^2}\frac{\partial^2\mathbf{E}}{\partial t^2}&=0\\ \frac{\partial^2\mathbf{B}}{\partial\zeta^2}-\frac{1}{c^2}\frac{\partial^2\mathbf{B}}{\partial t^2}&=0\end{aligned}\right\} \tag{5.15}$$

We may develop plane wave solutions for propagation in the direction of positive ζ and with harmonic time variation as†

$$\mathbf{E} = \mathbf{E}_0 e^{-i(\omega t - k\zeta)} \tag{5.16a}$$

$$\mathbf{B} = \mathbf{B}_0 e^{-i(\omega t - k\zeta)} \tag{5.16b}$$

where $\mathbf{E}_0$ and $\mathbf{B}_0$ are time-independent vector amplitudes which may be complex. Now, differentiating Eq. (5.16a),

$$\frac{\partial \mathbf{E}}{\partial \zeta} = ik\mathbf{E}$$

and, from Eq. (5.16b),

$$\frac{\partial \mathbf{B}}{\partial t} = -i\omega\mathbf{B}$$

so that Eq. (5.10c) becomes

$$\mathbf{k} \times \mathbf{E} - \frac{\omega}{c}\mathbf{B} = 0$$

or,

$$\frac{1}{k}(\mathbf{k} \times \mathbf{E}) = \mathbf{B} \tag{5.17}$$

If we define $\mathbf{e}_3 \equiv \mathbf{k}/k$ to be the unit vector in the direction of $\mathbf{k}$, we may write

$$\boxed{\mathbf{B} = \mathbf{e}_3 \times \mathbf{E}} \tag{5.17a}$$

Thus, **E** and **B**, in addition to being perpendicular to the direction of propagation [Eq. (5.14)] are also perpendicular to each other. Furthermore, if $|\mathbf{E}|$ is expressed in statvolts per cm and if $|\mathbf{B}|$ is expressed in Gauss, these magnitudes are equal.‡ The set of vectors (**E**, **B**, **k**) therefore constitute an orthogonal set, and, if taken in the order listed, are a right-handed orthogonal set, as in Fig. 5-2.

5.3 Polarization

According to Eq. (5.16a), the direction of **E** is constant in time and the wave is said to be *linearly polarized.* This is the simplest type of polarized vector wave. In general, however, in order to completely specify the electric vector in a plane, we must write **E** as a superposition of two linearly independent (i.e., perpendicular) solutions of the wave equation

$$\mathbf{E} = (\mathbf{e}_1 E_1 + \mathbf{e}_2 E_2) e^{-i(\omega t - k\zeta)} \tag{5.18}$$

† This entails no loss of generality since we may consider these solutions as Fourier components of the general solutions, as in Eq. (5.5a).

‡ This is one of the minor benefits of using Gaussian units.

where E_1 and E_2 are complex amplitudes and where $\mathbf{e}_1$ and $\mathbf{e}_2$ are unit vectors, called the *polarization vectors*; these latter vectors are perpendicular to each other and lie in the plane of propagation. The quantities $(\mathbf{e}_1, \mathbf{e}_2, \mathbf{e}_3)$ are chosen to form a right-handed orthogonal set of unit vectors.

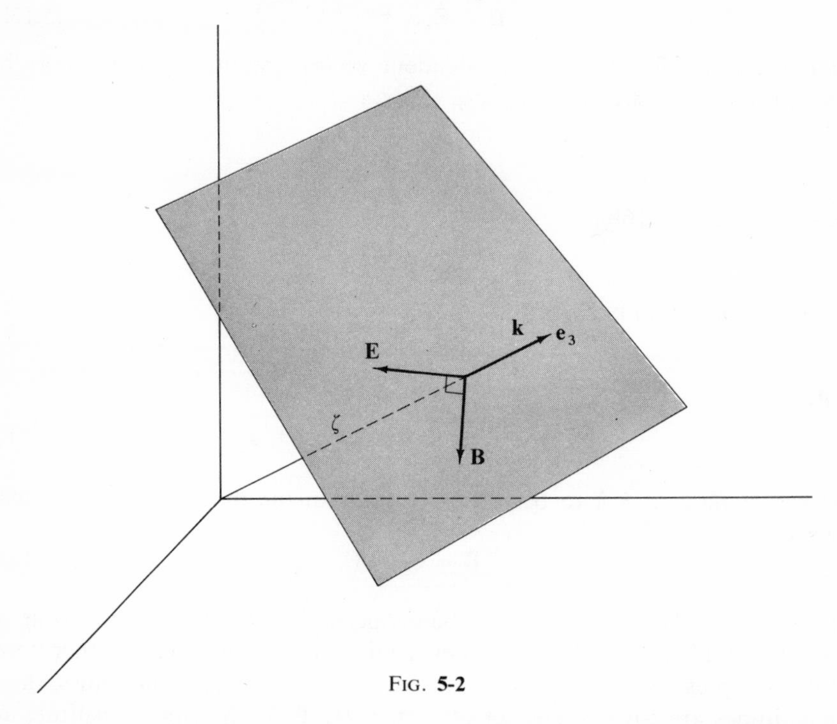

FIG. **5-2**

Since any complex quantity can be expressed as the product of a real quantity and a complex phase factor, we may write for E_1 and E_2,

$$\left.\begin{aligned} E_1 &= E_1^0 e^{i\alpha} \\ E_2 &= E_2^0 e^{i\beta} \end{aligned}\right\} \tag{5.19}$$

where E_1^0 and E_2^0 are real amplitudes.† This is, of course, equivalent to writing the two linearly independent solutions of which $\mathbf{E}$ is constructed as

$$\left.\begin{aligned} \mathbf{E}_1 &= \mathbf{e}_1 E_1 e^{-i(\omega t - k\zeta)} = \mathbf{e}_1 E_1^0 e^{-i(\omega t - k\zeta - \alpha)} \\ \mathbf{E}_2 &= \mathbf{e}_2 E_2 e^{-i(\omega t - k\zeta)} = \mathbf{e}_2 E_2^0 e^{-i(\omega t - k\zeta - \beta)} \end{aligned}\right\} \tag{5.20}$$

which explicitly illustrates the phase nature of α and β. Therefore, $\mathbf{E}$ becomes

$$\mathbf{E} = (\mathbf{e}_1 E_1^0 e^{i\alpha} + \mathbf{e}_2 E_2^0 e^{i\beta}) e^{-i(\omega t - k\zeta)} \tag{5.21}$$

† We shall, in general, use a superscript zero to denote a real, scalar amplitude.

The absolute magnitudes of α and β are not meaningful; it is only the *phase difference* that is physically significant. In the event that E_1 and E_2 have the same phase, or phases differing by an integral multiple of π, then $\beta = \alpha \pm m\pi$, $m = 0, 1, 2, \ldots$, and

$$\mathbf{E} = (\mathbf{e}_1 E_1^0 \pm \mathbf{e}_2 E_2^0) e^{-i(\omega t - k\zeta - \alpha)} \tag{5.22}$$

Thus, the direction of $\mathbf{E}$ is independent of time, and therefore the wave is *linearly polarized.*

The next most simple case of polarization is that in which the amplitudes of the components are equal, $E_1^0 = E_2^0 \equiv E_0^0$ but the phases differ by $\pi/2$, i.e., $\beta = \alpha \pm \pi/2$. Then,

$$\mathbf{E} = E_0^0(\mathbf{e}_1 \pm i\mathbf{e}_2) e^{-i(\omega t - k\zeta - \alpha)} \tag{5.23}$$

Such a wave is said to be *circularly polarized.* To illustrate this point, let us, for simplicity, choose a set of coordinate axes such that $(\mathbf{e}_1, \mathbf{e}_2, \mathbf{e}_3) = (\mathbf{e}_x, \mathbf{e}_y, \mathbf{e}_z)$. Then,

$$\left.\begin{aligned} E_x &= E_0^0 e^{-i(\omega t - kz - \alpha)} \\ E_y &= \pm i E_0^0 e^{-i(\omega t - kz - \alpha)} \end{aligned}\right\} \tag{5.24}$$

And, taking the real parts of these expressions, we have

$$\left.\begin{aligned} E_x &= E_0^0 \cos(\omega t - kz - \alpha) \\ E_y &= \pm E_0^0 \sin(\omega t - kz - \alpha) \end{aligned}\right\} \tag{5.25}$$

On a fixed plane $z =$ const. these are just the parametric equations of a circle. That is, as a function of time, the vector $\mathbf{E}$ traces out a circle, the direction of rotation being determined by whether the plus or the minus sign applies in the expression for E_y [(i.e., whether $\beta = \alpha + \pi/2$ or $\beta = \alpha - \pi/2$ in Eq. (5.21)]. If the plus sign applies, the rotation is counterclockwise if the wave is observed by looking at the on-coming wave front (i.e., by looking along negative z); such a wave is said to have *left circular polarization.* For the minus sign, the wave is said to be *right circularly polarized.*

If we take the most general case in which $E_1^0 \neq E_2^0$ and $\alpha \neq \beta$, then, in analogy with Eqs. (5.20), we have

$$E_x = E_x^0 e^{-i(\omega t - kz - \alpha)}$$

$$E_y = E_y^0 e^{-i(\omega t - kz - \beta)}$$

Taking the real parts of these expressions, we find

$$E_x = E_x^0 \cos(\omega t - kz - \alpha)$$

$$E_y = E_y^0 \cos(\omega t - kz - \beta)$$

If we define

$$\gamma \equiv \beta - \pi/2 \tag{5.26}$$

then the expression for E_y may be written as a sine:

$$\left.\begin{aligned} E_x &= E_x^0 \cos(\omega t - kz - \alpha) \\ E_y &= E_y^0 \sin(\omega t - kz - \gamma) \end{aligned}\right\} \tag{5.27}$$

But the forms of these expressions are exactly the same as those for the general two-dimensional harmonic oscillator,† and hence we know that the vector **E** performs elliptical motion as a function of time in the plane z = const.

We have discussed the phenomenon of polarization entirely from the standpoint of the electric field vector. This is all that is required, however, since the magnetic induction vector may always be obtained from **E** for the case of plane waves by using Eq. (5.17a).

[It should be noted that the convention in discussing *optical* polarization is to define the *plane of polarization* as the plane normal to **E** which contains **B** and **k**.]

5.4. Poynting's Theorem for Complex Field Vectors

In the preceding section we found that in general it is convenient to express the field vectors in terms of complex amplitudes. Of course, it is only the real part of a complex vector that is physically meaningful, but since we have chosen to write the time variation in the form $\exp(-i\omega t)$ we must allow an *imaginary* term in the amplitude so that it may combine with $i \sin \omega t$ to produce a *real* contribution. Thus, in order to pay for the luxury of the compact complex notation, we must exercise some caution when combining complex quantities to produce real physical quantities. A case in point is the calculation of the Poynting vector **S** when the field vectors **E** and **B** are expressed as complex quantities. If we wish to consider the average energy flow when **E** and **B** vary harmonically with time, we must average our expression over one complete period of oscillation. Therefore, we write

$$\left.\begin{aligned} \mathbf{E} &= \mathbf{E}_0 e^{-i\omega t} = (\mathbf{E}_1 + i\mathbf{E}_2)e^{-i\omega t} \\ \mathbf{B} &= \mathbf{B}_0 e^{-i\omega t} = (\mathbf{B}_1 + i\mathbf{B}_2)e^{-i\omega t} \end{aligned}\right\} \tag{5.28}$$

where $\mathbf{E}_1$, $\mathbf{E}_2$, $\mathbf{B}_1$, and $\mathbf{B}_2$ are real. Then the desired quantity is‡

$$\langle \mathbf{S} \rangle = \frac{c}{4\pi} \langle (\mathrm{Re}\,\mathbf{E}) \times (\mathrm{Re}\,\mathbf{B}) \rangle \tag{5.29}$$

† See Marion (Ma65a, Eq. (6.99) in Section 6.9).

‡ Angular brackets are used exclusively to denote *time* averages.

It should be noted that $\langle \mathbf{S} \rangle$ is *not* given by $(c/4\pi)\langle \mathrm{Re}(\mathbf{E} \times \mathbf{B})\rangle$ nor by $(c/4\pi)\, \mathrm{Re}\langle \mathbf{E} \times \mathbf{B}\rangle$. From Eqs. (5.28), we write

$$\mathrm{Re}\, \mathbf{E} = \mathbf{E}_1 \cos \omega t + \mathbf{E}_2 \sin \omega t$$

$$\mathrm{Re}\, \mathbf{B} = \mathbf{B}_1 \cos \omega t + \mathbf{B}_2 \sin \omega t$$

and then,

$$(\mathrm{Re}\, \mathbf{E}) \times (\mathrm{Re}\, \mathbf{B}) = (\mathbf{E}_1 \times \mathbf{B}_1) \cos^2 \omega t + (\mathbf{E}_2 \times \mathbf{B}_2) \sin^2 \omega t + (\mathbf{E}_1 \times \mathbf{B}_2 + \mathbf{E}_2 \times \mathbf{B}_1) \sin \omega t \cos \omega t$$

Taking the time average over one complete period of oscillation,

$$\langle \cos^2 \omega t \rangle = \langle \sin^2 \omega t \rangle = \tfrac{1}{2}$$

$$\langle \sin \omega t \cos \omega t \rangle = 0$$

Thus,

$$\langle (\mathrm{Re}\, \mathbf{E}) \times (\mathrm{Re}\, \mathbf{B}) \rangle = \tfrac{1}{2}(\mathbf{E}_1 \times \mathbf{B}_1 + \mathbf{E}_2 \times \mathbf{B}_2) \tag{5.30}$$

Let us now consider the quantities

$$\mathbf{E} = (\mathbf{E}_1 + i\mathbf{E}_2)(\cos \omega t - i \sin \omega t)$$

$$\mathbf{B}^* = (\mathbf{B}_1 - i\mathbf{B}_2)(\cos \omega t + i \sin \omega t)$$

$$\mathbf{E} = \mathbf{E}_1 \cos \omega t + \mathbf{E}_2 \sin \omega t + i(\mathbf{E}_2 \cos \omega t - \mathbf{E}_1 \sin \omega t)$$

$$\mathbf{B}^* = \mathbf{B}_1 \cos \omega t + \mathbf{B}_2 \sin \omega t - i(\mathbf{B}_2 \cos \omega t - \mathbf{B}_1 \sin \omega t)$$

Then, we compute

$$\begin{aligned}\mathrm{Re}(\mathbf{E} \times \mathbf{B}^*) = {} & (\mathbf{E}_1 \times \mathbf{B}_1) \cos^2 \omega t + (\mathbf{E}_1 \times \mathbf{B}_2) \cos \omega t \sin \omega t \\ & + (\mathbf{E}_2 \times \mathbf{B}_1) \cos \omega t \sin \omega t + (\mathbf{E}_2 \times \mathbf{B}_2) \sin^2 \omega t \\ & + (\mathbf{E}_2 \times \mathbf{B}_2) \cos^2 \omega t - (\mathbf{E}_2 \times \mathbf{B}_1) \cos \omega t \sin \omega t \\ & - (\mathbf{E}_1 \times \mathbf{B}_2) \cos \omega t \sin \omega t + (\mathbf{E}_1 \times \mathbf{B}_1) \sin^2 \omega t\end{aligned}$$

or, upon canceling the terms involving $\cos \omega t \sin \omega t$ and combining the terms involving $\cos^2 \omega t$ and $\sin^2 \omega t$, we find

$$\mathrm{Re}(\mathbf{E} \times \mathbf{B}^*) = (\mathbf{E}_1 \times \mathbf{B}_1) + (\mathbf{E}_2 \times \mathbf{B}_2) \tag{5.31}$$

Thus, in general, we have

$$\langle(\mathrm{Re}\,\mathbf{E}) \times (\mathrm{Re}\,\mathbf{B})\rangle = \tfrac{1}{2}\,\mathrm{Re}(\mathbf{E} \times \mathbf{B}^*) \tag{5.32}$$

We may then write

$$\boxed{\langle\mathbf{S}\rangle = \frac{c}{8\pi}\,\mathrm{Re}(\mathbf{E} \times \mathbf{B}^*)} \tag{5.33}$$

Therefore, we have the result that the time-averaged energy flow may be computed from the complex field vectors without explicitly performing an average since the time factors are automatically canceled by taking the product of **E** and **B***.

▶ **Example 5.4.** Let us compute the average energy flow in a plane wave which is elliptically polarized. The electric field vector for such a wave is given by Eq. (5.21):

$$\mathbf{E} = (\mathbf{e}_1 E_1^0 e^{i\alpha} + \mathbf{e}_2 E_2^0 e^{i\beta})e^{-i(\omega t - k\zeta)} \tag{1}$$

The magnetic induction vector may be calculated from Eq. (5.17a). Recalling that $(\mathbf{e}_1, \mathbf{e}_2, \mathbf{e}_3)$ form a right-handed orthogonal set, we have

$$\mathbf{B} = [(\mathbf{e}_3 \times \mathbf{e}_1)E_1^0 e^{i\alpha} + (\mathbf{e}_3 \times \mathbf{e}_2)E_2^0 e^{i\beta}]e^{-i(\omega t - k\zeta)}$$

$$= (\mathbf{e}_2 E_1^0 e^{i\alpha} - \mathbf{e}_1 E_2^0 e^{i\beta})e^{-i(\omega t - k\zeta)} \tag{2}$$

so that

$$\mathbf{B}^* = (\mathbf{e}_2 E_1^0 e^{-i\alpha} - \mathbf{e}_1 E_2^0 e^{-i\beta})e^{i(\omega t - k\zeta)} \tag{3}$$

Therefore,

$$\mathrm{Re}(\mathbf{E} \times \mathbf{B}^*) = (\mathbf{e}_1 E_1^0 e^{i\alpha} + \mathbf{e}_2 E_2^0 e^{i\beta}) \times (\mathbf{e}_2 E_1^0 e^{-i\alpha} - \mathbf{e}_1 E_2^0 e^{-i\beta})$$

$$= (\mathbf{e}_1 \times \mathbf{e}_2)(E_1^0)^2 - (\mathbf{e}_2 \times \mathbf{e}_1)(E_2^0)^2$$

$$= [(E_1^0)^2 + (E_2^0)^2]\mathbf{e}_3 \tag{4}$$

But,

$$|\mathbf{E}|^2 = E^2 = (E_1^0)^2 + (E_2^0)^2 \tag{5}$$

Thus,

$$\langle\mathbf{S}\rangle = \frac{c}{8\pi} E^2 \mathbf{e}_3 \tag{5.34a}$$

Since the magnitudes of **E** and **B** are equal in a plane wave with harmonic time variation [see Eq. (5.17a)], we may equally well write

$$\langle \mathbf{S} \rangle = \frac{c}{8\pi} B^2 \mathbf{e}_3 \tag{5.34b}$$

or,

$$\boxed{\langle \mathbf{S} \rangle = \frac{c}{16\pi}(E^2 + B^2)\mathbf{e}_3} \tag{5.35}$$

The time average of the energy density in a plane wave in free space is (see Problem 5-4)

$$\langle \mathscr{E} \rangle = \frac{1}{16\pi}(\mathbf{E} \cdot \mathbf{E}^* + \mathbf{B} \cdot \mathbf{B}^*) \tag{5.36}$$

But,

$$\mathbf{E} \cdot \mathbf{E}^* = |\mathbf{E}|^2 = E^2$$

$$\mathbf{B} \cdot \mathbf{B}^* = |\mathbf{B}|^2 = B^2$$

so that

$$\langle \mathscr{E} \rangle = \frac{1}{16\pi}(E^2 + B^2) \tag{5.37}$$

and then

$$\langle \mathbf{S} \rangle = c\langle \mathscr{E} \rangle \mathbf{e}_3 \tag{5.38}$$

Therefore, we see that the time-averaged energy flow is equal to the velocity of propagation of the wave multiplied by the average energy density in the wave. That is, the velocity of energy flow is just equal to the velocity c of the propagation of the wave.

In a medium (not a vacuum), the time average of the Poynting vector may be computed from

$$\langle \mathbf{S} \rangle = \frac{c}{16\pi}(\mathbf{E} \cdot \mathbf{D}^* + \mathbf{B} \cdot \mathbf{H}^*)\mathbf{e}_3 \tag{5.39}$$

Further consideration of energy flow will be presented from a relativistic viewpoint in Chapter 13.

5.5 The Field Equations in a Conducting Medium

For our discussion of electromagnetic waves in a conducting medium we must return to the complete forms for Maxwell's equations [Eqs. (4.18)]. We shall assume throughout that $\mathbf{J} = \sigma\mathbf{E}$, and that free charges are absent in the medium (i.e., $\rho = 0$). If we use the constitutive relations $\mathbf{D} = \varepsilon\mathbf{E}$ and $\mathbf{B} = \mu\mathbf{H}$, the field equations become

$$\operatorname{div} \mathbf{E} = 0 \tag{5.40a}$$

$$\operatorname{div} \mathbf{B} = 0 \tag{5.40b}$$

$$\mathbf{curl}\, \mathbf{E} + \frac{1}{c}\frac{\partial \mathbf{B}}{\partial t} = 0 \tag{5.40c}$$

$$\mathbf{curl}\, \mathbf{B} - \frac{\varepsilon\mu}{c}\frac{\partial \mathbf{E}}{\partial t} = \frac{4\pi\sigma\mu}{c}\mathbf{E} \tag{5.40d}$$

We are again interested in plane wave solutions to these equations, and we take $\mathbf{e}_3$ to be the unit vector along the direction of propagation of the wave; that is, $\mathbf{e}_3 = \mathbf{k}/k$. We shall also take (as in Section 5.2) the measure of the distance along $\mathbf{e}_3$ to be ζ. Therefore, in analogy with Eqs. (5.10), Maxwell's equations for a charge-free conducting medium become

$$\mathbf{e}_3 \cdot \frac{\partial \mathbf{E}}{\partial \zeta} = 0 \tag{5.41a}$$

$$\mathbf{e}_3 \cdot \frac{\partial \mathbf{B}}{\partial \zeta} = 0 \tag{5.41b}$$

$$\mathbf{e}_3 \times \frac{\partial \mathbf{E}}{\partial \zeta} + \frac{1}{c}\frac{\partial \mathbf{B}}{\partial t} = 0 \tag{5.41c}$$

$$\mathbf{e}_3 \times \frac{\partial \mathbf{B}}{\partial \zeta} - \frac{\varepsilon\mu}{c}\frac{\partial \mathbf{E}}{\partial t} = \frac{4\pi\sigma\mu}{c}\mathbf{E} \tag{5.41d}$$

Following the procedure used in Section 5.2, we take the scalar product of $\mathbf{e}_3$ with Eq. (5.41d):

$$\mathbf{e}_3 \cdot \left(\mathbf{e}_3 \times \frac{\partial \mathbf{B}}{\partial \zeta}\right) - \frac{\varepsilon\mu}{c}\frac{\partial \mathbf{E}}{\partial t} \cdot \mathbf{e}_3 = \frac{4\pi\sigma\mu}{c}\mathbf{e}_3 \cdot \mathbf{E}$$

The first term vanishes identically, so that

$$\mathbf{e}_3 \cdot \frac{\partial \mathbf{E}}{\partial t} = -\frac{4\pi\sigma}{\varepsilon}\mathbf{e}_3 \cdot \mathbf{E} \tag{5.42}$$

Multiplying this expression by dt and adding the result to Eq. (5.41a) multiplied by $d\zeta$, we have

$$\mathbf{e}_3 \cdot \left(\frac{\partial \mathbf{E}}{\partial \zeta} d\zeta + \frac{\partial \mathbf{E}}{\partial t} dt \right) = \mathbf{e}_3 \cdot d\mathbf{E} = -\frac{4\pi\sigma}{\varepsilon} \mathbf{e}_3 \cdot \mathbf{E}\, dt$$

or,

$$\mathbf{e}_3 \cdot \left(\frac{d\mathbf{E}}{dt} + \frac{4\pi\sigma}{\varepsilon} \mathbf{E} \right) = 0 \tag{5.43}$$

Therefore, the component of **E** along the direction of propagation (i.e., the longitudinal component, E_l) satisfies the equation

$$\frac{dE_l}{dt} + \frac{4\pi\sigma}{\varepsilon} E_l = 0 \tag{5.44}$$

If $E_l(t = 0) \equiv E_{l0}$, then integration yields

$$E_l(t) = E_{l0} e^{-(4\pi\sigma/\varepsilon)t} = E_{l0} e^{-t/\tau} \tag{5.45}$$

where

$$\tau \equiv \frac{\varepsilon}{4\pi\sigma} \tag{5.46}$$

is the *relaxation time* introduced in Section 4.2. Thus, we have the result that in a medium with finite conductivity there can be at most an exponentially decaying longitudinal component of the electric field vector. For a perfect conductor, there is no longitudinal component at all. This result is in contrast to that found in Section 5.2 for free space where we concluded that a static longitudinal electric field could exist. A conducting medium, of course, cannot support such a static field without a current flow and an external emf.

[Equation (5.44) gives the *time* dependence of the electric field in a conductor. We shall, in the next section, investigate the *spatial* dependence of the field and find the depth to which an electric field can penetrate a conducting medium.]

If we perform the above operations on Eqs. (5.41c) and (5.41b), then since Eq. (5.41c) is a *homogeneous* equation, we find

$$\mathbf{e}_3 \cdot d\mathbf{B} = 0 \tag{5.47}$$

from which we conclude (as in Section 5.2) that only a static longitudinal component of **B** may exist in the medium. Apart from this uninteresting static longitudinal component of **B** and the decaying longitudinal component of **E**, we have established the *transverse* nature of a plane electromagnetic wave in a conducting medium.

Returning to the field equations in the forms given by Eq. (5.40), if we take the curl of Eq. (5.40c), we obtain

$$\mathbf{curl\ curl\ E} + \frac{1}{c}\,\mathbf{curl}\,\frac{\partial \mathbf{B}}{\partial t} = 0$$

If we use the identity for the curl of the curl of a vector and interchange the order of space and time differentiation of **B**, then since div **E** $= 0$, we find

$$\nabla^2\mathbf{E} - \frac{1}{c}\frac{\partial}{\partial t}\,\mathbf{curl\ B} = 0$$

Substituting for **curl B** from Eq. (5.40d), there results

$$\boxed{\nabla^2\mathbf{E} - \frac{4\pi\sigma\mu}{c^2}\frac{\partial \mathbf{E}}{\partial t} - \frac{\varepsilon\mu}{c^2}\frac{\partial^2 \mathbf{E}}{\partial t^2} = 0} \tag{5.48a}$$

A similar development for **B**, starting with Eq. (5.40d), results in

$$\boxed{\nabla^2\mathbf{B} - \frac{4\pi\sigma\mu}{c^2}\frac{\partial \mathbf{B}}{\partial t} - \frac{\varepsilon\mu}{c^2}\frac{\partial^2 \mathbf{B}}{\partial t^2} = 0} \tag{5.48b}$$

Thus, we find that in a conducting medium **E** and **B** satisfy identical wave equations which contain damping terms proportional to the conductivity of the medium.

For a plane wave propagating in the direction of $\mathbf{e}_3$, these equations become, in the notation of Eq. (5.41),

$$\frac{\partial^2 \mathbf{E}}{\partial \zeta^2} - \frac{4\pi\sigma\mu}{c^2}\frac{\partial \mathbf{E}}{\partial t} - \frac{\varepsilon\mu}{c^2}\frac{\partial^2 \mathbf{E}}{\partial t^2} = 0 \tag{5.49a}$$

$$\frac{\partial^2 \mathbf{B}}{\partial \zeta^2} - \frac{4\pi\sigma\mu}{c^2}\frac{\partial \mathbf{B}}{\partial t} - \frac{\varepsilon\mu}{c^2}\frac{\partial^2 \mathbf{B}}{\partial t^2} = 0 \tag{5.49b}$$

That damped wave equations result for the field vectors in a conducting medium is reasonable since in such a medium there will be Ohmic losses, and energy will continually be removed from the wave and converted into heat. (See also the remarks at the end of Section 4.7.)

5.6 Plane Waves in Conducting Media

We shall now consider the plane wave solutions of Maxwell's equations for a conducting medium. We assume that the field vectors vary harmonically with time and write

$$\left.\begin{aligned}\mathbf{E} &= \mathbf{E}_0 e^{-i(\omega t - \mathbf{k}\cdot\mathbf{r})} \\ &= \mathbf{E}_0 e^{-i(\omega t - k\zeta)}\end{aligned}\right\} \tag{5.50a}$$

$$\left.\begin{aligned}\mathbf{B} &= \mathbf{B}_0 e^{-i(\omega t - \mathbf{k}\cdot\mathbf{r})} \\ &= \mathbf{B}_0 e^{-i(\omega t - k\zeta)}\end{aligned}\right\} \tag{5.50b}$$

where $\mathbf{E}_0$ and $\mathbf{B}_0$ are the *time-independent*, *transverse* amplitudes of the field vectors. (We take E_l and B_l to be identically zero.) Using these forms in Eq. (5.49), we find

$$\left[k^2 - i\frac{4\pi\omega\sigma\mu}{c^2} - \frac{\varepsilon\mu\omega^2}{c^2}\right]\mathbf{E}_0 e^{-i(\omega t - k\zeta)} = 0 \tag{5.51}$$

with a similar equation involving $\mathbf{B}_0$. Since this result must be valid for arbitrary $\mathbf{E}_0$, we have

$$\boxed{\hat{k}^2 = \frac{\mu\varepsilon\omega^2}{c^2}\left[1 + i\frac{4\pi\sigma}{\varepsilon\omega}\right]} \tag{5.52}$$

Thus, the propagation constant $\hat{k}$ is complex† and may be expressed as

$$\hat{k} \equiv \alpha + i\beta \tag{5.53}$$

Therefore, the portion of the field vectors that represents the spatial variation becomes

$$e^{ik\zeta} = e^{-\beta\zeta} e^{i\alpha\zeta}$$

The fields evidently are spatially attenuated in the medium, and the quantity β is a measure of this attenuation.

We note that in free space (i.e., $\varepsilon = 1$, $\mu = 1$, $\sigma = 0$), we have

$$\hat{k}^2 \to \omega^2/c^2 = k^2,$$

which is the familiar result. Therefore, in extracting the square root of $\hat{k}^2$ from Eq. (5.52), we must insure that we obtain $k = \omega/c$ as the limiting value.

Squaring Eq. (5.53) we have

$$\hat{k}^2 = (\alpha^2 - \beta^2) + 2i\alpha\beta$$

† When quantities such as the propagation constant, conductivity, dielectric constant, etc., are complex, we shall denote this by a "roof" above the symbol: $\hat{k}$, $\hat{\sigma}$, $\hat{\varepsilon}$, etc.

Comparing with Eq. (5.52), we identify

$$\left.\begin{aligned} \alpha^2 - \beta^2 &= \frac{\mu\varepsilon\omega^2}{c^2} \\ 2\alpha\beta &= \frac{4\pi\omega\sigma\mu}{c^2} \end{aligned}\right\} \tag{5.54}$$

These equations may be solved simultaneously with the result

$$\left.\begin{aligned} \alpha &= \frac{\omega}{c}\sqrt{\frac{\mu\varepsilon}{2}}\left[\sqrt{1 + \left(\frac{4\pi\sigma}{\omega\varepsilon}\right)^2} + 1\right]^{\frac{1}{2}} \\ \beta &= \frac{\omega}{c}\sqrt{\frac{\mu\varepsilon}{2}}\left[\sqrt{1 + \left(\frac{4\pi\sigma}{\omega\varepsilon}\right)^2} - 1\right]^{\frac{1}{2}} \end{aligned}\right\} \tag{5.55}$$

If the *positive* square roots are taken, this solution is seen to yield the proper form for $\hat{k}$ in the limit $\varepsilon = 1$, $\mu = 1$, $\sigma = 0$; that is, $\alpha = \omega/c$, $\beta = 0$.

Since $\hat{k} = \alpha + i\beta$, Eq. (5.50) for **E** and **B** may now be written as

$$\left.\begin{aligned} \mathbf{E} &= \mathbf{E}_0 e^{-\beta\zeta} e^{-i(\omega t - \alpha\zeta)} \\ \mathbf{B} &= \mathbf{B}_0 e^{-\beta\zeta} e^{-i(\omega t - \alpha\zeta)} \end{aligned}\right\} \tag{5.56a}$$

Using these expressions in Eq. (5.41c), we find

$$\left.\begin{aligned} \mathbf{B}_0 &= \frac{c}{\omega}(\alpha + i\beta)\mathbf{e}_3 \times \mathbf{E}_0 \\ &= \frac{c}{\omega}\hat{k}\mathbf{e}_3 \times \mathbf{E}_0 \end{aligned}\right\} \tag{5.56b}$$

Because of the imaginary factor in the relation connecting $\mathbf{E}_0$ and $\mathbf{B}_0$, the field vectors are in general *out of phase* in a conductor. We may write the complex propagation constant as the product of the magnitude and a phase factor:

$$\hat{k} = |\hat{k}|e^{i\phi} = \sqrt{\alpha^2 + \beta^2}\, e^{i\phi} \tag{5.57}$$

where

$$\left.\begin{aligned} \sqrt{\alpha^2 + \beta^2} &= \frac{\omega\sqrt{\mu\varepsilon}}{c}\left[1 + \left(\frac{4\pi\sigma}{\omega\varepsilon}\right)^2\right]^{\frac{1}{4}} \\ \phi &= \tan^{-1}(\beta/\alpha) = \tfrac{1}{2}\tan^{-1}(4\pi\sigma/\omega\varepsilon) \end{aligned}\right\} \tag{5.58}$$

Then,

$$\mathbf{B}_0 = \sqrt{\mu\varepsilon}\left[1 + \left(\frac{4\pi\sigma}{\omega\varepsilon}\right)^2\right]^{\frac{1}{4}} e^{i\phi}\mathbf{e}_3 \times \mathbf{E}_0 \tag{5.59}$$

from which it is seen that there is a time lag of **B** behind **E** by an amount equal to the phase angle ϕ. The magnitudes of $\mathbf{B}_0$ and $\mathbf{E}_0$ are related according to

$$|\mathbf{B}_0| = \sqrt{\mu\varepsilon}\left[1 + \left(\frac{4\pi\sigma}{\omega\varepsilon}\right)^2\right]^{\frac{1}{4}}|\mathbf{E}_0| \tag{5.60}$$

We note that in Eq. (5.51), the term $i(4\pi\omega\sigma\mu/c^2)$ arose from the term involving $\partial\mathbf{E}/\partial t$ in Eq. (5.48a), i.e., from the *conduction current*. On the other hand, $\varepsilon\mu\omega^2/c^2$ in Eq. (5.51) resulted from $\partial^2\mathbf{E}/\partial t^2$ in Eq. (5.48a), i.e., from the *displacement current*. The ratio of the conduction current to the displacement current (apart from the factor i) is therefore just the term $4\pi\sigma/\omega\varepsilon$ which occurs in $\hat{k}^2$ [Eq. (5.52)] and in the expressions for α and β [Eqs. (5.55)]. We now wish to distinguish two important cases which depend upon the magnitude of $4\pi\sigma/\omega\varepsilon$.

Case 1. $(4\pi\sigma/\omega\varepsilon) \ll 1$: the conduction current is much less than the displacement current. Such a situation obtains for poor conductors or for even moderately good conductors at very high frequencies. Expanding Eq. (5.55), we find

$$\left.\begin{aligned} \alpha &\cong \frac{\omega\sqrt{\mu\varepsilon}}{c}\left[1 + \frac{1}{2}\left(\frac{2\pi\sigma}{\omega\varepsilon}\right)^2\right] \\ \beta &\cong \frac{2\pi\sigma}{c}\sqrt{\frac{\mu}{\varepsilon}} \end{aligned}\right\} \tag{5.61}$$

Therefore, we see that, insofar as the frequency dependence of the conductivity may be neglected, the attenuation factor β is independent of the frequency.

If σ is sufficiently small, we have approximately

$$\left.\begin{aligned} |\hat{k}| = \sqrt{\alpha^2 + \beta^2} &\cong \frac{\omega\sqrt{\mu\varepsilon}}{c} \\ \phi &\cong 0 \end{aligned}\right\} \tag{5.62}$$

so that

$$|\mathbf{B}_0| \cong \sqrt{\mu\varepsilon}|\mathbf{E}_0| \tag{5.63}$$

and $\mathbf{E}_0$ and $\mathbf{B}_0$ are approximately in phase.

Case 2. $(4\pi\sigma/\omega\varepsilon) \gg 1$: the conduction current is much greater than the displacement current. For most metals, $\sigma/\varepsilon \approx 10^{18}$, so the conduction current always dominates for frequencies below about $10^{17}\ \text{sec}^{-1}$ which includes all of the radio, microwave, and visible light frequencies, as well as part of the X-ray region. For frequencies above the visible light region, however, resonance absorption effects are frequently important and the simple theory is no longer valid.† With this restriction, then, we may write

$$\alpha \cong \beta \cong \frac{1}{c}\sqrt{2\pi\omega\mu\sigma} \tag{5.64}$$

and we have

$$\left.\begin{aligned} |\hat{k}| = \sqrt{\alpha^2 + \beta^2} \cong \frac{1}{c}\sqrt{4\pi\omega\mu\sigma} \\ \phi \cong \pi/4 \end{aligned}\right\} \tag{5.65}$$

For this case we have

$$|\mathbf{B}_0| \cong \sqrt{\mu\varepsilon}\sqrt{\frac{4\pi\sigma}{\omega\varepsilon}}|\mathbf{E}_0|$$

Since $\sqrt{\mu\varepsilon} \approx 1$, we conclude that

$$|\mathbf{B}_0| \gg |\mathbf{E}_0| \tag{5.66}$$

Thus, **B** and **E** are approximately 45° out of phase, and $|\mathbf{B}|$ dominates $|\mathbf{E}|$ so that the energy density in the medium is largely magnetic in character. For $\omega = 0$, the energy density is *entirely* magnetic, in agreement with our previous conclusion that a conductor cannot support a static electric field.

5.7 Current Distribution in Conductors—The "Skin Depth"

In a good conductor, as we have noted, the conduction current dominates the displacement current. If we neglect the term in the wave equation for **E** [Eq. (5.48a)] that arises from $\partial\mathbf{D}/\partial t$, then we have

$$\nabla^2\mathbf{E} - \frac{4\pi\sigma\mu}{c^2}\frac{\partial\mathbf{E}}{\partial t} = 0 \tag{5.67a}$$

and, since $\mathbf{J} = \sigma\mathbf{E}$, we also have

$$\nabla^2\mathbf{J} - \frac{4\pi\sigma\mu}{c^2}\frac{\partial\mathbf{J}}{\partial t} = 0 \tag{5.67b}$$

† See Section 9.7 for some additional comments.

These equations are of a familiar form—they are just diffusion equations. If we write

$$\mathbf{J}(t) = \mathbf{J}_0 e^{i\omega t} \tag{5.68}$$

then,

$$\nabla^2 \mathbf{J}_0 - \tau^2 \mathbf{J}_0 = 0 \tag{5.69}$$

where

$$\tau^2 \equiv i\frac{4\pi\sigma\mu\omega}{c^2} \tag{5.70}$$

Now,

$$\sqrt{i} = \frac{\sqrt{2}}{2}(1 + i)$$

so that

$$\begin{aligned} \tau &= (1 + i)\frac{\sqrt{2\pi\sigma\mu\omega}}{c} \\ &= \frac{1 + i}{\delta} \end{aligned} \tag{5.71}$$

where [see Eq. (5.64)]

$$\delta \equiv \frac{c}{\sqrt{2\pi\sigma\mu\omega}} = \frac{1}{\beta} \tag{5.72}$$

If we consider a conductor which has infinite dimensions in the y- and z-directions and is semi-infinite in the x-direction, then we know that the solution for, say, the z-component of Eq. (5.69) is

$$J_z(x) = \text{const.}\, e^{-\tau x}$$

where x is the depth in the conductor and where we have suppressed the subscript zero. If J_s is the value of J_z at the surface of the conductor (the surface is taken to be the plane $x = 0$), then the magnitude of J_z/J_s is

$$\left|\frac{J_z(x)}{J_s}\right| = |e^{-\tau x}| = |e^{-(1+i)x/\delta}| = e^{-x/\delta} \tag{5.73}$$

Thus, we have the result that the current density decreases exponentially within the conductor. The quantity, δ, is called the *skin depth* and measures, for a particular material and a given frequency, the depth in the material at which the current density has decreased to $1/e$ of the value at the surface. (In MKS units, the skin depth is given by $\delta = \sqrt{2/\sigma\mu\omega}$.)

At high frequencies the skin depth in metals is extremely small. In silver, for example, at the typical microwave frequency of 100 Mc/sec,

$\delta \cong 10^{-4}$ cm, and for copper the penetration depth for ultraviolet radiation ($\lambda \approx 10^{-5}$ cm) is only 6×10^{-8} cm. On the other hand, at 30 kc/sec, the skin depth for sea water is approximately 10^2 cm. Thus, from the results for metals we see that in order to insure good conduction at microwave frequencies it is only necessary to have a thin coating of silver (or copper) on even a poor conductor. The sea water figure indicates that radio communication with submarines becomes increasingly difficult at depths of several meters. Extremely high power transmitters are necessary in order to maintain radio contact with submerged vessels.

Let us now calculate in detail a case of obvious importance, viz., the current distribution in a conductor of circular cross section. We assume only a radial variation for the component of the current density in the z-direction (i.e., the direction of the axis of the wire). Therefore, we need to retain only the radial portion of Eq. (5.69) when this equation is expressed in cylindrical coordinates:

$$\nabla^2 \mathbf{J}_0 - \tau^2 \mathbf{J}_0 = \frac{1}{r}\frac{d}{dr}\left(r\frac{dJ_z}{dr}\right) + \gamma^2 J_z = 0 \tag{5.74}$$

where we have written $\gamma^2 \equiv -\tau^2$ so that

$$\gamma = i\tau = i\sqrt{i}\,\frac{\sqrt{2}}{\delta} \tag{5.75}$$

Comparison with Eq. (3.80) shows that Eq. (5.74) is just Bessel's equation with $n = 0$. The solutions are therefore the zero-order Bessel and Neumann functions:

$$J_z(r) = C_1 \mathscr{J}_0(\gamma r) + C_2 \mathscr{N}_0(\gamma r) \tag{5.76}$$

where we have used script letters instead of ordinary capitals for the Bessel and Neumann functions in order to avoid confusion with the symbol for the current density.

Now, γr is a complex quantity, so it is necessary to investigate the expressions for Bessel functions of complex arguments. First, we remark that $\mathscr{N}_0(\gamma r)$ is irregular at the origin even for complex arguments; therefore, it is sufficient to consider only $\mathscr{J}_0(\gamma r)$ for the present case which involves the interior of the wire. We use the following definition† for the separation of a Bessel function into its real and imaginary parts:

$$\mathscr{J}_0(i\sqrt{i}x) \equiv \operatorname{ber} x + i \operatorname{bei} x \tag{5.77}$$

where ber x and bei x are real functions ‡ defined by the series (see Problem 5-13):

† See, for example, Dwight (Dw61, Eq. 820.1).
‡ ber = "Bessel, real"; bei = "Bessel, imaginary."

$$\left.\begin{aligned} \text{ber}\, x &= 1 - \frac{(x/2)^4}{(2!)^2} + \frac{(x/2)^8}{(4!)^2} - \cdots \\ \text{bei}\, x &= \frac{(x/2)^2}{(1!)^2} - \frac{(x/2)^6}{(3!)^2} + \frac{(x/2)^{10}}{(5!)^2} - \cdots \end{aligned}\right\} \tag{5.78}$$

Now,

$$\gamma r = i\tau r = i\sqrt{i}\left(\frac{\sqrt{2}}{\delta} r\right) \tag{5.79}$$

Therefore,

$$\mathscr{J}_0(\gamma r) = \mathscr{J}_0\left(i\sqrt{i}\,\frac{\sqrt{2}}{\delta} r\right)$$

$$= \text{ber}\left(\frac{\sqrt{2}}{\delta} r\right) + i\,\text{bei}\left(\frac{\sqrt{2}}{\delta} r\right) \tag{5.80}$$

Now, if r_0 is the radius of the circular wire and if $J_z(r_0) \equiv J_s$, then

$$J_z(r) = J_s \frac{\mathscr{J}_0(\gamma r)}{\mathscr{J}_0(\gamma r_0)} \tag{5.81}$$

and using Eq. (5.80), we have

$$J_z(r) = J_s \frac{\text{ber}(\sqrt{2}r/\delta) + i\,\text{bei}(\sqrt{2}r/\delta)}{\text{ber}(\sqrt{2}r_0/\delta) + i\,\text{bei}(\sqrt{2}r_0/\delta)}$$

Thus, for the magnitude of J_z/J_s, there results

$$\left|\frac{J_z(r)}{J_s}\right| = \left[\frac{\text{ber}^2(\sqrt{2}r/\delta) + \text{bei}^2(\sqrt{2}r/\delta)}{\text{ber}^2(\sqrt{2}r_0/\delta) + \text{bei}^2(\sqrt{2}r_0/\delta)}\right]^{\frac{1}{2}} \tag{5.82}$$

For a 1-mm diameter wire made of copper ($\sigma \cong 5.14 \times 10^{17}$ sec^{-1}†, $\mu \cong 1$), we calculate the quantities shown in Table 5.1. The current

Table 5.1

SKIN DEPTHS FOR A COPPER WIRE

Case	$\nu = \omega/2\pi$ (sec^{-1})	δ (mm)	$r_0/\delta = 0.5/\delta$
1	10^3	2.1	0.24
2	10^4	0.66	0.76
3	10^5	0.21	2.39
4	10^6	0.066	7.55

† As will be noted in Section 9.3, it is permissible to use the static value of σ for frequencies less than about 10^{13} sec^{-1}.

distribution for these cases are shown in Fig. 5-3. It will be seen that for frequencies of the order of a few kilocycles per second or less there is essentially a uniform current distribution in the wire, but that for frequencies in the megacycle range, the current is confined to a relatively small region near the surface.

If the frequency is sufficiently low (i.e., if δ is relatively large), then the series expansions of the ber and bei functions may be used. Retaining only the first terms in r and r_0, Eq. (5.82) becomes

$$\left|\frac{J_z(r)}{J_s}\right| \cong \sqrt{\frac{8\delta^4 + r^4}{8\delta^4 + r_0^4}} \tag{5.83}$$

On the scale of Fig. 5-3, the approximate result [Eq. (5.83)] cannot be distinguished from the curves for Cases 1 and 2. The dashed line in Fig. 5-3 shows the approximation for Case 3. Equation (5.83) is no longer adequate for Case 4.

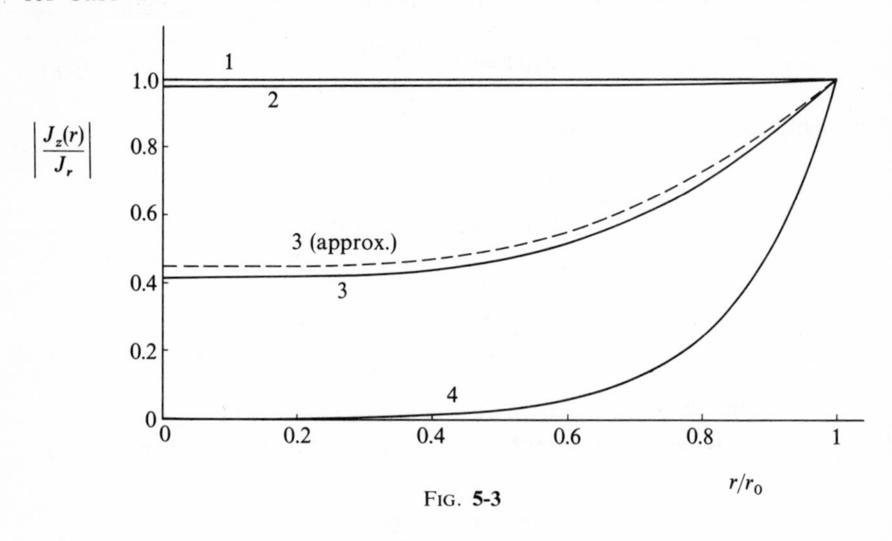

FIG. 5-3

Suggested References

The topics of electromagnetic waves in free space and in conducting media and the polarization of such waves are treated in many books. One of the more complete discussions is that in Stratton (St41, Chapter 5); see also Born and Wolf (Bo59, Chapter 1), Corson and Lorrain (Co62, Chapters 9, 10), Jackson (Ja62, Chapter 7), Panofsky and Phillips (Pa60, Chapter 11), Slater (Sl42, Chapter 2), Tralli (Tr63, Chapter 10), and Wangsness (Wa63, Chapter 28).

Skin effects are discussed in detail by Ramo and Whinnery (Ra44, Chapter 6) and by Sommerfeld (So52, Sections 20, 21). Engineering texts may be consulted for additional material.

Problems

5-1. Consider a dielectric medium which is charge-free but whose dielectric constant, ε, is a function of position; take $\mu = 1$. Derive the wave equations for **E** and **B** in such a medium. Show that they are different and can be written in the forms

$$\textbf{curl curl E} + \frac{\varepsilon}{c^2}\frac{\partial^2 \mathbf{E}}{\partial t^2} = 0$$

$$\textbf{curl curl B} + \frac{\varepsilon}{c^2}\frac{\partial^2 \mathbf{B}}{\partial t^2} = \varepsilon\, \textbf{curl B} \times \textbf{grad}(1/\varepsilon)$$

5-2. If the phase difference between the rectangular components of the electric field vector for an elliptically polarized plane wave is $\alpha - \beta = 30°$, plot the ellipses traced out by **E** and by **B**. Take $E_2^0 = 2E_1^0$.

5-3. Find the direction of **E** relative to $\mathbf{e}_1$ and $\mathbf{e}_2$ in terms of E_1^0 and E_2^0 for the case of a polarized plane wave in which the amplitudes of the rectangular components are different and the phases differ by π. Demonstrate that the direction of **E** does not change with time.

5-4. Show that the energy density in an elliptically polarized plane wave which has a sinusoidal time variation and which propagates in a medium (not a vacuum) is

$$\langle \mathscr{E} \rangle = \frac{1}{16\pi}(\mathbf{E} \cdot \mathbf{D}^* + \mathbf{B} \cdot \mathbf{H}^*)$$

$$= \frac{1}{16\pi}(\mathbf{E}^* \cdot \mathbf{D} + \mathbf{B}^* \cdot \mathbf{H})$$

5-5. Use the complex forms for the field vectors **E** and **B** given in Eq. (5.28) and verify that the time average of Poynting's vector is *not* given by $(c/4\pi)\langle \mathrm{Re}(\mathbf{E} \times \mathbf{B})\rangle$ nor by $(c/4\pi)\,\mathrm{Re}\langle \mathbf{E} \times \mathbf{B}\rangle$.

5-6. Show, in general, that for any pair of complex vectors, **F** and **G**, which have the same harmonic time variation, the time average of the product is given by

$$\langle (\mathrm{Re}\,\mathbf{F}) \otimes (\mathrm{Re}\,\mathbf{G})\rangle = \tfrac{1}{2}\mathbf{F} \otimes \mathbf{G}^* = \tfrac{1}{2}\mathbf{F}^* \otimes \mathbf{G}$$

where the symbol $\otimes$ denotes either scalar or vector multiplication.

5-7. Four electromagnetic waves are represented by the following expressions, which, in each case, are the only nonvanishing components of the field vectors:

$$\begin{aligned}
&\text{Wave 1:} && \mathbf{E}_1 = \mathbf{e}_x E_1^0 e^{-i(\omega t - kz)}; && \mathbf{B}_1 = \mathbf{e}_y E_1^0 e^{-i(\omega t - kz)} \\
&\text{Wave 2:} && \mathbf{E}_2 = \mathbf{e}_y E_2^0 e^{-i(\omega t - kz + \alpha)}; && \mathbf{B}_2 = -\mathbf{e}_x E_2^0 e^{-i(\omega t - kz + \alpha)} \\
&\text{Wave 3:} && \mathbf{E}_3 = \mathbf{e}_x E_3^0 e^{-i(\omega t - kz + \alpha)}; && \mathbf{B}_3 = \mathbf{e}_y E_3^0 e^{-i(\omega t - kz + \alpha)} \\
&\text{Wave 4:} && \mathbf{E}_4 = \mathbf{e}_x E_1^0 e^{-i(\omega t + kz)}; && \mathbf{B}_4 = -\mathbf{e}_y E_1^0 e^{-i(\omega t + kz)}
\end{aligned}$$

(a) Calculate $\mathbf{S}$ and $\langle \mathbf{S} \rangle$ for the superposition of Wave 1 and Wave 2. Show that these quantities are just the sums of the corresponding quantities for the waves taken separately. Why?

(b) Calculate $\mathbf{S}$ and $\langle \mathbf{S} \rangle$ for the superposition of Wave 1 and Wave 3. Compare with the results of (a) and explain the difference.

(c) Calculate $\mathbf{S}$ for the superposition of Wave 1 and Wave 4. Show that the energy oscillates, being purely electric then purely magnetic. Show that $\langle \mathbf{S} \rangle$ vanishes. Explain this result.

5-8. Consider the two waves represented by the following field vectors:

$$\text{Wave 1:} \quad \mathbf{E}_1 = (\mathbf{e}_1 E_{11}^0 e^{i\alpha_1} + \mathbf{e}_2 E_{21}^0 e^{i\beta_1}) e^{-i(\omega_1 t - k_1 \zeta)}$$

$$\mathbf{B}_1 = \frac{\mathbf{k}_1}{k_1} \times \mathbf{E}_1$$

$$\text{Wave 2:} \quad \mathbf{E}_2 = (\mathbf{e}_1 E_{12}^0 e^{i\alpha_2} + \mathbf{e}_2 E_{22}^0 e^{i\beta_2}) e^{-i(\omega_2 t - k_2 \zeta)}$$

$$\mathbf{B}_2 = \frac{\mathbf{k}_2}{k_2} \times \mathbf{E}_2$$

That is, the two waves are propagating in the same direction but with different frequencies and with different polarizations. Calculate $\mathbf{S}$ and $\langle \mathbf{S} \rangle_\infty$ for the superposition of the two waves, where $\langle \mathbf{S} \rangle_\infty$ is the time average over an infinitely long time. (Compute the average for a time τ and take the limit as $\tau \to \infty$.) Show that $\langle \mathbf{S} \rangle_\infty = \langle \mathbf{S}_1 \rangle + \langle \mathbf{S}_2 \rangle$, where $\mathbf{S}_1$ and $\mathbf{S}_2$ are the Poynting vectors for the individual waves. Discuss this result.

5-9. The series expansion for the zero-order Bessel function is

$$J_0(\xi) = 1 - \frac{(\xi/2)^2}{(1!)^2} + \frac{(\xi/2)^4}{(2!)^2} - \frac{(\xi/2)^6}{(3!)^2} + \cdots$$

Show that if $\xi = i\sqrt{i}\,x$ the series may be separated into real and imaginary parts which are equal to the functions ber x and bei x as defined by Eqs. (5.78).

5-10. A plane electromagnetic wave is incident on a thin (i.e., thickness $\ll \delta$) sheet of conducting material. Show, from considerations of the Poynting vector, that the energy lost to the medium by the wave is just equal to the Joule heating of the medium.

5-11. Use the asymptotic forms of the zero-order Bessel functions in Eq. (5.81) to obtain an approximate expression for $|J_z(r)/J_s|$ for the case in which the skin depth δ is small. Show that the result is the same as Eq. (5.73) with x replaced by $r_0 - r$.

CHAPTER 6

Reflection and Refraction

6.1 Introduction

In this chapter we shall study the behavior of electromagnetic waves at the boundaries between various media. We shall find that the dielectric constant and the conductivity of a medium determine the character of the reflection and refraction of a wave that is incident upon the medium. The derivations will be based on the general electromagnetic equations which have been developed in the preceding chapters, and the results will be familiar from geometrical and physical optics. Indeed, many of the experimental verifications of electromagnetic theory and many of the most important applications are in the field of optics. An appreciable fraction of the remaining material in this book is also optical in nature.

We begin by treating the case of normal incidence of an electromagnetic wave on a dielectric medium and then proceed to the general case of oblique incidence. Reflection, transmission, and polarization are discussed in detail, and then some of the more simple aspects of metallic reflection and refraction are examined. The chapter concludes with a brief discussion of guided waves. The interaction of electromagnetic waves with both dielectric and conducting media will be discussed from a *microscopic* viewpoint in Chapter 9.

6.2 Reflection and Transmission for Normal Incidence on a Dielectric Medium

In Section 1.10 we found that the field vectors satisfy the following conditions at the boundary between two media:

E: Tangential component continuous

D: Normal component continuous (for the case of no surface charge)

B: Normal component continuous

H: Tangential component continuous (for the case of no surface current)

We shall now consider a plane electromagnetic wave which is incident upon the boundary (assumed to be a plane surface) between two dielectric media and shall inquire as to the behavior of the field vectors brought about by the requirement that the above boundary conditions must be satisfied. We shall consider only nonmagnetic media, so that all permeabilities μ may be replaced by unity;† furthermore, the media are assumed to be *perfect* dielectrics (i.e., $\sigma = 0$, so that there are no energy losses). We treat first the case of normal incidence of the wave on the interface between the media. The situation for the incidence of the wave from the less dense of the two media is depicted in Fig. 6-1, in which the subscript 0 on the field vectors denotes the incident wave, 1 denotes the reflected wave, and 2 denotes the transmitted wave. For the incident electric field polarized in the x-direction, and for $n_2 > n_1$, we have‡

$$\left.\begin{aligned} \mathbf{E}_0 &= \mathbf{e}_x E_0^0 e^{-i(\omega t - k_1 z)} \\ \mathbf{E}_1 &= -\mathbf{e}_x E_1^0 e^{-i(\omega t + k_1 z)} \\ \mathbf{E}_2 &= \mathbf{e}_x E_2^0 e^{-i(\omega t - k_2 z)} \end{aligned}\right\} \tag{6.1}$$

where E_0^0, E_1^0, and E_2^0 are time-independent scalar amplitudes which may be complex. Thus, $\mathbf{E}_0$ and $\mathbf{E}_2$ represent waves propagating to the right and

† The quantities **B** and **H** are therefore equal. However, since it is the boundary condition on **H** that is important in these calculations, we shall use **H** rather than **B** in the discussions.

‡ Figure 6-1 and Eq. (6.1) (in which E_0^0, E_1^0, and E_2^0 are all *positive*) have been arranged to represent the situation for $n_2 > n_1$; i.e., the reflected electric wave suffers a phase change of π. It is, of course, not necessary to know this result beforehand. If we did not specify the relative magnitudes of n_1 and n_2 and if we were to write

$$\mathbf{E}_1 = +\mathbf{e}_x E_1^0 \exp[-i(\omega t + k_1 z)]$$

then we would find $E_1^0 < 0$ for $n_2 > n_1$.

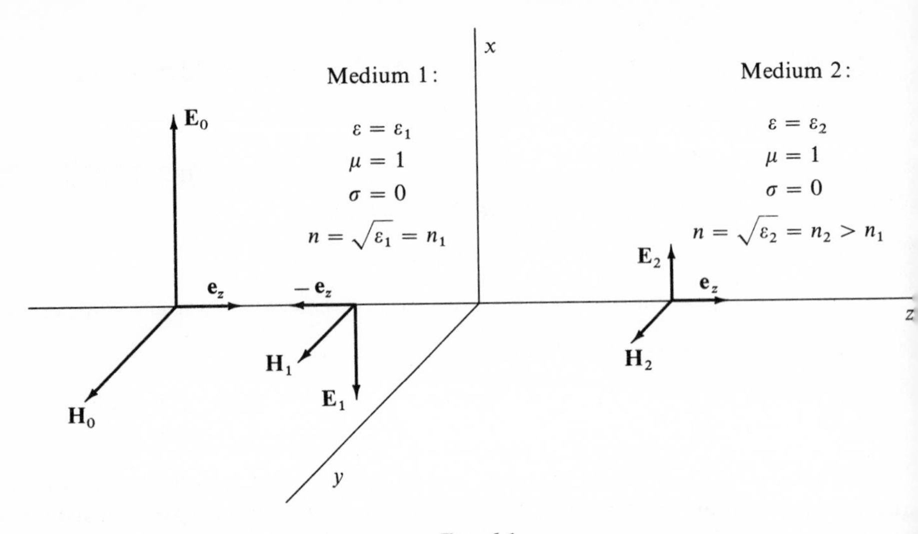

FIG. **6-1**

$\mathbf{E}_1$ represents a wave propagating to the left. The propagation constants are given by

$$\left.\begin{aligned} k_1 &= \frac{\omega}{V_1} = \frac{\omega}{c}n_1 = \frac{\omega}{c}\sqrt{\varepsilon_1} \\ k_2 &= \frac{\omega}{V_2} = \frac{\omega}{c}n_2 = \frac{\omega}{c}\sqrt{\varepsilon_2} \end{aligned}\right\} \tag{6.2}$$

The magnetic field vectors are given by [cf. Eq. (5.56b)]

$$\mathbf{H} = \frac{1}{\mu}\mathbf{B} = \frac{c}{\omega}k\mathbf{e}_3 \times \mathbf{E} = n\mathbf{e}_3 \times \mathbf{E} \tag{6.3}$$

where the unit vector in the direction of propagation, $\mathbf{e}_3$, is equal to $\mathbf{e}_z$ for the incident and transmitted waves, and is equal to $-\mathbf{e}_z$ for the reflected wave. Therefore,

$$\left.\begin{aligned} \mathbf{H}_0 &= \mathbf{e}_y n_1 E_0^0 e^{-i(\omega t - k_1 z)} \\ \mathbf{H}_1 &= \mathbf{e}_y n_1 E_1^0 e^{-i(\omega t + k_1 z)} \\ \mathbf{H}_2 &= \mathbf{e}_y n_2 E_2^0 e^{-i(\omega t - k_2 z)} \end{aligned}\right\} \tag{6.4}$$

Applying the boundary conditions on the tangential components of the field vectors we find

$$E_0^0 - E_1^0 = E_2^0 \tag{6.5a}$$

and,

$$H_0^0 + H_1^0 = H_2^0 \tag{6.5b}$$

or,

$$n_1(E_0^0 + E_1^0) = n_2 E_2^0 \tag{6.6}$$

If we solve for E_1^0 and E_2^0 in terms of E_0^0, the result is

$$\left.\begin{aligned} E_1^0 &= \frac{n_2 - n_1}{n_2 + n_1} E_0^0 \\ E_2^0 &= \frac{2n_1}{n_2 + n_1} E_0^0 \end{aligned}\right\} \tag{6.7}$$

Thus, the field vectors $\mathbf{E}_1$, $\mathbf{E}_2$, $\mathbf{H}_0$, $\mathbf{H}_1$, and $\mathbf{H}_2$ may all be specified in terms of the incident electric field vector and the indices of refraction of the media. We note that, as we have indicated, if $n_2 > n_1$, then $E_1^0 > 0$; that is, there is a phase change of π for reflection at the boundary of a medium with optical density greater than that in which the wave originates. For $n_1 > n_2$, we have $E_1^0 < 0$ so that $\mathbf{E}_0$ and $\mathbf{E}_1$ have the same polarization; there is no phase change.

The average energy flux in the incident wave is given by [see Eq. (5.33)]

$$\langle \mathbf{S}_0 \rangle = \frac{c}{8\pi} \operatorname{Re}(\mathbf{E}_0 \times \mathbf{H}_0^*) \tag{6.8}$$

The *reflection coefficient* R is defined to be the relative amount of energy flux which is reflected at the boundary; i.e.,

$$R \equiv \frac{\langle \mathbf{S}_1 \rangle \cdot (-\mathbf{e}_z)}{\langle \mathbf{S}_0 \rangle \cdot \mathbf{e}_z} = \frac{|\mathbf{E}_1 \times \mathbf{H}_1^*|}{|\mathbf{E}_0 \times \mathbf{H}_0^*|} = \frac{|E_1^0|^2}{|E_0^0|^2} \tag{6.9}$$

Thus,

$$R = \left(\frac{n_2 - n_1}{n_2 + n_1}\right)^2 \tag{6.10}$$

Similarly, the *transmission coefficient* T is defined by

$$T \equiv \frac{\langle \mathbf{S}_2 \rangle \cdot \mathbf{e}_z}{\langle \mathbf{S}_0 \rangle \cdot \mathbf{e}_z} = \frac{n_2}{n_1} \frac{|E_2^0|^2}{|E_0^0|^2} \tag{6.11}$$

so that

$$T = \frac{n_2}{n_1} \left(\frac{2n_1}{n_2 + n_1}\right)^2 \tag{6.12}$$

There can be no energy stored in the interface; energy conservation therefore leads to

$$R + T = 1 \tag{6.13}$$

which is readily verified from Eqs. (6.10) and (6.12).

Ordinary glass has an index of refraction of approximately 1.5, so that if a beam of light in air ($n = 1$) is incident normally on a sheet of glass, we find $R = 0.04$ and $T = 0.96$. Hence, most of the light is transmitted (as we know!) and very little is reflected.

[The expressions for R and T given here are of exactly the same form as those which were obtained in *Classical Dynamics of Particles and Systems* (Ma65a, Section 15.9) for the case of propagation of mechanical waves in a string with a discontinuity in the density; see Ma65a, Eqs. (15.105) and (15.106).]

6.3 Oblique Incidence—The Fresnel Equations

Having used the case of normal incidence to obtain a simple picture of the physical process that takes place at the boundary between two dielectric media, let us now examine the more general case of oblique incidence. Figure 6.2 describes the situation, and the field vectors for the incident wave are given by

$$\left.\begin{aligned} \mathbf{E}_0 &= \mathbf{E}_0^0 e^{-i(\omega t - \mathbf{k}_0 \cdot \mathbf{r})} \\ \mathbf{H}_0 &= \frac{n_1}{k_0}\mathbf{k}_0 \times \mathbf{E}_0 \end{aligned}\right\} \tag{6.14}$$

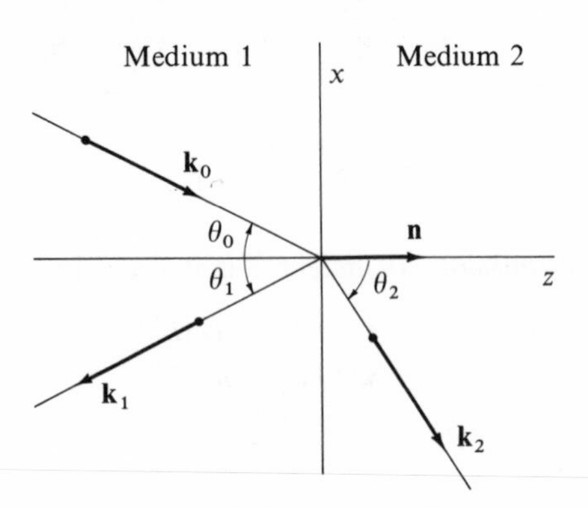

FIG. 6-2

where it is now more convenient to describe the direction of propagation in terms of the propagation vector. For the reflected wave we have

$$\left.\begin{aligned}\mathbf{E}_1 &= \mathbf{E}_1^0 e^{-i(\omega t - \mathbf{k}_1 \cdot \mathbf{r})} \\ \mathbf{H}_1 &= \frac{n_1}{k_1}\mathbf{k}_1 \times \mathbf{E}_1\end{aligned}\right\} \tag{6.15}$$

and for the transmitted wave,

$$\left.\begin{aligned}\mathbf{E}_2 &= \mathbf{E}_2^0 e^{-i(\omega t - \mathbf{k}_2 \cdot \mathbf{r})} \\ \mathbf{H}_2 &= \frac{n_2}{k_2}\mathbf{k}_2 \times \mathbf{E}_2\end{aligned}\right\} \tag{6.16}$$

The tangential components of **E** and **H** can be continuous across the boundary only if the phases of the field vectors are all equal at the interface. Thus, at the boundary ($z = 0$) we have

$$\mathbf{k}_0 \cdot \mathbf{r} = \mathbf{k}_1 \cdot \mathbf{r} = \mathbf{k}_2 \cdot \mathbf{r} \tag{6.17}$$

Now, $\mathbf{k}_0$, $\mathbf{k}_1$, and $\mathbf{k}_2$ are all coplanar, so if **r** is chosen to lie in the interface and in the plane of the propagation vectors, we have immediately

$$k_0 \sin\theta_0 = k_1 \sin\theta_1 = k_2 \sin\theta_2$$

But $k_0 = k_1$ and $k_1/n_1 = k_2/n_2$, so that

$$\boxed{\theta_0 = \theta_1} \tag{6.18}$$

and,

$$\boxed{\frac{\sin\theta_0}{\sin\theta_2} = \frac{n_2}{n_1} = \frac{\sin\theta_1}{\sin\theta_2}} \tag{6.19}$$

Equation (6.18) expresses the fact that the angle of incidence equals the angle of reflection, and Eq. (6.19) is *Snell's law*† for the angle of refraction.

The relationships among the various field vectors may be obtained by applying the boundary conditions to Eqs. (6.14), (6.15), and (6.16). The

† Discovered experimentally by Willebrord Snell about 1621, although he never published the result. Descartes apparently attempted to take the credit by presenting as his own a deductive (and incorrect) theoretical derivation in his *Dioptrique*, 1637. Fermat was the first to give a correct derivation (1661), based upon his Principle of Least Time (1657). Fermat's principle was, however, based upon metaphysical rather than physical grounds and so it had no lasting influence in physical theory. It remained for Hamilton to give a firm foundation to variational principles in physics (1834).

requirements on the normal components of **D** and **B**, when coupled with Snell's law, yield no information not included in the equations for the tangential components of **E** and **H**. Therefore, it is necessary to consider only these latter relations which are

$$(\mathbf{E}_0 + \mathbf{E}_1) \times \mathbf{n} = \mathbf{E}_2 \times \mathbf{n} \tag{6.20}$$

$$(\mathbf{H}_0 + \mathbf{H}_1) \times \mathbf{n} = \mathbf{H}_2 \times \mathbf{n} \tag{6.21}$$

where **n** is the unit vector normal to the plane of the interface (see Fig. 6-2). Equation (6.21) may be written in terms of the electric vectors; we find

$$(\mathbf{k}_0 \times \mathbf{E}_0 + \mathbf{k}_1 \times \mathbf{E}_1) \times \mathbf{n} = (\mathbf{k}_2 \times \mathbf{E}_2) \times \mathbf{n} \tag{6.22}$$

Any wave with arbitrary polarization which is incident on a plane surface may be considered as a superposition of two waves, one with the electric vector polarized parallel to the plane of incidence (i.e., the plane containing the propagation vectors $\mathbf{k}_j$), and one with the electric vector polarized perpendicular to the plane of incidence. Therefore, it is sufficient to consider these two cases separately; the general case may be obtained from the appropriate linear combination.

(a) **E** PERPENDICULAR TO THE PLANE OF INCIDENCE. This situation is shown in Fig. 6-3. The magnetic field vectors $\mathbf{H}_j$ and the propagation vectors $\mathbf{k}_j$ are indicated; the electric vectors $\mathbf{E}_j$ are all directed *into* the plane of

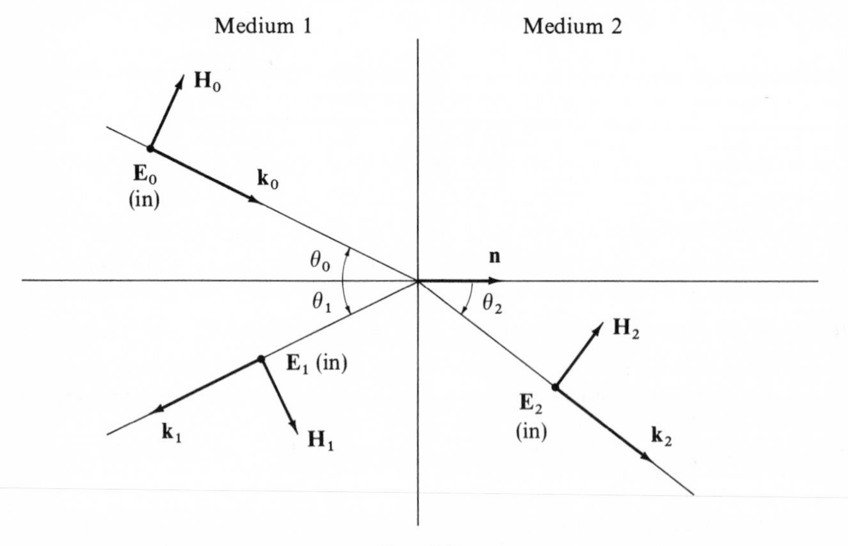

FIG. 6-3

the figure. Since the electric vectors are all parallel to the boundary surface, Eq. (6.20) gives

$$E_0^0 + E_1^0 = E_2^0 \tag{6.23}$$

where we have used the requirement on the phases at the interface given by Eq. (6.17). Expanding Eq. (6.22) we find

$$[(\mathbf{n}\cdot\mathbf{k}_0)\mathbf{E}_0 - (\mathbf{n}\cdot\mathbf{E}_0)\mathbf{k}_0] + [(\mathbf{n}\cdot\mathbf{k}_1)\mathbf{E}_1 - (\mathbf{n}\cdot\mathbf{E}_1)\mathbf{k}_1] = [(\mathbf{n}\cdot\mathbf{k}_2)\mathbf{E}_2 - (\mathbf{n}\cdot\mathbf{E}_2)\mathbf{k}_2]$$

The products $\mathbf{n}\cdot\mathbf{E}_j$ all vanish, and $\mathbf{n}\cdot\mathbf{k}_j = (-1)^j k_j \cos\theta_j$, $j = 0, 1, 2$, so that

$$E_0^0 \cos\theta_0 - E_1^0 \cos\theta_1 = \frac{k_2}{k_1} E_2^0 \cos\theta_2$$

or, since $\theta_0 = \theta_1$ and $k_2/k_1 = n_2/n_1$, we have

$$(E_0^0 - E_1^0)\cos\theta_0 = \frac{n_2}{n_1} E_2^0 \cos\theta_2 \tag{6.24}$$

Solving for E_1^0 and E_2^0 in terms of E_0^0 from Eqs. (6.23) and (6.24), we obtain

$$\left.\begin{aligned} E_1^0 &= \frac{\cos\theta_0 - (n_2/n_1)\cos\theta_2}{\cos\theta_0 + (n_2/n_1)\cos\theta_2} E_0^0 \\ &= \frac{\sin(\theta_2 - \theta_0)}{\sin(\theta_2 + \theta_0)} E_0^0 \end{aligned}\right\} \tag{6.25a}$$

$$\left.\begin{aligned} E_2^0 &= \frac{2\cos\theta_0}{\cos\theta_0 + (n_2/n_1)\cos\theta_2} E_0^0 \\ &= \frac{2\cos\theta_0 \sin\theta_2}{\sin(\theta_2 + \theta_0)} E_0^0 \end{aligned}\right\} \tag{6.25b}$$

where the second equation in each of the above pairs may be obtained from the first by using Snell's law. Thus, the second equations are not independent of the indices of refraction since these are implicitly contained in the angle θ_2.

(b) E PARALLEL TO THE PLANE OF INCIDENCE. This situation is shown in Fig. 6-4. In this case the magnetic field vectors $\mathbf{H}_j$ are all directed *out* of the plane of the figure. The boundary conditions on the tangential components of **E** and **H** give

$$\left.\begin{aligned} E_0^0 \cos\theta_0 - E_1^0 \cos\theta_1 &= E_2^0 \cos\theta_2 \\ k_0 E_0^0 + k_1 E_1^0 &= k_2 E_2^0 \end{aligned}\right\} \tag{6.26}$$

or,

$$\left.\begin{aligned} (E_0^0 - E_1^0)\cos\theta_0 &= E_2^0\cos\theta_2 \\ E_0^0 + E_1^0 &= \frac{n_2}{n_1}E_2^0 \end{aligned}\right\} \tag{6.27}$$

from which we obtain

$$\left.\begin{aligned} E_1^0 &= \frac{\cos\theta_0 - (n_1/n_2)\cos\theta_2}{\cos\theta_0 + (n_1/n_2)\cos\theta_2}E_0^0 \\ &= \frac{\tan(\theta_0 - \theta_2)}{\tan(\theta_0 + \theta_2)}E_0^0 \end{aligned}\right\} \tag{6.28a}$$

$$\left.\begin{aligned} E_2^0 &= \frac{2\cos\theta_0}{\cos\theta_2 + (n_2/n_1)\cos\theta_0}E_0^0 \\ &= \frac{2\cos\theta_0\sin\theta_2}{\sin(\theta_0 + \theta_2)\cos(\theta_0 - \theta_2)}E_0^0 \end{aligned}\right\} \tag{6.28b}$$

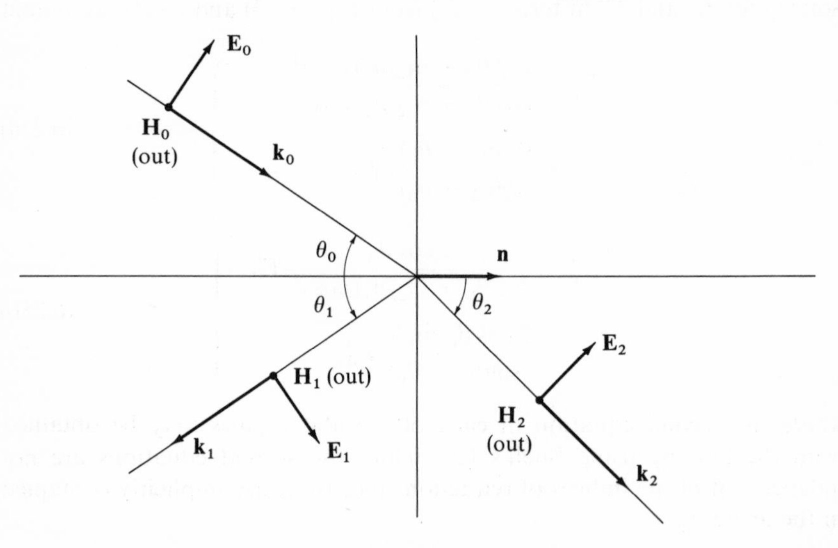

FIG. 6-4

Equations (6.25) and (6.28) are known as the *Fresnel equations.*† We note that these equations reduce to the case for normal incidence [Eqs. (6.7)] when $\theta_0 = \theta_2 = 0$.

† Derived in 1823 by Augustin Jean Fresnel (1788–1827) on the basis of his dynamical theory of light. The manuscript was lost, however, and not published until 1832.

From Eq. (6.28a) we see that E_1^0 will vanish when $\theta_0 = \theta_2$, or when $\theta_0 + \theta_2 = \pi/2$ (or, equivalently, when $\theta_1 + \theta_2 = \pi/2$). The first case is trivial since it implies that the two media are optically identical. But the second case shows that when the reflected and refracted rays are perpendicular there is no energy carried by the reflected ray. The incident angle for which this occurs is called *Brewster's angle*† θ_B. From Snell's law we have

$$\frac{n_2}{n_1} = \frac{\sin \theta_B}{\sin[(\pi/2) - \theta_B]} = \tan \theta_B \tag{6.29}$$

Thus, if an unpolarized wave is incident on the boundary surface with $\theta_0 = \theta_B$, only that portion of the wave with the electric vector perpendicular to the plane of incidence will be reflected and that portion with the electric vector parallel to the plane of incidence will be entirely transmitted. That is, the reflected wave will be *linearly polarized* perpendicular to the plane of incidence. Brewster's angle is therefore sometimes called the *polarizing angle*. For ordinary glass with $n_2 = 1.5$, a light ray incident from air at an angle of $\tan^{-1}(1.5) \cong 56°$ will be completely polarized upon reflection.

Brewster's law may be explained by the following physical argument. When an electromagnetic wave is incident on a plane surface, the electrons are set into motion by the action of the electric field of the wave. These vibrating electrons then give rise to the reflected and transmitted waves. But the direction of motion of the electrons must be parallel to the direction of the electric vector (if we neglect the effects of the magnetic portion of the Lorentz force and if the medium is nonmagnetic). Now, the energy radiated by an electron undergoing linear oscillations has a $\sin^2 \theta$ dependence on angle.‡ Thus, there is no radiation along the direction of motion ($\theta = 0$ or π). It follows, then, that if the direction of the transmitted wave is perpendicular to the direction of the reflected wave, the reflected wave receives no energy from electrons vibrating parallel to the plane of incidence.

The reflection and transmission coefficients for the cases of **E** perpendicular ($\perp$) and parallel ($\|$) to the plane of incidence may be obtained by computing the normal component of the Poynting vector for the various waves. For the perpendicular case we have

$$R_\perp = \frac{\langle \mathbf{S}_1 \rangle_\perp \cdot \mathbf{n}}{\langle \mathbf{S}_0 \rangle_\perp \cdot \mathbf{n}} = \frac{|E_1^0|^2}{|E_0^0|^2} = \frac{\sin^2(\theta_2 - \theta_0)}{\sin^2(\theta_2 + \theta_0)} \tag{6.30}$$

† Discovered experimentally in 1811 by the Scottish physicist Sir David Brewster (1781–1868), the inventor of the kaleidoscope.

‡ See Section 8.2. The angle θ here is measured relative to the direction of motion of the electron.

and

$$T_\perp = \frac{\langle \mathbf{S}_2 \rangle_\perp \cdot \mathbf{n}}{\langle \mathbf{S}_0 \rangle_\perp \cdot \mathbf{n}} = \frac{n_2 \cos\theta_2}{n_1 \cos\theta_0} \frac{|E_2^0|^2}{|E_0^0|^2}$$

$$= 4\frac{n_2 \cos\theta_0}{n_1 \cos\theta_0} \frac{\cos^2\theta_0 \sin^2\theta_2}{\sin^2(\theta_2 + \theta_0)} \tag{6.31}$$

Using Snell's law for n_2/n_1, we find

$$T_\perp = 4\frac{\sin\theta_0 \cos\theta_2}{\sin\theta_2 \cos\theta_0} \frac{\cos^2\theta_0 \sin^2\theta_2}{\sin^2(\theta_2 + \theta_0)}$$

$$= \frac{(2\sin\theta_0 \cos\theta_0)(2\sin\theta_2 \cos\theta_2)}{\sin^2(\theta_2 + \theta_0)}$$

$$= \frac{\sin 2\theta_0 \sin 2\theta_2}{\sin^2(\theta_2 + \theta_0)} \tag{6.31a}$$

For the parallel case, in similar fashion, we have

$$R_\parallel = \frac{\tan^2(\theta_2 - \theta_0)}{\tan^2(\theta_2 + \theta_0)} \tag{6.32}$$

$$T_\parallel = \frac{\sin 2\theta_0 \sin 2\theta_2}{\sin^2(\theta_0 + \theta_2)\cos^2(\theta_0 - \theta_2)} \tag{6.33}$$

The reflection coefficients for ordinary glass ($n = 1.5$) are plotted in Fig. 6-5 for the case of light incident from air. The *mean reflection coefficient* is $R_M \equiv (R_\perp + R_\parallel)/2$, and corresponds to the reflection of *unpolarized* light. We see the vanishing of $R_\parallel$ at Brewster's angle, and we see also that the reflected wave is largely polarized perpendicular to the plane of incidence for all angles of incidence except near 0° and 90°. The *degree of polarization* may be defined as

$$P(\theta_0) \equiv \frac{R_\parallel - R_\perp}{R_\parallel + R_\perp} \tag{6.34}$$

so that $P(0^0) = P(90^0) = 0$ and $P(\theta_B) = 1$; $P(\theta_0) > 0$ except for normal and for grazing incidence.

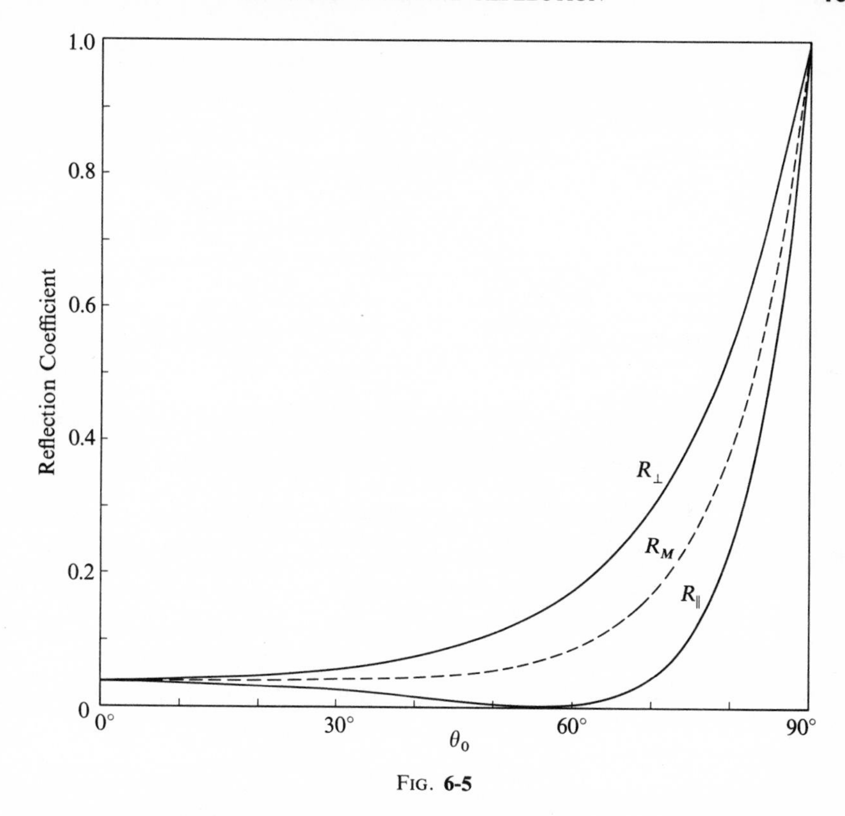

FIG. **6-5**

6.4 Total Internal Reflection

An interesting application of the Fresnel equations is to consider the electromagnetic wave to be incident on the boundary surface from the more dense of the two media; i.e., we have $n_1 > n_2$. If we start with $\theta_0 = 0$ and allow the angle of incidence to increase, all goes well until we reach an angle such that $\theta_2 = \pi/2$. From Snell's law this occurs when $\sin \theta_0 = n_2/n_1$, and the angle is called the *critical angle*:

$$\theta_c \equiv \sin^{-1}\left(\frac{n_2}{n_1}\right) \tag{6.35}$$

We may write the cosine of the angle of refraction as

$$\cos \theta_2 = \sqrt{1 - \sin^2 \theta_2}$$

$$= \sqrt{1 - \frac{\sin^2 \theta_0}{\sin^2 \theta_c}} \tag{6.36}$$

so that $\cos\theta_2 = 0$ for $\theta_0 = \theta_c$, but as θ_0 is increased beyond θ_c, $\cos\theta_2$ becomes a pure imaginary number. Therefore we write

$$\cos\theta_2 = iQ \tag{6.37a}$$

where Q is defined as the positive square root

$$Q \equiv \sqrt{\frac{\sin^2\theta_0}{\sin^2\theta_c} - 1}, \qquad \theta_0 > \theta_c \tag{6.37b}$$

In order to determine the effect on the field in Medium 2 when the angle of incidence exceeds the critical angle, we write $\mathbf{E}_2$ as [see Eq. (6.16)]

$$\mathbf{E}_2 = \mathbf{E}_2^0 e^{-i(\omega t - \mathbf{k}_2 \cdot \mathbf{r})} \tag{6.38}$$

If we take the coordinate axes as in Fig. 6-2, this becomes

$$\mathbf{E}_2 = \mathbf{E}_2^0 \exp[-i(\omega t + k_2 x \sin\theta_2 - k_2 z \cos\theta_2)] \tag{6.39}$$

But

$$\sin\theta_2 = \frac{n_1}{n_2}\sin\theta_0 = \frac{\sin\theta_0}{\sin\theta_c} \equiv W \tag{6.40}$$

where W is a real number, greater than unity. Thus, using Eq. (6.37a) for $\cos\theta_2$, we have

$$\mathbf{E}_2 = \mathbf{E}_2^0 e^{-k_2 z Q} e^{-i(\omega t + k_2 x W)} \tag{6.41}$$

We therefore see that for $\theta_0 > \theta_c$, the wave is propagated along the surface and is attenuated in the direction into the medium. The phase velocity of the surface wave is

$$|V| = \frac{\omega}{k_2 W} = \frac{\omega}{k_2}\frac{n_2}{n_1 \sin\theta_0} = \frac{c}{n_1}\frac{1}{\sin\theta_0}, \qquad \theta_0 > \theta_c \tag{6.42}$$

which is a function of the angle of incidence θ_0. We see that in the event Medium 1 is air ($n_1 = 1$), the phase velocity is just c for grazing incidence, as expected.

The amplitudes of the reflected electric vectors may be calculated from Fresnel's equations [Eqs. (6.25a) and (6.28a)]. For the case of $\mathbf{E}$ perpendicular to the plane of incidence, we have

$$\begin{aligned}(E_1^0)_\perp &= \frac{\cos\theta_0 - (n_2/n_1)\cos\theta_2}{\cos\theta_0 + (n_2/n_1)\cos\theta_2}(E_0^0)_\perp \\ &= \frac{\cos\theta_0 - i(n_2/n_1)Q}{\cos\theta_0 + i(n_2/n_1)Q}(E_0^0)_\perp\end{aligned}$$

so that

$$|(E_1^0)_\perp| = |(E_0^0)_\perp| \tag{6.43a}$$

Similarly, from Eq. (6.28a), we find

$$|(E_1^0)_\parallel| = |(E_0^0)_\parallel| \tag{6.43b}$$

We therefore have the result that the intensity of the reflected wave is equal to the intensity of the incident wave; i.e., the wave is *totally reflected.* Since this result applies to the case in which Medium 2 is the less dense (and is commonly air), while Medium 1 is some substance such as glass, this phenomenon is called *total internal reflection.*

Equation (6.43) shows that the reflection of the incident wave is complete; but we also know from Eq. (6.41) that because of the attenuation factor $\exp(-k_2 zQ)$ the field *does* exist in Medium 2. To investigate this point, we first calculate the average rate of energy flow across the boundary (i.e., across $z = 0$):

$$\langle \mathbf{S}_2 \rangle \cdot \mathbf{n} = \frac{c}{8\pi}(\mathbf{E}_2 \times \mathbf{H}_2^*) \cdot \mathbf{n} \tag{6.44}$$

where we understand that the real part of the right-hand side is to be taken. Using Eq. (6.16) this becomes

$$\begin{aligned} \langle \mathbf{S}_2 \rangle \cdot \mathbf{n} &= \frac{cn_2}{8\pi k_2}[\mathbf{E}_2 \times (\mathbf{k}_2 \times \mathbf{E}_2^*)] \cdot \mathbf{n} \\ &= \frac{cn_2}{8\pi k_2}[(\mathbf{E}_2 \cdot \mathbf{E}_2^*)\mathbf{k}_2 - (\mathbf{E}_2 \cdot \mathbf{k}_2)\mathbf{E}_2^*] \cdot \mathbf{n} \end{aligned} \tag{6.45}$$

But $\mathbf{E}_2$ is perpendicular to the propagation vector $\mathbf{k}_2$, so that the second term vanishes. Thus,

$$\begin{aligned} \langle \mathbf{S}_2 \rangle \cdot \mathbf{n} &= \frac{cn_2}{8\pi k_2}|\mathbf{E}_2|^2(\mathbf{k}_2 \cdot \mathbf{n}) \\ &= \frac{cn_2}{8\pi}|\mathbf{E}_2|^2 \cos\theta_2 \\ &= i\frac{cn_2}{8\pi}|\mathbf{E}_2|^2 Q \end{aligned} \tag{6.46}$$

Since we must take the real part of the right-hand side and since this expression is purely imaginary, we conclude that $\langle \mathbf{S}_2 \rangle \cdot \mathbf{n} \equiv 0$.

Although we have shown that there is no energy transport across the boundary, we still have not answered the question as to the origin of the decaying field within Medium 2. The explanation lies in the fact that our analysis has been based on the assumption of steady-state conditions. At the time that the incident wave first struck the surface, a small amount of energy penetrated the second medium and established the field. Once *done*, this transient effect cannot be *undone* since the steady-state solution does not allow any transfer of energy between the media. We hasten to add that even this explanation is not strictly correct if we allow the surface to be finite rather than infinite as has been implicit in all of the development above. For the finite case there is actually a small flow of energy into Medium 2.

6.5 Reflection from a Metallic Surface—Normal Incidence

We now consider the case in which the bounding surface separates a dielectric medium (Medium 1) from a conducting medium (Medium 2). For simplicity, we shall treat only the case of normal incidence. If the wave is allowed to be incident at an oblique angle, then interesting effects involving, for example, the elliptical polarization of the reflected wave, are found. The analysis of such effects is, however, a good deal more involved, and the reader is referred to the literature for a detailed account.†

We take for the incident wave [cf. Fig. 6-1 and Eqs. (6.1) and (6.4)]

$$\left.\begin{aligned} \mathbf{E}_0 &= \mathbf{e}_x E_0^0 e^{-i(\omega t - k_1 z)} \\ \mathbf{H}_0 &= \mathbf{e}_y \frac{c}{\omega} k_1 E_0^0 e^{-i(\omega t - k_1 z)} \end{aligned}\right\} \tag{6.47}$$

The reflected wave is given by

$$\left.\begin{aligned} \mathbf{E}_1 &= -\mathbf{e}_x E_1^0 e^{-i(\omega t + k_1 z)} \\ \mathbf{H}_1 &= \mathbf{e}_y \frac{c}{\omega} k_1 E_1^0 e^{-i(\omega t + k_1 z)} \end{aligned}\right\} \tag{6.48}$$

And the transmitted wave is

$$\begin{aligned} \mathbf{E}_2 &= \mathbf{e}_x E_2^0 e^{-i(\omega t - \hat{k}_2 z)} \\ \mathbf{H}_2 &= \mathbf{e}_y \frac{c}{\omega} \hat{k}_2 E_2^0 e^{-i(\omega t - \hat{k}_2 z)} \end{aligned} \tag{6.49}$$

where, since Medium 2 is conducting, the propagation constant in this medium is given by Eq. (5.52) (with μ_2 taken to be unity):

$$\hat{k}_2^2 = \frac{\varepsilon_2 \omega^2}{c^2}\left[1 + i\frac{4\pi\sigma_2}{\varepsilon_2 \omega}\right] \tag{6.50}$$

† See, for example, Stratton (St41, p. 500 ff.), or Born and Wolf (Bo59, p. 612 ff.).

The boundary conditions require

$$\left.\begin{aligned} E_0^0 - E_1^0 &= E_2^0 \\ k_1(E_0^0 + E_1^0) &= \hat{k}_2 E_2^0 \end{aligned}\right\} \tag{6.51}$$

Since $\hat{k}_2$ is complex, E_1^0 and E_2^0 cannot both be real. We must therefore expect that phase shifts different from 0 and π are to be found for the reflected and transmitted waves.

The simultaneous solution of Eqs. (6.51) yields

$$\left.\begin{aligned} E_1^0 &= \frac{\hat{k}_2 - k_1}{\hat{k}_2 + k_1} E_0^0 \\ E_2^0 &= \frac{2k_1}{\hat{k}_2 + k_1} E_0^0 \end{aligned}\right\} \tag{6.52}$$

These expressions for E_1^0 and E_2^0 should be compared with Eqs. (6.7). We note that if $\hat{k}_2$ were real, then $k_2 = (\omega/c)n_2$, and Eqs. (6.52) becomes identical to Eqs. (6.7).

If we substitute $k_1 = (\omega/c)\sqrt{\varepsilon_1}$ and Eq. (6.50) for $\hat{k}_2$, we find

$$\left.\begin{aligned} E_1^0 &= \frac{\sqrt{\dfrac{\varepsilon_2}{\varepsilon_1}\left(1 + i\dfrac{4\pi\sigma_2}{\varepsilon_2\omega}\right)} - 1}{\sqrt{\dfrac{\varepsilon_2}{\varepsilon_1}\left(1 + i\dfrac{4\pi\sigma_2}{\varepsilon_2\omega}\right)} + 1} E_0^0 \\ E_2^0 &= \frac{2}{\sqrt{\dfrac{\varepsilon_2}{\varepsilon_1}\left(1 + i\dfrac{4\pi\sigma_2}{\varepsilon_2\omega}\right)} + 1} E_0^0 \end{aligned}\right\} \tag{6.53}$$

In these forms the expressions for E_1^0 and E_2^0 are not amenable to further investigation in a simple way. We note, however, that if we assume Medium 2 to be a perfect conductor (i.e., $\sigma_2 = \infty$), then

$$\left.\begin{aligned} E_1^0 &= E_0^0 \\ E_2^0 &= 0 \end{aligned}\right\}, \qquad \sigma_2 = \infty \tag{6.54}$$

which shows that the reflection is complete and that there is a phase change of π between the incident and reflected waves. [Note that $\mathbf{E}_1$ was assumed to be in the direction of $-\mathbf{e}_x$; see Eq. (6.48).]

In order to find expressions for E_1^0 and E_2^0 that are somewhat more useful, we make the approximation that Medium 2 is a good (but not perfect) conductor. We then have $4\pi\sigma_2/\varepsilon_2\omega \gg 1$ and we may use the approximate formula for $\hat{k}_2$ which we have previously derived for this case [see Eq. (5.64)]. Thus,

$$\hat{k}_2 = \alpha + i\beta \cong (1 + i)\frac{\sqrt{2\pi\omega\sigma_2}}{c} \tag{6.55}$$

or, using the definition of the skin depth [Eq. (5.72)], we have

$$\hat{k}_2 \cong \frac{1 + i}{\delta} \tag{6.55a}$$

Now, the *reduced wavelength* of the incident radiation of frequency ω is $\lambdabar = c/\omega$. Therefore,

$$\frac{c}{\omega}\hat{k}_2 = (1 + i)\frac{\lambdabar}{\delta} \tag{6.56}$$

Also,

$$\frac{c}{\omega}k_1 = n_1 \tag{6.57}$$

Using these expressions for k_1 and $\hat{k}_2$ to evaluate E_1^0 [see Eqs. (6.52)], we find

$$E_1^0 = \frac{(1 + i)(\lambdabar/\delta) - n_1}{(1 + i)(\lambdabar/\delta) + n_1}E_0^0 \tag{6.58}$$

The reflection coefficient is given by

$$R = \frac{|E_1^0|^2}{|E_0^0|^2} = \frac{[1 - (\delta/\lambdabar)n_1]^2 + 1}{[1 + (\delta/\lambdabar)n_1]^2 + 1} \tag{6.59}$$

Now, even at optical frequencies $\delta/\lambdabar$ is small compared with unity. (As we found in Section 5.7, δ for copper is approximately 6×10^{-8} cm for ultraviolet radiation of wavelength $\lambda \cong 10^{-5}$ cm. Thus, for this case, $\delta/\lambdabar \cong 0.04$, and the ratio is even smaller for longer wavelengths.) Therefore, with the approximation $(\delta/\lambdabar)n_1 \ll 1$, an expansion of the expression for the reflection coefficient gives

$$R \cong 1 - 2\frac{\delta}{\lambdabar}n_1 \tag{6.60}$$

or,

$$R \cong 1 - 2n_1\sqrt{\frac{\nu}{\sigma_2}} \tag{6.60a}$$

The transmission coefficient is given by

$$T = 1 - R = 2\frac{\delta}{\lambda\!\!\!^{-}} n_1 \tag{6.61}$$

and represents the fraction of the average energy incident on the surface that is transmitted into the conducting medium.

If 3-cm waves ($\nu = 10^{10}\ \text{sec}^{-1}$) are incident from air on a copper surface, then $1 - R \cong 3 \times 10^{-4}$, a value so small that direct measurements are extremely difficult to perform. Values of the reflection coefficient are therefore usually determined by measuring the *emissivity* e of the surface, a quantity which is related to R by Kirchoff's† relation:

$$e = 1 - R = \frac{\text{(energy emitted by unit area of the metallic surface)}}{\text{(energy emitted by unit area of a } \textit{black body} \text{ at the same temperature)}} \tag{6.62}$$

According to Eqs. (6.60a) and (6.62), the quantity $(1 - R)\sqrt{\sigma} = e\sqrt{\sigma}$ should be a constant, independent of the material, for a given frequency of incident radiation. Extensive measurements by Hagen and Rubens in 1903 confirmed this prediction for a wide range of metals and for frequencies in the range 10^{13}–$10^{14}\ \text{sec}^{-1}$. The average value of $(1 - R)\sqrt{\sigma}$ obtained from measurements on 11 metals at $\lambda = 25.5 \times 10^{-4}$ cm was 6.96×10^6, whereas the calculated value was 6.86×10^6.

The predictions of this simple theory based on static values of σ are no longer valid at optical frequencies ($\nu \approx 10^{15}\ \text{sec}^{-1}$), as we shall see in Section 9.7.

Since the reflection coefficient is almost unity for a metallic surface, the magnitudes of the vectors $\mathbf{E}_0$ and $\mathbf{E}_1$ are almost equal. Therefore, we may write

$$\left.\begin{aligned} \mathbf{E}_0 &= \mathbf{e}_x E_0^0 e^{-i(\omega t - k_1 z)} \\ \mathbf{E}_1 &\cong -\mathbf{e}_x E_0^0 e^{-i(\omega t + k_1 z)} \end{aligned}\right\} \tag{6.63}$$

The total electric field in Medium 1 will be given by the sum of $\mathbf{E}_0$ and $\mathbf{E}_1$. We have approximately

$$\mathbf{E} \equiv \mathbf{E}_0 + \mathbf{E}_1 \cong \mathbf{e}_x E_0^0 e^{-i\omega t}(e^{ik_1 z} - e^{-ik_1 z})$$

or, upon taking the real part of this expression, we have

$$\mathbf{E} \cong 2\mathbf{e}_x E_0^0 \sin \omega t \sin k_1 z \tag{6.64}$$

† After the German physicist Gustav Robert Kirchhoff (1824–1887).

The total electric field is therefore represented by a standing wave, rather than a propagating wave. The argument of the sine term that depends on the space variable is $k_1 z = n_1(\omega/c)z = (2\pi n_1/\lambda)z$. Therefore, the standing wave shows nodes separated by a distance $\lambda/2n_1$. These standing waves have been detected by several methods, including the use of photographic plates and by means of the photoelectric effect.†

Our results show, therefore, that the electric field behaves as shown in Fig. 6-6.

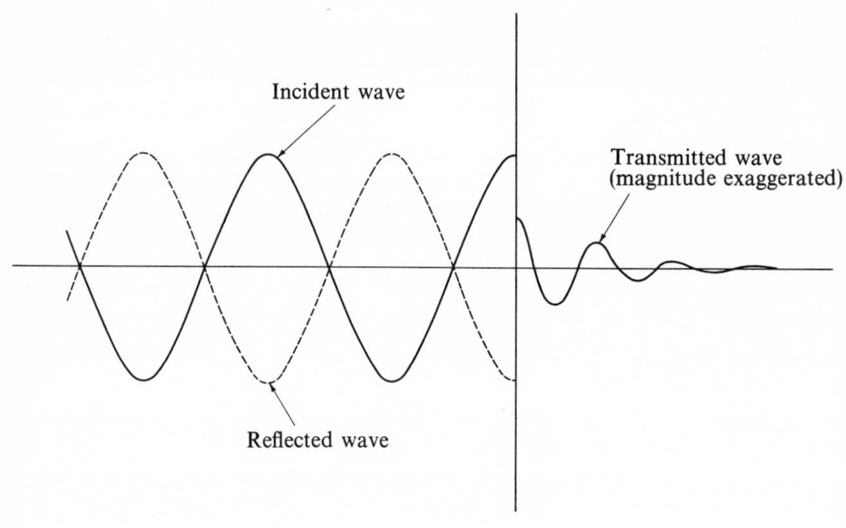

FIG. **6-6**

6.6 Refraction at a Metallic Surface

Having discussed the reflection of an electromagnetic wave at the surface of a conductor, we turn now to the subject of metallic *refraction*. We may begin by formally writing the expression for the electric vector in the conductor as in Eq. (6.16):

$$\mathbf{E}_2 = \mathbf{E}_2^0 e^{-i(\omega t - \hat{\mathbf{k}}_2 \cdot \mathbf{r})} \tag{6.65}$$

But now the medium has a nonvanishing conductivity and is therefore an absorbing medium. Consequently, the propagation constant is complex:

$$\hat{k}_2 = \frac{\omega}{c}\hat{n}_2 = \frac{\omega}{c}n(1 + i\kappa) \tag{6.66}$$

† See Section 11.3 for further discussion of these standing waves.

We may also formally write an expression analogous to Snell's law (we take $n_1 = 1$):

$$\sin\theta_0 = \hat{n}_2 \sin\theta_2' \tag{6.67}$$

Again, we have a fundamental difference from the previous result: $\hat{n}_2$ is complex, so that it is not possible to interpret the angle θ_2' in the ordinary sense of an "angle of refraction."

The interesting aspects of the wave propagation will be revealed by an examination of the spatial portion of the phase of the electric vector, $\hat{\mathbf{k}}_2 \cdot \mathbf{r}$. We choose a coordinate system (see Fig. 6-7) similar to that of Fig. 6-2. Then the phase is given by [cf. Eq. (6.39)]

$$\hat{\mathbf{k}}_2 \cdot \mathbf{r} = \frac{\omega}{c} n(1 + i\kappa)(x \sin\theta_2' + z\cos\theta_2') \tag{6.68}$$

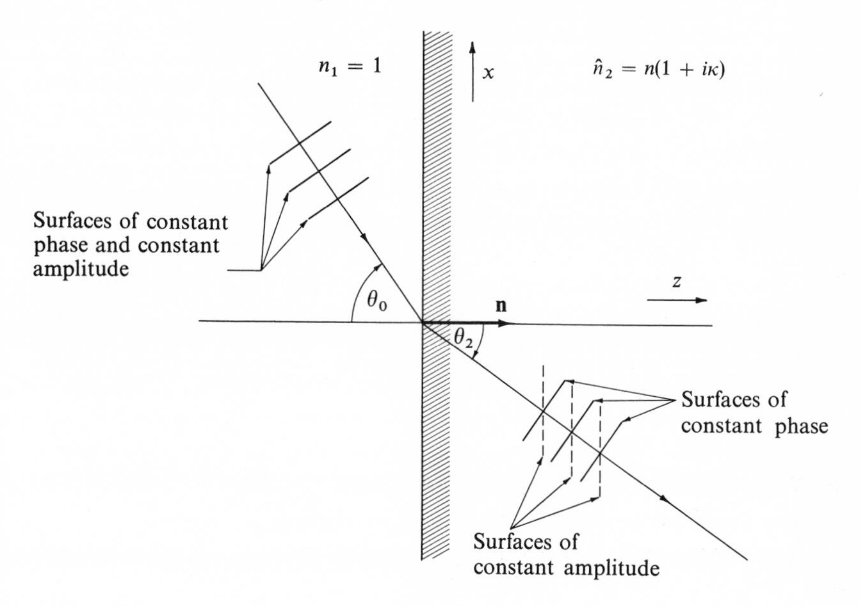

FIG. **6-7**

Now, we may express $\sin\theta_2'$ and $\cos\theta_2'$ as

$$\sin\theta_2' = \frac{\sin\theta_0}{\hat{n}_2} = \frac{\sin\theta_0}{n(1 + i\kappa)}$$

$$= \frac{1 - i\kappa}{n(1 + \kappa^2)} \sin\theta_0 = \gamma(1 - i\kappa)\sin\theta_0 \tag{6.69a}$$

$$\cos\theta_2' = \sqrt{1 - \sin^2\theta_2'}$$

$$= \sqrt{1 - \gamma^2(1 - \kappa^2)\sin^2\theta_0 + i2\kappa\gamma^2\sin^2\theta_0} \tag{6.69b}$$

where

$$\gamma \equiv [n(1 + \kappa^2)]^{-1} \tag{6.70}$$

Next, the complex quantity $\cos\theta_2'$ may be written as the product of a real magnitude and a complex phase factor:

$$\cos\theta_2' \equiv \alpha e^{i\phi} = \alpha(\cos\phi + i\sin\phi) \tag{6.71}$$

Then, substitution of the expressions for $\sin\theta_2'$ and $\cos\theta_2'$ into Eq. (6.68) for the phase yields

$$\hat{\mathbf{k}}_2 \cdot \mathbf{r} = \frac{\omega}{c} n(1 + i\kappa)[x\gamma(1 - i\kappa)\sin\theta_0 + z\alpha(\cos\phi + i\sin\phi)]$$

$$= \frac{\omega}{c}[x\sin\theta_0 + zn\alpha(\cos\phi - \kappa\sin\phi)$$

$$+ izn\alpha(\kappa\cos\phi + \sin\phi)] \tag{6.72}$$

where the phase has been separated into its real and imaginary parts. The imaginary part of the phase, since it occurs in the expression for $\mathbf{E}_2$ as $\exp(i\hat{\mathbf{k}}_2 \cdot \mathbf{r})$, produces an attenuation term

$$\exp\left[-z\left(\frac{\omega}{c} n\alpha(\kappa\cos\phi + \sin\phi)\right)\right]$$

Therefore, even though the wave is penetrating obliquely into the conductor, the attenuation is a function only of z. That is, the surfaces of *constant amplitude* are those for which $z =$ const.

The surfaces of *constant phase* may be determined by the requirement that the real part of $\hat{\mathbf{k}}_2 \cdot \mathbf{r}$ be constant:

$$x\sin\theta_0 + zn\alpha(\cos\phi - \kappa\sin\phi) = \text{const.} \tag{6.73}$$

These surfaces may be interpreted as planes that are perpendicular to a line defined by an angle θ_2 if

$$\sin\theta_2 = \frac{\sin\theta_0}{N(\theta_0)} \tag{6.74a}$$

$$\cos\theta_2 = \frac{n\alpha(\cos\phi - \kappa\sin\phi)}{N(\theta_0)} \tag{6.74b}$$

where

$$N(\theta_0) \equiv \sqrt{\sin^2 \theta_0 + n^2\alpha^2(\cos\phi - \kappa \sin\phi)^2} \tag{6.75}$$

The surfaces of constant phase in the conductor therefore do not coincide with the surfaces of constant amplitude (see Fig. 6-7). As a result, the phase velocity of the wave depends on the angle between the surfaces of constant phase and those of constant amplitude; this is independent of the fact that the medium is isotropic. An additional anomaly is that the phase velocity in the medium can exceed the velocity of light.† We also note that the field vector has a component in the direction of propagation, so that the field is not transverse in the conductor.

Equation (6.74a) has the form of Snell's law [cf. Eq. (6.67)], if the quantity $N(\theta_0)$ is interpreted as an index of refraction that depends upon the angle of incidence.

6.7 Propagation of Waves between Perfectly Conducting Planes

In the following sections we shall investigate some of the basic properties of *wave guides*. By way of introduction to the subject it is instructive to examine first the propagation of an electromagnetic wave that is confined to the region between two parallel and perfectly conducting planes.

If the planes are indeed perfect conductors, then the electric and magnetic fields are excluded completely from the interiors. But because of the conducting nature of the planes, *surface charges* and *surface currents* can exist. These charges and currents then determine the boundary conditions on the vectors **D** and **H**, as discussed in Section 1.10. Since we do not in general wish to evaluate explicitly the surface charges and currents, we shall instead make use of the following boundary conditions on **E** and **B**:

E: tangential component vanishes at the surface
B: normal component vanishes at the surface

For simplicity, we shall assume that the space between the planes is vacuum and accordingly set $\varepsilon = 1$, $\mu = 1$, $\rho = 0$, $\sigma = 0$ in this region.

As we have already seen (Section 5.2), plane electromagnetic waves in free space are *transverse waves*; that is, in such waves the vectors **E** and **B** are both perpendicular to the direction of propagation of the wave. We call these waves TEM (transverse electric and magnetic) waves. If we

† This does not contradict the fact that a signal cannot be transmitted with a velocity greater than c since the phase velocity does not correspond to the velocity with which energy is transferred in an absorbing medium. See, for example, Stratton (St41, p. 333 ff.).

introduce an electromagnetic wave into the region between two conducting planes, it is clear that by a process of multiple reflections the wave will propagate in a direction parallel to the planes. An individual wave front, however, will not in general be moving parallel to the planes. Figure 6-8 shows an instantaneous position of such a wave front. If we arrange the electric vector **E** to be directed vertically (direction of positive x), then the magnetic vector **B**, which must be perpendicular to **E** and must lie in the instantaneous plane of propagation, will have a component in the direction parallel to the conducting planes. Therefore, **B** has a component in the ultimate direction of wave propagation, whereas **E** does not. (See the projections of **B** shown in the y-z plane of Fig. 6-8.) Such a wave is called a *transverse electric* (TE) wave. Similarly, we could orient **E** and **B** so that **B** is entirely transverse but **E** has a longitudinal component; such a wave is called a *transverse magnetic* (TM) wave. We shall find that all waves that can propagate in hollow conducting pipes are either TE or TM waves; TEM waves do not occur.

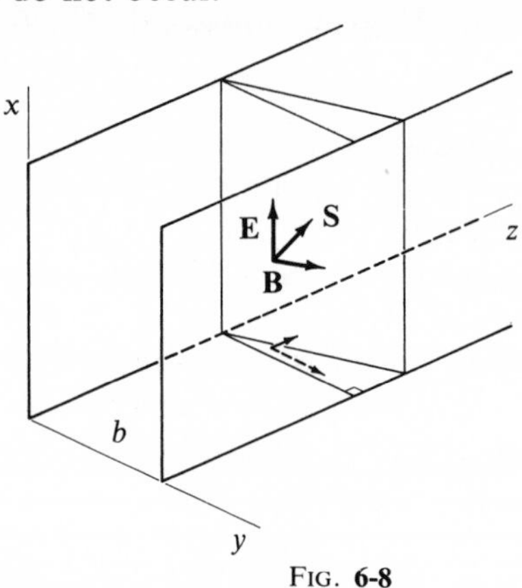

FIG. 6-8

Let us now investigate more closely the process of multiple reflections between two conducting planes. Figure 6-9 shows the top view of the situation represented in Fig. 6-8. The upper plane is located along $y = 0$, and the lower along $y = b$. The electric vector is chosen to be polarized in the x-direction; the wave is therefore a TE wave. The wave is incident on the upper plane at an angle θ_0; the dashed lines represent corresponding positions on successive wave fronts and are therefore separated by one free space wavelength λ_0 (or by any integral multiple of λ_0). The electric vector of the incident wave may be represented in the standard manner as

$$\begin{aligned}\mathbf{E}_0 &= \mathbf{e}_x E_0^0 \exp[-i(\omega t - \mathbf{k}_0 \cdot \mathbf{r})] \\ &= \mathbf{e}_x E_0^0 \exp(-i\omega t) \exp[ik_0(-y\cos\theta_0 + z\sin\theta_0)] \qquad (6.76\text{a})\end{aligned}$$

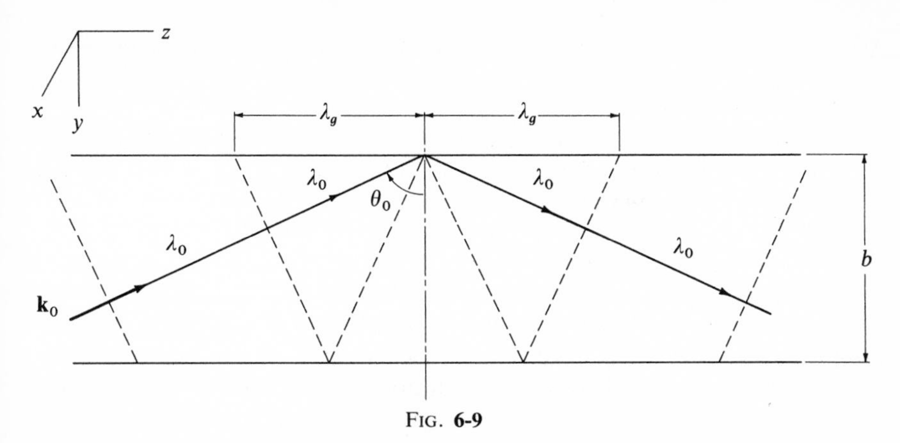

FIG. **6-9**

where $|\mathbf{k}_0| = k_0 = \omega/c$ is the free space propagation constant and is related to the free space wavelength by $k_0 = 2\pi/\lambda_0$. For the reflected wave we may explicitly take account of the phase change at the surface and write

$$\mathbf{E}_1 = -\mathbf{e}_x E_0^0 \exp[-i\omega t] \exp[ik_0(y \cos\theta_0 + z \sin\theta_0)] \tag{6.76b}$$

The total electric vector is therefore

$$\begin{aligned}\mathbf{E}_{\text{total}} &= \mathbf{E}_0 + \mathbf{E}_1 \\ &= \mathbf{e}_x E_0^0 e^{-i\omega t} e^{ik_0 z \sin\theta_0}[e^{-ik_0 y \cos\theta_0} - e^{ik_0 y \cos\theta_0}] \\ &= -2i\mathbf{e}_x E_0^0 e^{-i(\omega t - k_0 z \sin\theta_0)} \sin(k_0 y \cos\theta_0)\end{aligned} \tag{6.77}$$

Now, the electric vector is entirely transverse, so that the boundary condition becomes $\mathbf{E}_{\text{total}}\ (y = 0) = 0$; this condition is satisfied by Eq. (6.77). Along the plane $y = b$, the vector $\mathbf{E}_{\text{total}}$ must also vanish, so that

$$\sin(k_0 b \cos\theta_0) = 0$$

This condition leads immediately to

$$k_0 b \cos\theta_0 = n\pi, \qquad n = 0, 1, 2, \ldots \tag{6.78}$$

If we define an effective wavelength along y according to

$$\lambda_c = \frac{2\pi c}{\omega \cos\theta_0} = \frac{2\pi}{k_0 \cos\theta_0} = \frac{\lambda_0}{\cos\theta_0} \tag{6.79}$$

then Eq. (6.78) may be expressed as

$$\lambda_c = 2b/n \tag{6.80}$$

Thus, the *mode number n* and the width b determine the values of the effective wavelength λ_c that are allowed by the boundary condition on the electric vector. Therefore, for a given angle of incidence θ_0, only waves with a discrete set of frequencies $\omega_n = n[\pi c/(b \cos \theta_0)]$ will be propagated between the conducting planes.

We may also define an effective wavelength for the propagation in the direction parallel to the planes (the z-direction). From Fig. 6-9 we see that the appropriate relation is

$$\lambda_g = \frac{\lambda_0}{\sin \theta_0} \tag{6.81}$$

The quantity λ_g is called the *guide wavelength* and is related to the guide *propagation constant* k_g according to $k_g = 2\pi/\lambda_g$. Equations (6.81) and (6.79) may be combined to yield a relation connecting the various wavelengths:

$$\frac{1}{\lambda_0^2} = \frac{1}{\lambda_c^2} + \frac{1}{\lambda_g^2} \tag{6.82a}$$

or, equivalently,

$$\boxed{k_0^2 = k_c^2 + k_g^2} \tag{6.82b}$$

The phase velocity u_g for the propagation of the wave along the guide is given by

$$u_g = \frac{\omega}{k_g} = \frac{c}{\sin \theta_0} \tag{6.83a}$$

Therefore, $u_g > c$.† This result is clear from Fig. 6-9, since the point of intersection of one of the dashed wave fronts with the conducting plane must travel with a velocity greater than the velocity of advance of the wave front itself. The z-component of the velocity of the wave front is

$$u_z = c \sin \theta_0 \tag{6.83b}$$

so that $u_z < c$. Combining Eqs. (6.83a) and (6.83b), we find

$$u_g u_z = c^2 \tag{6.84}$$

If we write $u_g = c\lambda_g/\lambda_0$ and substitute for λ_g from Eq. (6.82a), we obtain

$$u_g = \frac{c\lambda_c}{\sqrt{\lambda_c^2 - \lambda_0^2}} \tag{6.85}$$

For a fixed value of λ_c (i.e., for a definite mode number and for a given width b), then as λ_0 is increased (ω decreasing), $u_g \to \infty$ as $\lambda_0 \to \lambda_c$. For $\lambda_0 > \lambda_c$, the guide phase velocity u_g is purely imaginary. The wave is therefore attenuated, and λ_c is called the *cutoff wavelength.*

† *Energy,* of course, cannot be propagated with the velocity u_g.

6.8 Waves in Hollow Conductors

We now consider the propagation of electromagnetic waves in a general form of wave guide—a hollow conducting pipe of arbitrary (but uniform) cross section. Again, for simplicity, we assume the interior to be vacuum and the walls to be perfect conductors. We could approach the problem by the method of the previous section whereby the waves in the pipe are constructed by superimposing the various modes of reflected waves. It is easier and more instructive, however, to obtain a general result by solving the wave equation in the interior region of the pipe, subject to the boundary conditions and to the requirement that Maxwell's equations be satisfied.

The equations to be solved are

$$\left(\nabla^2 - \frac{1}{c^2}\frac{\partial^2}{\partial t^2}\right)\begin{bmatrix}\mathbf{E}\\ \mathbf{B}\end{bmatrix} = 0 \tag{6.86}$$

We seek solutions of the form

$$\begin{bmatrix}\mathbf{E}\\ \mathbf{B}\end{bmatrix} = \begin{bmatrix}\mathbf{E}_0(x, y)\\ \mathbf{B}_0(x, y)\end{bmatrix} e^{-i(\omega t - k_g z)} \tag{6.87}$$

That is, the desired solutions represent harmonic oscillations that propagate along the pipe (the z-direction) with a propagation constant k_g; the variations of $\mathbf{E}_0$ and $\mathbf{B}_0$ over the cross section of the pipe are to be determined. If we substitute Eq. (6.87) into (6.86), we obtain

$$\left(\frac{\partial^2}{\partial x^2} + \frac{\partial^2}{\partial y^2} - k_g^2 + \frac{\omega^2}{c^2}\right)\begin{bmatrix}\mathbf{E}_0\\ \mathbf{B}_0\end{bmatrix} e^{-i(\omega t - k_g z)} = 0 \tag{6.88}$$

If we define a *transverse Laplacian operator* according to

$$\nabla_t^2 \equiv \frac{\partial^2}{\partial x^2} + \frac{\partial^2}{\partial y^2} = \nabla^2 - \frac{\partial^2}{\partial z^2} \tag{6.89}$$

and if we note that

$$-k_g^2 + \frac{\omega^2}{c^2} = -k_g^2 + k_0^2 = k_c^2$$

then Eq. (6.88) becomes

$$(\nabla_t^2 + k_c^2)\begin{bmatrix}\mathbf{E}_0\\ \mathbf{B}_0\end{bmatrix} = 0 \tag{6.90}$$

Since **E** and **B** vary harmonically with time, Maxwell's equations in the vacuum of the pipe become

$$\left.\begin{aligned} \operatorname{div}\mathbf{E} &= 0; \qquad \mathbf{curl}\,\mathbf{E} = -\frac{1}{c}\frac{\partial \mathbf{B}}{\partial t} = ik_0\mathbf{B} \\ \operatorname{div}\mathbf{B} &= 0; \qquad \mathbf{curl}\,\mathbf{B} = \frac{1}{c}\frac{\partial \mathbf{E}}{\partial t} = -ik_0\mathbf{E} \end{aligned}\right\} \tag{6.91}$$

It is convenient to write **E** and **B** as sums of components parallel to and transverse to the axis of the pipe:

$$\left.\begin{aligned} \mathbf{E} &\equiv \mathbf{E}_z + \mathbf{E}_t \\ \mathbf{B} &\equiv \mathbf{B}_z + \mathbf{B}_t \end{aligned}\right\} \tag{6.92}$$

Thus,

$$\begin{bmatrix} \mathbf{E}_z \\ \mathbf{B}_z \end{bmatrix} = \mathbf{e}_z \begin{bmatrix} E_z^0(x, y) \\ B_z^0(x, y) \end{bmatrix} e^{-i(\omega t - k_g z)} \tag{6.93a}$$

$$\begin{aligned} \begin{bmatrix} \mathbf{E}_t \\ \mathbf{B}_t \end{bmatrix} &= \begin{bmatrix} \mathbf{E}_{t0}(x, y) \\ \mathbf{B}_{t0}(x, y) \end{bmatrix} e^{-i(\omega t - k_g z)} \\ &= \begin{bmatrix} \mathbf{e}_x E_x^0(x, y) + \mathbf{e}_y E_y^0(x, y) \\ \mathbf{e}_x B_x^0(x, y) + \mathbf{e}_y B_y^0(x, y) \end{bmatrix} e^{-i(\omega t - k_g z)} \end{aligned} \tag{6.93b}$$

Maxwell's equations may now be written as

$$\operatorname{div}\mathbf{E} = 0: \qquad \frac{\partial E_x^0}{\partial x} + \frac{\partial E_y^0}{\partial y} + ik_g E_z^0 = 0 \tag{6.94}$$

$$\operatorname{div}\mathbf{B} = 0: \qquad \frac{\partial B_x^0}{\partial x} + \frac{\partial B_y^0}{\partial y} + ik_g B_z^0 = 0 \tag{6.95}$$

$$\mathbf{curl}\,\mathbf{E} = ik_0\mathbf{B}: \qquad \frac{\partial E_z^0}{\partial y} - ik_g E_y^0 = ik_0 B_x^0 \tag{6.96a}$$

$$ik_g E_x^0 - \frac{\partial E_z^0}{\partial x} = ik_0 B_y^0 \tag{6.96b}$$

$$\frac{\partial E_y^0}{\partial x} - \frac{\partial E_x^0}{\partial y} = ik_0 B_z^0 \tag{6.96c}$$

$$\textbf{curl B} = -ik_0\mathbf{E}: \qquad \frac{\partial B_z^0}{\partial y} - ik_g B_y^0 = -ik_0 E_x^0 \tag{6.97a}$$

$$ik_g B_x^0 - \frac{\partial B_z^0}{\partial x} = -ik_0 E_y^0 \tag{6.97b}$$

$$\frac{\partial B_y^0}{\partial x} - \frac{\partial B_x^0}{\partial y} = -ik_0 E_z^0 \tag{6.97c}$$

If we solve Eqs. (6.96b) and (6.97a) for E_x^0, we find

$$E_x^0 = \frac{i}{k_c^2}\left(k_0 \frac{\partial B_z^0}{\partial y} + k_g \frac{\partial E_z^0}{\partial x}\right) \tag{6.98a}$$

where we have used $k_c^2 = k_0^2 - k_g^2$. Similarly, we may also solve for E_y^0 and for the transverse components of **B** with the results

$$E_y^0 = -\frac{i}{k_c^2}\left(k_0 \frac{\partial B_z^0}{\partial x} - k_g \frac{\partial E_z^0}{\partial y}\right) \tag{6.98b}$$

$$B_x^0 = -\frac{i}{k_c^2}\left(k_0 \frac{\partial E_z^0}{\partial y} - k_g \frac{\partial B_z^0}{\partial x}\right) \tag{6.98c}$$

$$B_y^0 = \frac{i}{k_c^2}\left(k_0 \frac{\partial E_z^0}{\partial x} + k_g \frac{\partial B_z^0}{\partial y}\right) \tag{6.98d}$$

This is a remarkable set of equations, for it indicates that all the *transverse* components of the field vectors are specified entirely in terms of the *longitudinal* components, $E_z^0(x, y)$ and $B_z^0(x, y)$. But notice that this result is valid only for $k_c \neq 0$; that is, $k_g \neq k_0$. Now, in order for the transverse field components to remain finite for $k_g = k_0$, Eqs. (6.98) indicate that each of the parentheses must vanish. The only way in which such a requirement can be met in general is for E_z^0 and B_z^0 to be constants. Such a solution does not represent wave propagation, so we may set $E_z^0 = 0 = B_z^0$ for $k_g = k_0$. We therefore conclude that the wave is TEM. (Notice that the argument may be inverted: if the wave is TEM so that the longitudinal field components vanish, then the transverse components remain finite only if $k_c = 0$.) In the event that $k_c = 0$ and the field is entirely transverse, then Eq. (6.90) for $\mathbf{E}_0$ becomes

$$\nabla_t^2 \mathbf{E}_0 = 0$$

That is, $\mathbf{E}_0$ satisfies the two-dimensional Laplace equation. We know that a quantity which satisfies such an equation can be represented as the gradient of a scalar potential function. But the conducting surface of the pipe is an equipotential, and therefore the potential is a constant, and the electric field vanishes inside the pipe. (See Property 1 of solutions of

Laplace's equation, Section 3.2.) Consequently, we conclude that TEM waves cannot be propagated in a hollow pipe.

The result obtained in the preceding paragraph is valid only in the event that the surface of the pipe is singly connected. If there are, instead, two or more bounding surfaces that are not connected (such as in a coaxial cable, a conducting wire inside a hollow conducting tube), then Laplace's equation can be satisfied with a nonvanishing electric field vector and TEM waves can be propagated inside such structures.

6.9 TE and TM Waves

Since TEM waves cannot be propagated in ordinary hollow conducting pipes, we turn our attention now exclusively to the allowed possibilities, TE and TM waves. We first consider the TE mode, in which $E_z^0 \equiv 0$, $B_z^0 \neq 0$. Equations (6.98) then become

$$\left.\begin{aligned} E_x^0 &= \frac{ik_0}{k_c^2}\frac{\partial B_z^0}{\partial y}; \qquad & E_y^0 &= -\frac{ik_0}{k_c^2}\frac{\partial B_z^0}{\partial x} \qquad (6.99a) \\ B_x^0 &= \frac{ik_g}{k_c^2}\frac{\partial B_z^0}{\partial x}; \qquad & B_y^0 &= \frac{ik_g}{k_c^2}\frac{\partial B_z^0}{\partial y} \qquad (6.99b) \end{aligned}\right\} \quad \text{TE}$$

From Eqs. (6.99b) we calculate

$$\begin{aligned} \mathbf{grad}\, B_z^0 &= \frac{\partial B_z^0}{\partial x}\mathbf{e}_x + \frac{\partial B_z^0}{\partial y}\mathbf{e}_y \\ &= \frac{k_c^2}{ik_g}(B_x^0\mathbf{e}_x + B_y^0\mathbf{e}_y) \end{aligned}$$

or,

$$\boxed{\mathbf{grad}\, B_z^0 = -\frac{ik_c^2}{k_g}\mathbf{B}_{t0}} \qquad \text{TE} \qquad (6.100)$$

If we set $E_z^0 = 0$ in Eqs. (6.96a) and (6.96b), we have

$$\left.\begin{aligned} B_x^0 &= -\frac{k_g}{k_0}E_y^0 \\ B_y^0 &= \frac{k_g}{k_0}E_x^0 \end{aligned}\right\} \qquad (6.101)$$

Using these relations, we may express $\mathbf{B}_{t0}$ as

$$\begin{aligned} \mathbf{B}_{t0} &= B_x^0\mathbf{e}_x + B_y^0\mathbf{e}_y \\ &= \frac{k_g}{k_0}(-E_y^0\mathbf{e}_x + E_x^0\mathbf{e}_y) \end{aligned}$$

or,

$$\boxed{\mathbf{B}_{t0} = \frac{k_g}{k_0}(\mathbf{e}_z \times \mathbf{E}_{t0})} \qquad \text{TE} \tag{6.102}$$

Similar relationships may be derived for the TM mode by setting $B_z^0 = 0$ in the corresponding equations. We then find

$$\mathbf{E}_{t0} = -\frac{k_g}{k_0}(\mathbf{e}_z \times \mathbf{B}_{t0}) \tag{6.103}$$

$$\text{TM}$$

$$\mathbf{grad}\, E_z^0 = -\frac{ik_c^2}{k_g}\mathbf{E}_{t0} \tag{6.104}$$

In the TE mode, $B_z^0(x, y)$ completely determines the field, whereas in the TM mode the field is determined by $E_z^0(x, y)$.† The functions $B_z^0(x, y)$ and $E_z^0(x, y)$ are obtained by applying the boundary conditions to solutions of the Helmholtz equations:

$$(\nabla_t^2 + k_c^2)B_z^0 = 0 \qquad \text{TE} \tag{6.105a}$$

$$(\nabla_t^2 + k_c^2)E_z^0 = 0 \qquad \text{TM} \tag{6.105b}$$

The boundary conditions to be satisfied are

$$\mathbf{E}_{\text{tangential}}\Big|_S = \mathbf{n} \times \mathbf{E}\Big|_S = 0; \qquad \mathbf{B}_{\text{normal}}\Big|_S = \mathbf{n} \cdot \mathbf{B}\Big|_S = 0 \tag{6.106a}$$

where $\mathbf{n}$ is unit normal at the surface of the conducting pipe. These conditions may alternatively be expressed as

$$E_z^0\Big|_S = 0; \qquad \mathbf{n} \cdot \mathbf{B}_{t0}\Big|_S = 0 \tag{6.106b}$$

For the TM mode, we need only to specify

$$\boxed{E_z^0\Big|_S = 0} \qquad \text{TM} \tag{6.107}$$

since the condition on the magnetic vector is automatically satisfied. To see this, we note that Eq. (6.103) may be written as‡

$$\mathbf{B}_{t0} = \frac{k_0}{k_g}(\mathbf{e}_z \times \mathbf{E}_{t0})$$

† Consequently, TM waves are sometimes called *E-waves* and TE waves are called *H-waves* (rather than *B-waves*).

‡ Take the vector product of $\mathbf{e}_z$ with Eq. (6.103) and then expand the triple vector product.

then,

$$\mathbf{n} \cdot \mathbf{B}_{t0}\Big|_S = \frac{k_0}{k_g}\mathbf{n} \cdot (\mathbf{e}_z \times \mathbf{E}_{t0})\Big|_S \equiv 0$$

which vanishes identically since $\mathbf{E}_{t0}$ *at the surface* is normal to the surface† and hence $\mathbf{e}_z \times \mathbf{E}_{t0}$ is parallel to the surface.

For the TE mode, $E_z^0 \equiv 0$, so that the boundary condition on the tangential component of the electric vector is automatically satisfied. According to Eq. (6.100), the condition $\mathbf{n} \cdot \mathbf{B}_{t0}|_S = 0$ is equivalent to

$$\mathbf{n} \cdot \mathbf{grad}\, B_z^0\Big|_S = 0$$

or,

$$\boxed{\frac{\partial B_z^0}{\partial n}\Big|_S = 0} \qquad \text{TE} \tag{6.108}$$

where $\partial/\partial n$ denotes the normal derivative.

6.10 Rectangular Wave Guides

The use of wave guides for the propagation of electromagnetic energy at microwave frequencies‡ is now a common practice.§ The systems most widely used employ either hollow cylindrical or rectangular pipes. We shall discuss here only the simpler case of rectangular geometry, as shown schematically in Fig. 6-10.

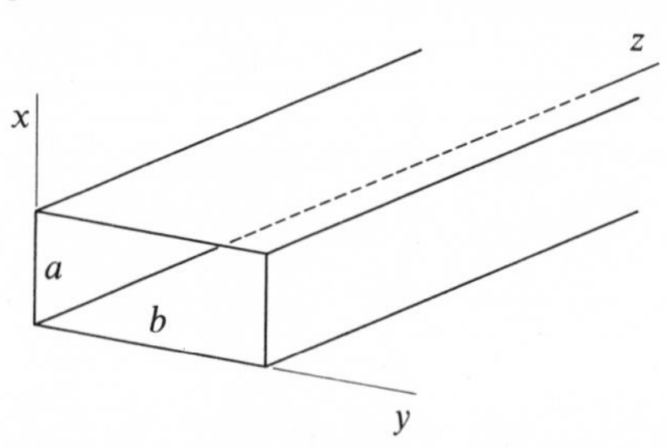

FIG. 6-10

† Because the surface is a perfect conductor.

‡ The microwave frequency range is from ≈ 3000 to ≈ 30,000 Mc/sec, corresponding to a free space wavelength range from ≈ 1 to ≈ 10 cm.

§ The first successful techniques were originated by George C. Southworth of the Bell Telephone Laboratories in the early 1930's. The theory was first discussed by Lord Rayleigh in 1897.

Consider the case of TE waves. The field is entirely determined by $B_z^0(x, y)$ which is a solution of

$$\left(\frac{\partial^2}{\partial x^2} + \frac{\partial^2}{\partial y^2} + k_c^2\right) B_z^0 = 0 \tag{6.109}$$

and subject to the boundary condition

$$\left.\frac{\partial B_z^0}{\partial n}\right|_S = 0$$

or,

$$\left.\frac{\partial B_z^0}{\partial x}\right|_{x=0,a} = 0; \qquad \left.\frac{\partial B_z^0}{\partial y}\right|_{y=0,b} = 0 \tag{6.110}$$

Such a solution is

$$B_z^0 = B^0 \cos\left(\frac{m\pi x}{a}\right) \cos\left(\frac{n\pi y}{b}\right) \tag{6.111}$$

with

$$k_c^2 = \pi^2\left(\frac{m^2}{a^2} + \frac{n^2}{b^2}\right) \tag{6.112}$$

The mode numbers m, n specify the cutoff frequency according to

$$\begin{aligned} \omega_{mn} &= ck_c \\ &= \pi c\sqrt{\frac{m^2}{a^2} + \frac{n^2}{b^2}} \end{aligned} \tag{6.113}$$

The mode corresponding to m, n is designated the TE_{mn} mode. The case $m = n = 0$ corresponds to the TEM situation discussed previously; therefore, the TE_{00} mode does not exist. If $a < b$, the lowest cutoff frequency results for $m = 0$, $n = 1$:

$$\omega_{01} = \frac{\pi c}{b}; \qquad k_c = \frac{\pi}{b} \tag{6.114}$$

The TE_{01} mode is called the *principal* or *dominant* mode. For any frequency of excitation ω, only those modes for which $\omega_{mn} < \omega$ will be propagated without attenuation. In practice it is frequently desirable to choose a wave guide with dimensions such that only the principal mode will be propagated at the operating frequency. Multimode operation is inefficient in several respects.

The field vector components are

$$\left.\begin{aligned} E_x^0 &= \frac{ik_0}{k_c^2}\frac{\partial B_z^0}{\partial y} = -i\frac{k_0 b}{\pi}B^0 \sin\left(\frac{\pi y}{b}\right) \\ E_y^0 &= 0; \qquad E_z^0 = 0; \qquad B_x^0 = 0 \\ B_y^0 &= \frac{ik_g}{k_c^2}\frac{\partial B_z^0}{\partial y} = -i\frac{k_g b}{\pi}B^0 \sin\left(\frac{\pi y}{b}\right) \\ B_z^0 &= B^0 \cos\left(\frac{\pi y}{b}\right) \end{aligned}\right\} \tag{6.115}$$

The complete space-time dependence of the field may be obtained by multiplying these components by $\exp[-i(\omega t - k_g z)]$. It is readily verified that the boundary conditions are all satisfied by Eqs. (6.115).

The energy flow in the wave guide may be obtained from

$$\langle \mathbf{S} \rangle = \frac{c}{8\pi}\,\mathrm{Re}(\mathbf{E} \times \mathbf{B}^*) \tag{6.116}$$

For the TE_{01} mode we have

$$\langle \mathbf{S} \rangle_{01} = \frac{c}{8\pi}\,\mathrm{Re}(-E_x^0 B_z^{0*}\mathbf{e}_y + E_x^0 B_y^{0*}\mathbf{e}_z)$$

But, according to Eqs. (6.115), $E_x^0 B_z^{0*}$ is purely imaginary so that the real part of this term vanishes. Thus,

$$\langle \mathbf{S} \rangle_{01} = \mathbf{e}_z \frac{c}{8\pi}\left(\frac{b}{\pi}B^0\right)^2 k_0 k_g \sin^2\left(\frac{\pi y}{b}\right) \tag{6.117}$$

The total transmitted power may be obtained by integrating this expression from $y = 0$ to $y = b$.

Some of the magnetic field lines in the median plane of a wave guide are shown in Fig. 6-11 for the TE_{01} mode. On the projected plane, some of the electric field lines for $y = b/2$ are indicated. Notice that the electric field (which has only an x component) is strongest at the positions where the magnetic field is almost entirely in the y-direction; the Poynting vector therefore lies predominantly in the z-direction, indicating energy flow down the guide. The *time average* of the Poynting vector lies entirely in the z-direction [Eq. (6.117)].

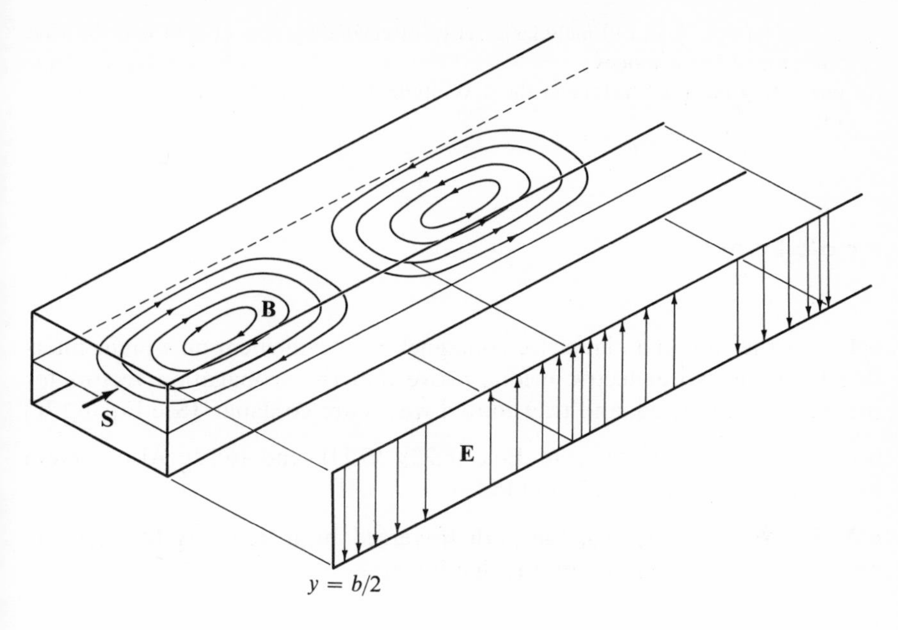

FIG. 6-11

Suggested References

The subject of reflection and refraction is treated in almost every text on electromagnetism or optics. A rather complete discussion at the intermediate level is contained in Corson and Lorrain (Co62, Chapter 11); more advanced coverage is that of Stratton (St41, Chapter 9) and of Landau and Lifshitz (La60, Chapter 10).

From the optics standpoint, detailed treatments are given by Born and Wolf (Bo59, Chapters 1, 3), Ditchburn (Di 62, Chapter 14), Jenkins and White (Je57, Chapter 25), Sommerfeld (So54, Chapter 1), and Vašíček (Va60, Chapter 2).

Discussions of a less comprehensive nature are those of Blass (Bl62, Chapter 31), Jackson (Ja62, Chapter 7), Panofsky and Phillips (Pa60, Chapter 11), Rossi (Ro57, Chapter 8), Stone (St63, Chapter 16), Tralli (Tr63, Chapter 11), and Wangsness (Wa63, Chapter 29).

The optics of metals is discussed in detail by Born and Wolf (Bo59, Chapter 13), Stratton (St41, Chapter 9), and Vašíček (Va60, Chapter 5).

Wave guide theory is given an intermediate treatment by Corson and Lorrain (Co62, Chapter 12), Holt (Ho63, Chapter 22), Skilling (Sk48, Chapter 13), Slater (Sl42, Chapter 3), Slater and Frank (Sl47, Chapter 11), and Wangsness (Wa63, Chapter 30). More advanced is the account of Jackson (Ja62, Chapter 8). A variety of electrical engineering texts treat wave guides in detail; see, for example, Plonsey and Collin (Pl61, Chapter 10) and Southworth (So50); the treatment by Ramo and Whinnery

(Ra44, Chapters 8 and 9) includes a series of clear diagrams of field lines in wave guides for different modes.

An interesting personal history of the development of wave guides is given by Southworth (So62).

Problems

6-1. For the case of a plane electromagnetic wave incident on a plane interface between two dielectric media, prove that the propagation vectors for the incident, reflected, and transmitted waves are coplanar. [See Eq. (6.17).]

6-2. Obtain Eqs. (6.25) from Eqs. (6.23), (6.24), and (6.19). Also, obtain Eqs. (6.28) from Eqs. (6.27) and (6.19).

6-3. The *optical length* of the path traversed by a light ray between the points P and Q is defined by the line integral

$$L = \int_P^Q n\,ds$$

where n is the index of refraction and may be a function of position. *Fermat's principle* states that the actual path followed by a light ray is that path for which the variation of L vanishes; i.e., $\delta L = 0$. Consider a light ray which originates at P in a medium with index of refraction n_1 and travels to point Q in another medium with index of refraction n_2. Let the x-y plane be the boundary between the media, and let the actual path of the ray pass through the origin. Show that if the varied path passes, not through the origin, but through the point $(\delta x, \delta y, 0)$, then the application of Fermat's principle results in Snell's law.

6-4. A beam of light is incident normally from air ($n_1 = 1$) on a plane slab of a transparent dielectric material with index of refraction n_2 and of thickness t. The light passes through the slab and enters a third medium with index of refraction n_3 and of infinite extent. Calculate the reflection coefficient R as a function of the thickness t for monochromatic light of wavelength λ_0. Plot R as a function of t for $n_3 = 1.5$ and $n_2 = 1.0$, 1.2, and 3.0. Suggest an application of these results in the design of optical instruments.

6-5. A plane electromagnetic wave is incident normally on the interface between two dielectric media. Find the condition on the indices of refraction that yields equal transmitted and reflected intensities.

6-6. A plane electromagnetic wave is incident from a dielectric medium whose index of refraction is n_1 and is reflected at the boundary of a medium whose index of refraction is slightly smaller than n_1; i.e., $n_2 = n_1(1 - \beta)$ where $\beta \ll 1$. Show that the reflection coefficients $R_\perp$ and $R_\parallel$ are both approximately

$$R_\perp \cong R_\parallel \cong \frac{1 - \sqrt{1 - 2\beta \tan^2 \theta_0}}{1 + \sqrt{1 - 2\beta \tan^2 \theta_0}}$$

6-7. A plane electromagnetic wave is incident from air ($n = 1$) at almost grazing incidence ($\theta_0 \cong \pi/2$) on a dielectric medium whose dielectric constant ε is almost unity. Show that $R_\perp$ and $R_\parallel$ are approximately equal and are given by

$$R_\perp \cong R_\parallel \cong \frac{\frac{\pi}{2} - \theta_0 - \sqrt{\frac{\pi}{2} - \theta_0 + (\varepsilon - 1)}}{(\varepsilon - 1)^2}$$

6-8. Derive the expressions for $R_\perp$ and $R_\parallel$ in the event that the reflecting medium has both ε and μ different from unity. Show that

$$\begin{pmatrix} R_\parallel \\ R_\perp \end{pmatrix} = \left| \frac{\mu \cos \theta_0 \pm \varepsilon\mu - \sin^2 \theta_0}{\mu \cos \theta_0 + \varepsilon\mu - \sin^2 \theta_0} \right|^2$$

6-9. Near the angle of total internal reflection, both $R_\perp$ and $R_\parallel$ approach unity. Find the functional form of this approach to unity; i.e., find $R = R(\theta)$ for $\theta \to \theta_c$.

6-10. A plane electromagnetic wave is incident normally on a slab of dielectric material. The back surface of the dielectric is in contact with a perfect conductor. Find the conditions under which there will be no multiple reflections within the dielectric.

6-11. An electromagnetic wave is incident on a slab of dielectric material which has parallel surfaces. If the wave is incident on the front surface at Brewster's angle, show that the refracted wave is incident on the rear surface at Brewster's angle also.

6-12. Construct a diagram similar to Fig. 6-5 for the case in which the wave is incident from the medium of greater optical density.

6-13. Consider an electromagnetic wave that is totally reflected at the boundary between two media. Calculate the time-averaged Poynting vector *along* the interface and just inside the second medium (i.e., calculate $\langle \mathbf{S}_2 \rangle \times \mathbf{n}$), and show that energy is propagated along the bounding surface.

6-14. A 100-kc/sec electromagnetic wave is incident normally on a sheet of copper which is 0.1 mm thick. Show that the amount of reflected energy is large compared to that which is lost in the Joule heating of the sheet. (The conductivity of copper is approximately 5.14×10^{17} sec^{-1}; the skin depth is given in Table 5.1, Section 5.7.)

6-15. Show that upon reflection at normal incidence from the surface of a conducting medium the electric vector undergoes a phase change ϕ which is given by

$$\tan \phi = \frac{2n\kappa}{n^2 - 1 + n^2\kappa^2}$$

where the index of refraction of the conductor is $\hat{n} = n(1 + i\kappa)$. Show that this result yields a phase change of π in the event that the medium is a perfect conductor.

6-16. For the case of an electromagnetic wave refracted at the surface of a metal, express the propagation constant k_2 in terms of the conductivity σ of the medium and the frequency ω of the incident wave. (Refer to Case 2 in Section 5.6.) Show that as the conductivity becomes extremely large or as the frequency approaches zero, $\theta_2 \to 0$ independent of the value of θ_0, so that the wave propagates normal to the surface and with the planes of constant amplitude and constant phase coinciding.

6-17. A plane electromagnetic wave is incident at an angle θ_0 on a plane conductor of conductivity σ ($\varepsilon = 1$, $\mu = 1$). Calculate the reduction in amplitude of the wave upon reflection. (Assume the conductivity to be large, but not infinite.)

6-18. Show that for TM waves propagating in a wave guide the surface currents are *longitudinal.*

6-19. Investigate the propagation of TM waves in a rectangular wave guide. Obtain expressions for the field quantities. Show that the principal mode is TM_{11} and find the ratio of the cutoff frequency in this mode to that for a TE_{01} wave propagating in the same wave guide.

6-20. Calculate the electric and magnetic energy densities in guided TE and TM waves. Compare the results and explain the difference.

6-21. Consider a rectangular wave guide in which is propagating a TE_{01} wave. Obtain an expression for the maximum power that can be transmitted if an electric field strength E_0 can be supported in the wave guide. If the wave guide has dimensions of 2.5×5.0 cm and if a field strength of 30,000 V/cm is possible, what is the maximum power that can be transmitted? Choose a frequency equal to the cutoff frequency of the next higher mode (i.e., the highest possible frequency for which only TE_{01} waves are propagated). (Note that conversion from volts/cm to statvolts/cm is necessary for this calculation.)

6-22. Consider a cylindrical coaxial line which consists of an outer (perfect) conductor of radius a and an inner (perfect) conductor of radius b. Show that TEM waves can be propagated in such a structure if the transverse electric field varies inversely with r, the distance from the axis of symmetry. Find the necessary potential difference between the outer and inner conductors. Find also the form of the magnetic induction vector.

6-23. Consider a closed cylindrical cavity of length l and radius a; the walls are perfect conductors. Obtain an expression for the frequencies of the allowed modes of standing electromagnetic waves within the cavity. (Set up Laplace's equation in cylindrical coordinates and obtain solutions in terms of Bessel functions. The mode frequencies depend on the roots of the Bessel functions.) Show that the lowest TE mode has the frequency

$$1.841(c/a)[1 + 2.912(a/l)^2]^{1/2}$$

CHAPTER 7

The Liénard-Wiechert Potentials and Radiation

7.1 Introduction

In this chapter we shall be concerned with the ultimate sources of all electromagnetic radiation, viz., moving charges. We shall find that radiation can be produced only if a charge undergoes acceleration. There are many interesting applications of accelerating charges—the production of X-rays, the acceleration of charged particles to velocities approaching the velocity of light, the radiation from antennas, etc. We shall study the radiation fields associated with these processes and will find a close similarity in the results. In Chapter 13 some of the results obtained here will be derived from the standpoint of relativity theory.

7.2 Retarded Potentials

We found in Section 4.6 that the scalar and vector potentials could be calculated from the expressions [cf. Eqs. (4.38) and (4.39)]

$$\Phi(\mathbf{r}) = \frac{1}{\varepsilon}\int_V \frac{\rho(\mathbf{r}')}{|\mathbf{r} - \mathbf{r}'|}\, dv'$$

$$\mathbf{A}(\mathbf{r}) = \frac{\mu}{c}\int_V \frac{\mathbf{J}(\mathbf{r}')}{|\mathbf{r} - \mathbf{r}'|}\,dv'$$

where ε and μ have been assumed constant throughout the volume V. In these equations we have explicitly indicated that the potentials are to be computed at a position designated by the radius vector $\mathbf{r}$ by integrating ρ and $\mathbf{J}$ throughout V by considering these quantities to be functions of the radius vector of integration $\mathbf{r}'$. The distance between the integration point $\mathbf{r}'$ and the point at which Φ and $\mathbf{A}$ are computed is $|\mathbf{r} - \mathbf{r}'|$, and dv' is the volume element at $\mathbf{r}'$.

The expression above for the scalar potential is correct if the charges are at rest. Similarly, if the currents are steady, the equation for the vector potential is valid. However, as soon as we allow the charges the freedom of motion or permit the currents to have a time dependence, a difficulty arises. Consider the calculation of the scalar potential at a position $\mathbf{r}$ and at a time t. We cannot compute $\Phi(\mathbf{r}, t)$ by integrating $\rho(\mathbf{r}', t)$ if the charges are in arbitrary motion since the electric fields associated with the charges propagate with the finite velocity c. Therefore, in order to calculate the potential at a given point and at a time t, we must know the positions of the charges, not at time t, but at previous times $t - |\mathbf{r} - \mathbf{r}'|/c$ which correspond to the times at which the electric fields must have been propagated from the charges at positions denoted by $\mathbf{r}'$ in order to arrive at $\mathbf{r}$ at the time t. Thus, the calculations of the individual fields must be performed at *retarded times*:

$$\text{Retarded time} = t - \frac{|\mathbf{r} - \mathbf{r}'|}{c} \tag{7.1}$$

Therefore, in the general case, we must modify the expressions for Φ and $\mathbf{A}$ to read*

$$\Phi(\mathbf{r}, t) = \int_V \frac{\rho(\mathbf{r}', t - |\mathbf{r} - \mathbf{r}'|/c)}{|\mathbf{r} - \mathbf{r}'|}\,dv' \tag{7.2}$$

$$\mathbf{A}(\mathbf{r}, t) = \frac{1}{c}\int_V \frac{\mathbf{J}(\mathbf{r}', t - |\mathbf{r} - \mathbf{r}'|/c)}{|\mathbf{r} - \mathbf{r}'|}\,dv' \tag{7.3}$$

where we have set $\varepsilon = 1$, $\mu = 1$ for the case of free space.† These potentials are called the *retarded potentials*; in the integrands for these potentials, $\rho(\mathbf{r}')$ and $\mathbf{J}(\mathbf{r}')$ are to be evaluated at the *retarded times* $t - |\mathbf{r} - \mathbf{r}'|/c$, where $\mathbf{r}'$ is *the radius vector at the retarded time.*

* Riemann suggested in 1858 that the potentials should be calculated by the retarded formulae, but Ludwig Lorenz (1829–1891) was the first to give a comprehensive treatment based on the retarded potentials (1867).

† For the remainder of this chapter and for the following chapter we consider only the free space situation.

We have argued on physical grounds that the potentials given by Eqs. (7.2) and (7.3) are the correct forms. We shall now prove that these potentials are indeed the solutions to the *inhomogeneous wave equations* for the potentials [cf. Eqs. (4.34) and 4.35)]. It will be sufficient to do this for Φ since the proof for $\mathbf{A}$ is entirely analogous.

The inhomogeneous wave equation for Φ is

$$\nabla^2\Phi - \frac{1}{c^2}\frac{\partial^2\Phi}{\partial t^2} = -4\pi\rho \tag{7.4}$$

We divide into two regions the volume V over which the integration in Eq. (7.2) is carried out:

$$V = V_1 + V_2$$

where V_1 is a small volume surrounding the point described by the radius vector $\mathbf{r}$; i.e., V_1 surrounds the point at which the potential is to be measured (the *observation point* or *field point*). The potential Φ is therefore composed of two parts,

$$\Phi = \Phi_1 + \Phi_2 \tag{7.5}$$

where

$$\Phi_i(\mathbf{r}, t) = \int_{V_i} \frac{\rho(\mathbf{r}', t - R'/c)}{R'}\, dv' \tag{7.6}$$

in which we have made the substitution

$$\mathbf{R}' \equiv \mathbf{r} - \mathbf{r}'; \qquad R' = |\mathbf{R}'| \tag{7.7}$$

The distance R', of course, is a function of t'.

We require that the volume V_1 be sufficiently small so that we may neglect the retardation effect for all points within V_1. (We shall eventually let $V_1 \to 0$.) Thus,

$$\rho(\mathbf{r}', t - R'/c) \to \rho(\mathbf{r}', t), \qquad \text{within } V_1$$

Therefore, Φ_1 becomes

$$\Phi_1(\mathbf{r}, t) = \int_{V_1} \frac{\rho(\mathbf{r}', t)}{R'}\, dv' \tag{7.8}$$

Since this expression is identical with that for the static case, we know [see Eqs. (1.9) and (1.13)] that Φ_1 is a solution of Poisson's equation:

$$\nabla^2\Phi_1(\mathbf{r}, t) = -4\pi\rho(\mathbf{r}, t) \tag{7.9}$$

The Laplacian of ρ/R' is (since $R' > 0$)

$$\nabla^2\left(\frac{\rho}{R'}\right) = \frac{1}{R'^2}\frac{\partial}{\partial R'}\left[R'^2\frac{\partial}{\partial R'}\left(\frac{\rho}{R'}\right)\right]$$

$$= \frac{1}{R'}\frac{\partial^2\rho}{\partial R'^2} \tag{7.10}$$

Therefore,

$$\nabla^2\Phi_2(\mathbf{r}, t) = \int_{V_2} \nabla^2\left\{\frac{\rho(\mathbf{r}', t - R'/c)}{R'}\right\} dv'$$

$$= \int_{V_2} \frac{1}{R'}\frac{\partial^2}{\partial R'^2}\rho(\mathbf{r}', t - R'/c)\, dv' \tag{7.11}$$

Now, an arbitrary function of the variable $t - R'/c$ is a solution of the one-dimensional wave equation [see Eq. (5.4)]. The charge density $\rho = \rho(\mathbf{r}', t - R'/c)$ is such a function, so we may write

$$\frac{\partial^2\rho}{\partial R'^2} - \frac{1}{c^2}\frac{\partial^2\rho}{\partial t^2} = 0 \tag{7.12}$$

Substituting for $\partial^2\rho/\partial R'^2$ in Eq. (7.11), we obtain

$$\nabla^2\Phi_2(\mathbf{r}, t) = \frac{1}{c^2}\int_{V_2} \frac{1}{R'}\frac{\partial^2}{\partial t^2}\rho(\mathbf{r}', t - R'/c)\, dv' \tag{7.13}$$

Interchanging the space and time derivatives, we have

$$\nabla^2\Phi_2(\mathbf{r}, t) = \frac{1}{c^2}\frac{\partial^2}{\partial t^2}\int_{V_2} \frac{\rho(\mathbf{r}', t - R'/c)}{R'}\, dv' \tag{7.14}$$

The integral in this equation would just be $\Phi(\mathbf{r}, t)$ if we let $V_1 \to 0$ so that $V_2 \to V$. Therefore, in this limit,

$$\nabla^2\Phi_2(\mathbf{r}, t) = \frac{1}{c^2}\frac{\partial^2\Phi}{\partial t^2} \tag{7.15}$$

Adding Eqs. (7.9) and (7.15), we obtain

$$\nabla^2\Phi = \nabla^2(\Phi_1 + \Phi_2) = \frac{1}{c^2}\frac{\partial^2\Phi}{\partial t^2} - 4\pi\rho \tag{7.16}$$

Thus, the proof is complete and the retarded potential is shown to be a solution of the inhomogeneous wave equation.*

* This result was first obtained in 1858 by the German mathematician Georg Friedrich Bernhard Riemann (1826–1866).

It should be noted that we chose the solution of the one-dimensional wave equation (7.12) to be $\rho(\mathbf{r}', t - R'/c)$; an equally acceptable solution is $\rho(\mathbf{r}', t + R'/c)$ [see Eq. (5.4)]. Therefore, the scalar potential

$$\Phi'(\mathbf{r}, t) = \int_V \frac{\rho(\mathbf{r}', t + R'/c)}{R'} dv' \tag{7.17}$$

is also a solution of the inhomogeneous wave equation. This so-called *advanced potential* appears to have no physical significance* since it corresponds to an anticipation of the charge distribution (and current distribution for the case of the vector potential) at a future time. Such a potential does not satisfy the requirement that causality must be obeyed by physical systems.

For the remainder of this chapter, if a quantity is to be evaluated at the retarded time, $t - R'/c$, we shall frequently enclose this quantity in square brackets in order to shorten the notation. Thus,

$$\rho(\mathbf{r}', t - R'/c) \equiv [\rho(\mathbf{r}')] \tag{7.18}$$

The potentials may therefore be written as

$$\Phi(\mathbf{r}, t) = \int_V \frac{[\rho(\mathbf{r}')]}{R'} dv' \tag{7.19}$$

$$\mathbf{A}(\mathbf{r}, t) = \frac{1}{c}\int_V \frac{[\mathbf{J}(\mathbf{r}')]}{R'} dv' \tag{7.20}$$

7.3 The Liénard-Wiechert Potentials

We wish ultimately to be able to calculate the electric and magnetic field vectors for charges which are in arbitrary motion. To do this we may use the potential functions Φ and $\mathbf{A}$. But in order to perform the integrations indicated in Eqs. (7.19) and (7.20) we must know the details of the motion of the charges since the calculations depend upon the positions and the velocities of the charges at the retarded time $t - R'/c$. Let us consider for simplicity a single particle (in fact, a *point* particle) carrying a charge e which undergoes an arbitrary motion having a trajectory described by a radius vector $\mathbf{r}_e(t')$ as in Fig. 7-1. The calculation of the potential according to Eq. (7.19) requires a retarded-time integration over the entire volume containing charge that contributes to the potential Φ. For a single, point charge e we may express the retarded-time calculation in terms of a delta-function:

$$\Phi(\mathbf{r}, t) = e\int_{-\infty}^{+\infty} \frac{\delta(t' - t + |\mathbf{r} - \mathbf{r}_e|/c)}{|\mathbf{r} - \mathbf{r}_e|} dt' \tag{7.21}$$

* See, however, J. A. Wheeler and R. P. Feynman, *Revs. Modern Phys.* **17**, 157 (1945).

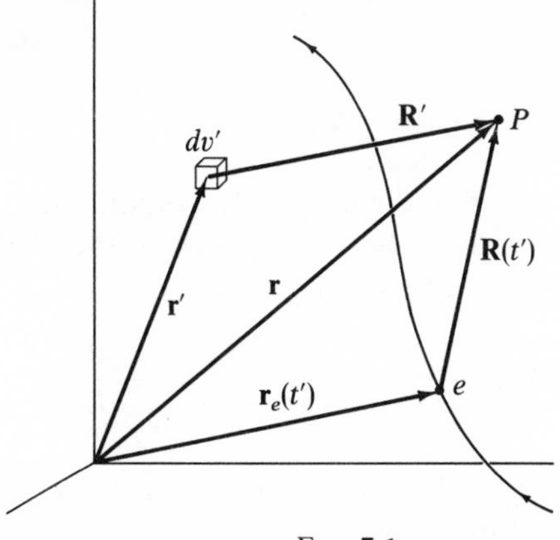

FIG. 7-1

In order to evaluate this integral we make a change of variable so that the integration variable is the same as the argument of the delta function. The integral is then just the value of the integrand taken at the time that is allowed by the delta function. It should be emphasized that the variable change is necessary because the vector $\mathbf{r}_e$ which describes the path of the charged particle is a function of the time variable, i.e., $\mathbf{r}_e = \mathbf{r}_e(t')$. Therefore, the integral that appears in Eq. (7.21) cannot yet be evaluated. We define a new variable t'' to be equal to the argument of the delta function:

$$t'' \equiv t' - t + \frac{|\mathbf{r} - \mathbf{r}_e(t')|}{c} \tag{7.22}$$

If we differentiate this expression and recall that $dt = 0$ since t is the fixed time of observation, we have

$$dt'' = dt' \left\{1 + \frac{1}{c}\frac{d}{dt'}|\mathbf{r} - \mathbf{r}_e(t')|\right\} \tag{7.23}$$

The quantity $|\mathbf{r} - \mathbf{r}_e|$ is just

$$|\mathbf{r} - \mathbf{r}_e| = \sqrt{\sum_i (x_i - x_{e,i})^2} \tag{7.24}$$

where $x_{e,i} = x_{e,i}(t')$ and where the x_i are *fixed* since they represent the coordinates of the fixed observation point. We note that although $|\mathbf{r} - \mathbf{r}_e|$ is a function of t', it is only an *implicit* dependence through the $x_{e,i}(t')$ which are *explicit* functions of t'. The derivative of $|\mathbf{r} - \mathbf{r}_e|/c$ with respect to t' is

$$\frac{1}{c}\frac{d}{dt'}|\mathbf{r} - \mathbf{r}_e| = \frac{1}{c}\sum_i \left(\frac{\partial}{\partial x_{e,i}}|\mathbf{r} - \mathbf{r}_e|\right)\frac{dx_{e,i}}{dt'} \tag{7.25}$$

which we may write as

$$\frac{1}{c}\frac{d}{dt'}|\mathbf{r} - \mathbf{r}_e| = \frac{1}{c}(\mathbf{grad}_{\mathbf{r}_e}|\mathbf{r} - \mathbf{r}_e|) \cdot \frac{d\mathbf{r}_e}{dt'} \tag{7.25a}$$

where the subscript $\mathbf{r}_e$ on the gradient operator signifies that the derivatives are to be taken with respect to the coordinates of the charge. Hence, the gradient operation may be expressed as

$$\mathbf{grad}_{\mathbf{r}_e}|\mathbf{r} - \mathbf{r}_e| = -\frac{\mathbf{r} - \mathbf{r}_e}{|\mathbf{r} - \mathbf{r}_e|} = -\frac{\mathbf{R}}{R} \tag{7.26}$$

Now, the derivative of $\mathbf{r}_e$ with respect to t' is just the velocity $\mathbf{u}$. If we define $\boldsymbol{\beta} \equiv \mathbf{u}/c$, Eq. (7.25a) becomes

$$\frac{1}{c}\frac{d}{dt'}|\mathbf{r} - \mathbf{r}_e| = -\frac{\boldsymbol{\beta} \cdot \mathbf{R}}{R} \tag{7.27}$$

Therefore,

$$\begin{aligned} dt'' &= dt' \left\{1 + \frac{1}{c}\frac{d}{dt'}|\mathbf{r} - \mathbf{r}_e|\right\} \\ &= dt' \left\{1 + \frac{1}{c}(\mathbf{grad}_{\mathbf{r}_e}|\mathbf{r} - \mathbf{r}_e|) \cdot \frac{d\mathbf{r}_e}{dt'}\right\} \\ &= dt' \left(1 - \frac{\boldsymbol{\beta} \cdot \mathbf{R}}{R}\right) \end{aligned}$$

or,

$$dt' = \frac{R}{R - \boldsymbol{\beta} \cdot \mathbf{R}} dt'' \tag{7.28}$$

With the change of variable defined by Eq. (7.22), the equation for $\Phi(\mathbf{r}, t)$ becomes

$$\Phi(\mathbf{r}, t) = e\int_{-\infty}^{+\infty} \frac{\delta(t'')}{R(t')}\left(\frac{R(t')}{R(t') - \boldsymbol{\beta}(t') \cdot \mathbf{R}(t')}\right) dt'' \tag{7.29}$$

Having accomplished the desired variable change to render the argument of the delta function identical to the integration variable, we have immediately

$$\Phi(\mathbf{r}, t) = \left.\frac{e}{R(t') - \boldsymbol{\beta}(t') \cdot \mathbf{R}(t')}\right|_{t''=0}$$

But $t'' = 0$ implies $t' = t - R(t')/c$, the retarded time. Thus,

$$\boxed{\Phi(\mathbf{r}, t) = \frac{e}{[R - \boldsymbol{\beta} \cdot \mathbf{R}]}} \tag{7.30}$$

Since the current density $\mathbf{J}$ is just equal to the charge density multiplied by the velocity, an analogous calculation can be carried out for $\mathbf{A}$ and we find that vector potential is just $\mathbf{u}/c$, or $\boldsymbol{\beta}$, times the scalar potential:

$$\boxed{\mathbf{A}(\mathbf{r}, t) = \frac{e[\boldsymbol{\beta}]}{[R - \boldsymbol{\beta} \cdot \mathbf{R}]}} \tag{7.31}$$

Equations (7.30) and (7.31) for $\Phi(\mathbf{r}, t)$ and $\mathbf{A}(\mathbf{r}, t)$, which explicitly exhibit the dependence of the potentials on the velocity of the particle, are called the *Liénard-Wiechert potentials.**

We may write the Liénard-Wiechert potentials in even more compact notation if we define

$$\left.\begin{aligned} K(t') &\equiv R(t') - \boldsymbol{\beta}(t') \cdot \mathbf{R}(t') \\ [K] &= [R - \boldsymbol{\beta} \cdot \mathbf{R}] \end{aligned}\right\} \tag{7.32}$$

Then, for a point charge,

$$\Phi(\mathbf{r}, t) = \frac{e}{[K]} \tag{7.33a}$$

$$\mathbf{A}(\mathbf{r}, t) = e\left[\frac{\boldsymbol{\beta}}{K}\right] \tag{7.33b}$$

We may gain some physical insight concerning the form of the Liénard-Wiechert potentials for moving charges by appealing to the following argument.† Let us consider the calculation of the potential Φ at some point P at some definite time t. In order to collect all of the information necessary to compute the potential, we use the following device. We surround the point P with a spherical shell of radius R', sufficiently large to include all the charge for which we desire the potential. Next, at the time $t - R'/c$, we allow the shell to start to collapse with a velocity c. As

* A. Liénard, 1898; and E. Wiechert, 1900.

† This discussion follows closely the elegant argument given by Panofsky and Phillips (Pa60, Chapter 18).

the collapsing shell sweeps through the charge distribution we gather information regarding the charge density. The shell will collapse to the point P at the time t and will have gathered all of the information necessary to compute $\Phi(P, t)$. For stationary charges, this method just yields Eq. (7.19). However, if the charge distribution has a net *outward* (inward) velocity, the volume integral measured by the collapsing sphere will yield a result that is *smaller* (larger) than the total charge of the system.

Consider a small amount of charge dq that is distributed uniformly with a charge density ρ throughout a volume element dv'. Let $\mathbf{R}$ be the vector from dv' to P. If the charge dq is stationary, the amount of charge that the spherical shell will cross as it contracts by an amount dR in a time dt is $[\rho]\, da\, dr = [\rho]\, dv'$. On the other hand, if the charge moves with a velocity $\mathbf{u}$, the amount of charge crossed by the spherical shell will be reduced to

$$dq = [\rho]\, dv' - [\rho]\frac{\mathbf{u}\cdot\mathbf{R}}{R}\, da\, dt$$

(If $\mathbf{u}$ is directed *outward*, then $\mathbf{u}\cdot\mathbf{R}$ is negative, and dq is *larger* than $[\rho]\, dv'$.) Now, $dv' = da\, dR$ and $R = ct$, so that

$$da\, dt = \left(\frac{dv'}{dR}\right)\left(\frac{dR}{c}\right) = \frac{dv'}{c}$$

Hence,

$$\frac{[\rho]}{R}\, dv' = \frac{dq}{R - \boldsymbol{\beta}\cdot\mathbf{R}}$$

where $\boldsymbol{\beta} = \mathbf{u}/c$. According to Eq. (7.19), we now have

$$\Phi = \int_V \frac{dq}{R - \boldsymbol{\beta}\cdot\mathbf{R}} \tag{7.34}$$

If the small charge distribution contains a total charge e that is confined to a small volume V, we can perform the integral by neglecting the variation of the denominator, with the result

$$\Phi = \frac{e}{[R - \boldsymbol{\beta}\cdot\mathbf{R}]}$$

which is just Eq. (7.30). A similar argument for $\mathbf{A}$ yields Eq. (7.31).

Notice, particularly in Eq. (7.34), that R, $\boldsymbol{\beta}$, and $\mathbf{R}$ are all functions of t'; that these quantities must be evaluated at the retarded time is explicitly indicated in the final expression by using the square-bracket notation.

In all of the preceding discussion we have been rather casual regarding *point charges*. Although it is clear that a "point charge" is a meaningless concept, the potentials derived by appealing to this idea are in fact correct. All that is required to obtain Φ for a moving, isolated charge by evaluating the integral in Eq. (7.34) is that the quantity $R - \boldsymbol{\beta}\cdot\mathbf{R}$ have a negligible variation over the spatial extent of the charge e.

7.4 The Field Produced by a Moving Charged Particle

We have thus far obtained the potentials for the electromagnetic field produced by a charged particle undergoing arbitrary motion in free space. The field vectors themselves must be calculated from [see Eqs. (4.22) and (4.20)]

$$\left.\begin{aligned} \mathbf{E} &= -\,\mathbf{grad}\,\Phi - \frac{1}{c}\frac{\partial\mathbf{A}}{\partial t} \\ \mathbf{B} &= \mathbf{curl}\,\mathbf{A} \end{aligned}\right\} \tag{7.35}$$

Since the time derivative of $\mathbf{A}$, and hence of $\boldsymbol{\beta}$, is involved, it is clear that the field vectors will be functions not only of the velocity $\mathbf{u}$, but also of the acceleration $\mathbf{a} = \partial\mathbf{u}/\partial t'$. We may therefore separate $\mathbf{E}$ and $\mathbf{B}$ into two components each, one which involves the acceleration and goes to zero for $\mathbf{a} = 0$, and one which involves only the velocity and yields the static field for a point charge having $\mathbf{u} = 0$:

$$\left.\begin{aligned} \mathbf{E} &= \mathbf{E}_v + \mathbf{E}_a \\ \mathbf{B} &= \mathbf{B}_v + \mathbf{B}_a \end{aligned}\right\} \tag{7.36}$$

$\mathbf{E}_v$ and $\mathbf{B}_v$ are called the *velocity fields* and $\mathbf{E}_a$ and $\mathbf{B}_a$ are called the *acceleration fields*.

The calculation of these field vectors* is complicated, although straightforward if proper consideration is given to the operations indicated in Eqs. (7.35). We give here only the results:

$$\mathbf{E}_v = \left[\frac{e}{K^3}(\mathbf{R} - R\boldsymbol{\beta})(1 - \beta^2)\right] \tag{7.37a}$$

$$\mathbf{E}_a = \left[\frac{e}{c^2K^3}(\mathbf{R}\cdot\mathbf{a})(\mathbf{R} - R\boldsymbol{\beta}) - \frac{e}{c^2K^2}R\mathbf{a}\right] \tag{7.37b}$$

$$\mathbf{B}_v = \left[\frac{e}{K^3}(\boldsymbol{\beta}\times\mathbf{R})(1 - \beta^2)\right] \tag{7.37c}$$

* See, for example, Landau and Lifshitz (La62, Chapter 8), Panofsky and Phillips (Pa60, Chapter 20), or Tralli (Tr63, Chapter 17).

$$\mathbf{B}_a = \left[\frac{e}{c^2K^3}(\mathbf{R}\cdot\mathbf{a})(\boldsymbol{\beta}\times\mathbf{R}) + \frac{e}{c^2K^2}(\mathbf{a}\times\mathbf{R})\right] \tag{7.37d}$$

From these equations it is apparent that the static limit (i.e., $\boldsymbol{\beta} = 0$, $\mathbf{a} = 0$) is satisfied, since

$$\begin{aligned}\mathbf{E}\text{ (static)} &= \mathbf{E}_v\text{ (static)} + \mathbf{E}_a\text{ (static)}\\ &= \frac{e\mathbf{R}}{K^3_{\text{static}}} + 0\\ &= \frac{e\mathbf{R}}{R^3}\end{aligned} \tag{7.38a}$$

$$\mathbf{B}\text{(static)} = 0 \tag{7.38b}$$

which are the appropriate equations. We also note that

$$\mathbf{B} = [\mathbf{n}] \times \mathbf{E} \tag{7.39}$$

where $\mathbf{n}$ is the unit vector in the direction of $\mathbf{R}$,

$$\mathbf{n} \equiv \frac{\mathbf{R}}{R} \tag{7.40}$$

In particular,

$$\mathbf{B}_v = [\mathbf{n}] \times \mathbf{E}_v \tag{7.41a}$$

$$\mathbf{B}_a = [\mathbf{n}] \times \mathbf{E}_a \tag{7.41b}$$

Therefore, $\mathbf{E}_v \perp \mathbf{B}_v$ and $\mathbf{E}_a \perp \mathbf{B}_a$.

It should be pointed out that the equations derived above are relativistically correct. Indeed, the velocity $\mathbf{u}$ may simply be considered the *relative* velocity between the charged particle and the observer. The Liénard-Wiechert potentials were derived prior to the advent of relativity theory; only after the same results were obtained relativistically did it become apparent that $\mathbf{u}$ could indeed be interpreted as the relative velocity. (Compare the results obtained in Chapter 13.)

Several interesting features of the effects produced by a moving charge can be easily deduced from Eqs. (7.37).

First, we note the following radial dependences:

$$\left.\begin{aligned}\mathbf{E}_v, \mathbf{B}_v &\propto \frac{1}{[R^2]}\\ \mathbf{E}_a, \mathbf{B}_a &\propto \frac{1}{[R]}\end{aligned}\right\} \tag{7.42}$$

Therefore, if we compute the Poynting vectors for the velocity and acceleration fields, we have

$$\left.\begin{aligned} \mathbf{S}_v &\propto \frac{1}{[R^4]} \\ \mathbf{S}_a &\propto \frac{1}{[R^2]} \end{aligned}\right\} \tag{7.43}$$

In order to calculate the energy radiated by a particle, we must integrate the normal component of **S** over the surface of a sphere. If we take the radius of the sphere to be large, then because the element of surface area involves R^2, we find that the integral containing $\mathbf{S}_v$ vanishes as $1/R^2$, whereas the integral containing $\mathbf{S}_a$ remains finite. We conclude, therefore, that a particle which moves with constant velocity, and so has $\mathbf{S}_a = 0$, cannot radiate energy; only a particle undergoing acceleration can produce radiation. The fact that a particle moving with a uniform velocity cannot radiate is consistent with the relativistic nature of the field quantities, for, if **u** is the *relative* velocity between particle and observer, there is a reference frame in which the particle is at rest and the observer is in uniform motion. A static charge clearly cannot radiate energy. That is, if it is possible to find an inertial reference frame with respect to which the charge is at rest, then radiation cannot occur.

The fact that only accelerated charges can radiate has important implications and applications. For example, electrons can be given high velocities in certain devices (e.g., betatrons and synchrotrons) by accelerating the electrons while they are confined by means of magnetic fields to move in circular orbits. Since a particle moving in a circular orbit undergoes acceleration (*centripetal* acceleration), the electrons in these machines radiate energy while they are being brought to high velocities, not only because of the acceleration process *per se* but also because they move in circular orbits. It is apparent that as the velocity is increased there will come a point at which energy is radiated away just as rapidly as it is supplied by the accelerator. Thus, there exists a practical upper limit for the energy of electrons that can be achieved in a circular machine. This limit apparently is in the energy range 10–20 BeV.* On the other hand, the radiation produced by the linear acceleration of electrons (which is small compared with the radiation produced by circular motion) appears to place no such severe upper limit on the energy at the present time (except financial!) and energies of 100–300 BeV seem feasible for linear electron accelerators. The radiation of energy by protons (hydrogen nuclei) moving in a circular orbit is much less than that for electrons of the same energy. As a consequence, the most economical way to accelerate protons to ultra-high energies is in circular machines.

* 1 BeV = 10^9 eV; see Appendix C.

Since radiation will occur whether **a** is positive or negative, energy will also be radiated upon deceleration. Thus, if a beam of electrons is projected into a block of material in which they are stopped, radiation will result. In this case the radiation is called *X-radiation* or *bremsstrahlung* ("braking radiation") and, indeed, this is precisely how X-ray beams are produced.

We shall now examine some special cases of motion which are of particular interest.

7.5 The Field Produced by a Charged Particle in Uniform Motion

In this case we clearly have $\mathbf{a} = 0$, $\boldsymbol{\beta} = \text{const}$. Therefore, the complete electric field is given by $\mathbf{E}_v$ alone:

$$\mathbf{E} = \left[\frac{e}{K^3}(\mathbf{R} - R\boldsymbol{\beta})(1 - \beta^2)\right] \tag{7.44}$$

We wish to express **E** in terms of the *present position* of the particle, **R**.

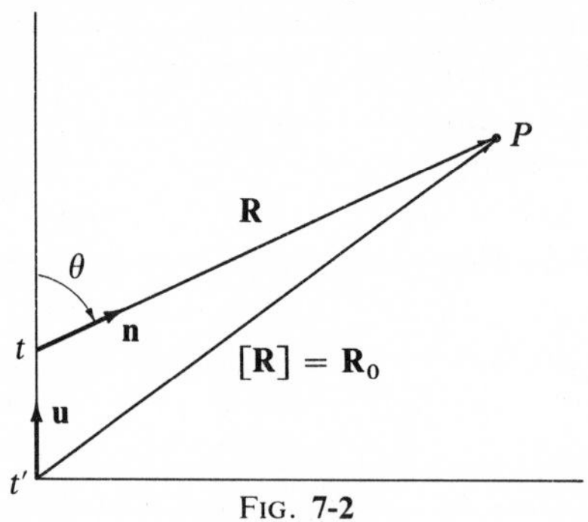

FIG. 7-2

To do this we refer to Fig. 7-2 where we have written $[\mathbf{R}] \equiv \mathbf{R}_0$ for simplicity. Since $\boldsymbol{\beta}$ is constant, we have $[\boldsymbol{\beta}] = \boldsymbol{\beta}$, so that

$$[K] = [R - \boldsymbol{\beta}\cdot\mathbf{R}] = R_0 - \boldsymbol{\beta}\cdot\mathbf{R}_0 \tag{7.45}$$

In order to express $[K^2]$ in terms of R, we start with

$$[K^2] = R_0^2 - 2R_0(\boldsymbol{\beta}\cdot\mathbf{R}_0) + (\boldsymbol{\beta}\cdot\mathbf{R}_0)^2 \tag{7.46}$$

We need two additional relations. First, we note that (see Fig. 7-2)

$$\mathbf{R} = \mathbf{R}_0 - \mathbf{u}(t - t')$$

But,

$$|\mathbf{R}_0| = R_0 = c(t - t')$$

so that

$$\mathbf{R} = \mathbf{R}_0 - R_0\boldsymbol{\beta} \tag{7.47}$$

Squaring, we find

$$R^2 = R_0^2 - 2R_0(\boldsymbol{\beta} \cdot \mathbf{R}_0) + R_0^2\beta^2 \tag{7.48}$$

Next, because triangles of equal areas are involved, we may write

$$|\mathbf{R} \times \mathbf{u}| = |\mathbf{R}_0 \times \mathbf{u}|$$

Therefore,

$$(\mathbf{R} \times \boldsymbol{\beta})^2 = (\mathbf{R}_0 \times \boldsymbol{\beta})^2 \tag{7.49}$$

Expanding both sides,

$$R^2\beta^2 - (\boldsymbol{\beta} \cdot \mathbf{R})^2 = R_0^2\beta^2 - (\boldsymbol{\beta} \cdot \mathbf{R}_0)^2 \tag{7.50}$$

Now, subtracting Eq. (7.50) from Eq. (7.48), we obtain

$$R^2 - R^2\beta^2 + (\boldsymbol{\beta} \cdot \mathbf{R})^2 = R_0^2 - 2R_0(\boldsymbol{\beta} \cdot \mathbf{R}_0) + (\boldsymbol{\beta} \cdot \mathbf{R}_0)^2 \tag{7.51}$$

Comparison of Eqs. (7.46) and (7.51) shows that

$$[K^2] = R^2 - R^2\beta^2 + (\boldsymbol{\beta} \cdot \mathbf{R})^2 \tag{7.52}$$

But from Fig. 7-2, we see that

$$\boldsymbol{\beta} \cdot \mathbf{R} = R\beta \cos\theta$$

Thus,

$$\begin{aligned} [K^2] &= R^2 - R^2\beta^2 + R^2\beta^2 \cos^2\theta \\ &= R^2(1 - \beta^2 \sin^2\theta) \end{aligned} \tag{7.53}$$

Also, in Eq. (7.44) for **E** we have the factor

$$[\mathbf{R} - R\boldsymbol{\beta}] = \mathbf{R}_0 - R_0\boldsymbol{\beta} = \mathbf{R} \tag{7.54}$$

where we have used Eq. (7.47). Substituting Eqs. (7.53) and (7.54) into the expression for **E**, we obtain

$$\boxed{\mathbf{E} = \frac{e\mathbf{R}(1 - \beta^2)}{R^3(1 - \beta^2 \sin^2\theta)^{\frac{3}{2}}}} \tag{7.55}$$

or,

$$\mathbf{E} = \frac{e(1 - \beta^2)}{R^2(1 - \beta^2 \sin^2\theta)^{\frac{3}{2}}}\,\mathbf{n} \tag{7.55a}$$

where **n** is the unit vector in the direction of **R**, as in Eq. (7.40).

The magnetic field is most easily calculated from Eq. (7.37c):

$$\mathbf{B} = \mathbf{B}_v = \left[\frac{e(1-\beta^2)}{K^3}(\boldsymbol{\beta} \times \mathbf{R})\right] \tag{7.56}$$

But,

$$[\boldsymbol{\beta} \times \mathbf{R}] = \boldsymbol{\beta} \times \mathbf{R}_0 = \boldsymbol{\beta} \times \mathbf{R} \tag{7.57}$$

where the last equality follows from Eq. (7.49). Therefore,

$$\boxed{\mathbf{B} = \frac{e(\boldsymbol{\beta} \times \mathbf{R})(1-\beta^2)}{R^3(1-\beta^2\sin^2\theta)^{\frac{3}{2}}}} \tag{7.58}$$

or,

$$\boxed{\mathbf{B} = \boldsymbol{\beta} \times \mathbf{E}} \tag{7.59}$$

It is evident from Eqs. (7.55a) and (7.59) that for high velocities, $u \to c$, the fields are increased in directions perpendicular to the direction of motion and decreased in the direction of motion. Thus, as $u \to c$, the total field begins to take on aspects of a plane wave, but no radiation can result because of the inverse R^2 dependence of the fields which leads to a vanishing of the surface integral of the Poynting vector at large distances.

Figure 7-3 shows the polar distribution of the electric field from an electric charge in uniform motion for different values of β.

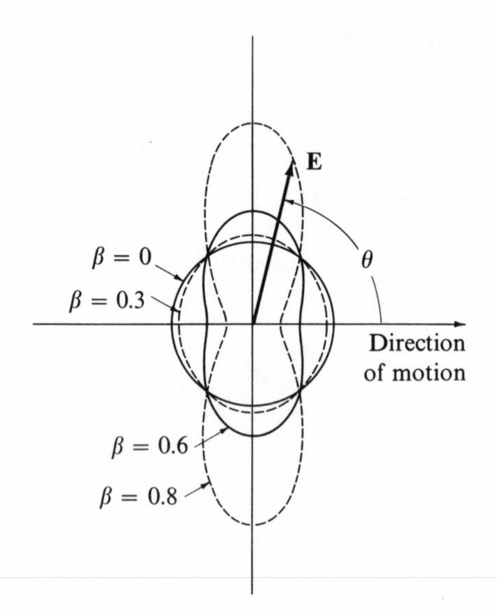

FIG. 7-3

7.6 Radiation from an Accelerated Charged Particle at Low Velocities

If the velocity of a particle is sufficiently small that it can be neglected in comparison with c, then $K \to R$ and the acceleration fields become* [see Eqs. (7.37b) and (7.41b)]

$$\mathbf{E}_a = \frac{e}{c^2 R^3}\{(\mathbf{R}\cdot\mathbf{a})\mathbf{R} - R^2\mathbf{a}\} \tag{7.60a}$$

$$\mathbf{B}_a = \frac{\mathbf{R}\times\mathbf{E}_a}{R} = \mathbf{n}\times\mathbf{E}_a \tag{7.60b}$$

Now,

$$\mathbf{E}_a \times \mathbf{B}_a = \frac{\mathbf{E}_a \times (\mathbf{R}\times\mathbf{E}_a)}{R}$$

$$= \frac{1}{R}\{E_a^2\mathbf{R} - (\mathbf{E}_a\cdot\mathbf{R})\mathbf{E}_a\} \tag{7.61}$$

But $\mathbf{E}_a$ is perpendicular to $\mathbf{R}$ (see Problem 7-2) so that the second term in Eq. (7.61) vanishes, and

$$\mathbf{E}_a \times \mathbf{B}_a = E_a^2\mathbf{n} \tag{7.62}$$

Thus, the portion of the Poynting vector that contributes to the radiation is

$$\mathbf{S}_a = \frac{c}{4\pi}(\mathbf{E}_a\times\mathbf{B}_a) = \frac{c}{4\pi}E_a^2\mathbf{n} \tag{7.63}$$

From Eq. (7.60a) we have

$$E_a^2 = \frac{e^2}{c^4 R^4}\{R^2 a^2 - (\mathbf{R}\cdot\mathbf{a})^2\} \tag{7.64}$$

If θ is the angle between $\mathbf{R}$ and $\mathbf{a}$, then

$$E_a^2 = \frac{e^2 a^2}{c^4 R^2}(1 - \cos^2\theta) = \frac{e^2 a^2}{c^4 R^2}\sin^2\theta \tag{7.65}$$

Therefore,

$$\mathbf{S}_a = \frac{e^2 a^2 \sin^2\theta}{4\pi c^3 R^2}\mathbf{n} \tag{7.66}$$

* In this section and in the following two sections, we suppress the square bracket notation; it will be understood that all quantities relating to the source are evaluated at the retarded time.

Since the Poynting vector represents an energy flow per unit area per unit time, we may express the angular distribution of the radiation as the power radiated per unit solid angle by multiplying $\mathbf{S}_a \cdot \mathbf{n}$ by R^2 (i.e., by the area per unit solid angle at the radius R). Thus,

$$\boxed{\frac{dP}{d\Omega} = (\mathbf{S}_a \cdot \mathbf{n})R^2 = \frac{e^2 a^2}{4\pi c^3} \sin^2 \theta} \tag{7.67}$$

This well-known $\sin^2 \theta$ distribution of radiated power (see Fig. 7-4) is an important result; we shall find a similar expression in the discussion of dipole radiation and antennas.

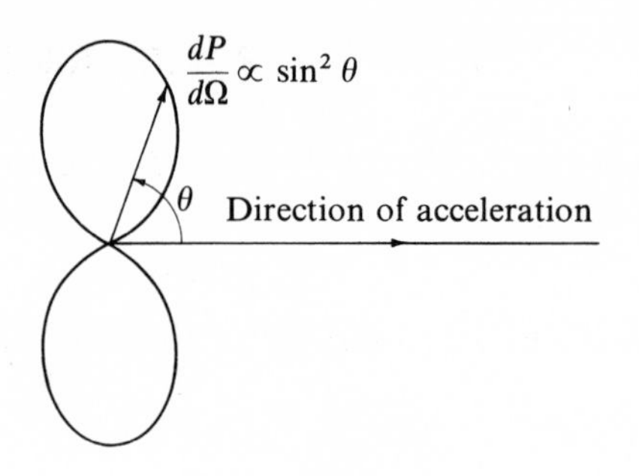

FIG. 7-4

The total radiated power is obtained by integrating over the entire sphere:

$$P = \int_{4\pi} \frac{dP}{d\Omega} \, d\Omega = \frac{e^2 a^2}{4\pi c^3} \int_0^{2\pi} d\varphi \int_0^{\pi} (\sin^2 \theta) \cdot \sin \theta \, d\theta$$

or,

$$\boxed{P = \frac{2e^2 a^2}{3c^3}} \tag{7.68}$$

This is the *Larmor formula** for the power radiated by a nonrelativistic accelerated charged particle.

* Derived first in 1897 by the English theoretical physicist Sir J. J. Larmor.

7.7 Radiation from a Charged Particle with Co-Linear Velocity and Acceleration

In order to discuss this case it is convenient to be able to express the electric field vector **E** in different terms. Again, since we are interested in radiation effects, it is sufficient to consider $\mathbf{E}_a$ alone. By expanding Eq. (7.37b), $\mathbf{E}_a$ may be written as

$$\mathbf{E}_a = \frac{e}{c^2K^3}\{(\mathbf{R}\cdot\mathbf{a})\mathbf{R} - R(\mathbf{R}\cdot\mathbf{a})\boldsymbol{\beta} - R^2\mathbf{a} + R(\mathbf{R}\cdot\boldsymbol{\beta})\mathbf{a}\} \tag{7.69}$$

We also note that

$$\mathbf{R}\times(\mathbf{R}\times\mathbf{a}) = (\mathbf{R}\cdot\mathbf{a})\mathbf{R} - R^2\mathbf{a}$$

$$\mathbf{R}\times(\boldsymbol{\beta}\times\mathbf{a}) = (\mathbf{R}\cdot\mathbf{a})\boldsymbol{\beta} - (\mathbf{R}\cdot\boldsymbol{\beta})\mathbf{a}$$

Using these last two expressions, $\mathbf{E}_a$ becomes

$$\mathbf{E}_a = \frac{e}{c^2K^3}\{\mathbf{R}\times(\mathbf{R}\times\mathbf{a}) - R\mathbf{R}\times(\boldsymbol{\beta}\times\mathbf{a})\} \tag{7.70}$$

We may also write this as

$$\mathbf{E}_a = \frac{eR^2}{c^2K^3}\mathbf{n}\times\{(\mathbf{n}-\boldsymbol{\beta})\times\mathbf{a}\} \tag{7.70a}$$

From Eq. (7.70) it is apparent that for the case in which the velocity and acceleration are parallel (so that $\boldsymbol{\beta}\times\mathbf{a} = 0$), we have

$$\mathbf{E}_a = \frac{e}{c^2K^3}\mathbf{R}\times(\mathbf{R}\times\mathbf{a})$$

$$= \frac{e}{c^2K^3}\{(\mathbf{R}\cdot\mathbf{a})\mathbf{R} - R^2\mathbf{a}\} \tag{7.71}$$

This is the same expression which we found for the case of low velocities [see Eq. (7.60a)] except that now the denominator contains K^3 instead of R^3. In order to obtain a quantitative description of the radiation produced under these conditions, we must take account of the fact that the radiation observed at a time t was emitted by the charged particle at the retarded time $t' = t - R/c$. We note first that

$$E_a^2 = \frac{e^2R^2}{c^4K^6}\{R^2a^2 - (\mathbf{R}\cdot\mathbf{a})^2\}$$

$$= \frac{e^2R^4a^2}{c^4K^6}\sin^2\theta \tag{7.72}$$

As before,

$$\mathbf{S}_a = \frac{c}{4\pi} E_a^2 \mathbf{n}$$

so that now we have

$$\mathbf{S}_a = \frac{e^2 a^2 R^4 \sin^2 \theta}{4\pi c^3 K^6} \mathbf{n} \tag{7.73}$$

Now, the incremental amount of energy lost by the particle, radiated into a unit solid angle at θ, and measured during the interval dt is

$$-dW(\theta) = (\mathbf{S}_a \cdot \mathbf{n}) R^2\, dt \tag{7.74}$$

where $\mathbf{S}_a \cdot \mathbf{n}$ is the outward component of the Poynting vector evaluated at the time t and corresponds to radiation emanating from the particle at the time t'. The amount of power that is radiated into a unit solid angle and crosses a surface at a distance R at a time t is equal to the energy per unit time lost by the particle at the time t':

$$\begin{aligned} \frac{dP}{d\Omega} &= -\frac{dW(\theta)}{dt'} = (\mathbf{S}_a \cdot \mathbf{n}) R^2 \frac{dt}{dt'} \\ &= \frac{e^2 a^2 R^6 \sin^2 \theta}{4\pi c^3 K^6} \frac{dt}{dt'} \end{aligned} \tag{7.75}$$

But, $t' = t - R/c$, and, according to Eq. (7.28),

$$\begin{aligned} \frac{dt'}{dt} &= 1 - \frac{\boldsymbol{\beta} \cdot \mathbf{R}}{R} \\ &= 1 - \beta \cos \theta \end{aligned} \tag{7.76}$$

We also have

$$K = R - \mathbf{R} \cdot \boldsymbol{\beta} = R(1 - \beta \cos \theta) \tag{7.77}$$

so that

$$\boxed{\frac{dP}{d\Omega} = \frac{e^2 a^2 \sin^2 \theta}{4\pi c^3 (1 - \beta \cos \theta)^5}} \tag{7.78}$$

For $\beta \ll 1$, we obtain the Larmor result [Eq. (7.67)], but as $\beta \to 1$, the angular distribution of the radiation is increased in the forward direction, as indicated in Fig. 7-5.

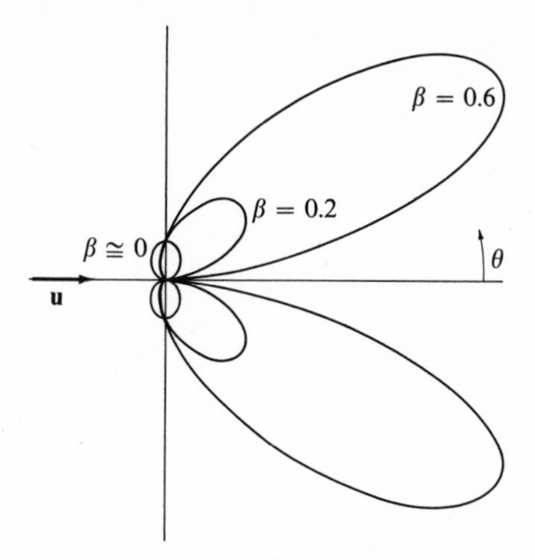

FIG. 7-5

Notice that there is no radiation produced exactly in the forward direction ($\theta = 0$). This result, which is predicted by the theory, is difficult to verify in practice.* For example, if the electrons are being accelerated linearly, the zone of no radiation lies directly in the path of the beam and measurements cannot be made precisely at $\theta = 0$ without introducing spurious effects. On the other hand, if a beam of electrons is stopped in a block of material, then during the process of stopping, scattering takes place so that the initial direction of motion is changed. For fast electrons this scattering serves to "smear out" the distribution of radiation and produce a single lobe of radiation in the forward direction.

The radiation emitted by decelerating electrons is called *bremsstrahlung* and the forward peaking is quite pronounced even for rather modest energies of a few hundred kiloelectron volts (keV).

7.8 Radiation from a Charged Particle Confined to a Circular Orbit

For this case the acceleration vector **a** is directed towards the center of the orbit circle and is therefore perpendicular to the velocity **u**. If the radius of the circular orbit is ρ, the angular frequency is

$$\omega = \frac{u}{\rho} \tag{7.79}$$

Also,

$$a = \rho\omega^2 \tag{7.80}$$

* The longitudinal observation of the normal Zeeman effect is an example of a process in which this result can be verified; see Section 9.7.

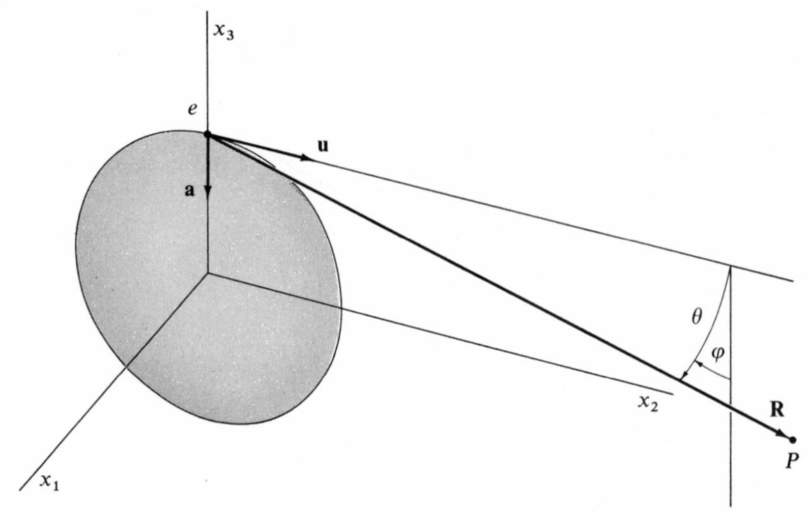

FIG. 7-6

Since **a** and **u** are perpendicular, in this problem we lose the symmetry about the direction of motion and must therefore introduce the azimuthal angle, φ, as in Fig. 7-6, where the orbit lies in the x_2-x_3 plane. Thus,

$$\mathbf{u} \cdot \mathbf{R} = uR \cos \theta$$

or,

$$\mathbf{n} \cdot \boldsymbol{\beta} = \beta \cos \theta \tag{7.81}$$

and,

$$\mathbf{a} \cdot \mathbf{R} = aR \sin \theta \cos \varphi$$

or,

$$\mathbf{n} \cdot \mathbf{a} = a \sin \theta \cos \varphi \tag{7.82}$$

From Eq. (7.70a) we may write

$$\mathbf{E}_a = \frac{eR^2}{c^2 K^3} \mathbf{n} \times (\mathbf{b} \times \mathbf{a}) \tag{7.83}$$

where

$$\mathbf{b} \equiv \mathbf{n} - \boldsymbol{\beta} \tag{7.84}$$

In order to calculate the radiation we wish to consider E_a^2; we therefore first compute

$$\{\mathbf{n} \times (\mathbf{b} \times \mathbf{a})\}^2 = \{(\mathbf{n} \cdot \mathbf{a})\mathbf{b} - (\mathbf{n} \cdot \mathbf{b})\mathbf{a}\}^2$$
$$= (\mathbf{n} \cdot \mathbf{a})^2 b^2 - 2(\mathbf{n} \cdot \mathbf{a})(\mathbf{n} \cdot \mathbf{b})(\mathbf{a} \cdot \mathbf{b}) + (\mathbf{n} \cdot \mathbf{b})^2 a^2 \tag{7.85}$$

We also have

$$b^2 = (\mathbf{n} - \boldsymbol{\beta}) \cdot (\mathbf{n} - \boldsymbol{\beta}) = \mathbf{n} \cdot \mathbf{n} - 2\mathbf{n} \cdot \boldsymbol{\beta} + \beta^2$$
$$= 1 - 2\beta \cos \theta + \beta^2$$
$$\mathbf{n} \cdot \mathbf{b} = \mathbf{n} \cdot (\mathbf{n} - \boldsymbol{\beta}) = \mathbf{n} \cdot \mathbf{n} - \mathbf{n} \cdot \boldsymbol{\beta}$$
$$= 1 - \beta \cos \theta$$
$$\mathbf{a} \cdot \mathbf{b} = \mathbf{a} \cdot (\mathbf{n} - \boldsymbol{\beta}) = \mathbf{a} \cdot \mathbf{n} - \mathbf{a} \cdot \boldsymbol{\beta}$$
$$= a \sin \theta \cos \varphi - 0$$

Then, Eq. (7.85) becomes

$$\{\mathbf{n} \times (\mathbf{b} \times \mathbf{a})\}^2 = (a \sin \theta \cos \varphi)^2 (1 - 2\beta \cos \theta + \beta^2)$$
$$-2(a \sin \theta \cos \varphi)^2 (1 - \beta \cos \theta) + a^2 (1 - \beta \cos \theta)^2$$
$$= a^2 \{(1 - \beta \cos \theta)^2 - (1 - \beta^2) \sin^2 \theta \cos^2 \varphi\} \tag{7.86}$$

and E_a^2 is found to be

$$E_a^2 = \frac{e^2 R^4 a^2}{c^4 K^6} \{(1 - \beta \cos \theta)^2 - (1 - \beta^2) \sin^2 \theta \cos^2 \varphi\} \tag{7.87}$$

where K is given by Eq. (7.77).

We must compute the angular distribution of the radiated energy as in the preceding example [see Eq. (7.75)], so we have

$$\frac{dP}{d\Omega} = -\frac{dW(\theta)}{dt'} = (\mathbf{S}_a \cdot \mathbf{n}) R^2 \frac{dt}{dt'}$$
$$= \frac{c}{4\pi} E_a^2 R^2 (1 - \beta \cos \theta)$$

or,

$$\boxed{\frac{dP}{d\Omega} = \frac{e^2 a^2}{4\pi c^3} \frac{(1 - \beta \cos \theta)^2 - (1 - \beta^2) \sin^2 \theta \cos^2 \varphi}{(1 - \beta \cos \theta)^5}} \tag{7.88}$$

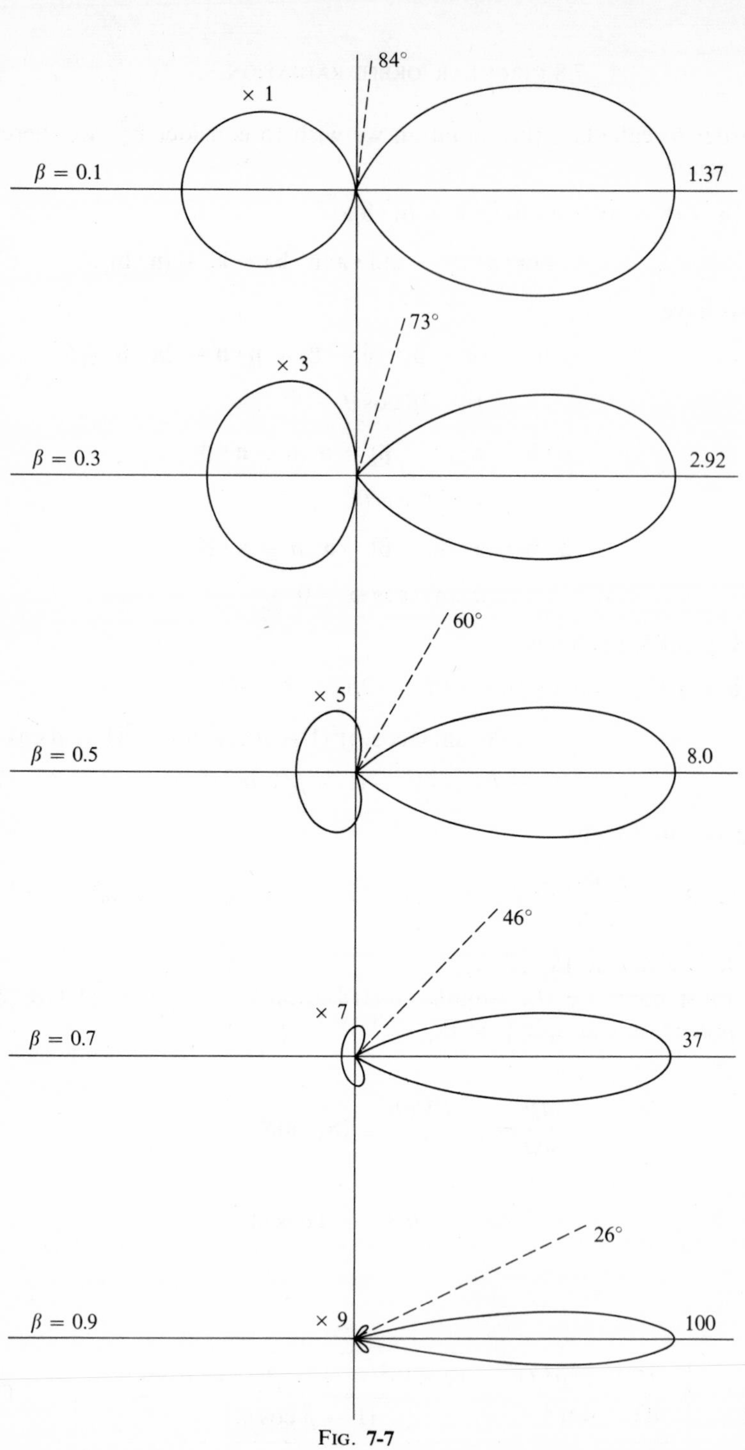

FIG. 7-7

For $\beta \cong 1$, the radiation has a sharp forward peak and a backward lobe of lesser intensity. Figure 7-7 shows the radiation pattern in the plane of the orbit ($\varphi = 0$) for several values of β. The dashed lines show the directions of zero intensity. In order to show the backward lobes more clearly, the radiation intensity in these lobes has been multiplied by 10β.

The total power radiated by a particle of charge e is (see Problem 7-10)

$$P = \int_{4\pi} \frac{dP}{d\Omega}\, d\Omega = \frac{2e^2a^2}{3c^3} \frac{1}{(1-\beta^2)^2} \tag{7.89}$$

or, in terms of the radius of the orbit,

$$P = \frac{2e^2\rho^2\omega^4}{3c^3} \frac{1}{(1-\beta^2)^2} \tag{7.90}$$

In the limit of low velocities the expression (7.89) for the radiated power reduces to that previously found [Eq. (7.68)] but rapidly becomes much larger as β becomes appreciable. It is clear that very fast electrons confined to a circular orbit will rapidly radiate away much of their energy.*

Suggested References

The Liénard-Wiechert potentials are derived in a manner similar to that given here by Becker and Sauter (Be64, Section 66), Owen (Ow63, Chapter 11), Jackson (Ja62, Chapter 14), and Tralli (Tr63, Chapter 17). Landau and Lifshitz (La62, Chapter 8) use the elegant, relativistic four-vector method. Corson and Lorrain (Co62, Chapter 14) use a straightforward "brute force" approach.

The expression for the velocity and acceleration field quantities are derived by Jackson (Ja62, Chapter 14) and by Landau and Lifshitz (La62, Chapter 8); a greater amount of detail is given in Panofsky and Phillips (Pa60, Chapter 20) and in Tralli (Tr63, Chapter 17).

Excellent accounts of the radiation produced by accelerated charges are to be found in Jackson (Ja62, Chapter 14) and in Panofsky and Phillips (Pa60, Chapter 20). The discussion of Sommerfeld (So52, Sections 19, 30, 36) is based on an older point of view.

Problems

7-1. Show by direct differentiation of the expressions for the retarded potentials [Eqs. (7.2) and (7.3)] that the Lorentz condition [Eq. (4.26)] is satisfied.

* The visible light radiated by artificially accelerated electrons was first observed in 1947: F. R. Elder, A. M. Gurewitsch, R. V. Langmuir, and H. C. Pollock, *Phys. Rev.* **71**, 829 (1947).

7-2. From Eq. (7.37b) show that $\mathbf{E}_a$ is perpendicular to $[\mathbf{R}]$.

7-3. The Biot-Savart law [Eq. (1.28)] states that the magnetic induction vector at a position $\mathbf{r}$ due to a current I flowing in an element $d\mathbf{l}$ of a conductor is given by

$$d\mathbf{B}(\mathbf{r}) = \frac{I}{c}\frac{d\mathbf{l} \times \mathbf{r}}{r^3}$$

Show that the fields calculated from this expression and from Eq. (7.58) for the field of a moving charge are identical in the limit that the velocity of the moving charge is small compared to the velocity of light.

7-4. Use Ampère's law to calculate the magnetic field at a distance R from an infinitely long straight conductor in which flows a current I. Show that the same result may be obtained from Eq. (7.58) without approximation as to the magnitude of $\mathbf{u}$.

7-5. Use Eq. (7.78) to show that the angle at which the radiation from an accelerating charged particle is a maximum is given by

$$\cos\theta_{\text{max}} = \frac{\sqrt{1 + 15\beta^2} - 1}{3\beta}$$

Show that as $\beta \to 1$,

$$\theta_{\text{max}} \to \frac{\sqrt{1 - \beta^2}}{2}$$

7-6. Calculate and plot the angular distribution of radiation from an accelerated electron when the kinetic energy of the electron is 100 keV. (Assume the acceleration is in the direction of motion and express the results in terms of a^2.) What is the angle of maximum radiation? Note that the velocity of the electron must be calculated from the relativistic expression for the kinetic energy (see Section 13.4):

$$T = m_e c^2[(1 - u^2/c^2)^{-\frac{1}{2}} - 1]$$

(See Appendix C for numerical values of the constants.)

7-7. A beam of electrons with initial velocity u_0 is brought to rest by being uniformly decelerated along the direction of initial motion. Calculate the angular distribution of the radiated energy. Plot the results for the case of a beam of electrons of initial energy 100 keV. Compare the results with those of the preceding problem.

7-8. Derive the expression for the total power radiated by a charge e moving in a circular orbit [Eq. (7.89)].

7-9. Use Eq. (7.90) to show that the energy lost per revolution by an electron in a circular orbit may be written approximately as

$$\Delta\varepsilon \cong \alpha \times \frac{\varepsilon^4}{\rho}$$

for $\beta \to 1$. Evaluate the constant α if $\Delta\varepsilon$ and ε are measured in MeV and ρ in centimeters. What is the result for an electron in (a) a betatron where $\varepsilon = 20$ MeV and $\rho = 50$ cm; and (b) an electron synchrotron where $\varepsilon = 1$ BeV $= 10^3$ MeV and $\rho = 500$ cm?

7-10. An early model of the hydrogen atom pictured an electron moving in a stationary circular orbit around a proton. If the radius of the orbit is 0.53×10^{-8} cm (the radius of the *first Bohr orbit*), show that on the basis of classical theory the electron would radiate energy at a rate of approximately 0.46 erg/sec and hence the atom would collapse almost instantaneously.

7-11. A low-energy electron has a velocity $u_0 \ll c$ at infinity. The velocity $\mathbf{u}_0$ is directed toward a fixed, repulsive Coulomb field, the potential for which is given by

$$U(r) = \frac{Ze^2}{r}$$

The electron is decelerated until it comes to rest and then is accelerated again in a direction opposite to the original direction of motion. Show that when the electron has again reached an infinite distance from the Coulomb scattering center, the kinetic energy of the electron is

$$\tfrac{1}{2}mu^2 = \tfrac{1}{2}mu_0^2 - \frac{8mu_0^5}{45Zc^3}$$

where the term depending on u_0^5 represents the energy radiated away during the deceleration and acceleration processes.

CHAPTER 8

Radiating Systems

8.1 Introduction

In this chapter we pursue the idea, established in the preceding chapter, that radiation is produced by electric charges undergoing acceleration. The arbitrary motion of a collection of charges will produce radiation which can be described by a multipole expansion. In addition to electric dipole radiation, electric quadrupole radiation, etc., there will also in general be magnetic radiation of all orders. We shall not attempt the general description of multipole radiation here, but will content ourselves with discussions of simple systems in which one or another of the multipole radiation terms is dominant.

We begin by establishing the criteria for electric dipole radiation and by examining the properties of such radiation. Application is made to the simple short, linear antenna. The Hertz potential functions are then introduced as an aid in describing the radiation from an oscillating dipole. The remainder of the chapter is devoted to antenna problems of various types: linear antennas, antenna arrays, and finally loop antennas which produce magnetic radiation. Antenna systems are of particular interest since the analysis requires the use of a basic principle concerning wave phenomena: the intensity of a wave which is derived from several sources must be computed by adding the individual amplitudes, each with its particular phase, and then squaring the result. Thus, the study of antenna systems affords an important practical application of *interference phenomena.* We shall have further use of the concept of interference when problems in wave optics are studied in Chapters 11 and 12.

8.2 Dipole Radiation*

Let us first consider a small region of space, V, which contains a collection of charged particles Such a system may possess multipole moments of all orders (see Section 2.3). We shall be interested for the present only in the dipole moment and in the radiation associated with it. The situation is depicted in Fig. 8-1. We wish to consider a field point P sufficiently far from the system so that, if d is a dimension characteristic of the system, we have $r \gg d$, or $\mathbf{r} \cong \mathbf{R}$.

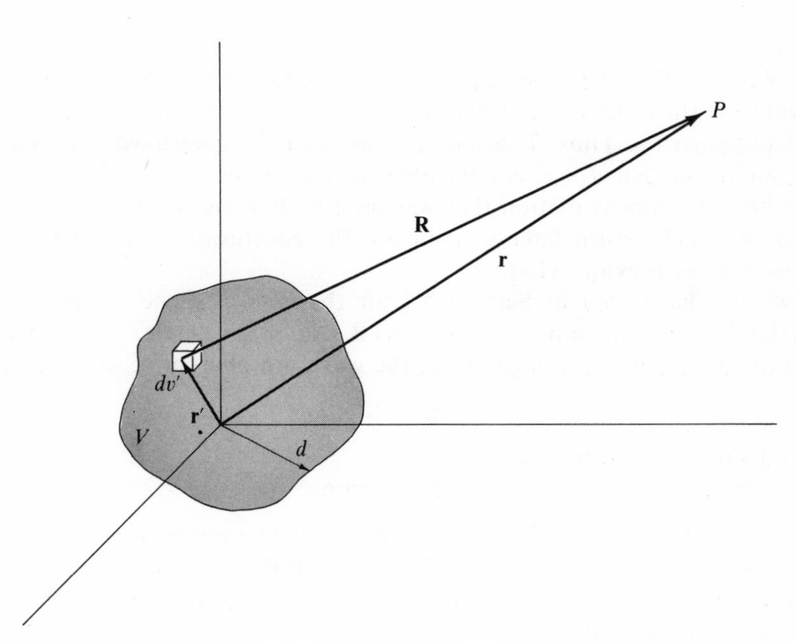

FIG. 8-1

* See also Section 8.3 for a derivation from a different viewpoint.

Now, we allow the charges within V to be in motion. We assume that a time interval T is required for any appreciable change to take place in the charge distribution of the system. That is, the system will have frequencies ν associated with the motion which are of order $1/T$. The requirement that $r \gg d$ means that we are neglecting times of the order of those necessary for the propagation of a signal across the system, i.e., we neglect times of the order of d/c. But these times must also be small compared to the time required for a significant change in the charge distribution to take place. Thus, we must have $d/c \ll T$, or $d \ll cT$. The product cT is just the wavelength associated with the frequency $\omega = 2\pi\nu$; that is, $cT/2\pi = c/\omega = \lambda/2\pi$. Therefore, our requirement may be stated as $d \ll \lambda$, i.e., the dimensions of the system must be small compared to the wavelength of the radiation.

We have a final condition which is imposed by the fact that we wish to interpret as a *plane wave* any radiation from the system of charges which arrives at the field point. In order to do this, the distance r to the field point P must be large compared to a wavelength λ. Therefore, the plane wave requirement may be stated as $r \gg \lambda$.

The three conditions which we have imposed on the problem (known as the *dipole approximation*) may be summarized as

$$d \ll \lambda \ll r \tag{8.1}$$

We note that the time required for a change in the charge distribution will be of the order of d/u, where u is the order of magnitude of the velocities of the particles. Thus, $T \approx d/u$, and since $cT = \lambda$, we have $\lambda \approx cd/u$. The requirement that $d \ll \lambda$ is equivalent to the requirement that $u \ll c$. This is the same approximation that was used in deriving the results of Section 7.6. We shall return later to compare the conclusions reached here with those of the previous chapter.

As we have seen in Section 5.2 for the case of plane waves, we may write the magnetic induction vector as $\mathbf{B} = \mathbf{n} \times \mathbf{E}$, where $\mathbf{n}$ is the unit vector in the direction of propagation of the wave. An alternative expression is

$$\mathbf{E} = \mathbf{B} \times \mathbf{n} \tag{8.2}$$

And since we also have

$$\mathbf{B} = \mathbf{curl\ A} \tag{8.3}$$

then, for the purposes of computing the field vectors, it is sufficient to consider only the vector potential, since both $\mathbf{B}$ and $\mathbf{E}$ may be obtained by performing the proper operations on $\mathbf{A}$. According to Eq. (7.20), the vector potential is given by

$$\mathbf{A}(\mathbf{r}, t) = \frac{1}{c} \int_V \frac{\mathbf{J}(\mathbf{r}', t - |\mathbf{r} - \mathbf{r}'|/c)}{|\mathbf{r} - \mathbf{r}'|} \, dv' \tag{8.4}$$

The approximation that $d \ll r$ allows us to neglect $\mathbf{r}'$ with respect to $\mathbf{r}$. Thus, we may write approximately,

$$\mathbf{A}(\mathbf{r}, t) = \frac{1}{cr}\int_V \mathbf{J}(\mathbf{r}', t - r/c)\, dv' \tag{8.5}$$

where $r = |\mathbf{r}|$ has been removed from the integral since the integration is only over $\mathbf{r}'$.

In order to identify the integral appearing in Eq. (8.5) we note that the current density is just the product of the charge density and the velocity,

$$\mathbf{J} = \rho\mathbf{u} \tag{8.6}$$

so that the integral of $\mathbf{J}$ may be written as

$$\int_V \mathbf{J}\, dv' = \int_V \rho\mathbf{u}\, dv' = \sum_\alpha q_\alpha \mathbf{u}_\alpha \tag{8.7}$$

where the sum is over all of the discrete particles; the αth particle carries a charge q_α and has a velocity $\mathbf{u}_\alpha$. Since the charges q_α are constant in time,

$$\sum_\alpha q_\alpha \mathbf{u}_\alpha = \frac{d}{dt'}\sum_\alpha q_\alpha \mathbf{r}'_\alpha \tag{8.8}$$

But the sum of the quantities $q_\alpha \mathbf{r}'_\alpha$ is just the dipole moment of the system $\mathbf{p}$ [see Eq. (2.22)], so we have

$$\int_V \mathbf{J}\, dv' = \dot{\mathbf{p}} \tag{8.9}$$

Therefore,*

$$\mathbf{A}(\mathbf{r}, t) = \frac{1}{cr}\dot{\mathbf{p}}(t') = \frac{1}{cr}[\dot{\mathbf{p}}] \tag{8.10}$$

where, in this approximation,

$$t' = t - r/c \tag{8.11}$$

In order to obtain $\mathbf{B}$ we must compute

$$\begin{aligned} \mathbf{B} &= \frac{1}{c}\,\mathbf{curl}\left(\frac{1}{r}[\dot{\mathbf{p}}]\right) \\ &= \frac{1}{c}\left(\mathbf{grad}\,\frac{1}{r}\right) \times [\dot{\mathbf{p}}] + \frac{1}{cr}\,\mathbf{curl}[\dot{\mathbf{p}}] \end{aligned} \tag{8.12}$$

* Notice that we use interchangeably the square bracket notation and the explicit indication of the dependence on t'.

where we have expanded the curl of the product of a scalar and a vector. Now, the term **grad**$(1/r)$ will produce a $1/r^2$ variation with distance. We are interested in discussing the *radiation* field, and since we know that $1/r^2$ terms give rise to a Poynting vector which varies as $1/r^4$, we may neglect **grad**$(1/r)$ as yielding no contribution to the radiation.* The region of space in which this approximation is valid is called the *radiation zone.* Consequently, the portion of **B** that contributes to the radiation is

$$\mathbf{B}_{\text{rad}} = \frac{1}{cr}\,\mathbf{curl}[\dot{\mathbf{p}}] \tag{8.13}$$

The computation of $\mathbf{curl}[\dot{\mathbf{p}}]$ may be accomplished in the following manner [see Eq. (A.28), Appendix A)]:

$$\begin{aligned}\mathbf{curl}[\dot{\mathbf{p}}] &= \sum_{i,j,k} \varepsilon_{ijk}\mathbf{e}_i \frac{\partial \dot{p}_k(t')}{\partial x_j}\\ &= \sum_{i,j,k} \varepsilon_{ijk}\mathbf{e}_i \frac{\partial \dot{p}_k(t')}{\partial t'}\frac{\partial t'}{\partial x_j}\end{aligned} \tag{8.14}$$

But,

$$t' = t - \frac{r}{c} = t - \frac{1}{c}\sqrt{\sum_i x_i^2} \tag{8.15}$$

so that

$$\frac{\partial t'}{\partial x_j} = -\frac{1}{c}\frac{x_j}{r} = -\frac{1}{c}n_j \tag{8.16}$$

where $x_j/r \equiv n_j$ is the jth rectangular component of the unit vector in the direction of **r**. Also,

$$\frac{\partial \dot{p}_k(t')}{\partial t'} = \ddot{p}_k(t') \tag{8.17}$$

Hence,

$$\mathbf{curl}[\dot{\mathbf{p}}] = -\frac{1}{c}\sum_{i,j,k} \varepsilon_{ijk}\mathbf{e}_i n_j \ddot{p}_k(t') \tag{8.18}$$

Now, the sum on the right-hand side is just the definition of the vector product of **n** and $[\ddot{\mathbf{p}}]$. Therefore,

$$\mathbf{curl}[\dot{\mathbf{p}}] = -\frac{1}{c}\mathbf{n} \times [\ddot{\mathbf{p}}] = \frac{1}{c}[\ddot{\mathbf{p}}] \times \mathbf{n} \tag{8.19}$$

Hence, the magnetic induction vector becomes

$$\mathbf{B}_{\text{rad}} = \frac{1}{c^2 r}[\ddot{\mathbf{p}}] \times \mathbf{n} \tag{8.20}$$

* This portion of the field is discussed briefly in Section 8.5.

and the electric vector is

$$\mathbf{E}_{\text{rad}} = \mathbf{B}_{\text{rad}} \times \mathbf{n} = \frac{1}{c^2 r}([\ddot{\mathbf{p}}] \times \mathbf{n}) \times \mathbf{n} \tag{8.21}$$

If we consider the vector $[\ddot{\mathbf{p}}]$ to be directed along the polar axis of a spherical coordinate system as in Fig. 8-2, then at a point in space at a distance r and in a direction defined by $\mathbf{n}$, we see that $\mathbf{B}$ is in the direction of $\mathbf{e}_\varphi$ and $\mathbf{E}$ is in the direction of $\mathbf{e}_\theta$. Thus,

$$\left.\begin{aligned} \mathbf{B}_{\text{rad}} &= B_\varphi^0 \sin\theta \mathbf{e}_\varphi = \frac{[\ddot{p}]}{c^2 r} \sin\theta \mathbf{e}_\varphi \\ \mathbf{E}_{\text{rad}} &= E_\theta^0 \sin\theta \mathbf{e}_\theta = \frac{[\ddot{p}]}{c^2 r} \sin\theta \mathbf{e}_\theta \end{aligned}\right\} \tag{8.22}$$

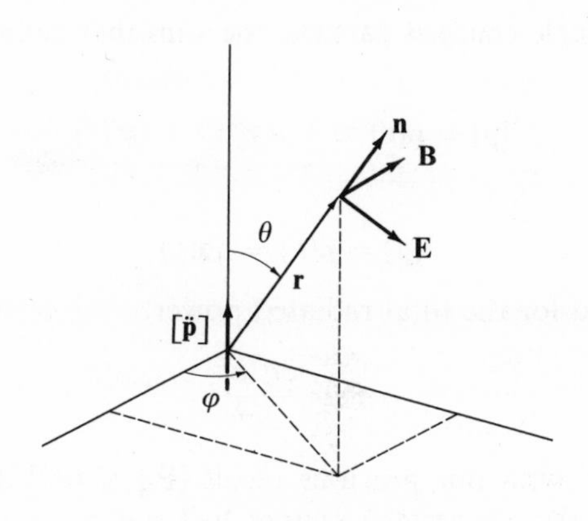

FIG. 8-2

The portion of the Poynting vector that describes the radiation is

$$\mathbf{S}_{\text{rad}} = \frac{c}{4\pi}(\mathbf{E}_{\text{rad}} \times \mathbf{B}_{\text{rad}}) = \frac{c}{4\pi} E_\theta B_\varphi \sin^2\theta \mathbf{n}$$

$$= \frac{c}{4\pi} E_{\text{rad}}^2 \mathbf{n} = \frac{c}{4\pi} B_{\text{rad}}^2 \mathbf{n} \tag{8.23}$$

Using Eq. (8.20) for $\mathbf{B}_{\text{rad}}$, we may rewrite this equation as

$$\mathbf{S}_{\text{rad}} = \frac{1}{4\pi c^3 r^2}([\ddot{\mathbf{p}}] \times \mathbf{n})^2 \mathbf{n} \tag{8.24}$$

The outward component of $\mathbf{S}_{\text{rad}}$ is

$$\mathbf{S}_{\text{rad}} \cdot \mathbf{n} = \frac{[\ddot{p}]^2}{4\pi c^3 r^2} \sin^2 \theta \tag{8.25}$$

The power emitted per unit solid angle is

$$\frac{dP}{d\Omega} = (\mathbf{S}_{\text{rad}} \cdot \mathbf{n}) r^2 = \frac{[\ddot{p}]^2}{4\pi c^3} \sin^2 \theta \tag{8.26}$$

and we find again the familiar $\sin^2 \theta$ dependence of the emitted radiation [cf. Eq. (7.67)]. The total radiated power is

$$\begin{aligned} P &= \int_{4\pi} \frac{dP}{d\Omega}\, d\Omega = \frac{[\ddot{p}]^2}{4\pi c^3} \int_{4\pi} (\sin^2 \theta) \cdot \sin \theta \, d\theta \, d\varphi \\ &= \frac{2[\ddot{p}]^2}{3c^2} \end{aligned} \tag{8.27}$$

If we have a single charged particle, the sum that defines $\mathbf{p}$ has only the one term

$$[\mathbf{p}] = \mathbf{p}(t') \equiv \sum_\alpha q_\alpha \mathbf{r}'_\alpha(t') = q\mathbf{r}'(t') \tag{8.28}$$

so that

$$[\ddot{\mathbf{p}}] = \ddot{\mathbf{p}}(t') = q\mathbf{a}(t') \tag{8.29}$$

Therefore, we find for the total radiated power,

$$P = \frac{2q^2 a^2}{3c^3} \tag{8.30}$$

which is identical with our previous result [Eq. (7.68)] derived under the assumption that the accelerated charge had $u \ll c$. As we saw earlier in this section, the *dipole approximation*, used to obtain Eq. (8.30), requires the assumption that the velocities in the system are small compared to the velocity of light.

Usually we are concerned with systems in which the dipole moment varies with time in a regular fashion. Then, the meaningful quantity is the radiated power averaged over one complete period of oscillation of the system. Thus,

$$\left\langle \frac{dP}{d\Omega} \right\rangle = \frac{\langle [\ddot{p}]^2 \rangle}{4\pi c^3} \sin^2 \theta \tag{8.31}$$

and

$$\langle P \rangle = \frac{2\langle [\ddot{p}]^2 \rangle}{3c^3} \tag{8.32}$$

In Eq. (8.27) it was necessary to consider the observation of the radiated power at a time t corresponding to the value of $\ddot{p}$ at the retarded time t'. For a system undergoing periodic motion, however, if a time average over one complete period is taken, then all times are equivalent and it is not necessary* to make the distinction between t and t'.

If the dipole moment varies harmonically with time,

$$[\mathbf{p}] = \mathbf{p}(t') = p_0 e^{-i\omega t'} \tag{8.33}$$

then†

$$\begin{aligned} \langle [\ddot{p}]^2 \rangle &= p_0^2 \omega^4 \langle \cos^2 \omega t' \rangle \\ &= \tfrac{1}{2} p_0^2 \omega^4 \end{aligned} \tag{8.34}$$

so that the expressions for the average radiated power [Eqs. (8.31) and (8.32)] become

$$\left\langle \frac{dP}{d\Omega} \right\rangle = \frac{p_0^2 \omega^4}{8\pi c^3} \sin^2 \theta = \frac{2\pi^3 p_0^2 c}{\lambda^4} \sin^2 \theta \tag{8.35}$$

$$\langle P \rangle = \frac{p_0^2 \omega^4}{3c^3} = \frac{16\pi^4 c p_0^2}{3\lambda^4} \tag{8.36}$$

where $\omega = 2\pi c/\lambda$. Thus, we find an inverse λ^4 dependence for the emitted power. Terms of this form $(1/\lambda^4)$ are characteristic of the radiation emitted from dipole systems. (See also Section 10.6.)

8.3 The Hertz Vectors

In the next section we shall describe the radiation field produced by an oscillator according to the method developed by Hertz. Preparatory to this discussion it is profitable to formulate the field equations in terms of the so-called Hertz vectors.‡ In order to do this, we first recall some of the basic properties of the electromagnetic field.

The vectors **E** and **B** are considered to be the fundamental field quantities; i.e., they specify the electromagnetic field in free space. In material media the electric polarization **P** and the magnetization **M** must be taken into

* It is assumed, of course, that the process of radiation does not alter the motion of the system; i.e., some mechanism exists to supply the energy that is radiated away. See also the comments in Section 9.9.

† Since **p** is now written as a complex quantity, the quantity $[\ddot{p}]^2$ should more properly be written as $|[\ddot{p}]|^2$. We shall assume that this is understood in such expressions.

‡ Introduced by Heinrich Hertz in 1888; a general treatment was given by Righi in 1901.

account. In these cases, the appropriate quantities are **D** and **H** [cf. Eqs. (1.19) and (1.53)]:

$$\left.\begin{aligned} \mathbf{D} &= \mathbf{E} + 4\pi\mathbf{P} \\ \mathbf{H} &= \mathbf{B} - 4\pi\mathbf{M} \end{aligned}\right\} \tag{8.37}$$

The vectors **P** and **M** represent the density of electric and magnetic dipole moments, respectively. These dipole moments may result from a combination of *induced* and *permanent* dipoles. Now, permanent electric dipoles do not exist in Nature,* so that such a contribution must be considered to result from the application of some external source. The permanent magnetic dipoles may arise from true permanent magnetic dipoles as well as from current loops supplied by an external power source.

Let us now consider the fields in a region which is characterized by $\rho = 0$, $\mathbf{J} = 0$, $\sigma = 0$; i.e., there are neither free charges nor free currents present, but there may still be polarization and magnetization. Maxwell's equations are

$$\left.\begin{aligned} \operatorname{div}\mathbf{D} &= 0 \\ \operatorname{div}\mathbf{B} &= 0 \\ \mathbf{curl}\,\mathbf{E} + \frac{1}{c}\frac{\partial \mathbf{B}}{\partial t} &= 0 \\ \mathbf{curl}\,\mathbf{H} - \frac{1}{c}\frac{\partial \mathbf{D}}{\partial t} &= 0 \end{aligned}\right\} \tag{8.38}$$

But now, if we use Eqs. (8.37) for **D** and **H**, we find

$$\left.\begin{aligned} \operatorname{div}\mathbf{E} &= -4\pi \operatorname{div}\mathbf{P} \\ \operatorname{div}\mathbf{B} &= 0 \\ \mathbf{curl}\,\mathbf{E} + \frac{1}{c}\frac{\partial \mathbf{B}}{\partial t} &= 0 \\ \mathbf{curl}\,\mathbf{B} - \frac{1}{c}\frac{\partial \mathbf{E}}{\partial t} &= \frac{4\pi}{c}\frac{\partial \mathbf{P}}{\partial t} + 4\pi\,\mathbf{curl}\,\mathbf{M} \end{aligned}\right\} \tag{8.39}$$

These equations are formally the same as Maxwell's equations for a vacuum [cf. Eqs. (4.18) with **D** = **E** and **B** = **H**], if we identify the charge and current densities as

$$\left.\begin{aligned} \rho &= -\operatorname{div}\mathbf{P} \\ \mathbf{J} &= \frac{\partial \mathbf{P}}{\partial t} + c\,\mathbf{curl}\,\mathbf{M} \end{aligned}\right\} \tag{8.40}$$

* Except for the so-called *electrets*.

Thus, as far as the field vectors are concerned, the presence of matter may be represented by an equivalent distribution of charge density, $-\operatorname{div} \mathbf{P}$, and an equivalent distribution of current density, $\partial \mathbf{P}/\partial t + c\, \mathbf{curl}\, \mathbf{M}$.

The electromagnetic field vectors in vacuum may then be obtained from the potentials by a retarded-time calculation [cf. Eqs. (7.19) and (7.20)]:

$$\Phi(\mathbf{r}, t) = -\int_V \frac{[\operatorname{div} \mathbf{P}(\mathbf{r}')]}{|\mathbf{r} - \mathbf{r}'|} dv' \tag{8.41a}$$

$$\mathbf{A}(\mathbf{r}, t) = \int_V \frac{\left[\mathbf{curl}\, \mathbf{M}(\mathbf{r}') + \dfrac{1}{c}\dfrac{\partial \mathbf{P}(\mathbf{r}')}{\partial t}\right]}{|\mathbf{r} - \mathbf{r}'|} dv' \tag{8.41b}$$

where the divergence and curl operations are performed with respect to the coordinates of the variable point of integration, $\mathbf{r}'$. In free space, Φ and $\mathbf{A}$ satisfy the inhomogeneous wave equations [cf. Eqs. (4.34) and (4.35) with $\varepsilon = 1$, $\mu = 1$]

$$\left.\begin{aligned} \nabla^2 \Phi - \frac{1}{c^2}\frac{\partial^2 \Phi}{\partial t^2} &= -4\pi\rho \\ \nabla^2 \mathbf{A} - \frac{1}{c^2}\frac{\partial^2 \mathbf{A}}{\partial t^2} &= -\frac{4\pi}{c}\mathbf{J} \end{aligned}\right\} \tag{8.42}$$

Therefore, the scalar and vector potentials may be obtained directly from the polarization and magnetization vectors, $\mathbf{P}$ and $\mathbf{M}$, but the relations are rather complicated. Hertz sought to remedy this difficulty by substituting a different pair of potentials from which the field vectors could be obtained but which could be more simply derived from the polarization and magnetization. We must expect, however, that a simplification of the forms of the potentials will complicate the equations which relate the potentials to the field vectors. In spite of this, a net simplification does in fact result since the complicated retarded-time calculation specified in Eqs. (8.41) will have been eliminated.

We introduce the Hertz vectors $\mathbf{\Pi}_e$ and $\mathbf{\Pi}_m$, which are related to the scalar and vector potentials according to

$$\left.\begin{aligned} \Phi &= -\operatorname{div} \mathbf{\Pi}_e \\ \mathbf{A} &= \frac{1}{c}\frac{\partial \mathbf{\Pi}_e}{\partial t} + \mathbf{curl}\, \mathbf{\Pi}_m \end{aligned}\right\} \tag{8.43}$$

We note that $\mathbf{\Pi}_e$ and $\mathbf{\Pi}_m$ are related to Φ and $\mathbf{A}$ in exactly the same manner that $\mathbf{P}$ and $\mathbf{M}$ are related to ρ and $\mathbf{J}$ [see Eqs. (8.40)].

As we shall see, the subscripts e and m on the Hertz vectors indicate that $\mathbf{\Pi}_e$ and $\mathbf{\Pi}_m$ are associated with *electric* and *magnetic* effects, respectively. (This is reasonable since Φ is expected to be related to electric charges and electric polarization, while the magnetic field must depend, through **A**, on currents—i.e., the time derivative of charge—and on magnetization.) In order to show these relationships explicitly, we use the inhomogeneous wave equations for Φ and **A** [Eqs. (8.42)] and substitute the expressions from Eqs. (8.43) and (8.40). The equation for Φ becomes

$$\nabla^2(-\operatorname{div}\mathbf{\Pi}_e) - \frac{1}{c^2}\frac{\partial^2}{\partial t^2}(-\operatorname{div}\mathbf{\Pi}_e) = 4\pi \operatorname{div}\mathbf{P}$$

Interchanging the derivatives, we find

$$\operatorname{div}\left(\nabla^2\mathbf{\Pi}_e - \frac{1}{c^2}\frac{\partial^2\mathbf{\Pi}_e}{\partial t^2} + 4\pi\mathbf{P}\right) = 0$$

which will be satisfied if

$$\nabla^2\mathbf{\Pi}_e - \frac{1}{c^2}\frac{\partial^2\mathbf{\Pi}_e}{\partial t^2} = -4\pi\mathbf{P} \tag{8.44}$$

Similarly, the equation for **A** becomes

$$\nabla^2\left(\frac{1}{c}\frac{\partial\mathbf{\Pi}_e}{\partial t} + \mathbf{curl}\,\mathbf{\Pi}_m\right) - \frac{1}{c^2}\frac{\partial^2}{\partial t^2}\left(\frac{1}{c}\frac{\partial\mathbf{\Pi}_e}{\partial t} + \mathbf{curl}\,\mathbf{\Pi}_m\right)$$
$$= -\frac{4\pi}{c}\left(\frac{\partial\mathbf{P}}{\partial t} + c\,\mathbf{curl}\,\mathbf{M}\right)$$

Again interchanging the derivatives and regrouping terms, we obtain

$$\frac{1}{c}\frac{\partial}{\partial t}\left(\nabla^2\mathbf{\Pi}_e - \frac{1}{c^2}\frac{\partial^2\mathbf{\Pi}_e}{\partial t^2} + 4\pi\mathbf{P}\right)$$
$$+\mathbf{curl}\left(\nabla^2\mathbf{\Pi}_m - \frac{1}{c^2}\frac{\partial^2\mathbf{\Pi}_m}{\partial t^2} + 4\pi\mathbf{M}\right) = 0$$

The first term vanishes in view of Eq. (8.44), so that the equation will be satisfied if

$$\nabla^2\mathbf{\Pi}_m - \frac{1}{c^2}\frac{\partial^2\mathbf{\Pi}_m}{\partial t^2} = -4\pi\mathbf{M} \tag{8.45}$$

Therefore, both $\mathbf{\Pi}_e$ and $\mathbf{\Pi}_m$ can be specified as solutions of inhomogeneous wave equations. The "source term" for $\mathbf{\Pi}_e$ is the polarization **P** while that for $\mathbf{\Pi}_m$ is the magnetization **M**. From the results of Section 7.2 we know that the solutions are

$$\mathbf{\Pi}_e(\mathbf{r}, t) = \int_V \frac{[\mathbf{P}(\mathbf{r}')]}{|\mathbf{r} - \mathbf{r}'|} dv' \tag{8.46a}$$

$$\mathbf{\Pi}_m(\mathbf{r}, t) = \int_V \frac{[\mathbf{M}(\mathbf{r}')]}{|\mathbf{r} - \mathbf{r}'|} dv' \tag{8.46b}$$

We have obtained expressions for the potentials $\mathbf{\Pi}_e$ and $\mathbf{\Pi}_m$ in terms of the polarization and magnetization which are much simpler than the corresponding expressions for Φ and **A** [Eqs. (8.41)]. It remains to express the field vectors, **E**, **D**, **B**, and **H**, in terms of the Hertz vectors. This may be accomplished by using Eqs. (8.43). Thus,

$$\begin{aligned}\mathbf{E} &= -\mathbf{grad}\,\Phi - \frac{1}{c}\frac{\partial \mathbf{A}}{\partial t} \\ &= \mathbf{grad}\,\mathrm{div}\,\mathbf{\Pi}_e - \frac{1}{c}\frac{\partial}{\partial t}\left(\frac{1}{c}\frac{\partial \mathbf{\Pi}_e}{\partial t} + \mathbf{curl}\,\mathbf{\Pi}_m\right)\end{aligned} \tag{8.47}$$

If we use the identity

$$\mathbf{grad}\,\mathrm{div} = \mathbf{curl}\,\mathbf{curl} + \nabla^2$$

then, Eq. (8.47) becomes

$$\begin{aligned}\mathbf{E} &= \mathbf{curl}\left(\mathbf{curl}\,\mathbf{\Pi}_e - \frac{1}{c}\frac{\partial \mathbf{\Pi}_m}{\partial t}\right) + \left(\nabla^2 \mathbf{\Pi}_e - \frac{1}{c^2}\frac{\partial^2 \mathbf{\Pi}_e}{\partial t^2}\right) \\ &= \mathbf{curl}\left(\mathbf{curl}\,\mathbf{\Pi}_e - \frac{1}{c}\frac{\partial \mathbf{\Pi}_m}{\partial t}\right) - 4\pi\mathbf{P}\end{aligned} \tag{8.48}$$

But, $\mathbf{E} + 4\pi\mathbf{P} = \mathbf{D}$. Therefore,

$$\mathbf{D} = \mathbf{curl}\left(\mathbf{curl}\,\mathbf{\Pi}_e - \frac{1}{c}\frac{\partial \mathbf{\Pi}_m}{\partial t}\right) \tag{8.49}$$

Also,

$$\begin{aligned}\mathbf{B} &= \mathbf{curl}\,\mathbf{A} \\ &= \mathbf{curl}\left(\frac{1}{c}\frac{\partial \mathbf{\Pi}_e}{\partial t} + \mathbf{curl}\,\mathbf{\Pi}_m\right) \\ &= \frac{1}{c}\frac{\partial}{\partial t}\mathbf{curl}\,\mathbf{\Pi}_e + \mathbf{grad}\,\mathrm{div}\,\mathbf{\Pi}_m - \nabla^2\mathbf{\Pi}_m \\ &= \frac{1}{c}\frac{\partial}{\partial t}\mathbf{curl}\,\mathbf{\Pi}_e + \mathbf{grad}\,\mathrm{div}\,\mathbf{\Pi}_m - \frac{1}{c^2}\frac{\partial^2 \mathbf{\Pi}_m}{\partial t^2} + 4\pi\mathbf{M}\end{aligned} \tag{8.50}$$

Using $\mathbf{H} = \mathbf{B} - 4\pi\mathbf{M}$, we have finally,

$$\mathbf{H} = \frac{1}{c}\frac{\partial}{\partial t}\left(\mathbf{curl}\,\mathbf{\Pi}_e - \frac{1}{c}\frac{\partial \mathbf{\Pi}_m}{\partial t}\right) + \mathbf{grad}\,\mathrm{div}\,\mathbf{\Pi}_m \tag{8.51}$$

The expressions for the field vectors are now more complicated than before, as predicted, but only simple differential operations are required, and since the Hertz vectors are given by the simplest type of retarded-time calculation, this formulation has the advantage of quite straightforward operations throughout.

8.4 The Field due to a Hertzian Dipole

We now use the method of Hertz to calculate the electromagnetic field due to an oscillating electric dipole. We consider a point dipole with moment $\mathbf{p} = p\mathbf{e}_3$ and located at the origin, as in Fig. 8-3. The dipole moment p is, of course, a function of the time: $p(t') = p_0 \exp(-i\omega t')$. The polarization vector $\mathbf{P}$ has a value only at the position of the dipole, i.e., at the origin:

$$\mathbf{P}(\mathbf{r}', t') = \mathbf{p}(t')\delta(\mathbf{r}') \tag{8.52}$$

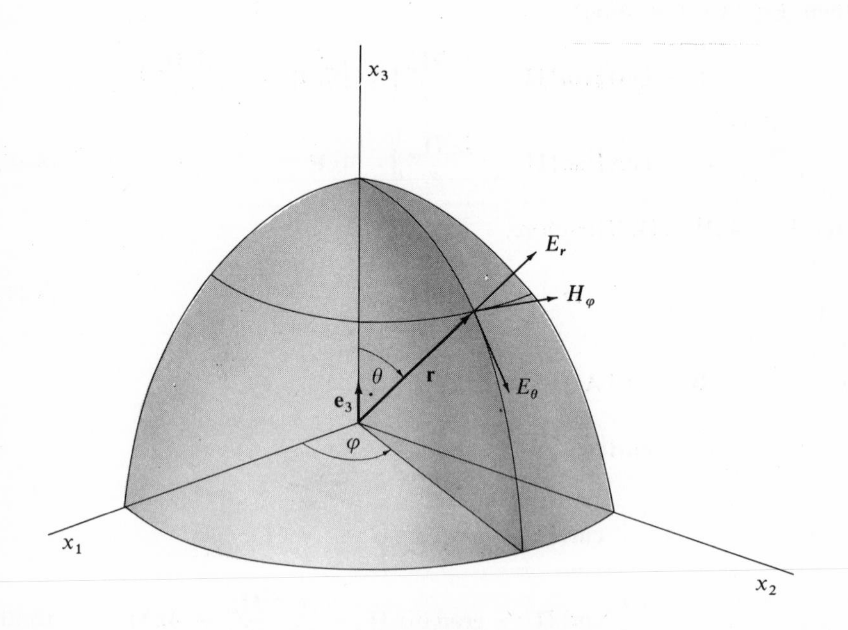

FIG. 8-3

From Eqs. (8.46) for the Hertz vectors, we have, therefore,

$$\mathbf{\Pi}_e = \frac{\mathbf{p}(t - |\mathbf{r} - \mathbf{r}'|/c)}{|\mathbf{r} - \mathbf{r}'|}$$

$$= \frac{\mathbf{p}(t - r/c)}{r} = \frac{[p]}{r}\mathbf{e}_3 \tag{8.53a}$$

$$\mathbf{\Pi}_m = 0 \tag{8.53b}$$

where $|\mathbf{r} - \mathbf{r}'|$ has been replaced by $|\mathbf{r}| = r$ since $\mathbf{r}' = 0$ for the point dipole. According to Eqs. (8.47) and (8.50), the field vectors are

$$\left.\begin{aligned} \mathbf{E} &= \mathbf{grad}\,\mathrm{div}\,\mathbf{\Pi} - \frac{1}{c^2}\frac{\partial^2 \mathbf{\Pi}}{\partial t^2} \\ \mathbf{B} &= \frac{1}{c}\frac{\partial}{\partial t}\,\mathbf{curl}\,\mathbf{\Pi} \end{aligned}\right\} \tag{8.54}$$

where the subscript e on $\mathbf{\Pi}_e$ has been suppressed. From Eq. (8.53a) and Fig. 8-3, we have for the components of $\mathbf{\Pi}$,

$$\left.\begin{aligned} \Pi_r &= \Pi\cos\theta = \frac{[p]}{r}\cos\theta \\ \Pi_\theta &= -\Pi\sin\theta = -\frac{[p]}{r}\sin\theta \\ \Pi_\varphi &= 0 \end{aligned}\right\} \tag{8.55}$$

In performing the differential operations in Eqs. (8.54), we may convert the differentiations with respect to r into differentiations with respect to time by using the fact that the argument of $\mathbf{p}$ is $t - r/c$. Thus,

$$\frac{\partial \mathbf{p}}{\partial r} = -\frac{1}{c}\frac{\partial \mathbf{p}}{\partial t} \tag{8.56}$$

Evaluating the vector quantities in Eqs. (8.54), we find

$$\begin{aligned} \mathrm{div}\,\mathbf{\Pi} &= \frac{1}{r^2}\frac{\partial}{\partial r}(r^2\Pi_r) + \frac{1}{r\sin\theta}\frac{\partial}{\partial\theta}(\Pi_\theta\sin\theta) \\ &= \frac{\cos\theta}{r^2}\frac{\partial}{\partial r}(r[p]) - \frac{[p]}{r^2\sin\theta}\frac{\partial}{\partial\theta}(\sin^2\theta) \\ &= \frac{\cos\theta}{r^2}\left(r\frac{\partial[p]}{\partial r} - [p]\right) \\ &= -\left(\frac{[\dot{p}]}{cr} + \frac{[p]}{r^2}\right)\cos\theta \end{aligned} \tag{8.57}$$

$$(\mathbf{grad}\,\mathrm{div}\,\mathbf{\Pi})_r = \frac{\partial}{\partial r}\mathrm{div}\,\mathbf{\Pi}$$

$$= -\frac{\partial}{\partial r}\left(\frac{[\dot{p}]}{cr} + \frac{[p]}{r^2}\right)\cos\theta$$

$$= \left(\frac{[\ddot{p}]}{c^2 r} + 2\frac{[\dot{p}]}{cr^2} + 2\frac{[p]}{r^3}\right)\cos\theta \tag{8.58a}$$

$$(\mathbf{grad}\,\mathrm{div}\,\mathbf{\Pi})_\theta = \frac{1}{r}\frac{\partial}{\partial\theta}\mathrm{div}\,\mathbf{\Pi}$$

$$= \left(\frac{[\dot{p}]}{cr^2} + \frac{[p]}{r^3}\right)\sin\theta \tag{8.58b}$$

$$(\mathbf{grad}\,\mathrm{div}\,\mathbf{\Pi})_\varphi = 0 \tag{8.58c}$$

$$(\mathbf{curl}\,\mathbf{\Pi})_r = 0\,; \qquad (\mathbf{curl}\,\mathbf{\Pi})_\theta = 0 \tag{8.59a}$$

$$(\mathbf{curl}\,\mathbf{\Pi})_\varphi = \frac{1}{r}\left(\frac{\partial}{\partial r}(r\Pi_\theta) - \frac{\partial\Pi_r}{\partial\theta}\right)$$

$$= -\frac{1}{r}\left(\sin\theta\frac{\partial[p]}{\partial r} + \frac{[p]}{r}\frac{\partial}{\partial\theta}\cos\theta\right)$$

$$= \left(\frac{[\dot{p}]}{cr} + \frac{[p]}{r^2}\right)\sin\theta \tag{8.59b}$$

The components of the field vectors may now be computed from Eqs. (8.54):

$$E_r = (\mathbf{grad}\,\mathrm{div}\,\mathbf{\Pi})_r - \frac{1}{c^2}\frac{\partial^2\Pi_r}{\partial t^2}$$

$$= \left(\frac{[\ddot{p}]}{c^2 r} + 2\frac{[\dot{p}]}{cr^2} + 2\frac{[p]}{r^3}\right)\cos\theta - \frac{[\ddot{p}]}{c^2 r}\cos\theta$$

$$= 2\left(\frac{[\dot{p}]}{cr^2} + \frac{[p]}{r^3}\right)\cos\theta \tag{8.60a}$$

$$E_\theta = (\mathbf{grad}\,\mathrm{div}\,\mathbf{\Pi})_\theta - \frac{1}{c^2}\frac{\partial^2\Pi_\theta}{\partial t^2}$$

$$= \left(\frac{[\ddot{p}]}{c^2 r} + \frac{[\dot{p}]}{cr^2} + \frac{[p]}{r^3}\right)\sin\theta \tag{8.60b}$$

$$E_\varphi = 0 \tag{8.60c}$$

$$B_r = 0; \qquad B_\theta = 0 \tag{8.61a}$$

$$\begin{aligned} B_\varphi &= \frac{1}{c}\frac{\partial}{\partial t}(\textbf{curl}\ \mathbf{\Pi})_\varphi \\ &= \left(\frac{[\ddot{p}]}{c^2 r} + \frac{[\dot{p}]}{c r^2}\right)\sin\theta \end{aligned} \tag{8.61b}$$

From these results, as in the previous analysis, we see that there are field components, E_θ and B_φ, which are mutually perpendicular and are both perpendicular to **r**. But in addition, there is a *radial* component of the electric field. Now, as we have noted previously, only terms of the form $|\mathbf{E}|^2 r^2$ and $|\mathbf{B}|^2 r^2$ which do not vanish as $r \to \infty$ can contribute to radiation. Then, for large r (i.e., in the *radiation zone*), the radial electric field becomes entirely negligible, as do all of the components of E_θ and B_φ except the first. Thus, for $r \to \infty$, we have

$$\left.\begin{aligned} E_\theta &= \frac{[\ddot{p}]}{c^2 r}\sin\theta \\ B_\varphi &= \frac{[\ddot{p}]}{c^2 r}\sin\theta \end{aligned}\right\} \quad \text{(Radiation zone)} \tag{8.62}$$

These field components correspond exactly to those found previously [Eqs. (8.22)]. The remainder of the results of Section 8.2 therefore follow immediately.

From Eqs. (8.60) and (8.61) we note that although **E** has a radial component in the near-field region, **B** has no such component in any region of space. The magnetic field due to an oscillating electric dipole is therefore everywhere transverse and the radiation from such a system consists of *transverse magnetic* (TM) radiation. In the radiation zone, $E_r \to 0$ so that the electric field also becomes transverse. Therefore, at large distances, the electric and magnetic fields are *both* transverse and the radiation is TEM (plane waves). The radiation from an oscillating *magnetic* dipole is everywhere transverse electric or TE (see Section 8.10).

8.5 The Near Field of an Oscillating Electric Dipole

Let us now return to the exact expressions for the field vector components [Eqs. (8.60) and (8.61)] and examine the field in the region near the dipole. Since $[p] = p_0 \exp(-i\omega t')$, we may write the previous results as

$$E_r = 2p_0 k^3 \left\{\frac{1}{(kr)^3} - \frac{i}{(kr)^2}\right\}\cos\theta\, e^{-i(\omega t - kr)} \tag{8.63a}$$

$$E_\theta = p_0 k^3 \left\{ \frac{1}{(kr)^3} - \frac{i}{(kr)^2} - \frac{1}{kr} \right\} \sin\theta \, e^{-i(\omega t - kr)} \tag{8.63b}$$

$$B_\varphi = -p_0 k^3 \left\{ \frac{i}{(kr)^2} + \frac{1}{kr} \right\} \sin\theta \, e^{-i(\omega t - kr)} \tag{8.63c}$$

where we have used $t' = t - r/c$ and $k = \omega/c$. These expressions may also be obtained from Eq. (8.12) by retaining the term containing **grad**$(1/r)$. [Note that the approximation $r \gg r'$ which was used in the derivation of Eq. (8.12) is still valid in the near-field region since we are now considering a *point* dipole; see Eq. (8.52).]

For the region very close to the dipole, $kr \ll 1$, and only the terms proportional to $1/r^3$ are important. Consequently, the components of the electric field reduce to

$$\left.\begin{aligned} E_r &\cong \frac{2p_0 \cos\theta}{r^3} e^{-i\omega t} \\ E_\theta &\cong \frac{p_0 \sin\theta}{r^3} e^{-i\omega t} \end{aligned}\right\} \quad \text{(Static zone)} \tag{8.64}$$

These expressions are equivalent to Eqs. (2.9) for the field of a static electric dipole, except that now we have $p = p_0 \exp(-i\omega t)$. The region in the immediate vicinity of an oscillating dipole is accordingly called the *static-field region.* (The field of course changes in this region, but at any instant it is equivalent to a static dipole field.)

We therefore find that the fields are rather simple in the two limiting cases, $kr \ll 1$ and $kr \gg 1$. In the intermediate region ($kr \approx 1$), however, the field of an oscillating dipole is quite complicated.*

The intermediate-zone electric field, obtained from Eqs. (8.63a) and (8.63b) is shown in Fig. 8-4 (adapted from Hertz, He93) for four different instants in a half cycle of the oscillation. At $t = 0$, the near field is just that of a static dipole (compare Fig. 2-2). As time increases, the field lines bulge, neck down, and finally are pinched off. The bundle of field lines then propagates outward and, for large r, becomes entirely transverse. As we have seen, it is only the $1/r$ term that contributes to the eventual propagation of energy to infinitely large r; the other terms give rise to an oscillation of energy back and forth in the intermediate (or *induction*) zone.

We may gain a bit more insight into the near-zone fields by examining the components in the plane defined by $\theta = \pi/2$. For this case, only E_θ

* The properties of the fields in the intermediate region were investigated in detail by Heinrich Hertz, beginning in about 1888 (see He93).

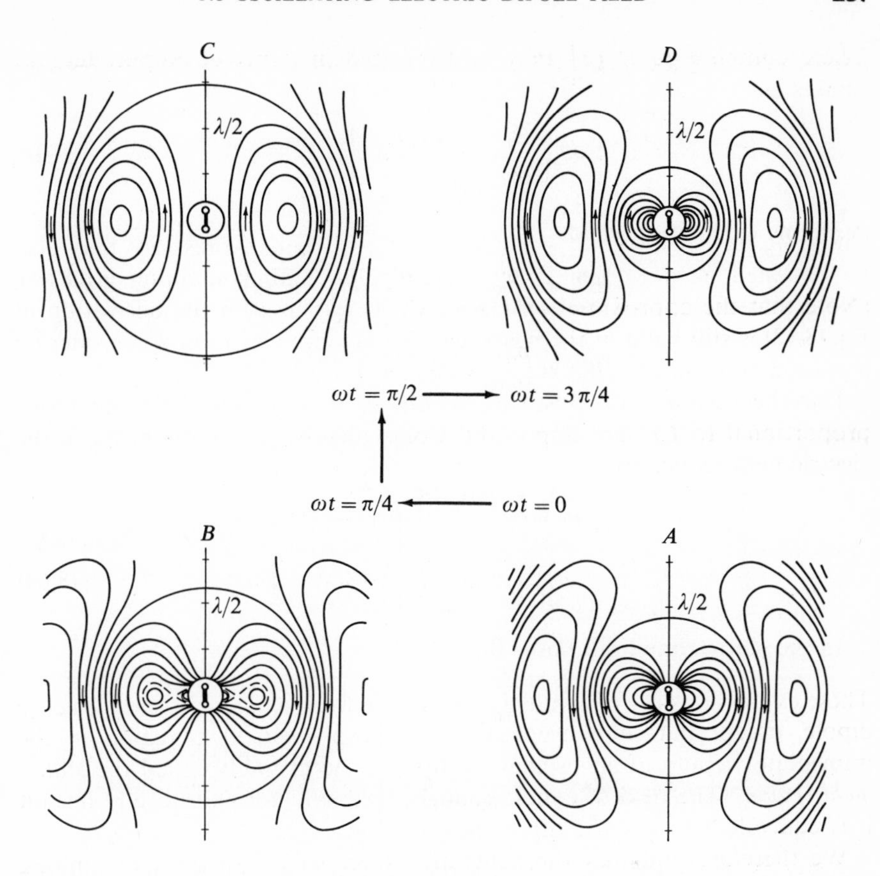

FIG. **8-4**

and B_φ are different from zero:

$$\left.\begin{aligned} E_\theta &= \quad E_\theta^0 e^{-i(\omega t - kr)} \\ B_\varphi &= -B_\varphi^0 e^{-i(\omega t - kr)} \end{aligned}\right\} \tag{8.65}$$

where

$$\left.\begin{aligned} E_\theta^0 &\equiv p_0 k^3 \left\{ \frac{1}{(kr)^3} - \frac{i}{(kr)^2} - \frac{1}{kr} \right\} \\ B_\varphi^0 &\equiv p_0 k^3 \left\{ \frac{i}{(kr)^2} + \frac{1}{kr} \right\} \end{aligned}\right\} \tag{8.66}$$

These complex quantities may be expressed in terms of amplitudes and phases as

$$\left.\begin{aligned} E_\theta^0 &= |E_\theta^0| e^{i\phi_E} \\ B_\varphi^0 &= |B_\varphi^0| e^{i\phi_B} \end{aligned}\right\} \tag{8.67}$$

A simple calculation yields

$$\left.\begin{aligned} |E_\theta^0| &= \frac{p_0 k^3}{(kr)^3}\sqrt{(kr)^4 - (kr)^2 + 1} \\ |B_\varphi^0| &= \frac{p_0 k^3}{(kr)^2}\sqrt{(kr)^2 + 1} \end{aligned}\right\} \tag{8.68}$$

and

$$\left.\begin{aligned} \phi_E &= \tan^{-1}\left(\frac{kr}{(kr)^2 - 1}\right) \\ \phi_B &= \tan^{-1}\left(\frac{1}{kr}\right) \end{aligned}\right\} \tag{8.69}$$

In the static-zone limit ($kr \to 0$), we have

$$\left.\begin{aligned} |E_\theta^0| &\to \frac{p_0}{r^3}; \qquad \phi_E \to \pi \\ |B_\varphi^0| &\to \frac{p_0 k}{r^2}; \qquad \phi_B \to \frac{\pi}{2} \end{aligned}\right\} \quad \text{(Static zone)} \tag{8.70}$$

We see, therefore, that very close to the dipole the magnitude of the electric field exhibits the $1/r^3$ variation characteristic of the static dipole. The magnetic field, on the other hand, depends on the frequency through the factor k. For the truly static case, $\omega = 0$ and $k = 0$, so that $|B_\varphi^0| = 0$. The ratio of the electric to the magnetic field as a function of k is

$$\frac{|E_\theta^0|}{|B_\phi^0|} = \frac{1}{kr} \tag{8.71}$$

Thus, the field is essentially entirely electric in the static zone.

In the radiation-zone limit ($kr \to \infty$), the fields become identical, as required for TEM waves:

$$\left.\begin{aligned} |E_\theta^0| &\to \frac{p_0 k^2}{r}; \qquad \phi_E \to 0 \\ |B_\varphi^0| &\to \frac{p_0 k^2}{r}; \qquad \phi_B \to 0 \end{aligned}\right\} \quad \text{(Radiation zone)} \tag{8.72}$$

The amplitudes and phases are shown as functions of kr in Figs. 8-5 and 8-6. From these curves it is apparent that the radiation zone may be considered to be that region for which kr exceeds a value of about 5 or 10; that is, $r \gtrsim 2\lambda$. At the other extreme, we may take the limit of the static

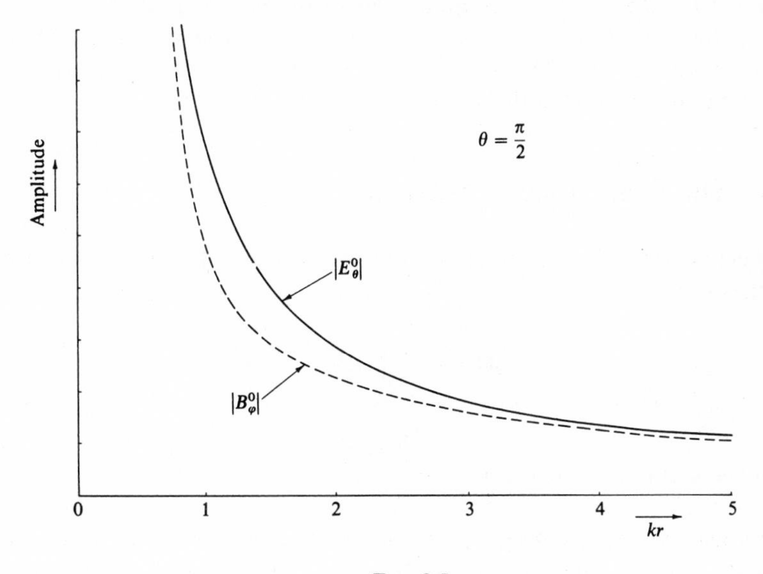

FIG. 8-5

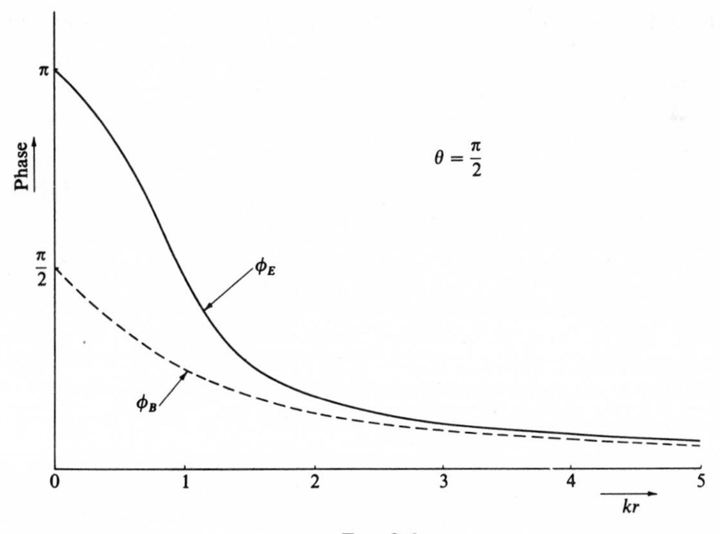

FIG. 8-6

zone to be the point at which $|B_{\varphi}^0|$ is no more than a few per cent of $|E_{\theta}^0|$. Equation (8.71) then indicates that we must have $r \lesssim \lambda/200$. That is, the static zone encompasses a region whose dimensions are only a small fraction of a wavelength of the radiation. For optical radiation, $\lambda \approx 5000$ Å $= 5 \times 10^{-5}$ cm, so that essentially all ordinary observations are carried out in the radiation zone. However, if the radiation is long radio waves ($\nu \approx 500$ kc/sec; $\lambda \approx 1500$ meters), the intermediate zone extends a considerable distance from the source.

8.6 The Short Linear Antenna

The first time derivative of the dipole moment of a system of discrete charges q_α is

$$\dot{\mathbf{p}}(t') = \frac{d}{dt'} \sum_\alpha q_\alpha \mathbf{r}'_\alpha(t')$$

$$= \sum_\alpha (q_\alpha \dot{\mathbf{r}}'_\alpha + \mathbf{r}'_\alpha \dot{q}_\alpha) \tag{8.73}$$

Previously, we have considered all of the charges to be of fixed magnitude so that the second term in Eq. (8.73) was not present. We now wish to alter our viewpoint and regard the vectors $\mathbf{r}'_\alpha$ as fixed, whereas the charges q_α are allowed to vary with time. The simplest example of such a situation is shown in Fig. 8-7. We may consider the time variation of the charges as

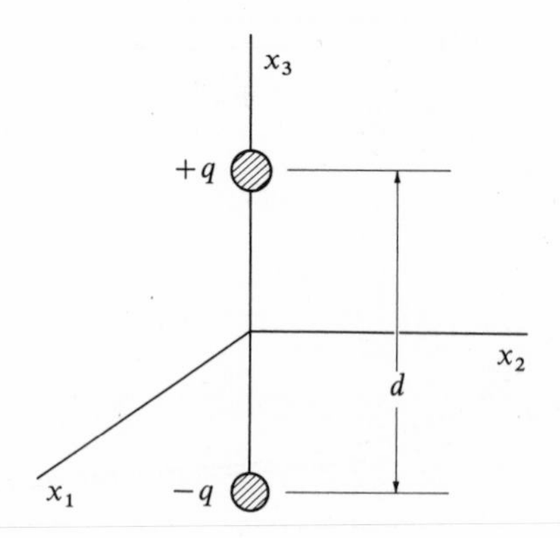

FIG. 8-7

being equivalent to the flow of a current between $x_3 = +d/2$ and $x_3 = -d/2$. The system therefore represents a simple linear antenna. Thus,

$$\dot{\mathbf{p}}(t') = \sum_{\alpha} \mathbf{r}'_{\alpha}\dot{q}_{\alpha} = I(t')d\,\mathbf{e}_3 \tag{8.74}$$

where the current I has been substituted for the time rate of change of the charge. If we have a harmonic time variation of the current,

$$I(t') = I_1 e^{-i\omega t'} \tag{8.75}$$

then,

$$\ddot{p}(t') = -i\omega I_1 d\, e^{-i\omega t'}$$

Hence,

$$\langle[\ddot{p}]^2\rangle = \tfrac{1}{2}I_1^2 d^2\omega^2 \tag{8.76}$$

The angular distribution of the average power radiated from such a system is

$$\left\langle\frac{dP}{d\Omega}\right\rangle = \frac{I_1^2 d^2\omega^2}{8\pi c^3}\sin^2\theta = \frac{\pi I_1^2}{2c}\left(\frac{d}{\lambda}\right)^2 \sin^2\theta \tag{8.77}$$

and the average total radiated power is

$$\langle P\rangle = \frac{I_1^2 d^2\omega^2}{3c^3} = \frac{4\pi^2 I_1^2}{3c}\left(\frac{d}{\lambda}\right)^2 \tag{8.78}$$

In order to maintain the radiation, it is, of course, necessary that power be continually supplied to the antenna. The oscillator which supplies this power must also furnish power which is dissipated as Joule heating.

If R_{eff} is the effective ohmic resistance* of the antenna, the power which goes into heating is

$$P_{\text{heat}} = I^2 R_{\text{eff}} \tag{8.79}$$

or,

$$\langle P\rangle_{\text{heat}} = \langle I^2\rangle R_{\text{eff}} = \tfrac{1}{2}I_1^2 R_{\text{eff}} \tag{8.80}$$

By analogy, the factor in Eq. (8.78) that multiplies $I_1^2/2$ is called the *radiation resistance* of the antenna, R_{rad}:

$$R_{\text{rad}} = \frac{8\pi^2}{3c}\left(\frac{d}{\lambda}\right)^2 \quad \text{statohms} \tag{8.81}$$

In MKS units, the radiation resistance may be expressed as

$$R_{\text{rad}} = 787\left(\frac{d}{\lambda}\right)^2 \quad \text{ohms} \tag{8.81a}$$

* Due to the concentration of the current on the surface of conductors at high frequencies (see Section 5.7), R_{eff} may not be equal to the dc resistance of the antenna.

It should be recalled that in order to obtain these results we have used the approximation that the dimensions of the system are small compared to the wavelength of the radiation. Therefore, the expressions above are valid only for $d \ll \lambda$. If we have an antenna for which $d = 0.01\lambda$, then the radiation resistance is approximately 0.08 ohm. The ohmic resistance of such an antenna could be appreciably larger than this value. Thus, most of the input power would be dissipated as heat and very little would be radiated as electromagnetic energy. A short dipole antenna is therefore in general only an inefficient radiator; d must be comparable with λ in order that electromagnetic energy can be efficiently radiated, but the dipole approximation is not valid for such a case. In the next sections we shall examine some more practical examples of antennas.

8.7 Linear Antennas

We shall consider first an antenna somewhat more realistic than that previously discussed—the linear center-driven antenna, shown schematically in Fig. 8-8. This antenna consists of two thin wires, each of length $d/2$ with a small separation between them for the purpose of applying the signal from an oscillator by means of, say, a coaxial cable. We shall consider the input signal to vary harmonically with time. The variation of the current

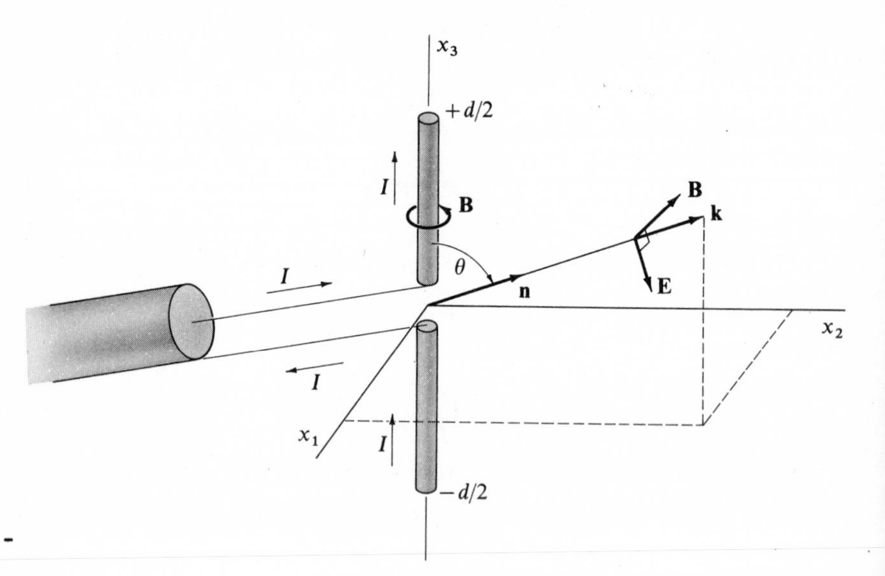

FIG. 8-8

density (now a *linear* current density) must also vary harmonically with time and with distance along the antenna wire. The current density obviously must vanish at the ends of the antenna; and, since the system is symmetric, we may write

$$\mathbf{J}(\mathbf{r}', t') = \mathbf{e}_3 I_0 e^{-i\omega t'} \sin\left(\frac{kd}{2} - k|x_3'|\right) \tag{8.82}$$

where the input signal (i.e., the current at the gap) is

$$I(t') = I_0 e^{-i\omega t'} \sin\frac{kd}{2} \tag{8.83}$$

That is,

$$\mathbf{J}(\mathbf{r}', t') = \mathbf{J}(\mathbf{r}')e^{-i\omega t'} = \mathbf{e}_3 J(x_3)e^{-i\omega t'} \tag{8.84}$$

In order to calculate the properties of the radiation field produced by this antenna, we begin with the general expression for the vector potential:

$$\mathbf{A}(\mathbf{r}, t) = \frac{1}{c}\int_V \frac{\mathbf{J}(\mathbf{r}', t')}{|\mathbf{r} - \mathbf{r}'|}\, dv' \tag{8.85}$$

At distances r that are large compared with the dimensions of the system (i.e., $r \gg d$), we may write [see Eq. (8.5)]

$$\mathbf{A}(\mathbf{r}, t) = \frac{1}{cr}\int_V \mathbf{J}(\mathbf{r}', t - r/c)\, dv' \tag{8.86}$$

The magnetic induction vector is given by the curl of this expression:

$$\mathbf{B} = \frac{1}{c}\,\mathbf{curl}\left\{\frac{1}{r}\int_V \mathbf{J}(\mathbf{r}', t')\, dv'\right\} \tag{8.87}$$

Expanding the curl and neglecting the term involving $\mathbf{grad}(1/r)$ [as in Eq. (8.13)] since it does not contribute to the radiation, we have

$$\begin{aligned}\mathbf{B}_{\text{rad}} &= \frac{1}{cr}\,\mathbf{curl}\left\{\int_V \mathbf{J}(\mathbf{r}', t')\, dv'\right\} \\ &= \frac{1}{cr}\,\mathbf{curl}\,\mathbf{f}(t')\end{aligned} \tag{8.88}$$

where

$$\mathbf{f}(t') \equiv \int_V \mathbf{J}(\mathbf{r}', t')\, dv' \tag{8.89}$$

Following the procedure of Eq. (8.14), we write

$$\begin{aligned}\mathbf{curl}\,\mathbf{f}(t') &= \sum_{i,j,k} \varepsilon_{ijk}\mathbf{e}_i \frac{\partial f_k}{\partial x_j} \\ &= \sum_{i,j,k} \varepsilon_{ijk}\mathbf{e}_i \frac{\partial f_k}{\partial t'}\frac{\partial t'}{\partial x_j} \\ &= -\frac{1}{c}\sum_{i,j,k} \varepsilon_{ijk}\mathbf{e}_i n_j \frac{\partial f_k}{\partial t'}\end{aligned} \tag{8.90}$$

Therefore,

$$\mathbf{curl}\,\mathbf{f}(t') = -\frac{1}{c}\mathbf{n} \times \frac{\partial \mathbf{f}}{\partial t'} \tag{8.91}$$

from which

$$\mathbf{B}_{\text{rad}} = -\frac{1}{c^2 r}\mathbf{n} \times \frac{\partial}{\partial t}\int_V \mathbf{J}(\mathbf{r}', t')\,dv' \tag{8.92}$$

where the substitution of $\partial/\partial t$ for $\partial/\partial t'$ in front of the integral is permissible in the approximation that $t' = t - r/c$, since r is constant. Thus,

$$\mathbf{B}_{\text{rad}} = -\frac{1}{c}\mathbf{n} \times \frac{\partial \mathbf{A}}{\partial t} \tag{8.93}$$

Now, we have assumed a harmonic dependence on time for $\mathbf{J}$, so we must also have the same form for $\mathbf{A}$:

$$\left.\begin{aligned}\mathbf{J}(\mathbf{r}', t') &= \mathbf{J}(\mathbf{r}')e^{-i\omega t'} \\ \mathbf{A}(\mathbf{r}, t) &= \mathbf{A}(\mathbf{r})e^{-i\omega t}\end{aligned}\right\} \tag{8.94}$$

Differentiating $\mathbf{A}$ and substituting into Eq. (8.93), we obtain

$$\begin{aligned}\mathbf{B}_{\text{rad}} &= i\frac{\omega}{c}\mathbf{n} \times \mathbf{A} \\ &= ik\mathbf{n} \times \mathbf{A}\end{aligned} \tag{8.95}$$

This expression, as well as Eq. (8.93), is a general result and depends only upon the assumption that the point at which $\mathbf{B}$ is measured is far from the source. The fact that we assumed harmonic time variations for $\mathbf{J}$ and $\mathbf{A}$ does not destroy the generality since we may always consider these terms as Fourier components of the general expressions. Any arbitrary time variation can then be represented as a Fourier integral.

Returning to Eq. (8.85) and explicitly writing the time dependence, we have

$$\mathbf{A}(\mathbf{r}, t) = \mathbf{A}(\mathbf{r})e^{-i\omega t} = \frac{1}{c}\int_V \frac{\mathbf{J}(\mathbf{r}')e^{-i\omega t}e^{ik|\mathbf{r}-\mathbf{r}'|}}{|\mathbf{r} - \mathbf{r}'|}\,dv' \tag{8.96}$$

where we have used $k = \omega/c$ in expressing $\exp(-i\omega t')$. Now, since $r \gg r'$, we have approximately (see Fig. 8-9),

$$|\mathbf{r} - \mathbf{r}'| \cong r - \mathbf{n}\cdot\mathbf{r}' = r\left(1 - \frac{\mathbf{n}\cdot\mathbf{r}'}{r}\right) \tag{8.97}$$

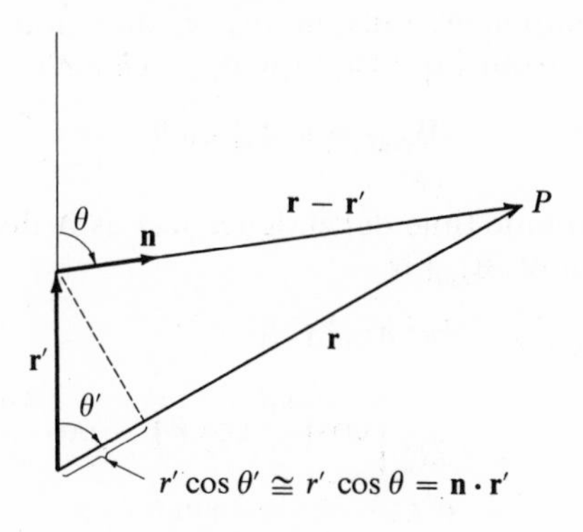

FIG. **8-9**

Therefore, Eq. (8.96) becomes

$$\mathbf{A}(\mathbf{r}) = \frac{e^{ikr}}{cr}\int_V \frac{\mathbf{J}(\mathbf{r}')e^{-ik(\mathbf{n}\cdot\mathbf{r}')}}{1 - [(\mathbf{n}\cdot\mathbf{r}')/r]}\,dv' \tag{8.98}$$

In the exponential term we write

$$\mathbf{n}\cdot\mathbf{r}' = r'\cos\theta \tag{8.99}$$

and if we neglect $(\mathbf{n}\cdot\mathbf{r}')/r$ as small compared with unity in the denominator of Eq. (8.98), we have

$$\mathbf{A}(\mathbf{r}) = \frac{e^{ikr}}{cr}\int_V \mathbf{J}(\mathbf{r}')e^{-ikr'\cos\theta}\,dv' \tag{8.100}$$

Again, we have a general result, dependent only on the assumption that our field point is at a distance large compared with the dimensions of the source. In this form, the expression for $\mathbf{A}$ may be integrated for the current distribution of the center-driven antenna [Eq. (8.83)]:

$$\mathbf{A}(\mathbf{r}) = \mathbf{e}_3\frac{I_0 e^{ikr}}{cr}\int_{-d/2}^{+d/2}\sin\left(\frac{kd}{2} - k|x_3'|\right)e^{-ikx_3'\cos\theta}\,dx_3' \tag{8.101}$$

from which (see Problem 8-6)

$$\mathbf{A}(\mathbf{r}) = \mathbf{e}_3 \frac{2I_0 e^{ikr}}{ckr} \left(\frac{\cos\left(\frac{kd}{2}\cos\theta\right) - \cos\frac{kd}{2}}{\sin^2\theta} \right) \tag{8.102}$$

Since $\mathbf{A}$ has a component only in the x_3-direction, $\mathbf{n} \times \mathbf{A} = |A_3| \sin\theta$ (see Fig. 8-8). Hence, from Eq. (8.95) for $\mathbf{B}_{\text{rad}}$, we have

$$|\mathbf{B}_{\text{rad}}| = k|A_3| \sin\theta \tag{8.103}$$

Now, $\mathbf{B}_{\text{rad}}$ has a harmonic time dependence just as $\mathbf{A}$ does, so that the time average of the square of $|\mathbf{B}_{\text{rad}}|$ is

$$\begin{aligned} \langle |\mathbf{B}_{\text{rad}}|^2 \rangle &= \tfrac{1}{2}k^2 A_3^2 \sin^2\theta \\ &= \frac{2I_0^2}{c^2 r^2} \left(\frac{\cos\left(\frac{kd}{2}\cos\theta\right) - \cos\frac{kd}{2}}{\sin\theta} \right)^2 \end{aligned} \tag{8.104}$$

The time average of the portion of the Poynting vector that contributes to the radiation is

$$\langle \mathbf{S}_{\text{rad}} \rangle = \frac{c}{4\pi} \langle |\mathbf{B}_{\text{rad}}|^2 \rangle \mathbf{n} \tag{8.105}$$

and the average power radiated into a unit solid angle is

$$\begin{aligned} \left\langle \frac{dP}{d\Omega} \right\rangle &= r^2 \langle \mathbf{S}_{\text{rad}} \rangle \cdot \mathbf{n} \\ &= \frac{I_0^2}{2\pi c} \left(\frac{\cos\left(\frac{kd}{2}\cos\theta\right) - \cos\frac{kd}{2}}{\sin\theta} \right)^2 \end{aligned} \tag{8.106}$$

The angular distribution of the radiated power depends upon the value of $kd/2$. Situations in which the antenna length bears a simple relationship to the wavelength of the driving oscillations are of particular interest. For example, if the oscillation frequency of the driver is such that the antenna length d is an integral number m of half wavelengths of the driving oscillations, then

$$d = m\frac{\lambda}{2} = \frac{m\pi}{k}$$

and, we have

$$\left\langle \frac{dP}{d\Omega} \right\rangle = \frac{I_0^2}{2\pi c} \left(\frac{\cos\left(\frac{m\pi}{2}\cos\theta\right) - \cos\left(\frac{m\pi}{2}\right)}{\sin\theta} \right)^2 \tag{8.107}$$

The current distributions for $m = 1, 2, 3, 4$ are shown in Fig. 8-10, in which the solid curves represent the forms of the distributions during one half of the cycle of the driving oscillations and the dotted curves represent the

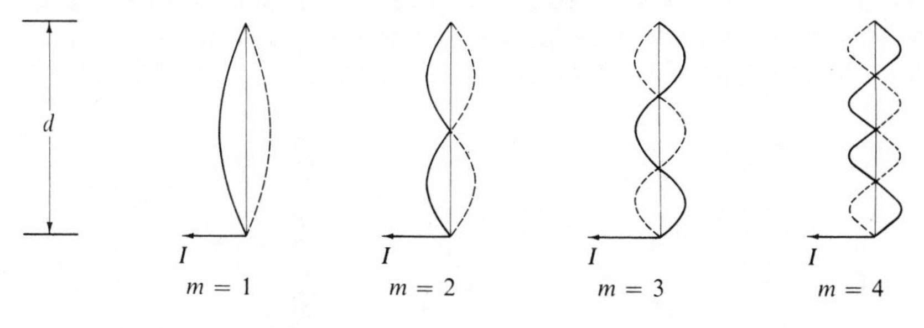

FIG. **8-10**

forms during the other half cycle. Positive and negative values of I mean, of course, different directions of current flow in the antenna. The angular distributions for the important cases of the half-wave ($m = 1$) and full-wave ($m = 2$) antennas are

$$\left\langle \frac{dP}{d\Omega} \right\rangle_{m=1} = \frac{I_0^2}{2\pi c} \frac{\cos^2\left(\frac{\pi}{2}\cos\theta\right)}{\sin^2\theta} \tag{8.108}$$

$$\left\langle \frac{dP}{d\Omega} \right\rangle_{m=2} = \frac{2I_0^2}{\pi c} \frac{\cos^4\left(\frac{\pi}{2}\cos\theta\right)}{\sin^2\theta} \tag{8.109}$$

The time average of the total power radiated by a half-wave center-driven antenna is (see Problem 8-8)

$$\langle P \rangle = 2.44\left(\frac{I_0^2}{2c}\right)$$

The radiation resistance of such an antenna is approximately 73 ohms. Therefore, the half-wave antenna is a much more efficient radiator than the short dipole (recall that for $d = 0.01\lambda$, the radiation resistance is approximately 0.08 ohm). The radiation resistance of the full-wave antenna is approximately 201 ohms and is therefore an even more efficient radiator.

From Fig. 8-10 it is apparent that the full-wave antenna can be represented by two half-wave antennas placed end-to-end and driven in phase. The half-wave antenna is in fact the basic unit of many antenna systems. By appropriate placement of such antennas and by proper choice of the relative phases of the driving current, it is possible to obtain a wide variety of radiation patterns (see Section 8.9).

We may also choose to drive an antenna such that the current density distributions are of the forms shown in Fig. 8-11. Such current distributions may be obtained, for example, by driving the antenna from one end (an *end-driven* antenna) or by using a center feed but driving the sections out of phase for even values of m.

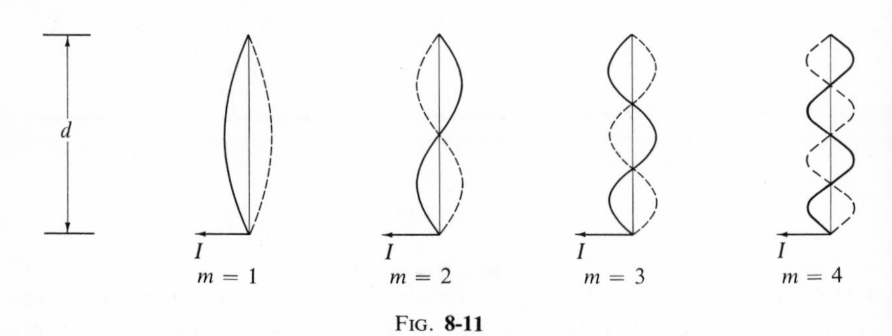

FIG. **8-11**

The radiation patterns for the current distributions of Fig. 8-11 may be obtained by calculating the integral for the vector potential in the same manner as above. For odd values of m, clearly the same results are obtained, namely,

$$\left\langle \frac{dP}{d\Omega} \right\rangle = \frac{I_0^2}{2\pi c} \frac{\cos^2\left(\dfrac{m\pi}{2}\cos\theta\right)}{\sin^2\theta}, \qquad m = 1, 3, 5, \cdots \tag{8.110}$$

where the term $\cos(m\pi/2)$ in Eq. (8.107) vanishes for odd values of m.

For even values of m, the current distribution is no longer symmetric about the mid-point of the antenna and we must therefore replace $|x_3'|$ in the expression for the vector potential [Eq. (8.101)] by x_3'. The integral now becomes complex (whereas before it was real), and the evaluation is a bit more complicated, but upon computing $|\mathbf{A}|^2 = |A_3|^2$, the average radiated power per unit solid angle is (see Problem 8-9)

$$\left\langle \frac{dP}{d\Omega} \right\rangle = \frac{I_0^2}{2\pi c} \frac{\sin^2\left(\dfrac{m\pi}{2}\cos\theta\right)}{\sin^2\theta}, \qquad m = 2, 4, 6, \cdots \tag{8.111}$$

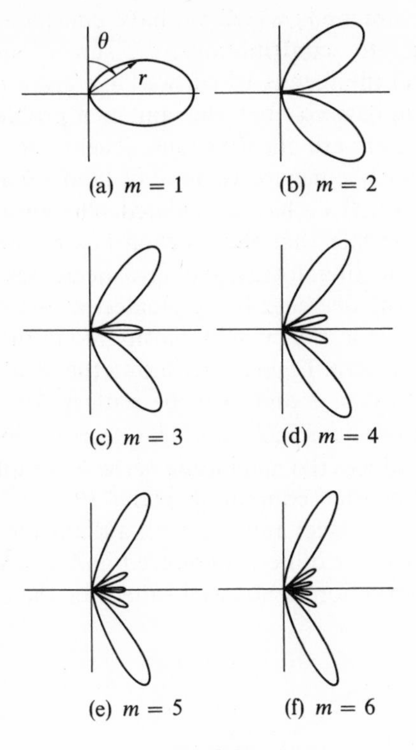

FIG. **8-12**

The radiation patterns for $m = 1$–6 are shown in Fig. 8-12. The more intense radiation lobe is always found nearest the antenna, and, as $m \to \infty$, this lobe corresponds with the antenna direction.

The radiation is, of course, symmetric about the axis of the antenna, so that the complete patterns are obtained by constructing the surfaces of revolution about the x_3'-axes (i.e., the *polar* axes).

The directionality of the radiation may be further enhanced by the use of reflectors of various types. Common reflector geometries are the parabolic dish (frequently used in radar antennas) and stacks of bars mounted parallel to the driven element (as seen in many television receiving antennas —the so-called *Yagi array*).

It should be noted that the angular distributions which we have derived for the radiated power are *exact*, at least in the sense that they are valid for an ideal, isolated antenna for observation points far removed from the antenna. That is to say, we have *not* made use of the dipole approximation [Eq. (8.1)] in the derivations; otherwise, we would be limited to $kd \ll 1$. Whereas it is possible to make a multipole expansion of the radiation from the antennas which we have considered and to obtain the dipole, quadrupole, etc., contributions, the sum of all of these individual terms will just equal the results which we have given for $\langle dP/d\Omega \rangle$.

It should be emphasized that the antenna problems which we have treated in this section are idealizations. There are several factors of a practical nature which conspire to modify (and often quite severely) the radiation patterns which we have calculated. The most crucial effect comes about because of the fact that the antenna has resistance [see Eq. (8.81)]. This gives rise to heating losses and also decreases the current density along the antenna, the decrease being greatest at the end or ends opposite the driver. The change in the current density along the wire can drastically alter the radiation pattern. Figure 8-13 shows the ideal pattern for a center-driven antenna with $m = 3$ and also the pattern for a real case in which the effects of the losses are included. The decrease in the current density along the antenna reduces the magnitude of the outer lobes and concentrates the radiation nearer the equatorial plane ($\theta = \pi/2$). The case shown approximates that for a steel antenna with a diameter of a few millimeters. The effect of the losses is quite pronounced and, obviously, an antenna of this particular construction is not well suited for the efficient transmission of power.

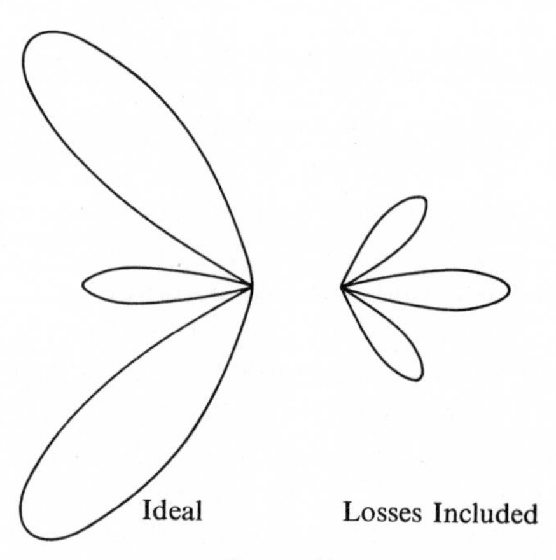

FIG. **8-13**

We must also remark that we have tacitly assumed all along that the antenna was isolated. In practice, of course, antennas are frequently mounted vertically above the earth. Since the earth is a conductor, reflection of the radiation will occur and the effect is that an "image antenna" is induced which can produce radiation that will interfere with the primary radiation.

In the preceding section we found that the angular distribution of power radiated by a short linear antenna is given by [Eq. (8.77)]:

$$\left\langle \frac{dP}{d\Omega} \right\rangle_{\text{short}} = \frac{\pi I_1^2}{2c} \left(\frac{d}{\lambda} \right)^2 \sin^2 \theta \tag{1}$$

From Eq. (8.106) we have the result for the power radiated from an antenna whose length is not restricted to be small compared to λ:

$$\left\langle \frac{dP}{d\Omega} \right\rangle = \frac{I_0^2}{2\pi c} \left(\frac{\cos\left(\frac{kd}{2} \cos \theta \right) - \cos \frac{kd}{2}}{\sin \theta} \right)^2 \tag{2}$$

These two expressions must, of course, yield the same result in the limit $\lambda \to \infty$ or, equivalently, $k \to 0$. In order to make such a comparison, we require that the *current densities* in the two equations refer to a common basis. In deriving Eq. (8.77), we used

$$[I(t')]_{\text{short}} = I_1 e^{-i\omega t'} \tag{3}$$

whereas in obtaining Eq. (8.106) we used

$$I(t') = I_0 e^{-i\omega t'} \sin\left(\frac{kd}{2} - k|x_3'| \right) \tag{4}$$

In the limit $k \to 0$, Eq. (4) becomes

$$I(t') = I_0 e^{-i\omega t'} \left(\frac{kd}{2} - k|x_3'| \right) \tag{4a}$$

Therefore, we identify

$$I_0 e^{-i\omega t'} \left(\frac{kd}{2} - k|x_3'| \right) = I_1 e^{-i\omega t'}$$

This requirement is clearly impossible to satisfy in general. It is possible, however, to equate the two *average* currents:

$$\langle [I(t')]_{\text{short}} \rangle = \langle I(t') \rangle$$

$$I_1 = I_0 \cdot \frac{1}{d} \int_{-d/2}^{+d/2} \left(\frac{kd}{2} - k|x_3'| \right) dx_3' = \frac{kd}{4} I_0 \tag{5}$$

If we substitute this result into Eq. (2) and make the small-angle approximation for the cosine, we find

$$\left\langle \frac{dP}{d\Omega} \right\rangle_{k \to 0} = \left(\frac{4I_1}{kd} \right) \frac{1}{2\pi c} \left(\frac{\left\{ 1 - \frac{1}{2} \left(\frac{kd}{2} \cos \theta \right)^2 \right\} - \left\{ 1 - \frac{1}{2} \left(\frac{kd}{2} \right)^2 \right\}}{\sin \theta} \right)$$

$$= \frac{(kd)^2}{8\pi c} I_1^2 \sin^2 \theta \tag{6}$$

And using $k = 2\pi/\lambda$, we have finally,

$$\left\langle \frac{dP}{d\Omega} \right\rangle_{k \to 0} = \frac{\pi I_1^2}{2c} \left(\frac{d}{\lambda} \right)^2 \sin^2 \theta \tag{7}$$

which is identical with Eq. (1).

8.8 Electric Quadrupole Radiation

In the preceding section we found that the angular distribution of radiation from a full-wave, end-driven antenna is given by [Eq. (8.111) with $m = 2$]

$$\left\langle \frac{dP}{d\Omega} \right\rangle = \frac{I_0^2}{2\pi c} \frac{\sin^2(\pi \cos \theta)}{\sin^2 \theta} \tag{8.112}$$

Let us approximate this antenna by two point dipoles separated linearly by a distance $d/2$ and oscillating out of phase, as in Fig. 8-14. The dipoles of such a pair always have their moments oppositely directed so that there is no net dipole moment. But the system possesses a quadrupole moment and since this moment varies with time we may expect that *quadrupole radiation* will be emitted.

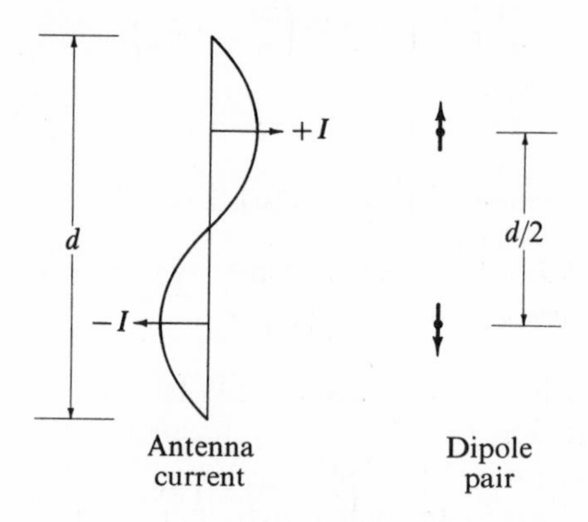

FIG. **8-14**

Recall that the derivation which resulted in Eq. (8.112) was exact (for the ideal case). We have now replaced the antenna current distribution by an oscillating quadrupole so that our result will be the quadrupole (or dipole-pair) approximation to Eq. (8.112). We may proceed with the derivation most easily by considering the quadrupole field to be the superposition (with the proper phases) of two dipole fields. If we had a single dipole located at the origin, the time dependence of the (scalar) dipole moment could be represented as

$$p(t') = [p] = p_0 e^{-i\omega t'} \tag{8.113}$$

so that

$$\ddot{p}(t') = [\ddot{p}] = -\omega^2 p_0 e^{-i\omega t'} \tag{8.114}$$

Then, according to Eq. (8.62), the only component of the electric vector in the radiation zone is

$$E_\theta = \frac{[\ddot{p}]}{c^2 r} \sin\theta$$

$$= -\frac{\omega^2 p_0}{c^2 r} \sin\theta\, e^{-i\omega t'} \tag{8.115}$$

We wish to determine the total electric field due to two dipoles displaced from the origin by $+d/4$ and $-d/4$, as in Fig. 8-15. The radiation from dipole 1 is closer to the field point P than is the origin by approximately $a = (d/4)\cos\theta$; similarly, dipole 2 is farther from the field point by the

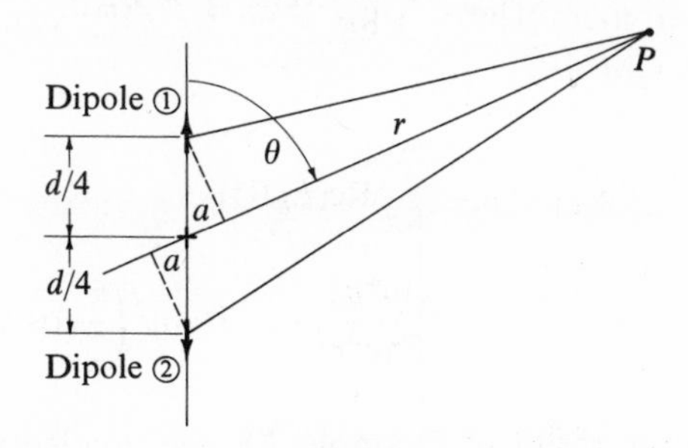

FIG. 8-15

same amount. Therefore, the phase of dipole 1 relative to the origin is $+(kd/4)\cos\theta$, where $k = \omega/c$. Similarly, the phase of dipole 2 relative to the origin is $-(kd/4)\cos\theta - \pi$, where the phase factor $-\pi$ enters since the two dipoles are assumed to oscillate exactly out of phase. The θ-component of the electric vector for the dipole pair is, therefore,

$$E_\theta = -\frac{\omega^2 p_0}{c^2 r}\sin\theta\left\{\exp\left[i\left(\frac{kd}{4}\cos\theta\right)\right] + \exp\left[-i\left(\frac{kd}{4}\cos\theta + \pi\right)\right]\right\}\exp[-i\omega t']$$

$$= -\frac{\omega^2 p_0}{c^2 r}\sin\theta\left\{\exp\left[i\left(\frac{kd}{4}\cos\theta\right)\right] - \exp\left[-i\left(\frac{kd}{4}\cos\theta\right)\right]\right\}\exp[-i\omega t'] \tag{8.116}$$

where we have used $\exp(-i\pi) = -1$. The curly brackets in Eq. (8.116) may be written as

$$\{\ \} = 2i \sin\left(\frac{kd}{4}\cos\theta\right)$$

Thus,

$$E_\theta = -2i\frac{\omega^2 p_0}{c^2 r}\sin\theta \sin\left(\frac{kd}{4}\cos\theta\right)e^{-i\omega t'} = B_\varphi \tag{8.117}$$

where we have indicated that $E_\theta = B_\varphi$ in the radiation zone [see Eqs. (8.62)]. If the dipoles are separated by a half wavelength, then $kd = 2\pi$, so that

$$E_\theta = B_\varphi = -2i\frac{\omega^2 p_0}{c^2 r}\sin\theta \sin\left(\frac{\pi}{2}\cos\theta\right)e^{-i\omega t'} \tag{8.117a}$$

The time-averaged Poynting vector is [Eq. (5.33)]

$$\langle \mathbf{S}_{\text{rad}} \rangle = \frac{c}{8\pi}\,\text{Re}(\mathbf{E}_{\text{rad}} \times \mathbf{B}^*_{\text{rad}}) \tag{8.118}$$

or,

$$\begin{aligned}\langle \mathbf{S}_{\text{rad}} \rangle \cdot \mathbf{n} &= \frac{c}{8\pi}\,\text{Re}(E_\theta B^*_\varphi) \\ &= \frac{\omega^4 p_0^2}{2\pi c^3 r^2}\sin^2\theta \sin^2\left(\frac{\pi}{2}\cos\theta\right)\end{aligned} \tag{8.119}$$

According to the result of Example 2.5, the quadrupole moment for the dipole pair in Fig. 8-15 is $Q = 2p_0 d$. Using also that $k = \omega/c = 2\pi/d$, we obtain

$$\begin{aligned}\left\langle \frac{dP}{d\Omega} \right\rangle &= r^2 \langle \mathbf{S}_{\text{rad}} \rangle \cdot \mathbf{n} \\ &= \frac{\omega^6 Q^2}{32\pi^3 c^5}\sin^2\theta \sin^2\left(\frac{\pi}{2}\cos\theta\right)\end{aligned} \tag{8.120}$$

Although the form of this expression for the angular distribution of the emitted radiation appears to be considerably different from that of the exact calculation [Eq. (8.112)], the two distributions are in fact quite similar. Figure 8-16 shows these radiation patterns, normalized to the same maximum value. It is apparent that the approximation of the dipole pair, or quadrupole, is very close to the exact result. The angles for maximum radiation emission are

$$\theta_{\max}\,(\text{exact}) \cong 54^\circ$$

$$\theta_{\max}\,(\text{dipole pair}) \cong 51^\circ$$

In the approximation above, the oscillating quadrupole consisted of two point dipoles separated by one-half of the antenna length. Let us now simplify the system even further, by collapsing the two dipoles to form a

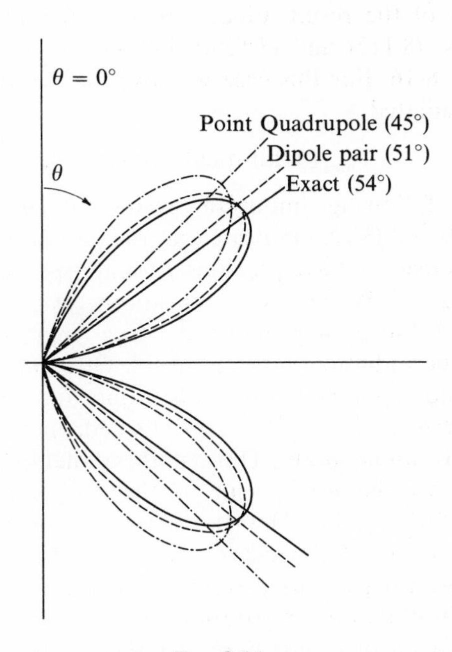

FIG. **8-16**

point quadrupole, located at the origin. (In passing to the limit $d \to 0$, we let p_0 increase as the separation decreases so that Q remains constant.) We may use the previous analysis with only one change, viz., kd is now a small quantity, so that in Eq. (8.117) we may write approximately

$$\sin\left(\frac{kd}{4}\cos\theta\right) \cong \frac{kd}{4}\cos\theta \tag{8.121}$$

Therefore,

$$E_\theta = -i\frac{\omega^2 p_0 kd}{2c^2 r}\sin\theta\cos\theta\, e^{-i\omega t'} \tag{8.112}$$

And the radiated power is

$$\left\langle \frac{dP}{d\Omega} \right\rangle = \frac{cr^2}{8\pi}\,\mathrm{Re}(E_\theta B_\varphi^*) = \frac{cr^2}{8\pi}|E_\theta|^2$$

$$= \frac{\omega^4 k^2 p_0^2 d^2}{32\pi c^3} \sin^2\theta \cos^2\theta$$

$$= \frac{\omega^6 Q^2}{128\pi c^5} \sin^2\theta \cos^2\theta \tag{8.123}$$

Again, the form of the result appears to be different from the previous expressions [Eqs. (8.112) and (8.120)], but in fact is quite similar, as is indicated in Fig. 8-16. For this case we have for the angle at which maximum power is radiated,

$$\theta_{\max}\,(\text{point quadrupole}) = 45°$$

We note the following important result for quadrupole radiation: Equations (8.120) and (8.123) indicate that the radiation from a quadrupole varies as ω^6, whereas we have previously found [see Eq. (8.35)] that dipole radiation varies as ω^4. We may state this another way: dipole radiation depends upon p_0^2/λ^4, but p_0 is proportional to a length characteristic of the system, so that the radiation varies as d^2/λ^4. Quadrupole radiation on the other hand depends upon Q^2/λ^6, but Q is proportional to $p_0 d$ or d^2, so that the radiation varies as d^4/λ^6. The ratio of quadrupole to dipole radiation therefore depends upon $(d/\lambda)^2$. Thus, if the dimensions of a system are small compared to the wavelength of the radiation, then, in general, dipole effects will dominate. This is exactly the condition on the size of the system given by Eq. (8.1) and referred to as the *dipole approximation.*

The quadrupole calculations carried out above were for a system consisting of two dipoles whose separation was in line with their moments; that is, they were *linearly* separated. Another interesting case is that in which the separation is *lateral*, as in Fig. 8-17. Each system, of course, has zero dipole moment and a nonvanishing quadrupole moment. In all

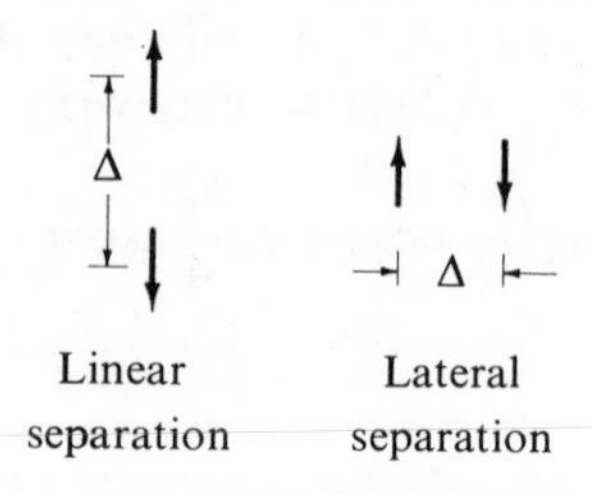

FIG. 8-17

of our previous discussions, the systems possessed azimuthal symmetry so that the field vectors, and hence the radiation, were independent of the angle φ. But for laterally separated dipoles, the phase difference will clearly depend upon φ as well as upon θ, so that the angular distribution of the radiation will be more complicated.

Let us consider the specific case for which the separation Δ is equal to one-half of the wavelength λ of the emitted radiation. The geometry of the system is shown in Fig. 8-18. We follow the procedure of Eq. (8.116) in which the phases of the field vectors in the direction of $\mathbf{r}$ are approximately $\pm(\Delta/2)\cos\psi = \pm(\lambda/4)\sin\theta\cos\varphi$. Thus, the θ-component of the electric vector is

$$E_\theta = -\frac{\omega^2 p_0}{c^2 r}\sin\theta\left\{\exp\left[i\left(\frac{k\lambda}{4}\sin\theta\cos\varphi\right)\right]\right.$$

$$\left.-\exp\left[-i\left(\frac{k\lambda}{4}\sin\theta\cos\varphi\right)\right]\right\}\exp[-i\omega t']$$

$$= -2i\frac{\omega^2 p_0}{c^2 r}\sin\theta\sin\left(\frac{\pi}{2}\sin\theta\cos\varphi\right)\exp[-i\omega t'] \tag{8.124}$$

where we have used $k = 2\pi/\lambda$. Therefore, the angular distribution of the emitted radiation is

$$\left\langle\frac{dP}{d\Omega}\right\rangle = \frac{\omega^4 p_0^2}{2\pi c^3}\sin^2\theta\sin^2\left(\frac{\pi}{2}\sin\theta\cos\varphi\right) \tag{8.125}$$

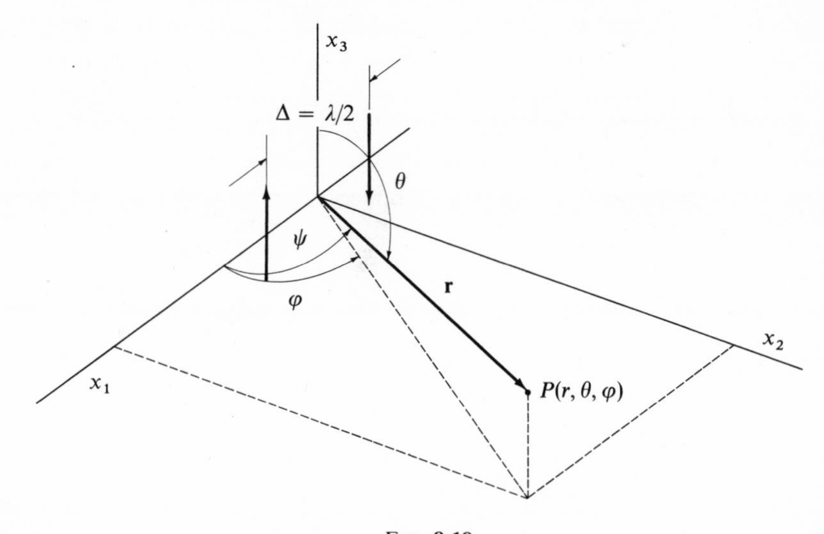

FIG. **8-18**

We may express this result in terms of the form of the angular distribution in the three mutually perpendicular planes:

$$x_1\text{-}x_3 \text{ plane} \quad (\varphi = 0): \qquad \sin^2\theta \sin^2\left(\frac{\pi}{2}\sin\theta\right)$$

$$x_2\text{-}x_3 \text{ plane} \quad (\varphi = \pi/2): \qquad 0$$

$$x_1\text{-}x_2 \text{ plane} \quad (\theta = \pi/2): \qquad \sin^2\left(\frac{\pi}{2}\cos\varphi\right)$$

The radiation patterns in the x_1-x_3 and x_1-x_2 planes are shown in Fig. 8-19. The forms of these radiation patterns confirm some of the qualitative statements which we could have made by referring to the geometry of Fig. 8-18: (a) There can be no radiation along $\theta = 0$ or π since the dipole fields vanish in these directions; (b) since the fields along the x_2-axis from the two dipoles exactly *cancel* because they oscillate out of phase, there can be no radiation for $\varphi = \pi/2$; (c) since the fields along the x_1-axis *add*, there is a maximum of the radiation for $\theta = \pi/2$.

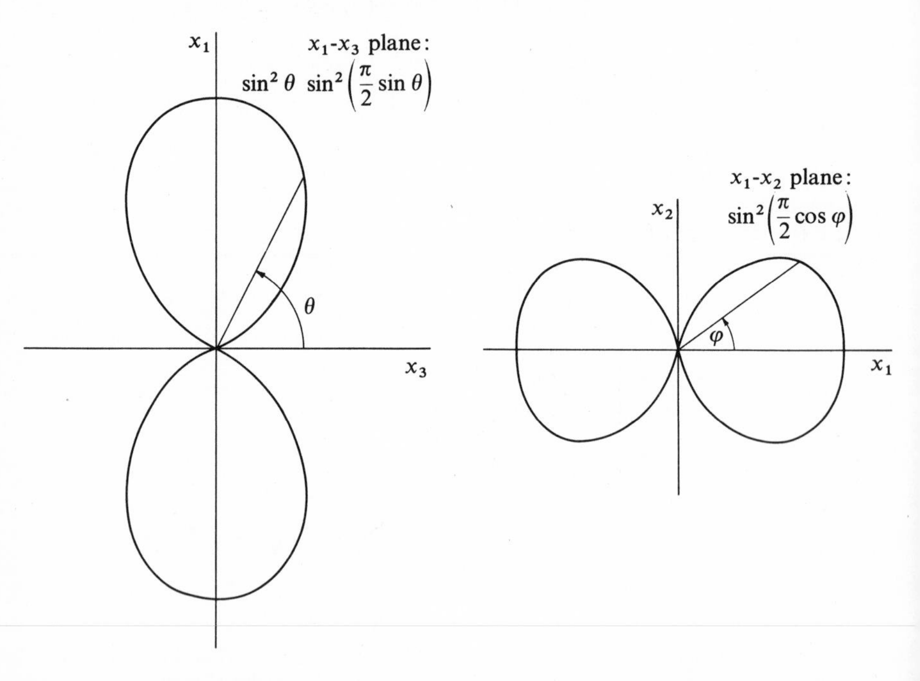

FIG. **8-19a** FIG. **8-19b**

It should be emphasized that the radiation patterns are sensitive to the value of the separation Δ in terms of the wavelength λ of the radiation. If we had chosen $\Delta = \lambda$ for this case, the patterns in both planes would have been similar to the curves shown in Fig. 8-16. This example shows that depending upon the exact geometry of the quadrupole, the radiation pattern can be significantly different from the $\sin^2 \theta \cos^2 \theta$ distribution that is characteristic of a point quadrupole.

8.9 Simple Arrays of Antennas

The method which we used in the preceding section to calculate the electric field and the radiation from a pair of dipoles may be applied equally well to linear antennas. Thus, we can compute the radiation pattern due to an array of half-wave antennas by simply adding the field components taken with the proper phases and squaring the result. By combining Eqs. (8.94) and (8.102), we have for the vector potential due to a center-driven antenna of length d which is oriented along the x_3-axis,

$$\mathbf{A}(\mathbf{r}, t) = \mathbf{e}_3 \frac{2I_0 e^{ikr}}{ckr} \left\{ \frac{\cos\left(\frac{kd}{2}\cos\theta\right) - \cos\frac{kd}{2}}{\sin\theta^2} \right\} e^{-i\omega t} \tag{8.126}$$

From Eq. (8.95) we have

$$\mathbf{B}_{\text{rad}}(\mathbf{r}, t) = ik\mathbf{n} \times \mathbf{A}(\mathbf{r}, t) = -ikA_3(\mathbf{r}, t) \sin\theta \, \mathbf{e}_\varphi \tag{8.127}$$

so that $\mathbf{B}_{\text{rad}}$ has only a component in the φ-direction:

$$B_\varphi = -2i\frac{I_0}{cr} \left\{ \frac{\cos\left(\frac{kd}{2}\cos\theta\right) - \cos\frac{kd}{2}}{\sin\theta} \right\} e^{-i(\omega t - kr)} \tag{8.128}$$

Therefore, specializing to the half-wave case for which $kd = \pi$, Eq. (8.128) becomes

$$B_\varphi = -2i\frac{I_0}{cr} \frac{\cos\left(\frac{\pi}{2}\cos\theta\right)}{\sin\theta} e^{-i\omega t'} = E_\theta \tag{8.129}$$

where we have replaced $\omega t - kr$ in the exponential by $\omega t' = \omega(t - r/c)$. Using this basic equation we may calculate the field for any given array of half-wave antennas. Let us consider first the situation illustrated in

Fig. 8-18 in which the dipoles are replaced by half-wave antennas that are driven out of phase. Then,

$$E_\theta = B_\varphi = -2i\frac{I_0}{cr}\frac{\cos\left(\frac{\pi}{2}\cos\theta\right)}{\sin\theta}\cdot\left\{\exp\left[i\left(\frac{\pi}{2}\sin\theta\cos\varphi\right)\right]\right.$$

$$\left.-\exp\left[-i\left(\frac{\pi}{2}\sin\theta\cos\varphi\right)\right]\right\}\exp[-i\omega t']$$

$$= 4\frac{I_0}{cr}\frac{\cos\left(\frac{\pi}{2}\cos\theta\right)}{\sin\theta}\sin\left(\frac{\pi}{2}\sin\theta\cos\varphi\right)\exp[-i\omega t'] \tag{8.130}$$

The angular distribution of the emitted radiation is given by

$$\left\langle\frac{dP}{d\Omega}\right\rangle = \frac{cr^2}{8\pi}|E_\theta|^2$$

$$= \frac{2I_0^2}{\pi c}\frac{\cos^2\left(\frac{\pi}{2}\cos\theta\right)\sin^2\left(\frac{\pi}{2}\sin\theta\cos\varphi\right)}{\sin^2\theta} \tag{8.131}$$

This radiation pattern is quite similar to that shown in Fig. 8-19 for the dipole case.

Next, we extend the discussion to consider a linear array of N half-wave antennas. Such an arrangement is shown in Fig. 8-20, in which there is a uniform spacing Δ between adjacent antennas. We assume that all of the antennas are driven in phase, and we select one end of the array as the origin. The field produced at the point $P(r, \theta, \varphi)$ by successive elements of the array will differ in phase by an amount $\alpha = k\Delta\sin\theta\cos\varphi$. Therefore, using Eq. (8.129) the total field is

$$E_\theta = B_\varphi = -2i\frac{I_0}{cr}\frac{\cos\left(\frac{\pi}{2}\cos\theta\right)}{\sin\theta}e^{-i\omega t'}$$

$$\cdot\{1 + e^{i\alpha} + e^{2i\alpha} + \cdots + e^{(N-1)i\alpha}\} \tag{8.132}$$

The series in the curly brackets is a geometrical progression in $\beta = \exp(i\alpha)$, the sum of which is

$$1 + \beta + \beta^2 + \cdots + \beta^{N-1} = \frac{\beta^N - 1}{\beta - 1} \tag{8.133}$$

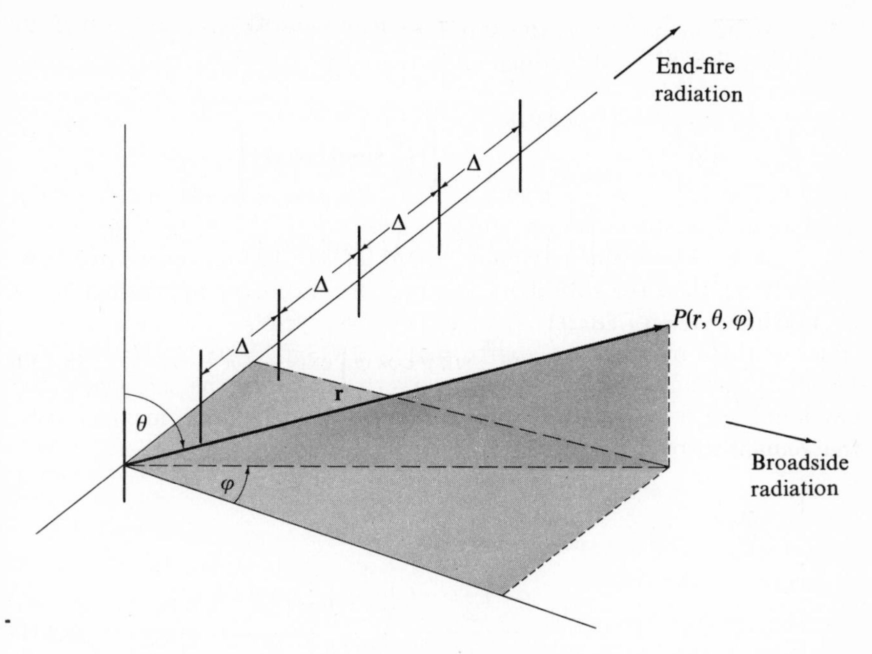

FIG. **8-20**

Thus,

$$\{\ \} = \frac{e^{iN\alpha} - 1}{e^{i\alpha} - 1} = \frac{e^{i(N/2)\alpha}(e^{i(N/2)\alpha} - e^{-i(N/2)\alpha})}{e^{i\alpha/2}(e^{i\alpha/2} - e^{-i\alpha/2})}$$

$$= e^{i(N-1)\alpha/2}\frac{\sin(N\alpha/2)}{\sin(\alpha/2)} \tag{8.134}$$

The magnitudes of the field quantities therefore become

$$|E_\theta| = |B_\varphi| = \frac{2I_0}{cr}\left|\frac{\cos\left(\frac{\pi}{2}\cos\theta\right)}{\sin\theta}\frac{\sin(N\alpha/2)}{\sin(\alpha/2)}\right| \tag{8.135}$$

and the angular distribution of the emitted radiation is

$$\left\langle\frac{dP}{d\Omega}\right\rangle = \frac{cr^2}{8\pi}|E_\theta|^2$$

$$= \frac{I_0^2}{2\pi c}\frac{\cos^2\left(\frac{\pi}{2}\cos\theta\right)}{\sin^2\theta}\frac{\sin^2(N\alpha/2)}{\sin^2(\alpha/2)} \tag{8.136}$$

The radiation pattern is the standard half-wave pattern [Eq. (8.108) or (8.110) and Fig. 8-12(a)] modulated by the term

$$f^2(\alpha) \equiv \frac{\sin^2(N\alpha/2)}{\sin^2(\alpha/2)} \tag{8.137}$$

The function $|f(\alpha)|$ is shown in Fig. 8-21; the zeroes of this function (and therefore nulls in the radiation pattern) occur at $|\alpha| = 2\pi/N, 4\pi/N, 6\pi/N, \cdots, 2(N-1)\pi/N$. The main maximum occurs at $\alpha = 0$, for which $f^2(0) = N$. If N is large, then the subsidiary maxima of $f^2(\alpha)$ occur approximately at the maxima of $\sin^2(N\alpha/2)$, i.e., at $|\alpha| = 3\pi/N$, $5\pi/N$, $7\pi/N$, etc., and the values of these maxima are approximately $2N/3\pi$, $2N/5\pi$, $2N/7\pi$, etc. The subsidiary maxima of the radiation pattern are called the *side lobes.* The function $f^2(\alpha)$ is shown in Fig. 8-22 where the side-lobe maxima have been expanded by a factor of 10 for clarity.

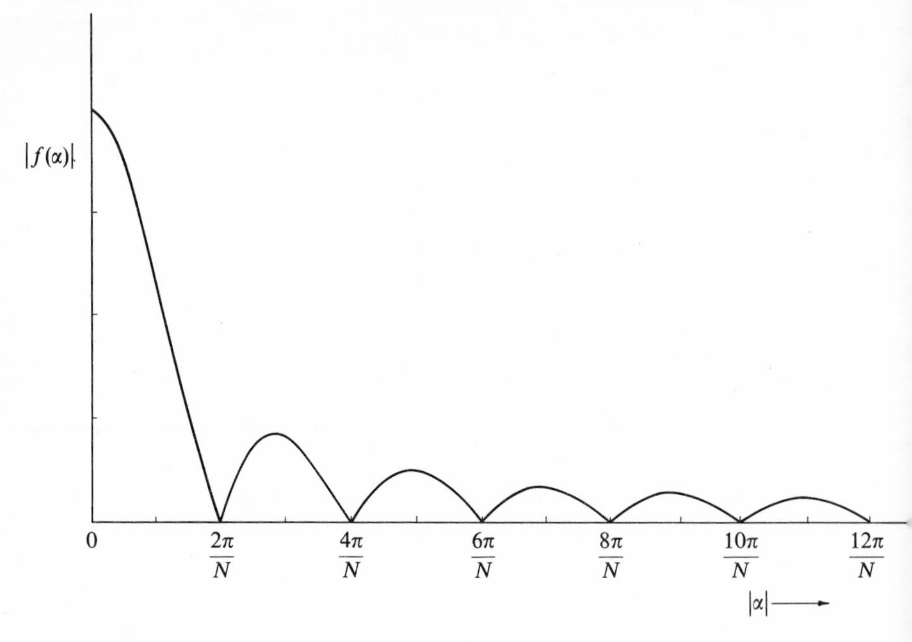

FIG. **8-21**

Notice that the main maximum in the radiation pattern at

$$\alpha = k\Delta \sin\theta \cos\varphi = 0$$

can result only for $\varphi = \pi/2$ since the other possibility, $\theta = 0$, is eliminated by the vanishing of E_θ for $\theta = 0$. The radiation is emitted predominantly in a direction perpendicular to the orientation of the array. Such a system

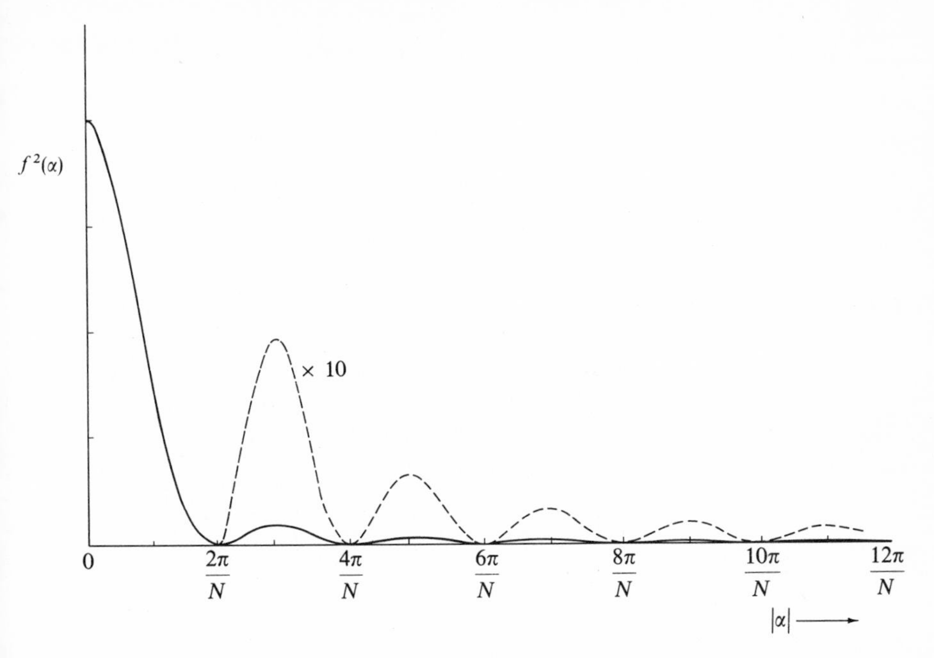

FIG. **8-22**

is called a *broadside array.* The radiation patterns for $\Delta = \lambda/2$ and $N = 1$ through 5 are shown in Fig. 8-23 as functions of φ for the plane $\theta = \pi/2$. The curves are drawn to scale, but the intensity of each pattern has been multiplied by a factor $1/N$ in order to allow more details to be shown. Notice that the intensity of the radiation emitted broadside to the array is proportional to the square of the sum of the individual amplitudes. Thus, the intensity at $\varphi = \pi/2$ for the five-element array is 25 times the intensity of a single half-wave antenna. Notice also that along $\varphi = 0$ or π, the amplitudes due to the individual elements of the array cancel in pairs so that the intensity of the radiation in these directions is zero for even N and nonzero for odd N.

A linear array of half-wave antennas which are spaced $\lambda/2$ apart and which are driven with *alternating* phases has its main radiation maximum along $\varphi = 0$ since the field amplitudes all add in the direction of the array. Such a system is called an *end-fire* array (see Problem 8-18).

It is apparent that a wide variety of radiation patterns can be produced by different geometrical and phase relations between antennas or dipoles. A large number of cases have been employed in engineering applications, including two- and three-dimensional arrays.*

* See, for example, F. E. Terman (Te55).

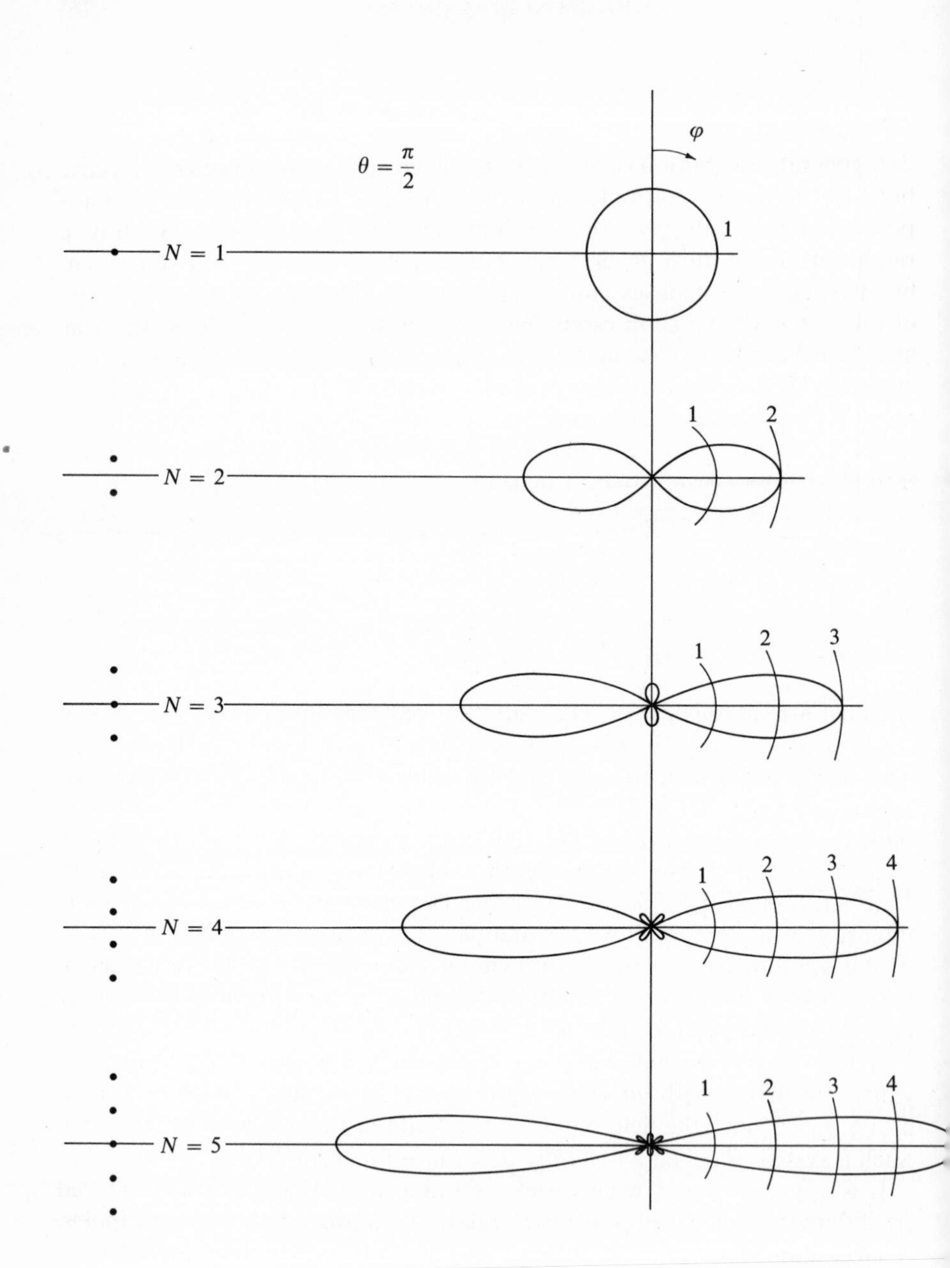

FIG. **8-23**

8.10 Magnetic Radiation

A general distribution of charge and current will possess not only electric but also magnetic multipole moments. The time variation of these multipole moments will give rise to both electric and magnetic multipole radiation. In the most general case both types of radiation will be present, but particular geometries can be arranged so that one or the other type of radiation will be suppressed. The systems we have considered thus far have been capable of emitting only electric radiation. We now turn our attention to systems that emit magnetic radiation. It will be convenient to employ the Hertz method again.

Let us consider a system that has a magnetization **M** but which has a zero electric polarization **P**. The Hertz potential $\mathbf{\Pi}_e$ vanishes for such a system, so that the scalar and vector potentials are simply [cf. Eq. (8.43)]

$$\left.\begin{aligned}\Phi &= 0\\ \mathbf{A} &= \mathbf{curl}\,\mathbf{\Pi}_m\end{aligned}\right\} \tag{8.138}$$

The electric and magnetic induction vectors in free space that arise from the magnetization are [see Eqs. (8.48) and (8.51)]

$$\left.\begin{aligned}\mathbf{E} &= -\frac{1}{c}\,\mathbf{curl}\,\mathbf{\Pi}\\ \mathbf{B} &= \mathbf{grad}\,\mathrm{div}\,\mathbf{\Pi} - \frac{1}{c^2}\frac{\partial^2\mathbf{\Pi}}{\partial t^2}\end{aligned}\right\} \tag{8.139}$$

where $\mathbf{\Pi}$ has been substituted for $\mathbf{\Pi}_m$. These field vectors are seen to be the same as those found for the case of electric polarization and no magnetization [Eqs. (8.54)], except that the roles of **E** and **B** have been interchanged and the sign of the curl term is reversed. (This change of sign is necessary in order to maintain an outward direction for the Poynting vector when **E** and **B** are interchanged.) The results for magnetic dipole radiation are therefore the same as those for electric dipole radiation [Eqs. (8.62)], except that the electric dipole moment **p** must be replaced by the magnetic dipole moment **m**.

As a specific example of magnetic dipole radiation, we consider a wire of length d that is formed into a circle and in which flows an oscillating current $I(t')$, as in Fig. 8-24. The Hertz potential at a point defined by the vector **r** and at a time t is given by [see Eq. (8.46b)]

$$\mathbf{\Pi}(\mathbf{r}, t) = \int_V \frac{[\mathbf{M}(\mathbf{r}')]}{|\mathbf{r} - \mathbf{r}'|}\,dv' \tag{8.140}$$

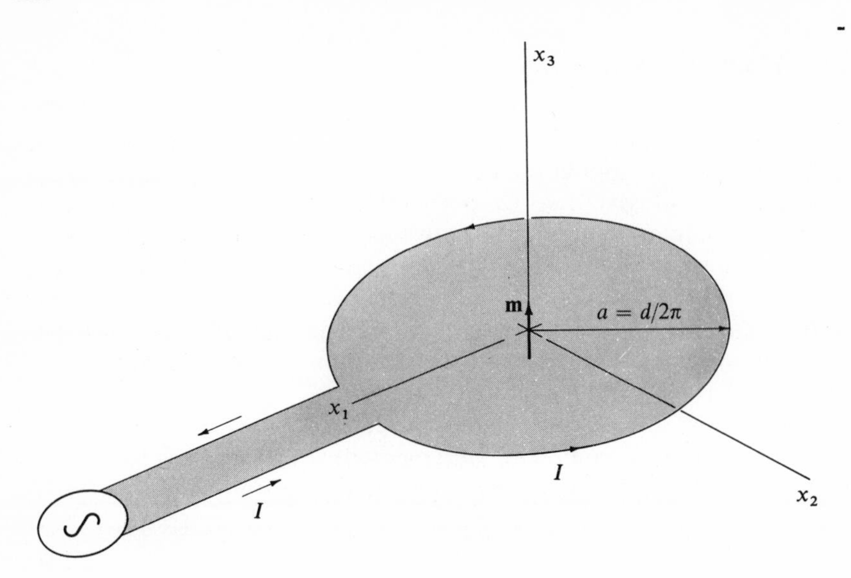

FIG. **8-24**

The magnetization **M** is [cf. Eq. (8.52)]

$$\mathbf{M}(\mathbf{r}', t') = \mathbf{m}(t')\delta(\mathbf{r}') \tag{8.141}$$

Now, according to Eq. (2.50a), the magnetic dipole moment is given by

$$\mathbf{m} = \frac{I}{c}\int_S d\mathbf{a} \tag{8.142}$$

For a plane, circular loop of radius $a = d/2\pi$ in which the current is $I(t') = I_0 \exp(-i\omega t')$, we have

$$\mathbf{m}(t') = \frac{I_0 S}{c} e^{-i\omega t'}\mathbf{e}_3 \tag{8.143}$$

where $S = d^2/4\pi$ is the area of the loop. The second time derivative of **m** is therefore

$$\ddot{\mathbf{m}} = -\frac{\omega^2 I_0 S}{c} e^{-i\omega t'}\mathbf{e}_3 \tag{8.144}$$

We may then substitute $[\ddot{m}]$ for $[\ddot{p}]$ in Eqs. (8.62) and obtain, for the case of magnetic dipole radiation,

$$E_\theta = B_\varphi = \frac{[\ddot{m}]}{c^2 r}\sin\theta \tag{8.145}$$

The angular distribution of the radiated power is

$$\left\langle \frac{dP}{d\Omega} \right\rangle = \frac{\omega^4 I_0^2 S^2}{8\pi c^5} \sin^2 \theta \tag{8.146}$$

and the total radiated power is

$$\langle P \rangle = \frac{\omega^4 I_0^2 S^2}{3c^5}$$

$$= \frac{2\pi^2}{3c} \frac{I_0^2}{2} \left(\frac{d}{\lambda}\right)^4 \tag{8.147}$$

The coefficient of $I_0^2/2$ is the radiation resistance [cf. Eq. (8.81)]:

$$R_{\text{rad}} = \frac{2\pi^2}{3c} \left(\frac{d}{\lambda}\right)^4 \quad \text{statohms}$$

$$= 197 \left(\frac{d}{\lambda}\right)^4 \quad \text{ohms} \tag{8.148}$$

The radiation resistance of a magnetic dipole therefore depends on $(d/\lambda)^4$, whereas that of an electric dipole depends on $(d/\lambda)^2$. (Both of these results require $d \ll \lambda$.) If $d = 0.01\lambda$, then the radiation resistance of a magnetic dipole is 2×10^{-6} ohms, whereas the resistance of an electric dipole with length equal to the circumference of the magnetic dipole current loop is 0.08 ohm (see Section 8.6). A magnetic dipole is therefore a far less efficient radiator than an electric dipole, for $d \ll \lambda$. The dependence on d/λ for magnetic dipole radiation (and also the order of magnitude of the radiation resistance) is the same as that for electric quadrupole radiation. Furthermore, magnetic quadrupole and electric octupole radiations are of the same order, and similarly for all higher-order multipole radiation. This result is of particular importance in considerations of the radiation emitted by atomic and nuclear systems.

A magnetic quadrupole radiator may be constructed, in analogy with the electric case, by arranging two current loops in parallel planes and by allowing the current to flow out of phase in the two loops. The radiation pattern for such a case is the same as that for a pair of electric dipoles in the analogous configuration.

Suggested References

One of the more complete accounts of radiation phenomena at the intermediate level is that of Corson and Lorrain (Co62, Chapter 13).

Brief treatments of dipole radiation are given, for example, by Becker and Sauter (Be64, Sections 67 and 68), Blass (Bl62, Chapter 28), and Scott (Sc59, Chapter 10); Stone (St63, Chapter 5) includes considerable detail.

Excellent discussions of radiation phenomena at the advanced level are those of Jackson (Ja62, Chapters 9, 16), Landau and Lifshitz (La62, Chapter 9), and Stratton (St41, Chapter 8).

The Hertz potentials are discussed by Aharoni (Ah46, Section I.6), Born and Wolf (Bo59, Chapter 2), Sommerfeld (So52, Section 19), and Stratton (St41, Chapter 1).

Antennas and antenna arrays are treated at the intermediate level by Harnwell (Ha49, Chapter 16), Plonsey and Collin (Pl61, Chapter 11), and Ramo and Whinnery (Ra44, Chapter 11). See also Slater (Sl42, Chapter 5).

There exist many excellent books on antenna theory, most of which stress the engineering aspects. A few of the better texts are those by Aharoni (Ah46), Kraus (Kr50), Schelkunoff (Sc52), and Schelkunoff and Friis (Sc52a).

Problems

8-1. Show that a system of charged particles all of which have identical charge-to-mass ratios e/m cannot emit dipole radiation if the center of mass of the system moves uniformly.

8-2. A spherical shell is uniformly charged and undergoes purely radial oscillations. Show that radiation cannot occur. (Show that there is no magnetic field.)

8-3. Show that the field vectors are invariant to a gauge transformation on the Hertz vectors of the form

$$\mathbf{\Pi}_e' = \mathbf{\Pi}_e + \mathbf{curl\ a} - \mathbf{grad}\, b$$

$$\mathbf{\Pi}_m' = \mathbf{\Pi}_m - \frac{1}{c}\frac{\partial \mathbf{a}}{\partial t}$$

if $\mathbf{a}$ and b satisfy homogeneous wave equations. Show that $\mathbf{\Pi}_e'$ and $\mathbf{\Pi}_m'$ satisfy inhomogeneous wave equations. Find the corresponding Φ' and $\mathbf{A}'$ [see Eqs. (4.23) and (4.25)] and find the condition on ξ.

8-4. For the case of the Hertzian dipole, show that the relevant vector quantities can be expressed in general as

$$\mathbf{grad}\ \mathrm{div}\,\mathbf{\Pi} = \left(\frac{[\ddot{p}]}{c^2r^3} + \frac{3[\dot{p}]}{cr^4} + \frac{3[p]}{r^5}\right)(\mathbf{e}_3 \cdot \mathbf{r})\mathbf{r} - \left(\frac{[\dot{p}]}{cr^2} + \frac{[p]}{r^3}\right)\mathbf{e}_3$$

$$\mathbf{curl}\,\mathbf{\Pi} = \left(\frac{[\dot{p}]}{cr^2} + \frac{[\dot{p}]}{cr^3}\right)(\mathbf{e}_3 \times \mathbf{r})$$

Show that for spherical coordinates these expressions reduce to Eqs. (8.58) and (8.59).

8-5. Use the results of the previous problem and derive the general expressions for **E** and **B**.

8-6. Integrate Eq. (8.101) to obtain Eq. (8.102).

8-7. Plot the radiation patterns for half-wave and full-wave center-driven antennas [Eqs. (8.108) and (8.109)]. Compare these patterns with that for the simple dipole antenna. Explain qualitatively why the full-wave pattern is narrower than the half-wave pattern.

8-8. Show that the time average of the total power radiated by a center-driven, half-wave antenna is given by

$$\langle P\rangle = \frac{I_0^2}{2c}\int_{-1}^{+1}\frac{1+\cos\pi u}{1+u}\,du = \frac{I_0^2}{2c}\int_0^{2\pi}\frac{1-\cos z}{z}\,dz$$

Express $\langle P\rangle$ in terms of the *cosine integral*

$$Ci(x) = -\int_x^\infty \frac{\cos z}{z}\,dz$$

Use a table of special functions (e.g., Jahnke and Emde, *Tables of Functions*) to evaluate the result, and show that

$$\langle P\rangle = 2.44(I_0^2/2c)$$

8-9. Derive Eq. (8.111).

8-10. Consider a center-driven antenna which has a length d equal to $\frac{3}{4}$ of a wavelength of the driving oscillations. Sketch the current density distribution in the antenna and plot the angular distribution of the radiated power.

8-11. The *directivity* of an antenna or an array is defined as the ratio of the maximum value of the power radiated per unit solid angle to the value of the total average power radiated per unit solid angle.* Show that the directivity of a simple, oscillating dipole is 1.5, whereas the directivity of a half-wave antenna is 1.64.

8-12. For a particular half-wave antenna it is found that if the antenna losses are included, the current distribution is given approximately by $I(x_3) = I_0\cos^2 kx_3$. Calculate the radiation pattern for such an antenna. Also, find the radiation resistance and the directivity (see Problem 8-11). [Use some numerical method (e.g., Simpson's rule) to evaluate the integral.] Compare the results with those obtained for a lossless half-wave antenna.

* This function is sometimes called the *gain* of the antenna, but, properly, the gain also takes into account the losses in the antenna and is defined as the ratio of the maximum value of the power radiated per unit solid angle to the total input power divided by 4π.

8-13. Consider the center-driven, full-wave antenna ($m = 2$ in Fig. 8-10) to be approximated by two point dipoles linearly separated by a distance $d/2$ and oscillating in phase. Show that the angular distribution of the radiated power is of the form $\sin^2\theta\cos^2[(\pi/2)\cos\theta]$. Plot this distribution and compare with that given by the exact formula [Eq. (8.109)].

8-14. Calculate and plot the angular distribution of the radiation emitted by a pair of electric dipoles that are laterally separated by a distance $\lambda/4$ and which oscillate with a phase difference of $\pi/2$.

8-15. Calculate and plot the radiation pattern for a pair of half-wave antennas which are laterally separated by a distance $\lambda/4$ and which oscillate with a phase difference of $\pi/2$. Compare with the results of the previous problem.

8-16. Calculate and plot the angular distribution of the radiation emitted by the system shown in Fig. 8-18 in the event that the dipoles oscillate *in phase*.

8-17. In Section 8.9 it was stated that the side-lobe maxima occur at approximately $|\alpha| = 3\pi/N$, $5\pi N$, $7\pi N$, etc. Derive an *exact* expression for the position of the maxima and compare the results with the approximate values for a 7-element broadside array. (The exact values may be obtained graphically or by a successive approximation procedure.)

8-18. Calculate the angular distribution of radiation from an N-element, end-fire array of half-wave antennas. Specialize to the case of $N = 5$ and plot the radiation pattern. Compare the result with Fig. 8-22 for a 5-element broadside array.

8-19. Two charges $+q$ and $-q$ are separated by a fixed distance d and rotate with a uniform angular velocity ω about an axis that passes mid-way between the charges and which is perpendicular to the line joining the charges. Discuss the radiation emitted in the plane of the motion and that emitted along the axis of rotation.

8-20. In the preceding problem replace the charge $-q$ by a charge $+q$ and add a charge $-2q$ located at the center of rotation. Discuss the radiation field.

8-21. Consider an oscillating electric quadrupole which is composed of four dipoles arranged in the following way:

Calculate the radiation pattern and compare with the results for magnetic dipole radiation given in Section 8.10. Comment on the comparison, especially on the relative intensity.

8-22. Calculate the field vectors and the angular distribution of the emitted radiation from a magnetic dipole by considering the dipole to be an oscillating current loop with $I = I_0 \exp(i\omega t')$. Perform the calculation by explicitly evaluating the vector potential. Then obtain **B** and **E** from $\mathbf{B} = \mathbf{curl}\,\mathbf{A}$ and $\mathbf{E} = -(1/c)(\partial\mathbf{A}/\partial t)$.

CHAPTER 9

Classical Electron Theory

9.1 Introduction

The treatment of the interaction of electromagnetic radiation with bulk matter can usually be handled quite adequately in classical terms. However, when it is necessary to inquire into the interaction between electromagnetic radiation and *microscopic* matter (i.e., individual electrons, atoms, or molecules), the description must properly be made in terms of quantum theory. Before the advent of quantum theory, however, a variety of interesting effects had been described in terms of a *mechanical* theory which treated the classical interaction of electromagnetic radiation with discrete charges. This approach is known as the *classical electron theory of matter* and takes two forms, both of which are concerned with the motion of electrons. In one form the electrons are considered to be *free*, i.e., not attached to atoms. This is the case, for example, in a metal or in an ionized gas in which the motion of the electrons can constitute a current. On the other hand, the electrons may be *bound* in atoms. Such electrons can still be set into motion by an electromagnetic wave but the motion is an oscillatory one since an electrical restoring force exists between the negative electron and the positive atomic nucleus.

We shall find that if we realize the importance of quantum effects in general and then choose cases in which we may make suitable approximations in order to avoid these effects, then the classical treatment will yield a variety of interesting results which agree quite closely with experiment. The danger in this approach, of course, is that we may be tempted to try to push the classical theory too far. With this word of caution, we undertake in this chapter to treat classically some of the problems involving the interaction of electromagnetic radiation with microscopic matter.

9.2 The Scattering of an Electromagnetic Wave by a Charged Particle

If we allow an electromagnetic wave to be incident on a system of charged particles, the electric and magnetic components of the wave will exert a Lorentz force on the charges and they will be set into motion. Since the electromagnetic wave is periodic in time, so will be the motion of the particles. Thus, there will be changes in the directions of motion and, hence, there will be accelerations. The system will therefore radiate; that is, energy will be absorbed from the incident wave by the particles and will be re-emitted into space. We may describe such a process as a *scattering* of the electromagnetic wave by the system of charged particles.

Let us first consider a linearly polarized plane electromagnetic wave incident on a single particle carrying a charge q. The electric vector of the wave will be

$$\mathbf{E} = \mathbf{e}E_0 e^{-i(\omega t - \mathbf{k}\cdot\mathbf{r}')} \tag{9.1}$$

where $\mathbf{e}$ is the polarization vector and $\mathbf{k}$ is the propagation vector [cf. Eq. (5.20)]. The electric field will exert a force $\mathbf{F} = q\mathbf{E}$ on the particle. We shall assume that the particle undergoes oscillations of small amplitude about a position of equilibrium which is chosen as the origin of the coordinate system. We assume further that the velocity acquired by the particle as a result of the interaction is small compared with the velocity of light. We may therefore neglect the magnetic portion of the Lorentz force (which depends upon u/c), and the equation of motion of the particle is approximately

$$\mathbf{F} = q\mathbf{E} = m\ddot{\mathbf{r}}' \tag{9.2}$$

where m is the mass of the particle. Now, the dipole moment is

$$\mathbf{p}(t') = q\mathbf{r}'(t') \tag{9.3}$$

so that Eq. (9.2) may be written as

$$\ddot{\mathbf{p}}(t') = \frac{q^2}{m}\mathbf{E}(t') \tag{9.4}$$

From Eq. (8.31) we have for the time average of the power radiated per unit solid angle,

$$\left\langle \frac{dP}{d\Omega} \right\rangle = \frac{\langle [\ddot{p}]^2 \rangle}{4\pi c^3} \sin^2\theta \tag{9.5}$$

But,

$$\langle [\ddot{p}]^2 \rangle = \frac{q^4}{m^2} \langle E^2 \rangle = \frac{q^4 E_0^2}{2m^2} \tag{9.6}$$

Hence,

$$\left\langle \frac{dP}{d\Omega} \right\rangle = \left(\frac{q^2}{mc^2} \right)^2 \frac{c}{8\pi} E_0^2 \sin^2\theta \tag{9.7}$$

The *differential scattering cross section* may be obtained by dividing the power radiated per unit solid angle by the incident flux,* where all quantities must, of course, be time averages. Thus,

$$\boxed{\left\langle \frac{d\sigma}{d\Omega} \right\rangle = \frac{\langle dP/d\Omega \rangle}{\langle \text{Incident flux} \rangle}} \tag{9.8}$$

But the average incident flux (i.e., the average incident energy per unit area per unit time) is just the average energy density in the wave:

$$\langle \mathbf{S} \rangle \cdot \mathbf{e}_3 = \frac{c}{8\pi} E_0^2 \tag{9.9}$$

Therefore,

$$\boxed{\left\langle \frac{d\sigma}{d\Omega} \right\rangle = \left(\frac{q^2}{mc^2} \right)^2 \sin^2\theta} \tag{9.10}$$

The angle θ, which appears in Eq. (9.10), is the angle between the dipole moment vector $\mathbf{p}$ and the direction of the outgoing radiation (described by the unit vector $\mathbf{n}$). In the present case, the dipole is induced by the electric field of the incident wave and therefore $\mathbf{p}$ has the same direction as $\mathbf{E}$.

* See also Eq. (10.30).

We must therefore interpret the angle θ in Eq. (9.10) as the angle between **E** (or the polarization vector **e**) and **n**, as in Fig. 9-1.

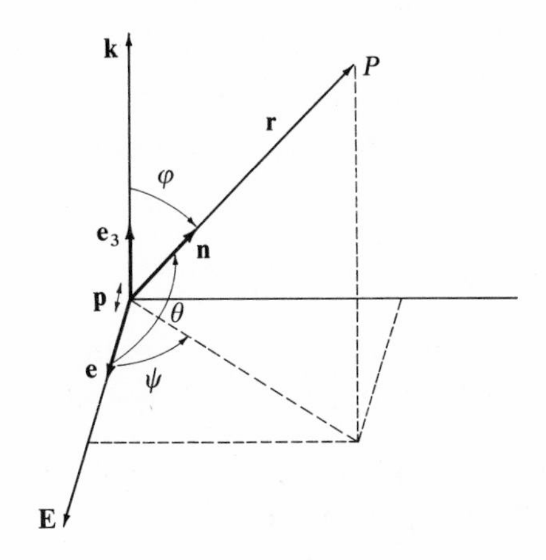

FIG. 9-1

Thus far we have considered only a linearly polarized wave. If we wish to describe the angular distribution of the scattered radiation for the more common case of unpolarized incident radiation, then we must modify the differential cross section as given by Eq. (9.10). We choose a coordinate system such as that in Fig. 9-1 in order to describe the process. Our previous result was expressed in terms of the angle θ between **E** and **n**. It is more useful to give the cross section in terms of the angle between the direction of the incident wave ($\mathbf{e}_3$) and the direction of the outgoing wave (**n**). To do this for an unpolarized incident wave means that we must average over all possible azimuthal orientations of the vector **E**; i.e. we must average over the angle ψ in Fig. 9-1. Now,

$$\cos\theta = \cos\psi \sin\varphi$$

or,

$$\sin^2\theta = 1 - \cos^2\psi \sin^2\varphi$$

Averaging over ψ,

$$\begin{aligned}\overline{\sin^2\theta} &= 1 - \overline{\cos^2\psi}\ \sin^2\varphi \\ &= 1 - \tfrac{1}{2}\sin^2\varphi \\ &= \tfrac{1}{2}(1 + \cos^2\varphi)\end{aligned}$$

where $\overline{\sin^2\theta}$ means the average of $\sin^2\theta$ taken over all angles ψ. Therefore, the differential cross section for the scattering of unpolarized radiation is obtained by substituting $\overline{\sin^2\theta}$ for $\sin^2\theta$ in Eq (9.10):

$$\left\langle \frac{d\sigma}{d\Omega} \right\rangle_{\text{unpolarized}} = \left(\frac{q^2}{mc^2} \right)^2 \frac{1 + \cos^2\varphi}{2} \tag{9.12}$$

The *total cross section* is obtained by integrating over the entire solid angle:

$$\langle \sigma \rangle_{\text{unpolarized}} = \int_{4\pi} \frac{d\sigma}{d\Omega}\, d\Omega = \frac{8\pi}{3} \left(\frac{q^2}{mc^2} \right)^2 \tag{9.13}$$

This expression gives the cross section for the scattering of an unpolarized plane electromagnetic wave by a free charged particle and is known as the *Thomson scattering cross section*,* denoted by σ_T. For the case of scattering by a free electron (so that q and m assume the values appropriate for an electron), the numerical result is

$$\sigma_T = 0.665 \times 10^{-24}\ \text{cm}^2 \tag{9.14}$$

The result given by Eq. (9.13) is strictly valid only in the limit $\omega \to 0$, but the error in the classical calculation is not too important for frequencies up to and including the X-ray region. Real radiation never takes the ideal form of a monochromatic plane wave as supposed in this derivation; rather, the radiation is composed of discrete quanta, or *photons* (see Chapter 11). The energy of a photon having a frequency ω is $\hbar\omega$, where $\hbar$ is Planck's constant divided by 2π. A quantum mechanical calculation shows that deviations from Thomson's result become significant for photon energies $\hbar\omega$ than are comparable with or larger than the rest energy of the scattering electron, $m_e c^2$. The scattering of a photon by a free electron is known as *Compton scattering*† and the quantum mechanical calculation of the cross section is known as the *Klein-Nishina formula.* Figure 9-2 shows the Compton scattering angular distribution given by the Klein-Nishina formula for several values of the parameter $\alpha \equiv \hbar\omega/m_e c^2$ which measures the photon energy in units of the electron rest energy; $\alpha = 0$ is the classical result. It is evident that a strong deviation from the classical result takes place for $\alpha \gtrsim 1$. Even for $\alpha = 0.1$, there is a significant difference for large scattering angles, although the distributions in the forward direction are almost the same. Notice, also, that the Klein-Nishina formula predicts the classical result at $\theta \cong 0°$ for all values of α.

* First derived by Sir Joseph John Thomson (1856–1940), discoverer of the electron and the founder of modern atomic physics. Sir Joseph was the 1906 Nobel Laureate in physics.

† After the American physicist Arthur Holly Compton (1892–1962) who discovered the effect in 1923. Compton was awarded the 1927 Nobel prize in physics for this work.

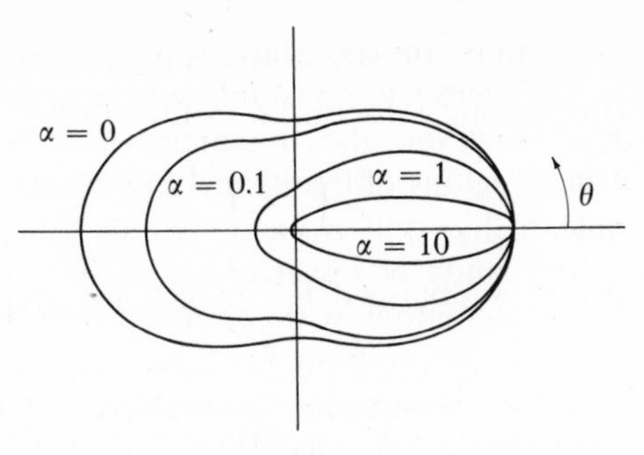

FIG. 9-2

9.3 Dispersion in Gases

In this section we shall discuss the propagation of an electromagnetic wave in a dilute gas, i.e., in a medium in which the constituent particles are sufficiently far apart so that we may neglect the mutual interactions. We shall be interested, in particular, in the velocity of propagation of waves in such a medium. If the medium is nonconducting (i.e., if the gas is not ionized), then the differential equation satisfied by **E** is just Eq. (5.48a) with $\sigma = 0$. Thus, we have the familiar wave equation

$$\nabla^2 \mathbf{E} - \frac{\varepsilon\mu}{c^2}\frac{\partial^2 \mathbf{E}}{\partial t^2} = 0 \tag{9.15}$$

We know that the coefficient of the second time derivative of **E** may be interpreted as the reciprocal of the square of the velocity of propagation v. That is,

$$\frac{1}{v^2} = \frac{\varepsilon\mu}{c^2}$$

or,

$$\frac{c}{v} = \sqrt{\varepsilon\mu}$$

Now, the ratio of the propagation velocity in free space to the propagation velocity* in a medium is called the *index of refraction n* of the medium:

$$n \equiv \frac{c}{v} = \sqrt{\varepsilon\mu} \tag{9.16}$$

For all of the media with which we shall be concerned, we have $\mu \cong 1$ (i.e., we exclude magnetic materials). Therefore, we have approximately

$$n \cong \sqrt{\varepsilon} \qquad (\mu \cong 1) \tag{9.17}$$

* Actually, the *phase* velocity; see Eq. (9.26).

We shall find that we must modify the above expression for the index of refraction because the dielectric constant is in general complex and a function of frequency. However, the imaginary (or absorptive) part is important only in certain regions of frequency. For simple gases it is found that the dielectric constant has only a weak frequency dependence, except in the relatively narrow bands of absorption. In fact, if static electrical measurements of $\sqrt{\varepsilon}$ are compared with optical values for n, the deviations are only a few parts per million for gases such as air, hydrogen, carbon dioxide, and carbon monoxide. Gases having a molecular structure somewhat more complicated would be expected to exhibit more regions of absorption and hence the comparison of n and $\sqrt{\varepsilon}$ would be subject to greater deviations. However, even for benzene vapor, the difference is only 0.5% (for optical measurements with sodium D light). For solids and liquids, on the other hand, strong deviations are found, demonstrating the effects of complicated interactions. Water, for example, shows a difference of a factor of 7 between the sodium D measurement of n and the static electrical result for $\sqrt{\varepsilon}$; this behavior is due largely to the fact that the water molecule is *polar*.

In order to investigate the frequency dependence of ε and to discuss dispersive effects, we take the following simple model of a gas. First, we assume that there is no appreciable interaction between molecules; this is certainly justified for a sufficiently dilute gas. As an electromagnetic wave passes through the gas, the electric field is able to induce a dipole moment in the gas molecule; that is, the molecule is *polarized* by the electric field, and the positions of the electrons are altered from their equilibrium values. We shall assume that the nuclei are stationary and that their positions are not affected by the passage of the wave. If the electrons are bound by a linear restoring force and if there is damping proportional to the velocity, then the equation of motion for the αth electron (with charge e) is

$$m\ddot{\mathbf{r}}_\alpha + l_\alpha \dot{\mathbf{r}}_\alpha + \gamma_\alpha \mathbf{r}_\alpha = e\mathbf{E} \tag{9.18}$$

or,

$$\ddot{\mathbf{r}}_\alpha + 2\beta_\alpha \dot{\mathbf{r}}_\alpha + \omega_\alpha^2 \mathbf{r}_\alpha = \frac{e}{m}\mathbf{E}_0 e^{-i\omega t} \tag{9.18a}$$

where $2\beta_\alpha \equiv l_\alpha/m$ and $\omega_\alpha^2 \equiv \gamma_\alpha/m$, and where we have used $\mathbf{E} = \mathbf{E}_0 \exp(-i\omega t)$. The simple form of Eq. (9.18) needs justification. First, the determination of the restoring force on an electron in an atom is a complicated problem that can be solved only by a quantum mechanical calculation. To a good approximation, however, the rigorous theory shows that the restoring force may be represented by a term linear in the displacement, $\mathbf{r}_\alpha$. Further, the innocuous-looking damping term $l_\alpha \dot{\mathbf{r}}_\alpha$ must be defended. Damping arises because the oscillating electron loses energy by radiation (*radiation damping*). But the justification of approximating this effect by a term proportional to the electron velocity is beset with some fundamental difficulties. (See Section 9.9 for a brief discussion.)

Equation (9.18a) is identical with that for a damped, driven mechanical harmonic oscillator,* and the solution is

$$\mathbf{r}_\alpha(t) = \frac{(e/m)\mathbf{E}_0}{(\omega_\alpha^2 - \omega^2) - 2i\beta_\alpha\omega} e^{-i\omega t} \tag{9.19}$$

Therefore, the dipole moment which results from the displacement of the αth electron is

$$\mathbf{p}_\alpha = e\mathbf{r}_\alpha(t) = \frac{(e^2/m)\mathbf{E}}{(\omega_\alpha^2 - \omega^2) - 2i\beta_\alpha\omega} \tag{9.20}$$

Now, if there are N electrons per unit volume in the gas and if a fraction f_α have the characteristic resonance frequency ω_α, then the total dipole moment per unit volume is

$$\mathbf{P} = \sum_\alpha N f_\alpha \mathbf{p}_\alpha = \mathbf{E} \sum_\alpha \frac{N f_\alpha e^2/m}{(\omega_\alpha^2 - \omega^2) - 2i\beta_\alpha\omega} \tag{9.21}$$

According to Eq. (1.21), the electric susceptibility $\hat{\chi}_e$ is given by the coefficient of $\mathbf{E}$; hence, the dielectric constant is [see Eq. (1.23)]

$$\hat{\varepsilon} = 1 + 4\pi\hat{\chi}_e = 1 + 4\pi \sum_\alpha \frac{N f_\alpha e^2/m}{(\omega_\alpha^2 - \omega^2) - 2i\beta_\alpha\omega} \tag{9.22}$$

Values of the dielectric constants for gases do not differ appreciably from unity, so the summation term in Eq. (9.22) is small. We may therefore calculate $\sqrt{\hat{\varepsilon}}$ by retaining only the first two terms of a binomial expansion. Therefore, we have approximately

$$\sqrt{\hat{\varepsilon}} \cong 1 + 2\pi \sum_\alpha \frac{N f_\alpha e^2/m}{(\omega_\alpha^2 - \omega^2) - 2i\beta_\alpha\omega} \tag{9.23}$$

Separating into real and imaginary parts, we obtain

$$\sqrt{\hat{\varepsilon}} \cong 1 + 2\pi \sum_\alpha \frac{(\omega_\alpha^2 - \omega^2) N f_\alpha e^2/m}{(\omega_\alpha^2 - \omega^2)^2 + 4\beta_\alpha^2\omega^2} + i4\pi \sum_\alpha \frac{N f_\alpha \omega \beta_\alpha e^2/m}{(\omega_\alpha^2 - \omega^2)^2 + 4\beta_\alpha^2\omega^2} \tag{9.23a}$$

The electromagnetic wave propagates in the gas with space and time

* Except for the minus sign in the exponential, Eq. (9.18a) is the same as Eq. (6.105a) of Marion (Ma65a); this changes the sign of the imaginary term, $2i\beta_\alpha\omega$, in the solution.

variation according to the term $\exp[-i(\omega t - \hat{k}\zeta)]$, where $\hat{k} = (\omega/c)\sqrt{\hat{\varepsilon}}$. We define a complex index of refraction $\hat{n}$ according to

$$\frac{c}{\omega}\hat{k} = \sqrt{\hat{\varepsilon}} = \hat{n} \equiv n(1 + i\kappa) \tag{9.24}$$

where n and κ are real. The quantity κ is called the *attenuation index* since the exponential space-time variation of the wave now becomes

$$e^{-i(\omega t - \hat{k}\zeta)} = e^{-(\omega n/c)\kappa\zeta}e^{-i[\omega t - (\omega/c)n\zeta]} \tag{9.25}$$

so that κ determines the spatial damping or the *attenuation* of the wave.

According to Eq. (9.25), the phase velocity of the wave is

$$V = \frac{\omega}{(\omega/c)n} = \frac{c}{\operatorname{Re}\hat{n}}$$

or,

$$n = \frac{c}{V} \tag{9.26}$$

Thus, n is identical to the quantity that we originally called the index of refraction for the case of zero attenuation [see Eq. (9.16)].

We may identify the real and imaginary parts of $\sqrt{\hat{\varepsilon}}$ from Eq. (9.23a):

$$\operatorname{Re}(\sqrt{\hat{\varepsilon}}) = n \cong 1 + 2\pi \sum_{\alpha} \frac{(\omega_\alpha^2 - \omega^2)Nf_\alpha e^2/m}{(\omega_\alpha^2 - \omega^2)^2 + 4\beta_\alpha^2\omega^2} \tag{9.27a}$$

$$\operatorname{Im}(\sqrt{\hat{\varepsilon}}) = n\kappa \cong 4\pi \sum_{\alpha} \frac{Nf_\alpha \omega\beta_\alpha e^2/m}{(\omega_\alpha^2 - \omega^2)^2 + 4\beta_\alpha^2\omega^2} \tag{9.27b}$$

Equation (9.27a) shows that the index of refraction (and, hence, the phase velocity) is a function of frequency. The medium is therefore *dispersive*.*

The quantities $n - 1$ and $n\kappa$ are shown in Fig. 9-3 for the case of a single term in the summations in Eqs. (9.27). Between the frequencies ω_1 and ω_2 the index of refraction decreases (and hence the phase velocity increases) as the frequency increases. The dispersion is then said to be *anomalous* (see the comments below). The region of anomalous dispersion, $\omega_1 \leq \omega \leq \omega_2$, corresponds to the region in which the absorption is greatest (ω_1 and ω_2 are actually the half-intensity points of $n\kappa$; see Problem 9-4), and therefore the region in which the imaginary part of the propagation constant is significant. Thus, the anomalous behavior of the phase velocity (i.e., $dV/d\omega > 1$) requires that the imaginary part of $\hat{k}$ (or $\hat{n}$) be large and therefore that the absorption also be large. The medium may

* A discussion of dispersion in mechanical systems is given by Marion (Ma65a, Section 15.3).

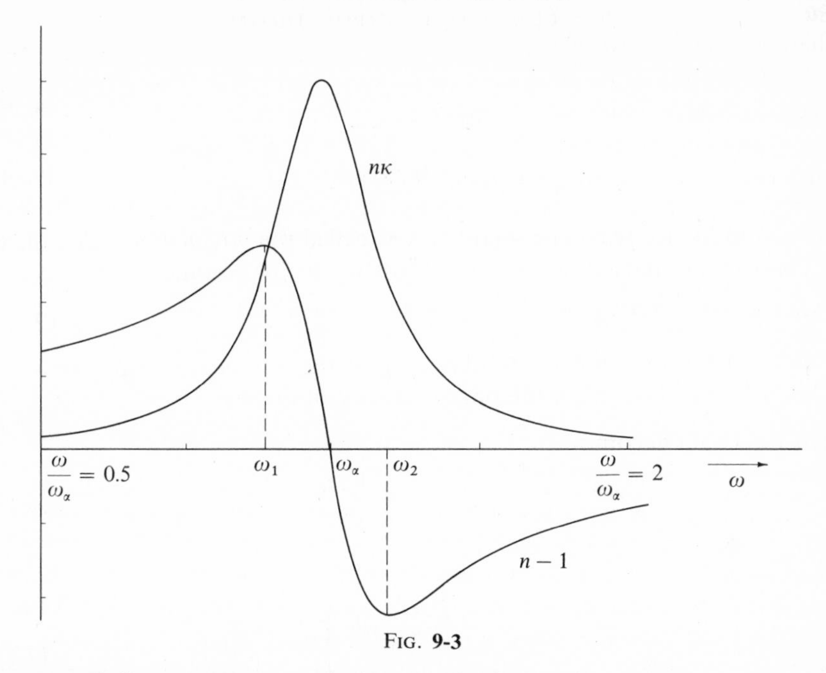

FIG. 9-3

be essentially opaque to radiation in the frequency range $\omega_1 \lesssim \omega \lesssim \omega_2$ if κ is large.

The origin of the term "anomalous dispersion" to describe the situation pictured in Fig. 9-3 is due to the fact that since $dn/d\omega < 1$ in the region $\omega_1 \leq \omega \leq \omega_2$, the rays of shorter wavelength are refracted *less* than those of longer wavelengths. This results in a reversal of the usual ordering of prismatic colors, and hence the term "anomalous" is used, although such regions of absorption and reversed dispersion are quite common.

It will be noted in Fig. 9-3 that for frequencies just above the resonance frequency* the index of refraction is less than unity. Since $n = c/V$, this implies $V > c$. But V is the phase velocity, and for a dispersive medium does not correspond to the signal velocity; the latter quantity is always less than the velocity of light in free space.

If we consider a case of optical radiation in which the frequency of the incident light is not close to one of the resonance frequencies ω_α, and if the damping coefficient β_α is not too large, then it is permissible to approximate n by neglecting the term $4\beta_\alpha^2\omega^2$ in the denominator of Eq. (9.27a). Thus, the index of refraction is approximately

$$n \cong 1 + 4\pi^2 c^2 \sum_\alpha \frac{\rho_\alpha}{\omega_\alpha^2 - \omega^2} \tag{9.28}$$

* This effect is indeed confined to a limited frequency range since $n - 1$ will eventually cross the ω-axis and become positive as the next higher resonance frequency is approached.

where we have substituted

$$\rho_\alpha \equiv \frac{N f_\alpha e^2}{2\pi m c^2} \tag{9.29}$$

Since $\omega/2\pi = c/\lambda$, we may write Eq. (9.28) as*

$$n \cong 1 + \sum_\alpha \frac{\lambda^2 \lambda_\alpha^2 \rho_\alpha}{\lambda^2 - \lambda_\alpha^2} \tag{9.30}$$

If we use the identity

$$\frac{\lambda^2}{\lambda^2 - \lambda_\alpha^2} = 1 + \frac{\lambda_\alpha^2}{\lambda^2 - \lambda_\alpha^2}$$

then Eq. (9.30) becomes

$$n \cong 1 + a + \sum_\alpha \frac{b_\alpha}{\lambda^2 - \lambda_\alpha^2} \tag{9.31}$$

where

$$\left.\begin{aligned} a &\equiv \sum_\alpha \lambda_\alpha^2 \rho_\alpha \\ b_\alpha &\equiv \lambda_\alpha^4 \rho_\alpha \end{aligned}\right\} \tag{9.32}$$

If we confine our attention to a certain optical wavelength range which does not contain any of the resonance frequencies ω_α, then we may obtain an expression for n which is even simpler than Eq. (9.31) by expanding the denominator of the sum. Denoting by λ_r those wavelengths λ_α which correspond to resonances lying in the longer (or *red*) wavelength region and denoting by λ_v those lying in the shorter (or *violet*) region, the expansion becomes (see Problem 9-5)

$$\begin{aligned} n \cong 1 + A_v(\rho_v, \lambda_v) + \frac{B_v(\rho_v, \lambda_v)}{\lambda^2} + \frac{C_v(\rho_v, \lambda_v)}{\lambda^4} + \cdots \\ - B_r(\rho_r)\lambda^2 - C_r(\rho_r, \lambda_r)\lambda^4 - \cdots \end{aligned} \tag{9.33}$$

The terms B_r, C_r, ... which arise from resonances in the infrared usually do not contribute significantly. Then, if we retain only the first term depending on λ, we obtain *Cauchy's equation*†:

$$n - 1 \cong A\left(1 + \frac{B}{\lambda^2}\right) \tag{9.34}$$

* This is equivalent to Sellmeier's dispersion formula, derived in 1871.

† First derived in 1836 by the French mathematician Baron Angustin Louis Cauchy (1789–1857).

The quantity A is called the *coefficient of refraction* and B is the *coefficient of dispersion*. The ratio of these two quantities is independent of the resonance frequency ω_α and has dimensions of [mass]^2. This expression is found to give quite accurate results in the visible light region for a variety of gases (see, for example, Problems 9-6 and 9-7).

The classical theory cannot, of course, *predict* the values of the resonance frequencies ω_α; only a correlation of observations relating to the optical properties of matter can be attempted. Within this limitation there are notable successes as well as gross failures (as, for example, in the explanation of the anomalous Zeeman effect; see Section 9.6). Quantum theory must be used for a complete description, and even though a quantum calculation can, in principle, yield values for the resonance frequencies, the computations can be carried out exactly only in the most simple cases.

9.4 Dispersion in Liquids and Solids

In order to discuss dispersive effects in liquids and solids, we must adopt a somewhat different approach from that used for gaseous media. The electric field within a liquid or a solid subjected to an external field will clearly depend upon the polarizability of the medium. For simplicity we shall assume that the molecules of the medium do not possess an intrinsic dipole moment; i.e., the molecules are assumed to be nonpolar. Now, we have previously seen that the displacement vector $\mathbf{D}$ is related to the electric and polarization vectors according to

$$\mathbf{D} = \mathbf{E} + 4\pi\mathbf{P}$$

For an ideal dielectric we also have

$$\mathbf{D} = \varepsilon\mathbf{E}$$

Since the index of refraction is given by the square root of the dielectric constant [Eq. (9.24)], we may write

$$\hat{n}^2 = \hat{\varepsilon} = 1 + 4\pi\frac{P}{E} \tag{9.35}$$

where P and E are the magnitudes of the polarization and electric field vectors.

Within the medium the local field $\mathbf{E}'$ is the sum of the external field $\mathbf{E}$ and a polarization field $\mathbf{E}_p$ which is proportional to $\mathbf{P}$:

$$\begin{aligned} \mathbf{E}' &= \mathbf{E} + \mathbf{E}_p \\ &= \mathbf{E} + \eta\mathbf{P} \end{aligned} \tag{9.36}$$

For a random distribution of dipoles within an ideal dielectric, the factor η is equal to $4\pi/3$ (see Problem 1-3).

We may now proceed with our calculations for a liquid or a solid medium in the same manner as for a gaseous medium if we replace the electric field vector $\mathbf{E}$ in Eq. (9.21) by the resultant field $\mathbf{E}' = \mathbf{E} + 4\pi\mathbf{P}/3$:

$$\mathbf{P} = (\mathbf{E} + 4\pi\mathbf{P}/3) \sum_\alpha \frac{Nf_\alpha e^2/m}{(\omega_\alpha^2 - \omega^2) - 2i\beta_\alpha\omega} \tag{9.37}$$

Using the expressions for $\mathbf{D}$ above, we may verify that

$$\frac{P}{E + 4\pi P/3} = \frac{3}{4\pi}\left(\frac{\hat{\varepsilon} - 1}{\hat{\varepsilon} + 2}\right) \tag{9.38}$$

Then, Eq. (9.37) becomes

$$\frac{\hat{\varepsilon} - 1}{\hat{\varepsilon} + 2} = \frac{4\pi}{3} \sum_\alpha \frac{Nf_\alpha e^2/m}{(\omega_\alpha^2 - \omega^2) - 2i\beta_\alpha\omega} \tag{9.39}$$

For gases, $\hat{\varepsilon} \cong 1$, and for such a case this expression becomes identical with the previous result, Eq. (9.22). On the right-hand side of Eq. (9.39), N is the number of electrons per unit volume and is therefore proportional to the number of atoms per unit volume or to the density ρ of the medium. No other quantity on the right-hand side of Eq. (9.39) is dependent on the density; hence, for a given frequency ω we may write

$$\boxed{\frac{\hat{\varepsilon} - 1}{\hat{\varepsilon} + 2} \cdot \frac{1}{\rho} = \text{const.}} \tag{9.40}$$

This result is known as the *Clausius-Mossotti relation.**

If we consider a transparent medium, so that $\kappa = 0$, then $\hat{\varepsilon} = \varepsilon = n^2$. Thus,

$$\boxed{\frac{n^2 - 1}{n^2 + 2} \cdot \frac{1}{\rho} = \text{const.} \equiv A} \tag{9.41a}$$

In this form the result is called the *Lorentz–Lorenz formula*† and is quite accurate for a wide variety of substances. The quantity A is known as the

* O. F. Mossotti originally derived an equivalent expression in 1850 on the basis of a crude model; R. Clausius refined the derivation in 1879.

† Derived independently and almost simultaneously on the basis of an atomistic view of matter by the Dutch physicist H. A. Lorentz (1880) and by L. Lorenz of Copenhagen (1881). (The two names have identical pronunciations!)

atomic refractivity of the medium (for the case of a *monatomic* substance). For a molecular substance of molecular weight W, the *molar refractivity* is

$$A_m = \frac{n^2 - 1}{n^2 + 2} \cdot \frac{W}{\rho} \tag{9.41b}$$

Table 9.1 indicates the high degree of accuracy possessed by this expression, even for different forms of the media which have quite different indices of refraction.

Table 9.1

MOLAR REFRACTIVITIES OF VARIOUS SUBSTANCES IN THE LIQUID AND VAPOR PHASE FOR SODIUM D LIGHT[a]

Substance		Index of Refraction, n	Molar Refractivity, A_m
Oxygen, O_2	liquid	1.221	2.00
	vapor	1.000271	2.01
Hydrochloric acid, HCl	liquid	1.245	6.88
	vapor	1.000447	6.62
Water, H_2O	liquid	1.334	3.71
	vapor	1.000249	3.70
Carbon disulfide, CS_2	liquid	1.628	21.33
	vapor	1.00147	21.78

[a] Values taken from Born and Wolf (Bo59, p.88).

9.5 Conductivity of Media Containing Free Electrons*

A metallic conductor is unlike a dielectric in the important respect that in a metal not all of the electrons are bound to the atoms, but some are free to move about within the material. In the absence of an applied electric field this motion is random and there is no net current flow. As soon as an electric field is applied, however, each electron acquires an additional velocity component in a direction opposite (since $e < 0$) to the field direction and a current results. As these free electrons flow under the influence of the field, from time to time they encounter the atoms of the material (which are essentially stationary) and are scattered. This scattering may be represented by a damping term which clearly must depend inversely

* This simple model of conductivity was first constructed in 1900 by the German physicist Paul Karl Ludwig Drude (1863–1906).

on the time between collisions and is therefore proportional to the electron velocity.* Hence, the equation of motion of a free electron in a metal may be written as

$$m\ddot{\mathbf{r}}_\alpha + l_\alpha \dot{\mathbf{r}}_\alpha = e\mathbf{E} \tag{9.42}$$

If the electric field varies harmonically with the time, this equation becomes

$$m\dot{\mathbf{u}}_\alpha + l_\alpha \mathbf{u}_\alpha = e\mathbf{E}_0{}^{-i\omega t} \tag{9.43}$$

where $\mathbf{u}_\alpha \equiv \dot{\mathbf{r}}_\alpha$ is the velocity of the αth electron. The solution is

$$\mathbf{u}_\alpha = \frac{e\mathbf{E}}{l_\alpha - im\omega} \tag{9.44}$$

If there are N equivalent electrons per unit volume (i.e., all have the common velocity $\mathbf{u}$), then the current density is given by

$$\mathbf{J} = \sum_\alpha e\mathbf{u}_\alpha = Ne\mathbf{u} = \frac{Ne^2\mathbf{E}}{l - im\omega} \tag{9.45}$$

Now, the coefficient of $\mathbf{E}$ may be interpreted as the conductivity of the metal, so we define a complex conductivity by

$$\boxed{\hat{\sigma} \equiv \frac{Ne^2}{l - im\omega}} \tag{9.46}$$

where $\hat{\sigma} \to \sigma$ (the normal dc conductivity) for $\omega \to 0$. The propagation of the wave may now be obtained by calculating $\hat{k}$ from [cf. Eq. (5.52)]

$$\hat{k}^2 = \frac{\mu\varepsilon\omega^2}{c^2}\left[1 + i\frac{4\pi\hat{\sigma}}{\varepsilon\omega}\right] \tag{9.47}$$

Equation (9.46) shows that for sufficiently low frequencies the conductivity is essentially real. In fact, dc values of σ may be used for most metals without appreciable error well into the infrared region $\lambda \gtrsim 3 \times 10^{-5}$ cm, $\nu \lesssim 10^{13}$ sec^{-1}).† For shorter wavelengths, however, a strong frequency dependence sets in and the current and field are no longer in phase.

* This damping term also includes the effects of radiation damping (see Section 9.9), but in general the collision damping will dominate. As always, the details are given only by a quantum-mechanical calculation.

† As, for example, in the Hagen-Rubens experiment discussed in Section 6.5.

9.6 Propagation in a Plasma—Ionospheric Propagation

We wish to discuss next another important case in which the electrons in the medium may be considered free, viz., the propagation of an electromagnetic wave in a dilute, ionized gas or *plasma*. In such a medium the collision time is long and the damping is relatively unimportant. Equation (9.46) shows that under such conditions $\hat{\sigma}$ becomes essentially a pure imaginary quantity. Since for a plasma $\varepsilon \cong 1$, $\mu \cong 1$, Eq. (9.47) for $\hat{k}^2$ becomes approximately

$$\left.\begin{aligned} \hat{k}^2 &\cong \frac{\omega^2}{c^2}\left[1 - \frac{4\pi N e^2}{m\omega^2}\right] \\ &\cong \frac{\omega^2}{c^2}\left[1 - \frac{\omega_p^2}{\omega^2}\right] \end{aligned}\right\} \tag{9.48}$$

where we have used the expression for the so-called *plasma frequency*:

$$\omega_p^2 \equiv \frac{4\pi N e^2}{m} \tag{9.49}$$

For frequencies $\omega > \omega_p$, the propagation constant is real and we may write for the index of refraction,

$$n \cong \frac{ck}{\omega} = \sqrt{1 - \frac{\omega_p^2}{\omega^2}}, \qquad \omega > \omega_p \tag{9.50}$$

On the other hand, for $\omega < \omega_p$, $\hat{k}$ is purely imaginary. If we write $\hat{k} \equiv i(\omega/c)n\kappa$, the description of a harmonic plane wave will contain the factor

$$e^{-i(\omega t - \hat{k}\zeta)} = e^{-(\omega n/c)\kappa\zeta} e^{-i\omega t}$$

Thus, we see that attenuation will result and that there will be no propagation in the medium. Therefore, an electromagnetic wave with frequency below the plasma frequency will be reflected at the plasma boundary and will have a decaying amplitude extending into the plasma. The effect of the index of refraction for $\omega > \omega_p$ is examined in Problem 9-15.

If we wish to extend the analysis to the propagation of electromagnetic waves in the ionized upper atmosphere, it is necessary to take into account the effects produced by the existence of the Earth's magnetic field in this region.

We assume that we may represent the magnetic field of the Earth by a static, uniform magnetic induction vector $\mathbf{B}_0$. If we consider as small the electron oscillations induced by the passage of the wave, we have approximately

$$m\ddot{\mathbf{r}} \cong e\mathbf{E} + \frac{e}{c}\dot{\mathbf{r}} \times (\mathbf{B}_0 + \mathbf{B}) \tag{9.51}$$

where $\mathbf{B}$ represents the transverse magnetic field of the electromagnetic wave. For all practical cases of the propagation of radio waves in the ionosphere, $|\mathbf{B}_0| \gg |\mathbf{B}|$. Consequently, for propagation in the direction of $\mathbf{B}_0$ (so that $\mathbf{B}_0 = \mathbf{e}_3 B_0$) we have

$$m\ddot{\mathbf{r}} \cong e\mathbf{E} + \frac{e}{c}B_0\dot{\mathbf{r}} \times \mathbf{e}_3 \tag{9.52}$$

If we choose axes such that $(\mathbf{e}_1, \mathbf{e}_2, \mathbf{e}_3) = (\mathbf{e}_x, \mathbf{e}_y, \mathbf{e}_z)$, then the component equations of Eq. (9.52) are approximately

$$\left.\begin{aligned} m\ddot{x} &= eE_x + \frac{e}{c}B_0\dot{y} \\ m\ddot{y} &= eE_y - \frac{e}{c}B_0\dot{x} \\ m\ddot{z} &= 0 \end{aligned}\right\} \tag{9.53}$$

If we multiply the second of these equations by i and add to the first, then

$$m(\ddot{x} + i\ddot{y}) = e(E_x + iE_y) - i\frac{e}{c}B_0(\dot{x} + i\dot{y}) \tag{9.54}$$

Define

$$\left.\begin{aligned} w &\equiv x + iy \\ E &\equiv E_x + iE_y \end{aligned}\right\} \tag{9.55}$$

Then, Eq. (9.54) may be written as

$$\ddot{w} = \frac{e}{m}E - i\frac{eB_0}{mc}\dot{w} \tag{9.56}$$

We assume solutions of the form

$$\left.\begin{aligned} w &= w_0 e^{\pm i(\omega t - kz)} \\ E &= E_0 e^{\pm i(\omega t - kz)} \end{aligned}\right\} \tag{9.57}$$

Substituting these expressions into Eq. (9.56) gives

$$-\omega^2 w_0 = \frac{e}{m} E_0 \pm \omega \frac{eB_0}{mc} w_0$$

or,

$$w_0 = -\frac{(e/m)E_0}{\omega^2 \pm \omega\omega_L} \tag{9.58}$$

where ω_L is the Larmor precession frequency* of an electron in the field B_0.

Now, the wave equation for $\mathbf{E}$ is [see Eq. (5.48a)]

$$\nabla^2 \mathbf{E} - \frac{4\pi\sigma\mu}{c^2} \frac{\partial \mathbf{E}}{\partial t} - \frac{\varepsilon\mu}{c^2} \frac{\partial^2 \mathbf{E}}{\partial t^2} = 0 \tag{9.59}$$

Because this equation is satisfied for each rectangular component of $\mathbf{E}$, it will also be satisfied for $E = E_x + iE_y$. In addition, $\sigma\mathbf{E} = \mathbf{J}$, where $\mathbf{J} = Ne\dot{\mathbf{r}}$, with N equal to the number of electrons per unit volume. Writing $J \equiv J_x + iJ_y$, we have

$$J = \sigma E = Ne\dot{w}$$

Then, for $\varepsilon = 1$, $\mu = 1$, Eq. (9.59) becomes

$$\frac{\partial^2 E}{\partial z^2} - \frac{4\pi Ne}{c^2} \frac{\partial^2 w}{\partial t^2} - \frac{1}{c^2} \frac{\partial^2 E}{\partial t^2} = 0 \tag{9.60}$$

Using Eqs. (9.57) for w and E, we find

$$-k^2 E_0 + \frac{4\pi Ne\omega^2}{c^2} w_0 + \frac{\omega^2}{c^2} E_0 = 0$$

Substituting for w_0 from Eq. (9.58), we have

$$\frac{\hat{k}^2 c^2}{\omega^2} = 1 - \frac{4\pi Ne^2/m}{\omega^2 \pm \omega\omega_L} \tag{9.61}$$

Where we have written $\hat{k}$ since it is now apparent that the propagation constant can be complex.

* The Lorentz magnetic force on an electron moving perpendicular to a field $\mathbf{B}$ is $e(u/c)B$. This must equal the centrifugal force mu^2/ρ, where ρ is the radius of the circular orbit. Since the angular frequency of rotation is $\omega = u/\rho$ we have

$$\omega = \frac{eB}{mc} \equiv \omega_L$$

where the frequency of precession is ω_L, the *Larmor frequency*.

Now, $\omega/\hat{k}$ is the phase velocity of the wave, so that $\hat{k}^2c^2/\omega^2$ is the square of the index of refraction. Thus, we have two possibilities for $\hat{n}^2$, depending on the sign in the denominator:

$$\hat{n}_{\pm}^2 = 1 - \frac{\omega_p^2}{\omega^2 \pm \omega\omega_L}$$

where we have substituted the plasma frequency ω_p in the numerator [see Eq. (9.49)].

Referring to Eqs. (9.55) and (9.56), we see that the waves associated with

$$E = E_x + iE_y = E_0 e^{+i(\omega t - \hat{k}z)}$$

and with the complex conjugate,

$$E^* = E_x - iE_y = E_0 e^{-i(\omega t - \hat{k}z)}$$

have different indices of refraction and therefore propagate with different phase velocities. Therefore, if a linearly polarized wave is incident upon the ionosphere, then choosing the polarization vector to coincide with $\mathbf{e}_x$, we may write

$$\mathbf{E} = \mathbf{e}_x E_x = \tfrac{1}{2}(\mathbf{E}_c + \mathbf{E}_c^*) \tag{9.63}$$

where $\mathbf{E}_c$ and $\mathbf{E}_c^*$ describe waves that are circularly polarized in opposite senses, i.e.,

$$\left.\begin{aligned} \mathbf{E}_c &= E_x(\mathbf{e}_x + i\mathbf{e}_y) \\ \mathbf{E}_c^* &= E_x(\mathbf{e}_x - i\mathbf{e}_y) \end{aligned}\right\} \tag{9.64}$$

But, as we have seen, $\mathbf{E}_c$ and $\mathbf{E}_c^*$ propagate differently. Thus, the effect of an ionized atmosphere in which there is a magnetic field is to separate a linearly polarized wave propagating along the magnetic field direction into two circularly polarized components which propagate with different phase velocities. In this sense, the ionosphere is similar to a double-refracting crystal and is *birefringent*.

This simple model which we have assumed for the ionosphere qualitatively accounts for the effect of the Kennelly-Heaviside layers on the propagation of radio signals. A more detailed account would have to consider the fact that the electron density, and hence ω_p, is a function of altitude (and *time*; day-night and seasonal effects are quite important) (see Problem 9-15). In addition, the precession frequency ω_L is due only to that component of $\mathbf{B}_0$ which lies along the direction of propagation, and therefore the index of refraction is a function of the angle between $\mathbf{B}_0$ and $\mathbf{e}_3$. Consequently, the upper atmosphere is not only nonuniform, but anisotropic as well. In our simple model we have also neglected damping. Thus, the index of refraction does not, of course, ever become infinite, although it can be much greater than unity.

9.7 The Zeeman Effect

We now turn to the discussion of another important result concerning electromagnetic radiation from electrons in a magnetic field. If the electrons are bound to an atom, then the radiation emitted by the atom in a magnetic field will exhibit the *Zeeman effect*.* We shall treat only the so-called *normal* Zeeman effect, for which the classical description is adequate.

The equation of motion of an electron in an electromagnetic field is given by the Lorentz expression,

$$\mathbf{F} = m\mathbf{a}_0 = e\mathbf{E} + \frac{e}{c}\mathbf{u}_0 \times \mathbf{B} \tag{9.65}$$

where the velocity $\mathbf{u}_0$ and the acceleration $\mathbf{a}_0$ are referred to a set of axes which are fixed with respect to an inertial reference frame. If we transform to a set of axes which are rotating with a constant angular velocity $\boldsymbol{\omega}$ with respect to the fixed set of axes, and if $\mathbf{a}$ and $\mathbf{u}$ are the acceleration and velocity referred to the rotating axes, we have

$$\mathbf{u}_0 = \mathbf{u} + \boldsymbol{\omega} \times \mathbf{r} \tag{9.66}$$

The force $m\mathbf{a}_0$ in the fixed coordinate system is equal to the "apparent force" $m\mathbf{a}$ in the rotating system plus the centrifugal and Coriolis terms (see, for example, Section 12.3 of Ma65a):

$$m\mathbf{a}_0 = m\mathbf{a} + 2m\boldsymbol{\omega} \times \mathbf{u} + m\boldsymbol{\omega} \times (\boldsymbol{\omega} \times \mathbf{r}) \tag{9.67}$$

Combining Eqs. (9.65), (9.66), and (9.67), we find

$$e\mathbf{E} + \frac{e}{c}[\mathbf{u} + \boldsymbol{\omega} \times \mathbf{r}] \times \mathbf{B} = m\mathbf{a} + 2m\boldsymbol{\omega} \times \mathbf{u} + m\boldsymbol{\omega} \times (\boldsymbol{\omega} \times \mathbf{r})$$

or,

$$m\mathbf{a} = e\mathbf{E} + 2m\mathbf{u} \times \left[\boldsymbol{\omega} + \frac{e}{2mc}\mathbf{B}\right] + m(\boldsymbol{\omega} \times \mathbf{r}) \times \left[\boldsymbol{\omega} + \frac{e}{mc}\mathbf{B}\right] \tag{9.68}$$

* The effect of a magnetic field on the optical radiation from atoms had been sought without success by Faraday. (His last recorded observation relates to these studies, 1862.) It was the Dutch physicist Pieter Zeeman (1865–1943) who first observed (1896) the effect that Faraday had thought should exist. The explanation in terms of classical electron theory was developed by H. A. Lorentz in 1896. Zeeman and Lorentz shared the 1902 Nobel prize for this work.

Choosing the particular frequency*

$$\boldsymbol{\omega} = -\frac{e}{2mc}\mathbf{B} \equiv \boldsymbol{\omega}_B \qquad (e < 0) \tag{9.69}$$

we have

$$\begin{aligned} m\mathbf{a} &= e\mathbf{E} + m(\boldsymbol{\omega}_B \times \mathbf{r}) \times (\boldsymbol{\omega}_B - 2\boldsymbol{\omega}_B) \\ &= e\mathbf{E} + m\boldsymbol{\omega}_B \times (\boldsymbol{\omega}_B \times \mathbf{r}) \end{aligned} \tag{9.70}$$

Now, if the electron is bound to an atom, the electric field $\mathbf{E}$ appearing in these equations is produced by the charge $+Ze$ of the nucleus combined with the $(Z - 1)$ negative charges of the other electrons. Thus, $\mathbf{E} \cong Z_{\text{eff}}e\mathbf{r}/r^3$, where Z_{eff} is the effective charge of the nucleus plus the $(Z - 1)$ electrons and is of the order of (but somewhat larger than) unity. Therefore, the ratio of the magnitudes of the two terms in Eq. (9.70) is

$$R \equiv \frac{|e\mathbf{E}|}{|m\boldsymbol{\omega}_B \times (\boldsymbol{\omega}_B \times \mathbf{r})|} = \frac{Z_{\text{eff}}e^2/r^2}{mr(eB/2mc)^2} = \frac{4Z_{\text{eff}}mc^2}{r^3B^2}$$

For an atomic system $r \approx 10^{-8}$ cm; also, $mc^2 \approx 10^{-6}$ CGS units (ergs), so that

$$R \approx \frac{10^{19}}{B^2}$$

The highest static fields attainable in the laboratory at present are of the order of 10^5 gauss. Hence, the value of R is at least 10^9, and we may safely neglect the second term in Eq. (9.70). Thus,

$$m\mathbf{a} = e\mathbf{E} \tag{9.70a}$$

But this is just the equation of motion in the absence of a magnetic field. Therefore, viewed in a coordinate system which rotates about the direction of the magnetic field with an angular velocity $\omega_B = eB/2mc$, the electron undergoes simple harmonic motion as if there were no magnetic field present. This result is known as *Larmor's theorem.*†

Consider, as in Fig. 9-4, a constant magnetic field directed along the X_0-axis. (Since the rotating coordinate system revolves with angular velocity ω_B about the field direction, the X- and X_0-axes coincide.) The electron oscillates with frequency ω_0 and amplitude A along the line OP and this line rotates about and makes a constant angle θ with the X_0-axis. The directions of $\boldsymbol{\omega}$ and $\mathbf{B}$ are the same since we are considering an electron

* We note that ω_B is just one half of the Larmor frequency ω_L.

† Derived by Sir J. J. Larmor in 1897.

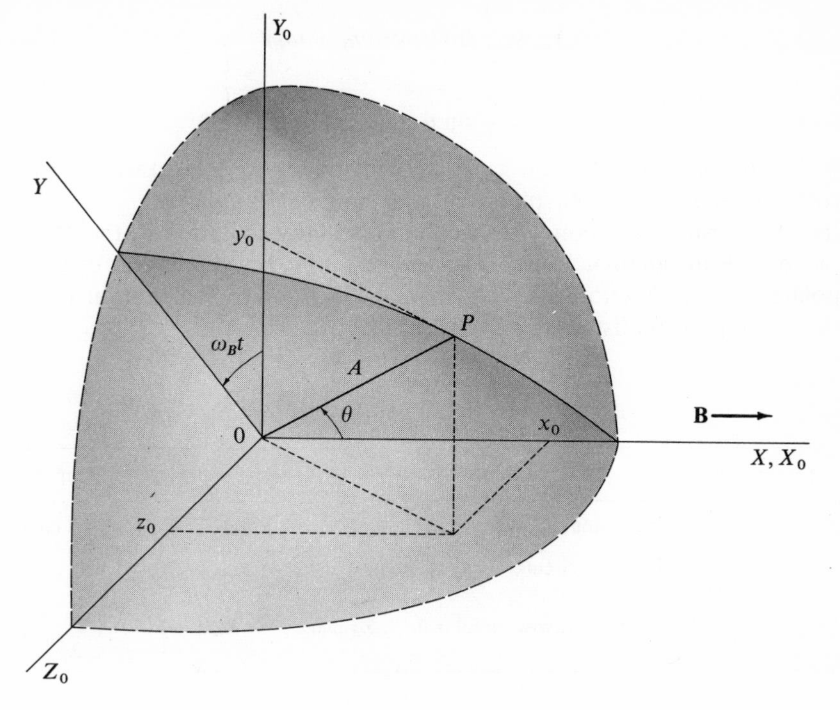

FIG. **9-4**

(with *negative* charge). The projections of the electron position vector on the three axes of the fixed coordinate system are

$$\left.\begin{aligned} x_0 &= A\ \cos\theta\cos\omega_0 t \\ y_0 &= A\sin\theta\cos\omega_0 t\cos\omega_B t \\ z_0 &= A\sin\theta\cos\omega_0 t\sin\omega_B t \end{aligned}\right\} \tag{9.71}$$

Now, consider the y_0 and z_0 projections; these may be written as

$$\left.\begin{aligned} y_0 &= y_1 + y_2 \\ z_0 &= z_1 + z_2 \end{aligned}\right\} \tag{9.72}$$

This latter separation may be accomplished by rewriting y_0 and z_0 in Eqs. (9.71):

$$\left.\begin{aligned} y_1 &= \frac{A}{2}\sin\theta\cos(\omega_0 - \omega_B)t \\ z_1 &= -\frac{A}{2}\sin\theta\sin(\omega_0 - \omega_B)t \end{aligned}\right\} \tag{9.73a}$$

$$\left.\begin{aligned} y_2 &= \frac{A}{2}\sin\theta\cos(\omega_0+\omega_B)t \\ z_2 &= \frac{A}{2}\sin\theta\sin(\omega_0+\omega_B)t \end{aligned}\right\} \tag{9.73b}$$

It will be seen that the y_1, z_1 pair corresponds to a clockwise* circular rotation in the $Y_0 - Z_0$ plane with an angular frequency $\omega_0 - \omega_B$, and the y_2, z_2 pair corresponds to a counterclockwise rotation in the $Y_0 - Z_0$ plane with an angular frequency $\omega_0 + \omega_B$. (See the discussion of circular polarization in Section 5.3.) Thus, we have resolved the motion into the three components listed in Table 9.2.

Table 9.2

FREQUENCY COMPONENTS IN THE NORMAL ZEEMAN EFFECT

Component	Motion	Frequency	Amplitude
1	Linear along X_0-axis	ω_0	$A\cos\theta$
2	Clockwise circular in Y_0-Z_0 plane	$\omega_0 - \omega_B$	$\frac{A}{2}\sin\theta$
3	Counterclockwise circular in Y_0-Z_0 plane	$\omega_0 + \omega_B$	$\frac{A}{2}\sin\theta$

An oscillating electron which undergoes the motion described in Table 9.2 will, of course, produce radiation. We may, however, consider the three components of the motion as independent oscillators and the frequency of the radiation from each component will be different. For example, let us view the oscillating system by looking along the X_0-axis (*longitudinal* observation). We know that a linear oscillation produces a radiation pattern which has a $\sin^2\theta$ dependence. Therefore, no radiation of frequency ω_0 will be emitted along the X_0-axis. The other two components will, however, produce longitudinal radiation, and, because of the circular character of the motion, the radiation will be circularly polarized.† Thus, the longitudinal spectrum will appear as in Fig. 9-5*a*, where the c denotes that the radiations are *circularly polarized.* On the other hand, if the system is viewed along the Z_0-axis (*transverse* observation), radiation with all three frequencies will be observed. The radiation with frequency ω_0 will be linearly polarized‡ *parallel* to the field and is designated π-radiation (or p-radiation). The radiation with frequency $\omega_0 \pm \omega_B$ will be linearly

* "Clockwise" when looking toward the origin along the $+x$-axis.

† The predicted circular polarization of this radiation was confirmed by M. A. Cornu and C. G. W. König in 1897.

‡ Recall that polarization is defined in terms of the behavior of the electric vector.

polarized *perpendicular* (German: *senkrecht*) to the field and is designated σ-radiation (or *s*-radiation). The transverse spectrum is shown in Fig. 9-5b.

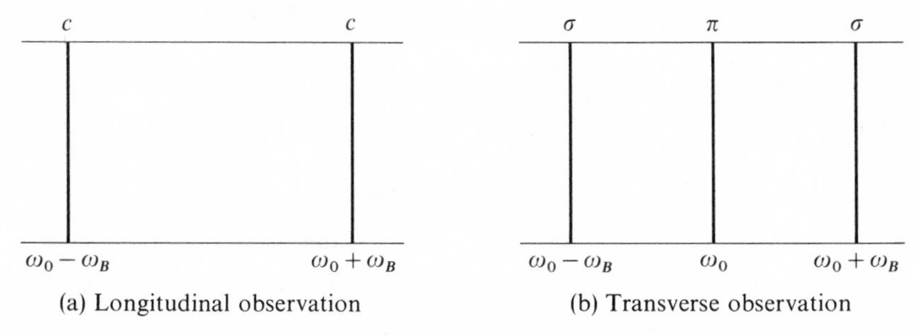

(a) Longitudinal observation (b) Transverse observation

FIG. **9-5**

The spectra of atoms which show this type of spectral splitting when placed in a magnetic field are said to exhibit the *normal Zeeman* (or *Lorentz*) *triplet*. However, only the most simple atoms display the normal Zeeman effect. Again, history has presented us with an unfortunate terminology: the "normal" pattern is rather anomalous, while the "anomalous" Zeeman pattern* (which we must invoke quantum theory in order to interpret) is quite normal.

9.8 Optical Properties of Metals

In Section 9.3 we discussed the dielectric constant and the index of refraction for a perfect dielectric gas by solving the equation of motion for an electron bound in a gas atom under the application of a harmonic electromagnetic field. The sum of all the individual dipole moments gave the polarization of the gas from which we were able to identify the (complex) dielectric constant. In the discussion of the conductivity of a metal on the free-electron model (Section 9.5), we adopted a slightly different point of view. The equation of motion was solved, not for $\mathbf{r}$, but for the velocity $\dot{\mathbf{r}} = \mathbf{u}$. The total current density was then calculated and the (complex) conductivity was identified.

Let us now return to the free-electron model of a metal and extend our calculation by solving for $\mathbf{r}$. Then, as in the case of the dielectric gas, we can find the dielectric constant by computing the polarization of the material.

The equation of motion for the αth free electron is [cf. Eq. (9.42)]

$$\ddot{\mathbf{r}}_\alpha + 2\beta_\alpha \dot{\mathbf{r}}_\alpha = \frac{e}{m}\mathbf{E} \tag{9.74}$$

* The "anomalous" radiation was discovered by Thomas Preston, 1897.

If $\mathbf{E}$ has a harmonic time variation, $\mathbf{E} = \mathbf{E}_0 \exp(-i\omega t)$, then, in analogy with Eq. (9.19), the solution is

$$\mathbf{r}_\alpha(t) = -\frac{(e/m)}{\omega^2 + 2i\beta_\alpha\omega}\mathbf{E} \tag{9.75}$$

The polarization vector $\mathbf{P}$ is the sum of all of the individual dipole moments $\mathbf{p}_\alpha = e\mathbf{r}_\alpha$. Thus, if all of the N electrons per unit volume are identical, we have

$$\mathbf{P} = \sum_{\alpha=1}^{N} \mathbf{p}_\alpha = -\frac{Ne^2/m}{\omega^2 + 2i\beta\omega}\mathbf{E} \tag{9.76}$$

The coefficient of $\mathbf{E}$ is identified as the (complex) electric susceptibility $\hat{\chi}_e$, and the (complex) dielectric constant is given by

$$\hat{\varepsilon} = 1 + 4\pi\hat{\chi}_e = 1 - \frac{4\pi Ne^2/m}{\omega^2 + 2i\beta\omega} \tag{9.77}$$

According to Eq. (9.24) we have

$$\sqrt{\hat{\varepsilon}} = n(1 + i\kappa) \tag{9.78}$$

or,

$$\hat{\varepsilon} = n^2(1 - \kappa^2) + 2in^2\kappa \tag{9.79}$$

Identifying the real and imaginary parts of Eqs. (9.77) and (9.79), we find

$$n^2(1 - \kappa^2) = 1 - \frac{4\pi Ne^2/m}{\omega^2 + 4\beta^2} \tag{9.80a}$$

$$n^2\kappa = \frac{4\pi Ne^2\beta/m\omega}{\omega^2 + 4\beta^2} \tag{9.80b}$$

From Eq. (9.80a) it is apparent that if β is small, then for a certain range of low frequencies, $n^2(1 - \kappa^2) < 0$. If we define ω_c to be the critical frequency at which $n^2(1 - \kappa^2)$ changes sign,

$$\omega_c^2 \equiv 4\pi Ne^2/m - 4\beta^2 \tag{9.81}$$

then,

$$n^2(1 - \kappa^2) = 1 - \frac{\omega_c^2 + 4\beta^2}{\omega^2 + 4\beta^2} \tag{9.82}$$

If both ω_c^2 and ω^2 are assumed large compared with $4\beta^2$ (a reasonable assumption for optical frequencies since the electron damping in a metal is rather small), then we have approximately

$$\left.\begin{aligned} n^2(1-\kappa^2) &\cong 1 - \frac{\omega_c^2}{\omega^2} \\ n^2\kappa &\cong \frac{\beta\omega_c^2}{\omega^3} \end{aligned}\right\} \tag{9.83}$$

From the first of these expressions we see that for $\omega^2 < \omega_c^2$ (but still $\omega^2 \gg 4\beta^2$) we have $\kappa^2 > 1$. But κ is a measure of the attenuation of the wave in the metal. Therefore, if κ is large, we expect a rapid attenuation of the wave and a small value of the transmission coefficient. Hence, for $\omega < \omega_c$, the reflection coefficient will be near unity. On the other hand, when ω exceeds the critical frequency, κ is small, giving rise to a small reflection coefficient and a large transmission coefficient. The medium therefore becomes transparent and is optically similar to a dielectric. To see this quantitatively, we return to Eq. (6.52). We have

$$\frac{E_1^0}{E_0^0} = \frac{\hat{k}_2 - k_1}{\hat{k}_2 + k_1}$$

Considering an air-metal system, we may write

$$\left.\begin{aligned} k_1 &= \frac{\omega}{c} \qquad (n_{\text{air}} \cong 1) \\ \hat{k}_2 &= \frac{\omega}{c}\sqrt{\hat{\varepsilon}} = \frac{\omega}{c} n(1 + i\kappa) \end{aligned}\right\} \tag{9.84}$$

Then the reflection coefficient is given by

$$\begin{aligned} R = \frac{|E_1^0|^2}{|E_0^0|^2} &= \frac{|n(1+i\kappa) - 1|^2}{|n(1+i\kappa) + 1|^2} \\ &= \frac{n^2(1+\kappa^2) + (1-2n)}{n^2(1+\kappa^2) + (1+2n)} \end{aligned} \tag{9.85}$$

From this expression for R, we may obtain the following approximate results for large and small κ:

$$\left.\begin{aligned} R &\cong 1 - \frac{4}{n\kappa^2}, \qquad \kappa \gg 1 \\ R &\cong \left(\frac{1-n}{1+n}\right)^2, \qquad \kappa \ll 1 \end{aligned}\right\} \tag{9.86}$$

Thus, R is essentially unity for large κ (i.e., $\omega < \omega_c$) and R becomes very small for small κ (i.e., $\omega > \omega_c$) since n is a number of the order of unity. The effects based on the qualitative argument given above are therefore correct. In fact, the optical properties of the alkali metals (Li, Na, K, Rb, Cs), in which the valence electrons are almost free, follow these predictions quite closely (see Problem 9-18). These metals are highly reflecting at frequencies below a certain frequency which lies in the optical region, whereas above this frequency, they become quite transparent. The qualitative behavior of n and κ is shown in Fig. 9-6.

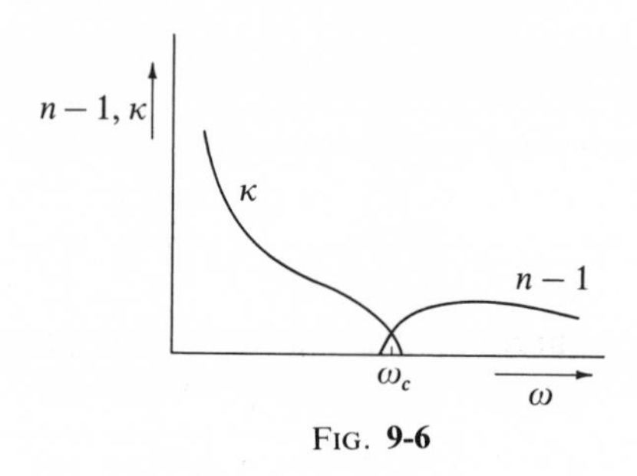

FIG. **9-6**

9.9 Radiation Damping

From time to time in the preceding developments we have made use of two basic facts: (a) the motion of a charged particle is influenced by the presence of electromagnetic fields and (b) a charged particle which undergoes acceleration produces electromagnetic radiation. Although we have treated several problems (and achieved quite satisfactory agreement with experiment) by considering these two facts to be independent and unrelated, it is clear that such an assumption is really unjustified. For, if a charged particle is accelerated and thereby produces an electromagnetic radiation field, the subsequent motion of the particle will be influenced by this field. This phenomenon is termed *radiation reaction* or *radiation damping*.* In many instances this damping effect is sufficiently small so that the problem may be divided into two separate parts as indicated above.

In the problem of dispersion in gases (Section 9.3), we assumed the existence of a damping term proportional to the velocity, and we found that the attenuation index κ was related to the damping parameter β_α [see Eq. (9.27b)]. We now seek to justify the inclusion of such a damping term in the equation of motion [Eq. (9.18)].

* For a detailed account of the (unsatisfactory) state of the fundamental theory of such processes, see, for example, Jackson (Ja62, p. 578 ff.).

According to Eq. (7.68) the energy radiated per unit time by a charge e which is moving with a velocity $u \ll c$ and which undergoes an acceleration $a = \dot{u}$ is

$$P = -\frac{dW}{dt} = \frac{2e^2a^2}{3c^3} = \frac{2e^2\dot{u}^2}{3c^3} \tag{9.87}$$

Therefore, in order to conserve energy, the Newtonian equation which describes the motion of a particle under the influence of a conservative external force $\mathbf{F}_e$,

$$m\dot{\mathbf{u}} = \mathbf{F}_e$$

must be modified by the addition of a *reaction force* $\mathbf{F}_r$ which describes the reaction of the radiation field on the particle; thus,

$$m\dot{\mathbf{u}} = \mathbf{F}_e + \mathbf{F}_r \tag{9.88}$$

This reaction force must satisfy the relation

$$\mathbf{F}_r \cdot \mathbf{u} = \frac{dW}{dt} = -\frac{2e^2}{3c^3}(\dot{\mathbf{u}} \cdot \dot{\mathbf{u}}) \tag{9.89}$$

Now, in general, $\mathbf{u}$ and $\dot{\mathbf{u}}$ are independent so that it is not possible to find a function $\mathbf{F}_r$ which satisfies this equation for all instants of time. By integrating over a short interval of time, however, we can obtain a solution which yields an *average* energy balance:

$$\int_{t_1}^{t_2} \mathbf{F}_r \cdot \mathbf{u}\, dt = -\frac{2e^2}{3c^3}\int_{t_1}^{t_2} \dot{\mathbf{u}} \cdot \dot{\mathbf{u}}\, dt \tag{9.90}$$

Integrating the right-hand side by parts, we have

$$\int_{t_1}^{t_2} \mathbf{F}_r \cdot \mathbf{u}\, dt = -\frac{2e^2}{3c^3}\Big[\mathbf{u} \cdot \dot{\mathbf{u}}\Big]_{t_1}^{t_2} + \frac{2e^2}{3c^3}\int_{t_1}^{t_2} \mathbf{u} \cdot \ddot{\mathbf{u}}\, dt$$

Now, if we consider the time interval $t_2 - t_1$ to be short, or if the motion is periodic (apart from the small energy loss in one period), then the state of the system will be approximately the same at t_2 as at t_1. Therefore, we may neglect the integrated term* and write approximately

$$\int_{t_1}^{t_2} \left(\mathbf{F}_r - \frac{2e^2}{3c^3}\ddot{\mathbf{u}}\right) \cdot \mathbf{u}\, dt \cong 0 \tag{9.91}$$

* This term represents energy which resides in the induction field and therefore oscillates between the source (i.e., the moving charge) and the field.

Hence, energy will be conserved *on the average* if*

$$\mathbf{F}_r = \frac{2e^2}{3c^3}\,\ddot{\mathbf{u}} = \frac{2e^2}{3c^3}\dddot{\mathbf{r}} \tag{9.92}$$

The modified equation of motion is then

$$m\ddot{\mathbf{r}} = \mathbf{F}_e + \frac{2e^2}{3c^3}\dddot{\mathbf{r}} \tag{9.93}$$

If the external force is a linear restoring force, $\mathbf{F}_e = -\gamma\mathbf{r}$, then

$$m\ddot{\mathbf{r}} - \frac{2e^2}{3c^3}\dddot{\mathbf{r}} + \gamma\mathbf{r} = 0 \tag{9.94}$$

We may assume that the radiation damping term is small, so that in a first approximation $\mathbf{r}$ is a solution of

$$m\ddot{\mathbf{r}} + \gamma\mathbf{r} = 0 \tag{9.95}$$

or,

$$\mathbf{r}(t) = \mathbf{r}_0 e^{-i\omega_0 t} \tag{9.96}$$

where $\omega_0^2 = \gamma/m$, as usual. The derivatives of $\mathbf{r}(t)$ are

$$\left.\begin{aligned} \dot{\mathbf{r}}(t) &= -i\omega_0\mathbf{r}(t) \\ \dddot{\mathbf{r}}(t) &= i\omega_0^3\mathbf{r}(t) \end{aligned}\right\} \tag{9.97}$$

so that we may write, approximately,

$$\dddot{\mathbf{r}}(t) = -\omega_0^2\dot{\mathbf{r}}(t) \tag{9.98}$$

With this substitution, Eq. (9.94) becomes approximately

$$m\ddot{\mathbf{r}} + l\dot{\mathbf{r}} + \gamma\mathbf{r} = 0 \tag{9.99}$$

where $l \equiv 2e^2\gamma/3mc^3$. This equation is just the homogeneous form of Eq. (9.18) and therefore justifies our procedure for calculating dispersive effects in gases, at least in the approximation of small radiation damping.

We must note, however, that the values of the damping terms calculated in this manner are in poor agreement with absorption measurements. Thus, the classical theory is not adequate to explain the details of dispersive phenomena; quantum theory must be used for a complete description, although the calculations are frequently too complicated to be carried out exactly.

* The derivation of an equivalent expression was first given by H. A. Lorentz (see Lo09).

Suggested References

Scattering of electromagnetic waves is treated by Panofsky and Phillips (Pa62, Chapter 22), Rosenfeld (Ro51, Chapter 5), Rossi (Ro57, Chapter 8), and Stone (St63, Chapter 14). A comprehensive account is given by Landau and Lifshitz (La62, Chapter 9).

Classical dispersion theory is discussed in a great number of texts. A particularly complete treatment is that of Rosenfeld (Ro51, Chapter 5). Briefer accounts are given, for example, by Blass (Bl62, Chapter 30), Ditchburn (Di62, Chapter 15), Joos and Freeman (Jo50, Chapter 25), Page (Pa52, Chapter 12), Seitz (Se40, Chapter 17), Slater and Frank (Sl47, Chapter 9), Sommerfeld (So54, Chapter 3), and Wangsness (Wa63, Chapter 34).

Plasmas are discussed by Jackson (Ja62, Chapter 7, 10); a brief, introductory survey is given by Whitmer (Wh62, Chapter 11). Spitzer's short book (Sp56) is quite readable.

The free electron theory of metals is discussed, for example, by Born and Wolf (Bo59, Chapter 13), Joos and Freeman (Jo50, Chapter 24), Kittel (Ki56, Chapter 10), and Slater and Frank (Sl47, Chapter 9). An authoritative account is given by Wilson (Wi53). In addition, many books on solid state physics treat this topic as well as the topics listed above.

Propagation in the ionosphere is discussed briefly by Harnwell (Ha49, Chapter 16), Jackson (Ja62, Chapter 7), Plonsey and Collin (Pl61, Chapter 12), and Stratton (St41, Chapter 5). Many electrical and radio engineering texts are also sources of such material.

The classical explanation of the Zeeman effect is given by Menzel (Me53, Section 35), Page (Pa52, Chapter 12), and Sommerfeld (So54, Chapter 3).

Radiation damping is discussed by Jackson (Ja62, Chapter 17), Landau and Lifshitz (La62, Chapter 9), Panofsky and Phillips (Pa62, Chapter 22), and Sommerfeld (So52, Section 36).

Of considerable historical importance in the development of classical electron theory is the book by Lorentz (Lo09), which may still be read with profit.

Problems

9-1. Obtain the expression for the differential scattering cross section for the case of an elliptically polarized incident plane wave scattered by a free charged particle.

9-2. Show that unpolarized radiation, when scattered by a collection of free charged particles, is always at least partially polarized and that the polarization is a maximum for scattering through 90°. (This is the case, for example, for the blue light from the sky.)

9-3. Calculate the differential and the total scattering cross sections for an electron which is bound harmonically to an atom and which experiences a damping linear in its velocity, when a linearly polarized plane electromagnetic wave is incident. Compare the angular distribution of the scattered radiation with that for Thomson scattering. Show that the cross section becomes very large near $\omega = \sqrt{\gamma/m} \equiv \omega_0$, where γ is the "spring constant" of the restoring force. Show also that for strong binding (i.e., large ω_0), the cross section varies as $1/\lambda^4$ (called *Rayleigh scattering*).

9-4. Show that in a region of anomalous dispersion in a gas, the frequencies at which the index of refraction assumes its maximum and minimum values correspond to the half-intensity points of the absorption coefficient. Under the assumption that $\beta_\alpha \ll \omega_\alpha$, express the frequency interval $\omega_2 - \omega_1$ (see Fig. 9-3) in terms of β_α. The quantity $\omega_2 - \omega_1 \equiv \omega_{1/2}$ is the full width at half intensity (i.e., the "half width") of the absorption band.

9-5. Verify the expansion given in Eq. (9.33) and obtain the expressions for A_v, B_v, C_v, B_r, and C_r in terms of the parameters ρ_v, ρ_r, λ_v, and λ_r.

9-6. The constants appearing in Cauchy's equation [Eq. (9.34)] which are appropriate for air under standard conditions are

$$A = 2.879 \times 10^{-4}; \qquad B = 0.567$$

for λ measured in units of 10^{-5} cm. The following are observed values of $n - 1$ for air:

λ	$n - 1$
6.563×10^{-5} cm	2.916×10^{-4}
5.184	2.940
4.308	2.966
3.441	3.016
2.948	3.065

Compare the experimental results with the values calculated from Cauchy's equation.

9-7. Accurate measurements of the refractive index of hydrogen (at 0°C and 760 mm Hg) have been made for the optical region. The results may be summarized as

$$n_H = 1 + 1.360 \times 10^{-4} + \frac{1.05}{\lambda^2} \times 10^{-14}$$

where λ is in cm. Show that the ratio of the constants A and B in the Cauchy equation [Eq. (9.34)] depends only upon the number of electrons per unit volume in the gas. Use this fact together with the above expression for n_H to evaluate e/m, the charge-to-mass ratio of the electron. Compare the result with the currently accepted value. This method was actually one of the earliest used to determine e/m. (The auxiliary data necessary for the computation may be found in, for example, *The Handbook of Chemistry and Physics*.) Assume that a single resonance is responsible for the dispersion.

Calculate the frequency of this resonance and show that it lies in the ultra-violet region, as required for the use of the Cauchy equation.

9-8. The densities at 15°C and the indices of refraction for sodium D light of acetone and ethyl ether are found to be:

Substance	ρ	n
Acetone	0.791	1.3589
Ethyl ether	0.720	1.3558

Calculate the indices of refraction for the vapor phases of these substances at NTP. Compare with the observed values of 1.00108 and 1.00152.

9-9. Show that for a compound the molar refractivity A_m [Eq. (9.41b)] equals the sum of the atomic refractivities of the constituent atoms of the substance. Neglect attenuation effects. Find also an expression for the refractivity of a mixture of two substances whose individual refractivities are A_1 and A_2 if there are N_1 molecules per unit volume of the first type and N_2 molecules per unit volume of the second type.

9-10. From the data of Table 9.1, Section 9.4, and the results of Problem 9-9, calculate the refractivity of hydrogen gas at NTP for sodium D light. Compare with results tabulated in *The Handbook of Chemistry and Physics.*

9-11. Consider a plasma consisting of helium gas at a pressure of 10^{-3} mm Hg in which essentially every atom is singly ionized. To what depth will a 10-kc/sec electromagnetic wave penetrate this plasma before it is reduced in intensity to 10% of its original value?

9-12. A plane electromagnetic wave travels through a uniform plasma. Show that the Poynting vector vanishes if the frequency of the wave is less than the plasma frequency.

9-13. Plot $\hat{n}_+^2$ and $\hat{n}_-^2$ [see Eq. (9.62)] as functions of ω/ω_B for the case in which $\omega_p = \omega_B$. What is the significance of the fact that for certain frequency ranges $\hat{n}_+^2 > 0$ while $\hat{n}_-^2 < 0$ (or $\hat{n}_+^2 < 0$ while $\hat{n}_-^2 > 0$)?

9-14. The density of matter in interstellar space is approximately one electron and one proton per cubic centimeter. What is the limit on the frequency of electromagnetic radiation which can be propagated through such a medium without attenuation? Explain this result physically.

9-15. An electromagnetic wave enters a plasma in which the electron density increases with depth (such as the ionosphere, in which the electron density increases with height for altitudes that are not too great). Show that if the wave enters the plasma at normal incidence, then reflection will occur at a depth at which the plasma frequency is equal to the frequency of the wave. If the entry is not normal, show that the maximum penetration of the wave is less.

9-16. Equation (9.52) describes the motion of a free electron in a magnetic field under the influence of an electromagnetic wave. Consider the modification of this equation if the electron is bound by a linear restoring force to an (immovable) atom. Show that the index of refraction is given by an expression similar to Eq. (9.62) but that now the characteristic frequency (i.e., the frequency of free oscillations) of the electron occurs in the denominator. Show that if a polarized electromagnetic wave is incident upon a system of such atoms in a direction that coincides with the direction of the external magnetic field, then the polarization vector will be rotated as the wave progresses through the medium. This is called the *Faraday effect*.* Show that if the medium is of length L, then the angle through which the polarization vector is rotated may be expressed as

$$\theta = VBL$$

The constant V is known as *Verdet's constant*. [Consider only the frequency region for which the index of refraction is real. It will be convenient to associate the propagation constants $\hat{k}_+$ and $\hat{k}_-$ with the indices $\hat{n}_+$ and $\hat{n}_-$. Introduce also the mean index of refraction $\bar{n} \equiv (\hat{n}_+ + \hat{n}_-)/2$ in order to simplify the expressions.]

9-17. Discuss the angular distribution (relative to the direction of the magnetic field) of the power radiated by the individual components of the normal Zeeman triplet. Calculate the total power radiated by each component and show that the sum is equal to the total power radiated by an identical oscillating electron in the absence of a magnetic field. Calculate also the angular distribution of the power radiated by each component of the triplet for an assembly of electrons for which there is a random distribution of the angles between the oscillation axes and the direction of the magnetic field.

9-18. The critical wavelengths λ_c which correspond to the critical frequencies ω_c [see Eq. (9.81)] for the alkali metals are:

Element	λ_c
Li	2.05×10^{-5} cm
Na	2.10
K	3.15
Rb	3.60
Cs	4.40

* Faraday's observation of this effect in 1845 constituted the first experimental connection between magnetism and light. Faraday had sought such an effect for 20 years.

Assume that each atom of the metal contributes one free electron and assume that the damping term $4\beta^2$ is small. Calculate the wavelengths at which the transition from high reflectivity to high transmission is expected. Also express the results in terms of the effective number of free electrons N_{eff} per atom which it is necessary to assume in order to make the calculated critical wavelengths agree with the observed values given above.

CHAPTER 10

Spherical Scalar Waves

10.1 Introduction

In the preceding chapters we have limited the discussion of electromagnetic waves to the case in which the wave function depends only upon one rectangular coordinate, i.e., the case of *plane waves*. The restriction to the one-dimensional case is not artificial; there are many important problems which can be analyzed in these terms, as we have seen. If one restricts the region of interest to have dimensions somewhat less than the distance to the source of the radiation, then the approximation of plane waves is quite adequate for many applications. For example, an oscillating electric dipole will generate spherical electromagnetic waves, just as a radially vibrating sphere which is immersed in a uniform, isotropic fluid will generate spherical pressure waves. But if we observe the radiation at a large distance from the source and over a limited region of space, the waves are essentially plane waves. On the other hand, if we wish to treat the *entire* radiation field in either case, then we must perform the analysis in terms of spherical waves.

In Chapter 3 we discussed the solution of Laplace's equation in three dimensions. We shall now make use of some of this formalism in order to develop solutions of the wave equation in spherical coordinates.

We must note that our attention here will be confined to spherical *scalar* waves. Therefore, although we shall be able to demonstrate many of the important features of electromagnetic waves, our results will not be correct *in detail*, since electromagnetic radiation is *vector* in character, rather than scalar. Thus, we shall not attempt to describe electromagnetic waves in terms of vector spherical harmonics.* The development presented will be adequate for our purposes, however, since in Chapter 12 we will treat only *scalar* diffraction theory; vector diffraction theory is quite complicated (indeed, only a few problems have been solved exactly) and actually adds very little to our basic understanding of diffraction phenomena.

10.2 Spherical Waves

We begin with the general expression for the scalar wave equation:

$$\nabla^2\Psi - \frac{1}{v^2}\frac{\partial^2\Psi}{\partial t^2} = 0 \tag{10.1}$$

and take, as usual, the time dependence of the wave function to be harmonic:

$$\Psi(\mathbf{r}, t) = \psi(\mathbf{r})e^{-i\omega t} \tag{10.2}$$

Thus, with the standard designation of the wave number, $k = \omega/v$, we have

$$\nabla^2\psi + k^2\psi = 0 \tag{10.3}$$

which is the general form of the *time-independent* wave equation (known also as the *Helmholtz equation*).

We note that there is no loss of generality in assuming a harmonic time variation of the wave function since we may always perform a Fourier analysis of $\Psi(\mathbf{r}, t)$,

$$\Psi(\mathbf{r}, t) = \int_{-\infty}^{+\infty} \psi(\mathbf{r}, \omega)e^{-i\omega t}\, d\omega \tag{10.4}$$

and each Fourier component $\psi(\mathbf{r}, \omega)$ satisfies Eq. (10.3). If we attempt a solution in spherical coordinates, we may express $\psi(\mathbf{r})$ [or, more properly, $\psi(\mathbf{r}, \omega)$] as a sum of products of radial functions and spherical harmonics:

$$\psi(\mathbf{r}) = \sum_{l,m} A_{lm}\, R_l(r) Y_l^m(\theta, \varphi) \tag{10.5}$$

We have already discussed the equation satisfied by the $Y_l^m(\theta, \varphi)$ and have listed their important properties (Section 3.5). The radial equation here is

* See *Suggested References* for sources of such material.

different from that encountered previously [Eq. (3.32)] due to the term $k^2\psi$ which occurs in the Helmholtz equation. We now have

$$\frac{d^2R_l}{dr^2} + \frac{2}{r}\frac{dR_l}{dr} + \left[k^2 - \frac{l(l+1)}{r^2}\right]R_l = 0 \tag{10.6}$$

If we make the substitution

$$R_l(r) = \frac{\mathscr{R}_l(r)}{\sqrt{r}} \tag{10.7}$$

then Eq. (10.6) becomes

$$\frac{d^2\mathscr{R}_l}{dr^2} + \frac{1}{r}\frac{d\mathscr{R}_l}{dr} + \left[k^2 - \frac{(l+\frac{1}{2})^2}{r^2}\right]\mathscr{R}_l = 0 \tag{10.8}$$

With the change of variable, $u \equiv kr$, we have

$$u_2\frac{d^2\mathscr{R}_l}{du^2} + u\frac{d\mathscr{R}_l}{du} + [u^2 - (l+\tfrac{1}{2})^2]\mathscr{R}_l = 0 \tag{10.9}$$

This equation is just Bessel's equation [Eq. (3.84)] with n replaced by $(l + \frac{1}{2})$. The solutions are just the Bessel and Neumann functions of half-integral order, and in analogy with Eq. (3.100) we write a particular solution as

$$\mathscr{R}_l(u) = A_l J_{l+\frac{1}{2}}(u) + B_l N_{l+\frac{1}{2}}(u) \tag{10.10}$$

Thus, dividing the arbitrary constants A_l and B_l by $\sqrt{k}$, we can write

$$R_l(kr) = \frac{A_l}{\sqrt{kr}} J_{l+\frac{1}{2}}(kr) + \frac{B_l}{\sqrt{kr}} N_{l+\frac{1}{2}}(kr) \tag{10.10a}$$

It is customary to define *spherical* Bessel and Neumann functions according to

$$j_l(kr) \equiv \sqrt{\frac{\pi}{2kr}}\, J_{l+\frac{1}{2}}(kr) \tag{10.11a}$$

$$n_l(kr) \equiv \sqrt{\frac{\pi}{2kr}}\, N_{l+\frac{1}{2}}(kr) \tag{10.11b}$$

The first few of these functions are (see Problems 10-1 through 10-4)

$$j_0(kr) = \frac{\sin kr}{kr} \tag{10.12a}$$

$$j_1(kr) = \frac{\sin kr}{(kr)^2} - \frac{\cos kr}{kr} \tag{10.12b}$$

$$j_2(kr) = \left[\frac{3}{(kr)^3} - \frac{1}{kr}\right] \sin kr - \frac{3 \cos kr}{(kr)^2} \tag{10.12c}$$

$$n_0(kr) = -\frac{\cos kr}{kr} \tag{10.12d}$$

$$n_1(kr) = -\frac{\cos kr}{(kr)^2} - \frac{\sin kr}{kr} \tag{10.12e}$$

$$n_2(kr) = -\left[\frac{3}{(kr)^3} - \frac{1}{kr}\right] \cos kr - \frac{3 \sin kr}{(kr)^2} \tag{10.12f}$$

The limiting values are [cf. Eqs. (3.101) to (3.104)]

$$j_l(kr) \sim \frac{(kr)^l}{(2l+1)!!}, \qquad kr \ll l \tag{10.13a}$$

$$j_l(kr) \sim \frac{1}{kr} \sin\left(kr - \frac{l\pi}{2}\right), \qquad kr \gg l \tag{10.13b}$$

$$n_l(kr) \sim -\frac{(2l-1)!!}{(kr)^{l+1}}, \qquad kr \ll l \tag{10.14a}$$

$$n_l(kr) \sim -\frac{1}{kr} \cos\left(kr - \frac{l\pi}{2}\right), \qquad kr \gg l \tag{10.14b}$$

where the double factorial is defined by

$$(2l+1)!! \equiv 1 \cdot 3 \cdot 5 \cdot 7 \cdot \cdots \cdot (2l+1)$$

Now, sine and cosine functions may be combined to yield an exponential function according to the Euler relation,

$$e^{ix} = \cos x + i \sin x$$

Since the spherical Bessel and Neumann functions involve sines and cosines, they may be similarly combined to form exponentials. For this purpose, one defines the *spherical Hankel functions**:

$$h_l^{(1)}(kr) = j_l(kr) + i n_l(kr) \tag{10.15a}$$

$$h_l^{(2)}(kr) = j_l(kr) - i n_l(kr) \tag{10.15b}$$

Thus, for real values of kr, $h_l^{(1)}(kr)$ and $h_l^{(2)}(kr)$ are complex conjugates:

$$h_l^{(1)}(kr) = h_l^{(2)*}(kr) \tag{10.16}$$

* Introduced by the German mathematician H. Hankel in 1869.

Using Eqs. (10.12) we find

$$h_0^{(1)}(kr) = \frac{e^{ikr}}{ikr} \tag{10.17a}$$

$$h_1^{(1)}(kr) = -\frac{e^{ikr}}{kr}\left(1 + \frac{i}{kr}\right) \tag{10.17b}$$

$$h_2^{(1)}(kr) = \frac{ie^{ikr}}{kr}\left(1 + \frac{3i}{kr} - \frac{3}{(kr)^2}\right) \tag{10.17c}$$

The asymptotic form is

$$h_l^{(1)}(kr) \sim (-1)^{l+1}\frac{e^{ikr}}{kr}, \qquad kr \gg l \tag{10.18}$$

The corresponding expressions for the $h_l^{(2)}(kr)$ are given by the complex conjugates of the $h_l^{(1)}(kr)$ in the event that kr is real.

If $z_l(kr)$ stands for *any* of the functions $j_l(kr)$, $n_l(kr)$, $h_l^{(1)}(kr)$, or $h_l^{(2)}(kr)$, then the following recursion relations are satisfied:

$$z_l(kr) = \frac{kr}{2l+1}[z_{l-1}(kr) + z_{l+1}(kr)], \qquad l > 0 \tag{10.19a}$$

$$\frac{d}{dr}z_l(kr) = \frac{k}{2l+1}[lz_{l-1}(kr) - (l+1)z_{l+1}(kr)] \tag{10.19b}$$

We may now write the general expression for the wave function $\psi(\mathbf{r})$ in spherical coordinates incorporating the linearly independent solutions, $j_l(kr)$ and $n_l(kr)$:

$$\psi(\mathbf{r}) = \sum_{l,m} [A_l^m j_l(kr) + B_l^m n_l(kr)] Y_l^m(\theta, \varphi) \tag{10.20a}$$

or, since $h_l^{(1)}$ and $h_l^{(2)}$ are also linearly independent, we may write

$$\psi(\mathbf{r}) = \sum_{l,m} [A_l^m h_l^{(1)}(kr) + B_l^m h_l^{(2)}(kr)] Y_l^m(\theta, \varphi) \tag{10.20b}$$

where the constants A_l^m and B_l^m are different in the two equations, but are written similarly for economy of notation.

Now, according to Eq. (10.18) the asymptotic form of $\psi(\mathbf{r})$ has the radial variation

$$R_l(r) \sim \alpha_l \frac{e^{ikr}}{kr} + \beta_l \frac{e^{-ikr}}{kr}, \qquad r \to \infty \tag{10.21a}$$

for real kr. Thus, the complete wave function has the asymptotic form

$$\Psi(\mathbf{r}, t) \sim \int_{-\infty}^{+\infty} \sum_{l,m} \frac{1}{kr}[\alpha_l e^{-i(\omega t - kr)} + \beta_l e^{-i(\omega t + kr)}] Y_l^m(\theta, \varphi)\, d\omega, \quad r \to \infty \tag{10.21b}$$

Therefore, we see that, just as in the case of plane waves, we have a combination of two wave forms—an *outgoing* wave represented by $\exp[-i(\omega t - kr)]$ and an *incoming* wave represented by $\exp[-i(\omega t + kr)]$. The factor $1/kr$ takes account of the expansion of the wave as r increases. We must therefore identify that portion of the wave function which depends on $h_l^{(1)}(kr)$ as an *outgoing* wave, and that portion which depends on $h_l^{(2)}(kr)$ as an *incoming* wave.*

10.3 Expansion of a Plane Wave in Spherical Waves

In discussing the interaction of a plane wave with any localized object it proves convenient to express the plane wave as a combination of spherical waves. For the case in which there is symmetry about the normal to the wave front of the plane wave, an expansion in terms of spherical harmonics reduces to one in terms of the normal Legendre functions, and we may write, for a wave traveling in the positive z-direction,

$$\begin{aligned} e^{ikz} &= e^{ikr\cos\theta} \\ &= \sum_{l=0}^{\infty} C_l(r) P_l(\cos\theta) \end{aligned} \tag{10.22}$$

In order to obtain an expression for the $C_l(r)$, we first multiply this equation by $P_{l'}(\cos\theta)$ and integrate over the range $-1 \leq \cos\theta \leq 1$. The result is

$$\begin{aligned} \int_{-1}^{+1} e^{ikr\cos\theta} P_{l'}(\cos\theta)\, d(\cos\theta) &= C_l(r) \int_{-1}^{+1} P_l(\cos\theta) P_{l'}(\cos\theta)\, d(\cos\theta) \\ &= C_l(r) \frac{2}{2l+1} \delta_{ll'} \\ &= \frac{2}{2l'+1} C_{l'}(r) \end{aligned}$$

where we have used the orthogonality condition given by Eq. (3.54). Thus,

$$C_l(r) = \frac{2l+1}{2} \int_{-1}^{+1} e^{ikr\cos\theta} P_l(\cos\theta)\, d(\cos\theta) \tag{10.23}$$

* This identification depends upon our arbitrary assumption [in Eq. (10.2)] that the time-dependent part of the wave function had the form $\exp(-i\omega t)$. We could just as well have chosen $\exp(i\omega t)$, and then this factor multiplied by, say, $h_l^{(1)}(kr)$ would yield $\exp[i(\omega t + kr)]$ which is an *incoming* wave. Thus, the identifications are reversed. Some authors adopt this latter convention.

Now, an integral form for the spherical Bessel functions is*

$$j_l(kr) = \frac{1}{2i^l}\int_{-1}^{+1} e^{ikr\cos\theta} P_l(\cos\theta)\, d(\cos\theta) \tag{10.24}$$

Therefore, $C_l(r)$ may be expressed as

$$C_l(r) = (2l + 1)i^l j_l(kr) \tag{10.25}$$

and the expansion of the plane wave is

$$\boxed{e^{ikz} = \sum_{l=0}^{\infty} (2l + 1)i^l j_l(kr) P_l(\cos\theta)} \tag{10.26}$$

10.4 Scattering of a Plane Wave

We now consider the effect on a plane wave produced by a symmetrical scattering object. The Fourier component of the incident wave corresponding to the frequency ω may be represented by

$$\psi_{\text{inc}}(\mathbf{r}) = Ae^{ikz} \tag{10.27}$$

which describes a plane wave of amplitude A moving in the positive z-direction. The interaction of the plane wave with the scattering sphere will produce outgoing waves which at large distances will appear to be spherical waves and must, therefore, asymptotically have the form of $h_l^{(1)}(kr)$. If we include a factor $f(\theta)$ to describe any angular dependence of the scattered wave, we have, asymptotically,

$$\psi_{\text{scatt}}(\mathbf{r}) \sim \frac{f(\theta)}{r} e^{ikr} \tag{10.28}$$

where we have assumed symmetry about the direction normal to the wave front of the plane wave. [Otherwise, we would write $f(\theta, \varphi)$ instead of $f(\theta)$.]

The complete wave function is

$$\psi(\mathbf{r}) = \psi_{\text{inc}}(\mathbf{r}) + \psi_{\text{scatt}}(\mathbf{r}) \tag{10.29}$$

the asymptotic form of which is therefore

$$\psi(\mathbf{r}) \sim A\left[e^{ikz} + \frac{f(\theta)}{r} e^{ikr}\right] \tag{10.29a}$$

* See, for example, Morse and Feshbach (Mo53, Part II, p. 1575).

Now, the definition of the differential scattering cross section can be written as [cf. Eq. (9.8)]

$$\frac{d\sigma(\theta)}{d\Omega} = \frac{\text{Scattered energy/unit solid angle at the angle } \theta\text{/unit time}}{\text{Incident energy/unit area/unit time}} \tag{10.30}$$

The energy density in a wave is proportional to the squared magnitude of the wave function. Thus, the energy per unit area in the incident wave is proportional to

$$|\psi_{\text{inc}}(\mathbf{r})|^2 = |A|^2$$

The energy density in the scattered wave is proportional to

$$|\psi_{\text{scatt}}(\mathbf{r})|^2 = |A|^2 \frac{|f(\theta)|^2}{r^2}$$

so that the scattered energy per unit solid angle is this quantity multiplied by r^2. Thus, the differential scattering cross section becomes

$$\frac{d\sigma(\theta)}{d\Omega} = \frac{r^2 |\psi_{\text{scatt}}(\mathbf{r})|^2}{|\psi_{\text{inc}}(\mathbf{r})|^2}$$

from which

$$\boxed{\frac{d\sigma(\theta)}{d\Omega} = |f(\theta)|^2} \tag{10.31}$$

The total cross section is

$$\boxed{\sigma = \int_{4\pi} \frac{d\sigma(\theta)}{d\Omega}\, d\Omega = \int_{4\pi} |f(\theta)|^2\, d\Omega} \tag{10.32}$$

To summarize, we have taken the total wave function which describes the interaction of the radiation field and the scattering object and have separated this wave function into two parts which describe an incident plane wave and a scattered wave. This clearly is a useful separation to make and can be understood by appealing to physical intuition in the following way. The wave function must satisfy certain boundary conditions imposed by the presence of the scattering object; i.e., the wave function, or possibly its derivative, must assume some certain value at the surface of the scatterer, the value dictated by the physical nature of the situation. In general, a plane wave will not fulfill such conditions and it is necessary to introduce an additional wave so that interference between the two waves will produce the desired result at the surface. Clearly, this additional wave must be an outgoing wave and, since we must account for the energy carried off in this manner, the outgoing wave must be a portion of the incident wave which is reflected by the scattering object.

In Eqs. (10.31) and (10.32) we have expressed the cross sections for the scattering in terms of the factor $f(\theta)$ which occurs in that portion of the wave function identified as the scattered wave. Since both portions of the total wave function extend throughout all space, the question arises as to how a measurement can be made on the scattered portion alone in order to determine the cross section. This will be possible only if we limit the extent of the incident wave, for example, by passing it through an opening in an impenetrable screen some distance away from the scattering object, as in Fig. 10-1. The resulting wave will no longer be a pure plane wave,

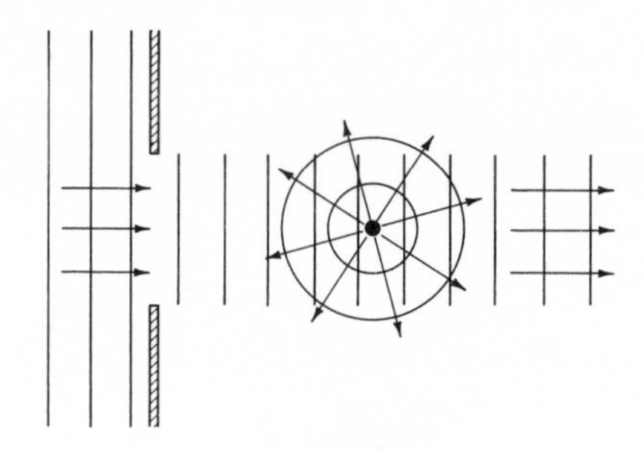

FIG. **10-1**

but if the dimensions of the opening are large compared with a wavelength, then little distortion of the wave will result. By this device it is possible to exclude the incident wave from the regions of space in which the measurements are to be carried out.

10.5 Calculation of the Cross Sections

We now wish to express the cross sections in terms of the wave number of the incident wave and the radius of the sphere which we assume as the scattering object.

A completely general form for the radial portion of the total wave function $\psi(\mathbf{r})$ for a particular value of l can be written as* [cf. Eq. (10.20a)]

$$R_l(kr) = C_l[A_l j_l(kr) - B_l n_l(kr)] \tag{10.33}$$

* We need not label the factor k with an index as was necessary in Eq. (3.106) since we are now considering only a *single* Fourier component of the solution [cf. Eq. (10.4)] in which the frequency ω corresponds to the wave number k according to $k = \omega/v$.

where we choose A_l and B_l to be real and take account of any complex factors by including the constant C_l. If we define

$$\cos \delta_l \equiv \frac{A_l}{\sqrt{A_l^2 + B_l^2}}; \qquad \sin \delta_l \equiv \frac{B_l}{\sqrt{A_l^2 + B_l^2}} \tag{10.34a}$$

and

$$D_l \equiv C_l \sqrt{A_l^2 + B_l^2} \tag{10.34b}$$

then we have

$$R_l(kr) = D_l[\cos \delta_l j_l(kr) - \sin \delta_l n_l(kr)] \tag{10.35}$$

where δ_l is real but where D_l may be complex. If we use Eqs. (10.13b) and (10.14b), the asymptotic radial solution is

$$R_l(kr) \sim \frac{D_l}{kr}\left[\cos \delta_l \sin\left(kr - \frac{l\pi}{2}\right) + \sin \delta_l \cos\left(kr - \frac{l\pi}{2}\right)\right]$$

or,

$$R_l(kr) \sim \frac{D_l}{kr} \sin\left(kr - \frac{l\pi}{2} + \delta_l\right) \tag{10.36}$$

Since the spherical harmonics are normal Legendre functions when there is azimuthal symmetry, we may write the asymptotic form of the total wave function as

$$\psi(\mathbf{r}) \sim \sum_{l=0}^{\infty} \frac{D_l}{kr} \sin\left(kr - \frac{l\pi}{2} + \delta_l\right) P_l(\cos \theta) \tag{10.37}$$

where the constants D_l are now considered to incorporate the constant factors appearing in the definition of the Y_l^0 [Eq. (3.69)]. Thus, the wave function $\psi(\mathbf{r})$ has the normal appearance of a spherical wave, but with a phase that is different by an amount δ_l. The quantity δ_l is called the *phase shift* and, as we shall see, is characteristic of the wave number of the incident wave and the properties of the scattering object, including the type of boundary condition imposed at the surface of the object.

The asymptotic wave function is also given by Eq. (10.29a), and we may use the expansion of the plane wave given in Eq. (10.26) to write

$$\psi(\mathbf{r}) \sim \frac{f(\theta)}{r} e^{ikr} + \sum_{l=0}^{\infty} \frac{(2l+1)i^l}{kr} \sin\left(kr - \frac{l\pi}{2}\right) P_l(\cos \theta) \tag{10.38}$$

where we have used the asymptotic form of $j_l(kr)$ and where we have set the amplitude of the incident wave equal to unity.

The asymptotic wave functions given by Eqs. (10.37) and (10.38) must, of course, be identical, so, expressing the sine terms as exponentials, we have

$$\sum_{l=0}^{\infty} \frac{D_l}{2ikr} P_l(\cos\theta)\{e^{ikr}e^{-i[(l\pi/2)-\delta_l]} - e^{-ikr}e^{i[(l\pi/2)-\delta_l]}\}$$

$$= \frac{f(\theta)}{r}e^{ikr} + \sum_{l=0}^{\infty} \frac{(2l+1)i^l}{2ikr} P_l(\cos\theta)\,[e^{ikr}e^{-i(l\pi/2)} - e^{-ikr}e^{i(l\pi/2)}] \qquad (10.39)$$

Since $\exp(ikr)$ and $\exp(-ikr)$ are linearly independent, the coefficients of these terms must separately be equal. For the terms involving $\exp(-ikr)$, we have

$$\sum_{l=0}^{\infty} D_l P_l(\cos\theta)e^{-i\delta_l} = \sum_{l=0}^{\infty} (2l+1)i^l P_l(\cos\theta) \qquad (10.40)$$

If we multiply this equation by $P_{l'}(\cos\theta)$, integrate, and use the orthogonality condition [Eq. (3.54)], we find

$$D_l = (2l+1)i^l e^{i\delta_l} \qquad (10.41)$$

The coefficients of the terms involving $\exp(ikr)$ in Eq. (10.39) yield

$$\sum_{l=0}^{\infty} D_l P_l(\cos\theta)e^{-i[(l\pi/2)-\delta_l]}$$

$$= 2ik f(\theta) + \sum_{l=0}^{\infty} (2l+1)i^l P_l(\cos\theta)e^{-i(l\pi/2)} \qquad (10.42)$$

Substituting the result for D_l from Eq. (10.41) and using the fact that

$$i^l e^{-i(l\pi/2)} = i^l \cdot (-i)^l = 1$$

we find

$$f(\theta) = \frac{1}{2ik}\sum_{l=0}^{\infty} (2l+1)P_l(\cos\theta)[e^{2i\delta_l} - 1] \qquad (10.43a)$$

or,

$$f(\theta) = \frac{1}{k}\sum_{l=0}^{\infty} (2l+1)P_l(\cos\theta)e^{i\delta_l}\sin\delta_l \qquad (10.43b)$$

Therefore, the differential scattering cross section is given by

$$\boxed{\frac{d\sigma(\theta)}{d\Omega} = |f(\theta)|^2 = \frac{1}{k^2}\left|\sum_{l=0}^{\infty}(2l+1)P_l(\cos\theta)e^{i\delta_l}\sin\delta_l\right|^2} \tag{10.44}$$

and the total scattering cross section is

$$\sigma = \int_{4\pi} |f(\theta)|^2\, d\Omega$$

$$= \frac{2\pi}{k^2}\int_0^{\pi}\left|\sum_{l=0}^{\infty}(2l+1)P_l(\cos\theta)e^{i\delta_l}\sin\delta_l\right|^2 \sin\theta\, d\theta \tag{10.45}$$

Because of the orthogonality of the $P_l(\cos\theta)$, the integrals of all the cross terms in the squared sum vanish, and we have

$$\sigma = \frac{2\pi}{k^2}\sum_{l=0}^{\infty}(2l+1)^2\sin^2\delta_l\int_0^{\pi}[P_l(\cos\theta)]^2\sin\theta\, d\theta$$

Using the orthogonality equation (3.54), we have the result

$$\boxed{\sigma = \frac{4\pi}{k^2}\sum_{l=0}^{\infty}(2l+1)\sin^2\delta_l} \tag{10.46}$$

10.6 Calculation of the Phase Shifts in the Long-Wavelength Limit for Different Boundary Conditions

In order to complete the calculation of the cross sections given by Eqs. (10.44) and (10.46), it is now necessary to find the phase shifts δ_l. This may be accomplished by imposing the appropriate boundary condition on the wave function at the surface of the scattering object. The exact form of the boundary condition will depend on the physical nature of the wave and of the object. For example, if we are considering the scattering of an electromagnetic wave by a perfect conductor, then we must require the wave function (i.e., the electric field) to vanish at the surface. On the other hand, if we have an acoustic wave which impinges on a perfectly rigid object immersed in a fluid medium, then the pressure will not vanish at the surface, but the velocity of the medium will do so, and we must therefore require the vanishing of the normal derivative of the wave function on the surface. These are two examples in which we entirely exclude the wave function from the interior of the object. We could, however, consider a light wave scattering from a refractive object or an acoustic wave scattering from a nonrigid object. In these cases there would be some penetration of the wave function into the interior and the appropriate boundary condition is that the wave function and its derivative must be continuous across the surface. (Note that in this latter case we must develop the interior solution entirely in terms of spherical Bessel functions since the Neumann functions cannot be used in a region which includes the origin.)

Let us first consider a case in which the wave function must vanish at the surface. Then, if the radius of the sphere is a, we have

$$R_l(ka) = 0 \tag{10.47}$$

and from Eq. (10.35), we find

$$\tan \delta_l = \frac{j_l(ka)}{n_l(ka)} \tag{10.48}$$

If we now limit the discussion to long wavelengths (i.e., small k) so that $ka \ll 1$, it is easy to compute the δ_l from the limiting expressions for $j_l(kr)$ and $n_l(kr)$ [see Eqs. (10.13a) and (10.14a)]:

$$\tan \delta_l \cong -\frac{(ka)^l}{(2l + 1)!!} \cdot \frac{(ka)^{l+1}}{(2l - 1)!!} \tag{10.49}$$

or, since ka is small,

$$\delta_l \cong -\frac{(ka)^{2l+1}}{(2l + 1)!!(2l - 1)!!} \tag{10.50}$$

Thus,

$$\delta_0 \cong -ka \tag{10.51a}$$

$$\delta_1 \cong -\frac{(ka)^3}{3} \tag{10.51b}$$

Therefore, in the long-wavelength limit, the phase shifts for $l > 0$ are negligible in comparison with δ_0. As a result, the cross section may be closely approximated by the $l = 0$ term alone:

$$\frac{d\sigma(\theta)}{d\Omega} \cong \frac{1}{k^2} \sin^2 \delta_0 \cong a^2 \tag{10.52}$$

and

$$\sigma \cong \frac{4\pi}{k^2} \sin^2 \delta_0 \cong 4\pi a^2 \tag{10.53}$$

We note that in the long-wavelength limit the total scattering cross section σ is approximately equal to *four times* the geometrical cross section of the sphere, πa^2. The reason for this effect is that we have imposed the condition that the wave function vanish at $r = a$. Therefore, because distortions of the wave function must take place in a continuous manner, the forcing of $\psi(\mathbf{r})$ to assume a definite value on the surface of the sphere affects the wave function even some distance away from the sphere.* This extension of the effective region of interaction increases the cross section by a factor of four.

The expression for the differential cross section [Eq. (10.44)] is, in general, rather complicated since it involves the absolute square of a sum of terms. However, if only the $l = 0$ term is important, then we note that the scattering is spherically symmetric, as indicated by Eq. (10.52).

We have obtained the solution to the problem of the scattering of a plane wave by a sphere for the case in which the boundary condition requires the vanishing of the wave function at the surface of the sphere. Let us next inquire as to the physical problems which will be described in this manner. It was remarked earlier that the scattering of electromagnetic waves by a perfect conductor requires the vanishing of $\psi(\mathbf{r})$ at the surface of the scattering object. The result we have obtained is not directly applicable to this problem however, since the electromagnetic field is a *vector field*, as contrasted to the *scalar field* which we have explicitly assumed in choosing the scalar function $\psi(\mathbf{r}, t)$ to describe our problem. One of the differences that arises when treating the scattering of electromagnetic waves is that the term $\sin^2 \delta_l$ in the expression for the total cross section [Eq. (10.46)] is replaced by $(\sin^2 \delta_l + \sin^2 \varepsilon_l)$, where the phase shifts δ_l and ε_l for the electric and magnetic waves are, in general, different.

Another important difference in our results when electromagnetic waves are considered is in the $l = 0$ term. The electromagnetic wave can be expanded in terms of multipoles, the index l indicating the multipole order: monopole ($l = 0$), dipole ($l = 1$), quadrupole ($l = 2$), etc. The monopole term arises from the total charge on the conductor. Thus, if the conducting sphere is grounded, there is no net charge and the $l = 0$ term does not occur. The lowest order term in the cross section therefore involves $l = 1$, and we find for the total cross section

$$\sigma(l = 1) \cong \frac{4\pi}{k^2} \cdot 3 \cdot \sin^2\left[-\frac{(ka)^3}{3}\right]$$

$$\cong \frac{4\pi}{3} k^4 a^6 \tag{10.54}$$

* Compare Fig. 3-5 which shows the distortion of a *static* electric field in the vicinity of a conducting sphere.

Since $k = 2\pi/\lambda$, we have

$$\sigma(l = 1) \cong \frac{64\pi^5 a^6}{3} \cdot \frac{1}{\lambda^4} \tag{10.54a}$$

(For the electromagnetic case, the coefficient of $1/\lambda^4$ is actually slightly different from that given here due to the particular nature of the electromagnetic field.) If all values of $l > 1$ can be neglected, the differential scattering cross section is no longer spherically symmetric, but involves* $[P_1(\cos\theta)]^2$. If the sphere carries a charge, there will also be $l = 0$ terms in the cross sections.

If an electromagnetic wave is incident on a conducting sphere, then the electric field will induce a dipole moment [cf. Eq. (16) of Example 3.4(a)]

$$p(t) = p_0 e^{-i\omega t} = E_0 a^3 e^{-i\omega t} \tag{10.55}$$

The oscillation of this dipole produces radiation which corresponds to the scattered wave. Notice that a^6 is proportional to p_0^2, so that the scattering cross section varies as p_0^2/λ^4. This is just the form we have previously found [see Eq. (8.36)] for the average power radiated by a dipole. The dependence of the scattering cross section on $1/\lambda^4$ is characteristic of a system that possesses a dipole moment (in the event that there is no monopole term which would otherwise dominate). Scattering of this type is known as *Rayleigh scattering*† (see also Problem 9-2).

The scattering problem which we have just solved is one that is found in virtually every quantum mechanics text—it corresponds to the scattering of a wave (or a particle represented by a *matter wave*) by an infinitely repulsive spherical potential. In this case, the index l refers to the various discrete units of angular momentum (in units of Planck's constant divided by 2π) that the system can possess. For low energies ($ka \gg 1$) only $l = 0$

* Actually, the differential cross section is more complicated than $[P_1(\cos\theta)]^2$ (but it still involves $\cos^2\theta$ as the highest order term) since there arise cross terms between the electric and magnetic contributions to the scattering.

† The variation of σ with $1/\lambda^4$ accounts for the blue of the sky since the shorter wavelengths of visible light are more strongly scattered by the "dipoles" in the atmosphere than are the long wavelengths. Since the range of wavelengths in the visible region is about a factor of 2, scattered blue light predominates over red light by about a factor of $2^4 = 16$. The same effect explains the redness of sunsets since the blue light is scattered and the red light is transmitted. Although the scattering of light by dust particles in the atmosphere does tend to give the sky a blue appearance, Lord Rayleigh showed in 1871 that even dust-free air will scatter light due to molecular fluctuations in density. This molecular effect alone is almost sufficient to account for the observed blueness, and the occurrence of dust particles enhances the effect. Dust particle scattering is particularly evident in the reddening of sunsets since the light must pass through a great length of air near the surface of the Earth and such air can contain much dust and smoke. Sunsets in smoggy areas tend to be quite red.

and, possibly, $l = 1$ are important, and the partial cross sections are just those which we have obtained in Eqs. (10.53) and (10.54a). It must be emphasized, however, that the basic development is *classical*, rather than quantal, in nature.

Let us now turn to the other possible boundary condition for an impenetrable sphere, viz., that the normal derivative of the wave function must vanish on the surface. This is the case, for example, of the scattering of an acoustic wave by a rigid sphere. We have

$$\left.\frac{\partial \psi}{\partial r}\right|_{r=a} = 0 \tag{10.56}$$

or,

$$\left.\frac{dR_l}{dr}\right|_{r=a} = 0 \tag{10.56a}$$

By differentiating Eq. (10.35) we find

$$R_l'(ka) = D_l[\cos \delta_l' j_l'(ka) - \sin \delta_l' n_l'(ka)] = 0 \tag{10.57}$$

where the prime on δ_l' denotes that this new phase shift is based on a boundary condition on the derivative of the wave function, and where the other primes denote differentiation with respect to r. Therefore, we have

$$\tan \delta_l' = \frac{j_l'(ka)}{n_l'(ka)} \tag{10.58}$$

The derivatives of the Bessel and Neumann functions may be evaluated by using the recursion relation given in Eq. (10.19b). For $l = 0$ we find

$$\tan \delta_0' = \frac{j_1(ka)}{n_1(ka)} = \tan \delta_1 \tag{10.59}$$

Thus, we have the result that the $l = 0$ phase shift for the case that the normal derivative of the wave function vanishes on the surface is equal to the $l = 1$ phase shift for the vanishing of the wave function itself. We have, in the long-wavelength approximation,

$$\delta_0' \cong -\frac{(ka)^3}{3} \tag{10.60}$$

and the total cross section is

$$\left.\begin{aligned} \sigma(l = 0) &\cong \frac{4\pi}{9} k^4 a^6 \\ &\cong \frac{64\pi^5 a^6}{9} \cdot \frac{1}{\lambda^4} \end{aligned}\right\} \tag{10.61}$$

We therefore find a cross section which is spherically symmetric and which varies as $1/\lambda^4$. In contrast with our previous $l = 0$ case [Eq. (10.53)], the total cross section for long wavelengths is now much *smaller* than the geometrical cross section.

10.7 The Short-Wavelength Limit of the Cross Sections

In the preceding section we considered the case in which the wavelength of the incident plane wave was large compared with the size of the scattering object, i.e., $ka \ll 1$. We now consider the other limiting case in which the wavelength is small compared with dimensions of the scattering object, i.e., $ka \gg 1$. Previously, we argued that forcing the wave function to vanish at the surface of the scattering sphere distorted the wave function for some distance from the sphere and that, therefore, the total scattering cross section was larger than the geometrical cross section. In the short-wavelength approximation we expect this effect to be small and, as a result, we might predict that the cross section is almost geometrical. Furthermore, in this limit, we expect a reasonably sharp shadow to be formed behind the sphere, such as that which occurs for an opaque object placed in a light beam. As we shall see, this latter expectation is correct, but the former needs some modification.

From the asymptotic expressions for $j_l(kr)$ and $n_l(kr)$ [Eqs. (10.13) and (10.14)], we find

$$\tan \delta_l = \frac{j_l(ka)}{n_l(ka)} \sim \begin{cases} -\tan\left(ka - \dfrac{l\pi}{2}\right), & ka \gg l \\ -\dfrac{(ka)^{2l+1}}{(2l+1)!!(2l-1)!!}, & ka \ll l \end{cases} \tag{10.62}$$

Therefore, the phase shifts δ_l are approximately equal to $-ka + (l\pi/2)$ for l less than ka. For l greater than ka, the factorials in the denominator increase more rapidly with l than does the power of ka in the numerator, so that the phase shifts tend to become quite small. If we neglect the latter values of δ_l, the expression for the total cross section [Eq. (10.46)] becomes

$$\sigma \cong \frac{4\pi}{k^2} \sum_{l=0}^{ka} (2l+1) \sin^2 \delta_l \tag{10.63}$$

Now, in view of Eq. (10.62), we have

$$\sin^2 \delta_l = \sin^2\left(\frac{l\pi}{2} - ka\right)$$

$$= \left(\sin\frac{l\pi}{2}\cos ka - \cos\frac{l\pi}{2}\sin ka\right)^2$$

$$= \sin^2\frac{l\pi}{2}\cos^2 ka + \cos^2\frac{l\pi}{2}\sin^2 ka$$

where the cross term, which involves $\sin(l\pi/2)\cos(l\pi/2)$, vanishes for all integral values of l. Thus,

$$\sigma \cong \frac{4\pi}{k^2}\sum_{l=0}^{ka}(2l+1)\left[\sin^2\frac{l\pi}{2}\cos^2 ka + \cos^2\frac{l\pi}{2}\sin^2 ka\right] \tag{10.64}$$

As l runs through $0, 1, 2, \ldots$, the terms $\sin^2(l\pi/2)$ and $\cos^2(l\pi/2)$ alternately vanish or become 1, and we have

$$\sigma \cong \frac{4\pi}{k^2}[1\cdot\sin^2 ka + 3\cdot\cos^2 ka + 5\cdot\sin^2 ka + 7\cdot\cos^2 ka + \cdots]$$

$$= \frac{4\pi}{k^2}[(1+5+9+\cdots)\sin^2 ka + (3+7+11+\cdots)\cos^2 ka]$$

We now use the arithmetic series

$$S = b + (b+d) + (b+2d) + \cdots + L = \frac{n}{2}(b+L)$$

where L is the last term:

$$L = b + (n-1)d$$

For our case, $L = 2ka + 1$, so that $n = (ka/2) + 1$, and

$$1 + 5 + 9 + \cdots + 2ka + 1 = \frac{(ka/2)+1}{2}[1 + (2ka+1)]$$

$$\cong \tfrac{1}{2}(ka)^2$$

since $ka \gg 1$. The same result is obtained for the series which is the coefficient of $\cos^2 ka$. The fact that ka is not, in general, an integer will introduce negligible error if ka is large. Therefore, we have approximately

$$\sigma \cong \frac{4\pi}{k^2}[\tfrac{1}{2}(ka)^2\sin^2 ka + \tfrac{1}{2}(ka)^2\cos^2 ka]$$

r,

$$\sigma \cong 2\pi a^2 \tag{10.65}$$

so that the cross section in this limit is *twice* the geometrical cross section. In order to understand this result, we note that in the short-wavelength limit, the portion of the incident wave that strikes the sphere will tend to be reflected, forming a shadow in the forward direction. The cross section for reflection will be approximately geometrical. But in order to form a shadow in the forward direction, there must be destructive interference between two waves. Consequently, in addition to the *reflected wave* of cross section πa^2, there must be an equal amount scattered into the forward direction (the *shadow-forming wave*) which just cancels with the incident wave function to produce a shadow region. Thus, the total scattering cross section must be approximately $2\pi a^2$. We have the result, therefore, that πa^2 is removed from the incident wave and appears in the reflected wave, but that in addition equal amounts of incident and scattered wave (πa^2) interfere to produce the shadow.

In order to measure the total scattering cross section, it is, of course, necessary to detect the scattered wave at all scattering angles and to integrate the results. If a sizeable fraction of the scattered wave lies in the forward direction, then, as a practical matter, it becomes increasingly difficult to separate this wave from the incident wave as we approach $\theta = 0$. In fact, as ka tends to infinity, the entire shadow-forming wave lies closer and closer to $\theta = 0$, so that in the limit it becomes impossible to separate the two waves experimentally and the measured cross section will equal $\sigma/2$, or the geometrical cross section.

A complicated calculation shows that the angular distribution of scattering intensity in the short-wavelength limit is given by*

$$\frac{d\sigma(\theta)}{d\Omega} = |f(\theta)|^2 \sim \frac{a^2}{4} + \frac{a^2}{4}\cot^2(\theta/2)J_1^2(ka\sin\theta) \tag{10.66}$$

where the first term is the spherically symmetrical reflected intensity (the integral of which alone is πa^2), and where the second term gives the sharply forward-peaked, shadow-forming wave intensity. The second term becomes small compared with the first term as soon as θ differs by a small amount from zero.

Suggested References

The solution of the scalar wave equation in three dimensions is discussed by Jackson (Ja62, Chapter 16) and by Slater and Frank (Sl47, Chapter 12). Infinite detail is given by Morse and Feshbach (Mo53, Part II, Chapter 11).

* See, for example, Morse and Feshbach (Mo53, Part II, p. 1551 ff).

Scattering theory is most commonly found in quantum mechanics texts. Many of these accounts can be appreciated without recourse to quantum concepts. See, for example, Houston (Ho51, Chapters 11, 12), Merzbacher (Me61, Chapter 12), Schiff (Sc55, Chapter 5), and Wu and Ohmura (Wu62, Chapter 1).

The vector wave equation is discussed in detail by Jackson (Ja62, Chapter 16) and by Stratton (St41, Chapter 7). Even more comprehensive is Morse and Feshbach (Mo53, Chapter 13).

Problems

10-1. Use Eq. (3.95b) to calculate $J_{\frac{1}{2}}(u)$ and $J_{\frac{3}{2}}(u)$, and use Eq. (3.100) to calculate $N_{\frac{1}{2}}(u)$ and $N_{\frac{3}{2}}(u)$. Show that these functions agree with Eqs. (10.12).

10-2. Use Eq. (3.108b) to prove the relation

$$u^{-(n+m)}J_{n+m}(u) = (-1)^m \frac{1}{u^m}\frac{d^m}{du^m}\left(\frac{1}{u^n}J_n(u)\right)$$

where m is a positive integer, but n is unrestricted. From this result, show that

$$J_{l+\frac{1}{2}}(u) = (-1)^l \frac{(2u)^{l+\frac{1}{2}}}{\sqrt{\pi}} \frac{d^l}{d(u^2)^l}\left(\frac{\sin u}{u}\right)$$

Use this expression and the relation

$$j_l(u) = \sqrt{\frac{\pi}{2u}}\, J_{l+\frac{1}{2}}(u)$$

to verify Eqs. (10.12a), (10.12b), and (10.12c).

10-3. Verify Eq. (10.24) by direct integration for j_0, j_1, and j_2.

10-4. The *generating functions* for the spherical Bessel and Neumann functions are

$$j_l(u) = (-1)^l u^l \left(\frac{1}{u}\frac{d}{du}\right)^l \left(\frac{\sin u}{u}\right)$$

$$n_l(u) = -(-1)^l u^l \left(\frac{1}{u}\frac{d}{du}\right)^l \left(\frac{\cos u}{u}\right)$$

where, for example,

$$\left(\frac{1}{u}\frac{d}{du}\right)^2 = \frac{1}{u}\frac{d}{du}\left(\frac{1}{u}\frac{d}{du}\right)$$

and so on, for higher values of l. Use these expressions to verify Eqs. (10.12) and, in addition, compute $j_3(kr)$ and $n_3(kr)$.

10-5. Consider the scattering of a plane wave from a sphere of radius a for the case in which the wave function vanishes on the surface. Take $ka = \frac{1}{2}$ and use Eq. (10.48) to compute the phase shifts δ_0, δ_1 and δ_2. Plot the differential scattering cross sections for the $l = 0$ contribution alone, then for $l = 0$ and $l = 1$, and finally for $l = 0$, $l = 1$, and $l = 2$. Comment on the comparison of these plots. Calculate the total cross section in similar approximations. Estimate the error involved in computing the total cross section by considering only the $l = 0$ term.

10-6. Work the above problem for the case in which the normal derivative of the wave function vanishes on the surface of the sphere. Use Eq. (10.57) to calculate the phase shifts δ_l'. In order to calculate δ_2' you will need the expressions for $j_3(kr)$ and $n_3(kr)$ from Problem 10-4. Comment on the magnitudes of the cross sections found in this and in the above problem.

CHAPTER 11

Interference Phenomena

11.1 Introduction

In a great many problems involving electromagnetic radiation, particularly in the field of optics, the interference of waves from two or more sources is of prime importance. We have already encountered several examples of interference effects: For example, in Section 6.5, the standing wave produced when an electromagnetic wave is incident normally on a perfect conductor is a result of the interference between the incident and reflected waves. In Section 10.4 we found that there was interference between the incoming and outgoing waves when radiation is scattered by an object. In both of these cases, the interference was between an *incident* and a *reflected* wave; i.e., both waves were derived ultimately from the same source. This is a crucial point, since the emission of radiation from a real physical source of light is not continuous but takes the form of great numbers of short bursts of radiation (*photons*). Thus, the light source is subject to fluctuations. But if the fluctuations in two beams of light are *correlated* (as they would be if they were derived from the same source), then interference between the beams is possible. Such beams are said to be *coherent*. The correlation of the fluctuations in two light beams can be stated in terms of the *phases* of the waves involved. Thus, two beams are coherent if there exists a *definite phase difference* between waves in the two beams. If no such definite phase relation exists (i.e., if the phases are *random*), then the beams are *incoherent*. Whereas coherent beams can interfere to produce regular variations of intensity, such effects tend to cancel in incoherent beams and the resultant intensity is just the sum of the individual intensities. These considerations will be discussed in detail in several of the later sections.

The possibility of interference between two beams of radiation is dependent upon the existence of a definite phase relation between the waves. It is not possible, of course, to *control* the phase of waves from a real light source,* so that coherent light beams can be produced only by dividing the light from a *single* source into two (or more) waves. (Methods for accomplishing this are described briefly in Sections 11.7 and 11.8.) On the other hand, it is a relatively easy matter to control the phase of certain other types of electromagnetic radiation, e.g., radio waves. Indeed, in the discussions of antenna arrays (Sections 8.8 and 8.9), the radiation patterns which we found were actually the result of interference between waves emitted by different sources. Radiation of controlled phase is limited to the range of frequencies that can be generated by electronic methods. At present, wavelengths shorter than a millimeter or so ($\nu \gtrsim 300{,}000$ Mc/sec) cannot be generated with controlled phase.

11.2 Wiener's Experiment and the "Light Vector"

Before beginning the discussion of interference effects in general, we shall in this section describe the experiment performed by Wiener† which demonstrated that optical effects are caused predominantly by the *electric* vector of the electromagnetic wave rather than by the magnetic vector. This result considerably simplifies the general treatment of optical phenomena since we may then limit the discussion to **E** and essentially ignore **B**.

In Wiener's experiment, monochromatic light of wavelength λ is incident normally on a highly reflecting surface ($R \cong 1$), as in Fig. 11-1. A detector, in the form of a thin ($<\frac{1}{20}\lambda$), transparent photographic film, is

* In certain special cases it is possible to produce optical radiation in which all of the photons are *in phase*. This is the situation in stimulated emission of radiation (*lasers*) and in the radiation produced when a charged particle traverses a dielectric material with a velocity greater than the velocity of light in that material (*Cherenkov radiation*). These interesting subjects are treated, for example, in the monographs by Lengyel (*Lasers*; Le62) and by Jelley (*Cherenkov Radiation*; Je58).

† O. Wiener, 1889.

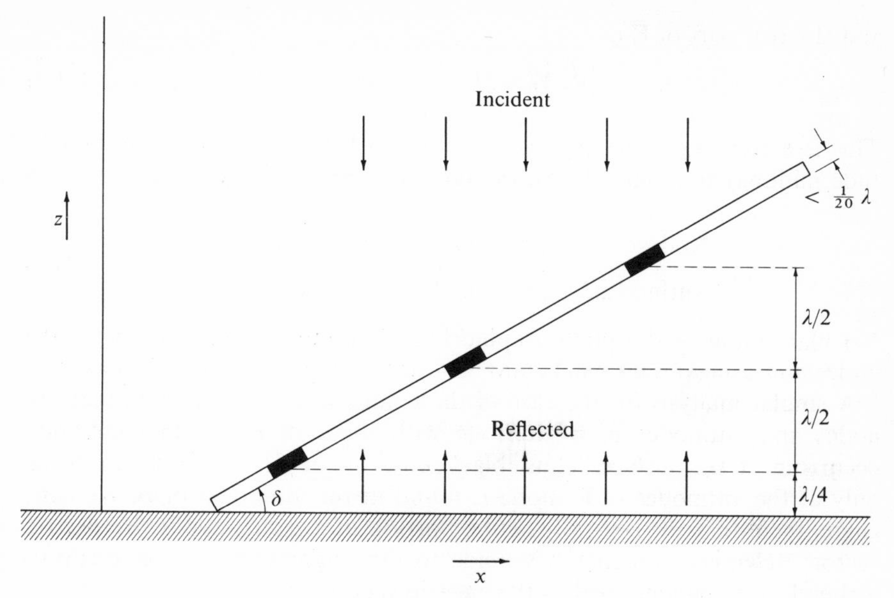

FIG. **11-1**

placed above the reflecting surface, making a small angle δ with the surface. Upon exposure to the radiation, the photographic film is observed to be blackened at regular intervals. Because δ is small,* the perpendicular distances from the reflecting surface to the film are magnified by a factor $1/\sin\delta \cong 1/\delta$ along the film so that the spacing between blackened strips is readily observable and accurately measureable. The blackened strips correspond to the regions in which the "light vector" is enhanced due to constructive interference. The first black strip occurs at a distance $\lambda/4$ above the surface and successive strips are found with a spacing of $\lambda/2$ (see Fig. 11-1).

If $\mathbf{E}_0$ is the incident electric vector (polarized in the x-direction) and if $\mathbf{E}_1$ is the reflected electric vector, then if the reflection coefficient is assumed to be unity, we may write

$$\left.\begin{aligned} \mathbf{E}_0 &= \quad \mathbf{e}_x E_0^0 e^{-i(\omega t + kz)} \\ \mathbf{E}_1 &= -\,\mathbf{e}_x E_0^0 e^{-i(\omega t - kz)} \end{aligned}\right\} \tag{11.1}$$

The minus sign in the expression for $\mathbf{E}_1$ occurs, of course, because there is a phase change of π upon reflection. The total electric vector is

$$\begin{aligned} \mathbf{E} &= \mathbf{E}_0 + \mathbf{E}_1 \\ &= \mathbf{e}_x E_0^0 (e^{-ikz} - e^{ikz}) e^{-i\omega t} \end{aligned} \tag{11.2}$$

* In Wiener's experiment, δ was equal to 4 minutes of arc.

and the real part of **E** is

$$|\text{Re}\,\mathbf{E}| = 2E_0^0 \sin kz \sin \omega t \tag{11.3}$$

This is a standing wave, just as we found in Eq. (6.64), with *nodes* (amplitude minima) and *antinodes* (amplitude maxima) given by

$$\left.\begin{array}{lll} \text{Nodes:} & z = m\lambda/2, & m = 0, 1, 2, \cdots \\ \text{Antinodes:} & z = n\lambda/2, & n = \frac{1}{2}, \frac{3}{2}, \frac{5}{2}, \cdots \end{array}\right\} \tag{11.4}$$

No blackening of the photographic film is found at the positions of the nodes and a maximum blackening is found at the antinode positions.

A similar analysis for the case of the magnetic vector **B** reveals that the nodes and antinodes of **B** alternate with those of **E**, the first antinode occurring at the surface. Thus, blackening of the film is found to occur only at the antinodes of **E**; none is found at the antinodes of **B**. We conclude, then, that the optically active portion of a light wave is the electric vector. Reference is sometimes made to the "light vector"; this quantity is therefore to be identified as the electric vector.

The magnetic effects of light waves are almost always negligible, since for optical frequencies only small velocities can be imparted to electrons in one oscillation period. The magnetic effects are proportional to u/c (as in the Lorentz force) and are therefore usually unimportant.

11.3 Coherence and Incoherence—"Almost Monochromatic" Radiation

In all of our previous discussion we have assumed the existence of *monochromatic* radiation. Truly monochromatic radiation, however, is an idealization since it requires the wave to be of infinite extent. Light, on the other hand, consists of finite wave trains emitted by atoms. These bursts of radiation (*photons*) generally contain $\approx 10^6$ wave oscillations which are emitted from an atom during a time $\approx 10^{-9}$ sec. Such a pulse of radiation, containing as it does a very large number of wave oscillations, is "almost monochromatic" (or *quasi-monochromatic**); i.e., the pulse consists of a band of frequencies, although the frequency spectrum may be rather narrow.

* We take the definition of quasi-monochromatic radiation to be that radiation for which the range of wavelengths involved, $\Delta\lambda$, is small compared with the mean wavelength λ_0: $\Delta\lambda/\lambda_0 \ll 1$; see Eq. (11.8b).

Let us suppose that an oscillator with a characteristic frequency ω_0 emits a pulse of radiation with unit amplitude in a time Δt. Then, the wave has the form

$$F(t) = \begin{cases} e^{-i\omega_0 t}, & |t| \leq \Delta t/2 \\ 0, & \text{otherwise} \end{cases} \tag{11.5}$$

As discussed in Marion (Ma65a, Section 15.6), the frequency distribution $f(\omega)$ of such a wave will be given by the Fourier transform of $F(t)$:

$$\begin{aligned} f(\omega) &= \int_{-\infty}^{+\infty} F(t)e^{i\omega t}\, dt \\ &= \int_{-\Delta t/2}^{+\Delta t/2} e^{-i(\omega_0 - \omega)t}\, dt \\ &= \left[\frac{\sin[(\omega_0 - \omega)\Delta t/2]}{(\omega_0 - \omega)\Delta t/2}\right]\Delta t \end{aligned} \tag{11.6}$$

The *intensity* of the light in the pulse as a function of frequency is given by the square of the amplitude distribution function:

$$I(\omega) = |f(\omega)|^2 \tag{11.7}$$

The intensity function $I(\omega)$ is shown in Fig. 11-2 for the case of the pulse described by Eq. (11.5). From the appearance of this curve it is clear that

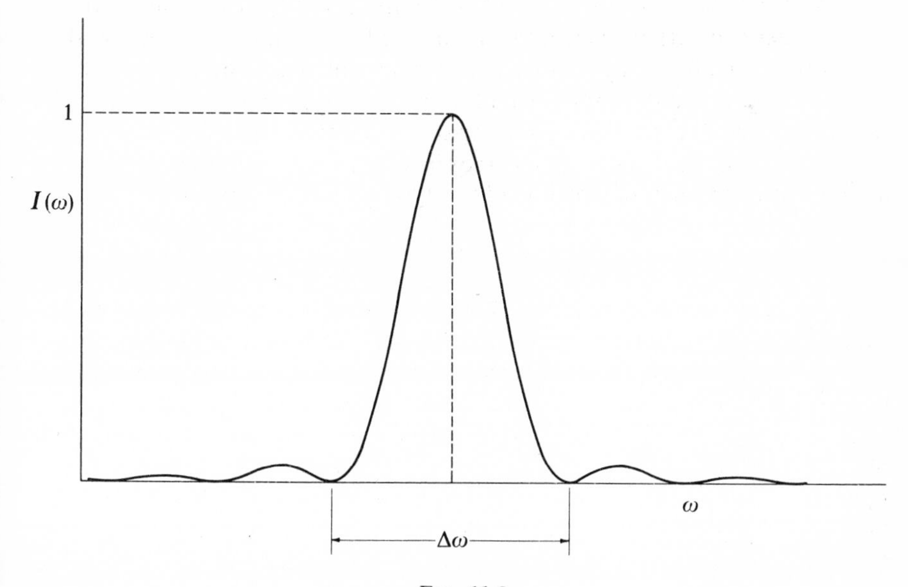

FIG. **11-2**

any statement regarding the "width of the frequency spectrum" must be somewhat arbitrary. However, on either side of the main maximum, the first minima occur at $|\omega_0 - \omega|\Delta t/2 = \pi$, and we take this interval to correspond to the "width" $\Delta\omega$ of the frequency distribution. Thus, we may write

$$\Delta\omega\,\Delta t \cong 2\pi \tag{11.8}$$

Since $k_0 = \omega_0/c$ and since the length of the pulse is $\Delta x = c\,\Delta t$, we have, equivalently,

$$\Delta k\,\Delta x \cong 2\pi \tag{11.8a}$$

This result is analogous to the Heisenberg uncertainty relation of quantum mechanics [see also Marion (Ma65a, Section 15.6)].

Equation (11.8a) confirms our remark that a monochromatic wave must be of infinite extent, since if $\Delta\omega = 0$ (and, hence, $\Delta k = 0$), then Δx must be infinite for the relation to hold.

Since $\omega_0 = ck_0 = 2\pi c/\lambda_0$, we may express Eq. (11.8) in still another way:

$$\Delta\lambda \cong \frac{\lambda_0^2}{c\,\Delta t} \tag{11.8b}$$

Thus, for an oscillator whose characteristic wavelength is 5000 Å $= 5 \times 10^{-5}$ cm and which radiates for a time 10^{-9} sec, we find a wavelength spread $\Delta\lambda \cong 0.01$ Å. One of the narrowest spectral lines is the red cadmium line at 6438 Å which has $\Delta\lambda \cong 0.013$ Å. The limiting width of *any* spectral line (independent of its wavelength) is due to radiation damping and is 0.000116 Å, or about the diameter of a heavy nucleus (see Problem 11-2).

Because they are of infinite extent, ideal monochromatic waves have the same (sinusoidal) form throughout space. Therefore, the calculation of the interference of two such waves requires only the addition of the two wave functions,* each of which is of the type (in one dimension)

$$\Psi(x, t) = Ae^{-i(\omega t - kx - \phi)}$$

As we have seen above, however, real light waves are only quasi-monochromatic and cannot be represented by an expression as simple as that above. Consequently, the interference effects are subject to some restrictions. Consider, for example, a real light source which is radiating at a certain average rate. The emission of light is not continuous, but individual photons are radiated from the atoms of the source in a random manner. Thus, there is no definite phase relation between any two photons and the interference effects that take place also occur in a random way. Therefore, even though interference *does* take place, it will sometimes be constructive

* A simple case is worked out in Section 11.9.

and sometimes destructive, and the net effect is to produce an intensity which is the sum of the intensities of the individual photons.* The radiation from a real light source is therefore *incoherent.*

Consider next the result of passing a beam of light from a real source through a half-silvered mirror so that two beams of equal intensity are produced. Each wave from the source will have been divided with one half appearing in each of the two resultant beams. If these beams are brought together again (as could be accomplished with a set of mirrors), then each wave in one beam has a counterpart in the other beam and, furthermore, *the phase difference between each such pair is the same.* Therefore, a definite interference effect between the two beams will result; whether the interference is constructive or destructive will depend upon the exact value of the phase difference that was introduced by the process of splitting and recombining the beam. The two beams that were produced by the splitting are *coherent.*

It is important to realize that the *only* way† in which it is possible to produce a coherent light beam is to split a single beam either by reflection or refraction or by passing the beam through two or more slits. Thus, a light source and its optical image are coherent. We shall investigate various methods of producing coherent light beams later in this chapter.

In the argument above, we have neglected an important consideration, viz., the finite extent of quasi-monochromatic radiation. Thus, if a finite wave train is split into two wave trains (of equal length) and the two parts are permitted to travel different distances before being recombined, then interference between the parts will be possible only if the difference in the path lengths does not exceed the length of the wave trains. Therefore, no interference will occur if one wave is delayed so that it falls a distance greater than Δx [see Eq. (11.8a)] behind the other wave. Appreciable interference will result only if the path difference is much less than Δx. The distance Δx is called the *coherence length* of the wave and may be expressed as

$$\Delta x = \frac{\lambda_0^2}{\Delta\lambda} \tag{11.9}$$

The red cadmium line ($\lambda_0 = 6438$ Å, $\Delta\lambda = 0.013$ Å) has a coherence length of approximately 32 cm. Michelson was able to observe interference effects with this radiation for path differences of ~ 30 cm.‡

If $\Delta\lambda$ were no larger than the value which results from radiation damping (0.000116 Å), then the coherence length would be enormous (~ 200 meters

* This point will be proved in Section 11.4.

† Apart from the special cases of lasers and Cherenkov radiation as mentioned earlier.

‡ Albert A. Michelson (1852–1931) used his famous interferometer for these measurements, 1891. Michelson was awarded the Nobel prize in physics in 1907.

for 5000 Å radiation). However, effects more important than radiation damping cause essentially all of the observed width of optical spectral lines. These effects are:

(a) DOPPLER EFFECT. A wavelength shift occurs when the radiating atom is in motion relative to the observer. Since the thermal motion of atoms is random, the net result of the Doppler effect is a broadening of the spectral line. This broadening is proportional to the square root of the absolute temperature and so can be reduced to some extent by maintaining the source at a reduced temperature, for example, by means of a liquid-nitrogen bath.

(b) PRESSURE BROADENING. Since the atoms of a source are in continual motion, collisions occur at frequent intervals. If the *mean free time* between collisions is smaller than the time Δt during which radiation occurs, then this interruption of the radiation process by the collision shortens the wave train and broadens the line.

By using low-pressure gaseous sources at low temperatures, the Doppler and pressure effects can be reduced, but a residual line width for optical radiation of ~0.005 Å is the best that has been achieved. The bright green line at 5461 Å in the spectrum of Hg^{198} has been observed with $\Delta\lambda \cong 0.005$ Å. The coherence length is therefore approximately 60 cm.

11.4 The Intensity of Incoherent Radiation

We now wish to prove the statement made in the preceding section that the intensity of radiation from a real light source is the sum of the intensities of the individual light waves emitted by the source. In constructing this proof we may limit the discussion to the electric vectors of the waves since we have already established that optical effects are due predominantly to the electric vector.

We consider a source which produces a number of waves with individual electric vectors $\mathbf{E}_r$. The total electric vector of the radiation field is then

$$\mathbf{E} = \sum_r \mathbf{E}_r \tag{11.10}$$

Now, the light from a real source will consist of radiation from a number of different spectral lines; we shall consider only one such line, but a sum over all of the lines may be performed to generalize the argument. We take the direction of propagation of the light waves to be the z-direction and we assume the radiation to be polarized in the x-direction.* The light,

* This is no restriction, since we may make the same argument for light polarized in the y-direction, and a linear combination of the two polarizations can represent *any* polarization.

even from a single spectral line, will not be monochromatic, but since it is nearly so we may write approximately for the rth electric vector,

$$\mathbf{E}_r = \mathbf{e}_x E^0 e^{-i(\omega t - kz)} e^{i\phi_r} \tag{11.11}$$

where E^0 is the amplitude (a real quantity and the same for each wave originating from the single spectral line) and where ϕ_r is the phase. The time average of the radiated power is just the *intensity* of the radiation:

$$\begin{aligned} I &= \langle P \rangle = \langle \mathbf{S} \rangle \cdot \mathbf{e}_z \\ &= \frac{c}{4\pi} \langle \mathbf{E} \cdot \mathbf{E}^* \rangle = \frac{c}{8\pi} |\mathbf{E}|^2 \end{aligned} \tag{11.12}$$

We have

$$\mathbf{E} = \mathbf{e}_x E^0 e^{-i(\omega t - kz)} \sum_{r=1}^{N} e^{i\phi_r} \tag{11.13}$$

so that

$$\begin{aligned} |\mathbf{E}|^2 &= \left| E^0 \sum_{r=1}^{N} e^{i\phi_r} \right|^2 \\ &= \left(E^0 \sum_r \cos \phi_r \right)^2 + \left(E^0 \sum_r \sin \phi_r \right)^2 \\ &= (E^0)^2 \Bigg[\sum_r \cos^2 \phi_r + \sum_r \sum_{\substack{s \\ r \neq s}} \cos \phi_r \cos \phi_s \\ &\qquad + \sum_r \sin^2 \phi_r + \sum_r \sum_{\substack{s \\ r \neq s}} \sin \phi_r \sin \phi_s \Bigg] \end{aligned} \tag{11.14}$$

If the number N of contributing waves is very large, and if the phases are truly random, the double sums in Eq. (11.14) each vanish by virtue of the fact that they contain equal positive and negative contributions. Then, combining the first and third terms of Eq. (11.14), we have

$$|\mathbf{E}|^2 = (E^0)^2 \sum_{r=1}^{N} 1 = N \cdot (E^0)^2 \tag{11.15}$$

or, equivalently,

$$|\mathbf{E}|^2 = \sum_{r=1}^{N} |\mathbf{E}_r|^2 \tag{11.15a}$$

Thus,

$$I = \frac{c}{8\pi} \sum_r |\mathbf{E}_r|^2 = \sum_r I_r \tag{11.16}$$

Hence, the total intensity is just the sum of the individual intensities.*

* This result was first obtained by Lord Rayleigh, who, in 1880, considered the problem from the standpoint of probability theory. For a brief account of Rayleigh's solution, see Feather (Fe61, pp. 207–209).

11.5 Interference of Two Coherent Light Beams

We have already noted that it is possible to produce two beams of light which are coherent by splitting a single original beam. Without yet inquiring exactly how these beams are produced, we wish to investigate the interference effects that occur. We shall assume that it is possible *to control the phase difference* between the two beams;* i.e., there is some mechanism to adjust the path length that one of the beams travels before it is recombined with the other beam. A device which accomplishes this is called an *interferometer*; we shall discuss some examples later in this chapter. For the moment, we also restrict our attention to path differences that are small compared with the coherence length of the radiation. Therefore, we may approximate the light by a monochromatic wave.

Our two beams of light will be assumed to be of the same frequency, to be propagating in the z-direction, and to be polarized in the x-direction. The electric vectors of the two waves will be denoted by $\mathbf{E}_1$ and $\mathbf{E}_2$:

$$\left.\begin{aligned}\mathbf{E}_1 &= \mathbf{e}_x E_1^0 e^{-i(\omega t - kz)} e^{i\phi_1}\\ \mathbf{E}_2 &= \mathbf{e}_x E_2^0 e^{-i(\omega t - kz)} e^{i\phi_2}\end{aligned}\right\} \tag{11.17}$$

The total electric vector is

$$\mathbf{E} = \mathbf{E}_1 + \mathbf{E}_2 \tag{11.18}$$

and the intensity is

$$\begin{aligned} I &= \frac{c}{4\pi}\langle \mathbf{E}\cdot\mathbf{E}^*\rangle = \frac{c}{8\pi}|\mathbf{E}|^2 \\ &= \frac{c}{8\pi}\left\{|\mathbf{E}_1|^2 + |\mathbf{E}_2|^2 + \mathbf{E}_1\cdot\mathbf{E}_2^* + \mathbf{E}_1^*\cdot\mathbf{E}_2\right\} \end{aligned} \tag{11.19}$$

We define component intensities so that

$$I = I_1 + I_2 + I_{12} \tag{11.20}$$

where,

$$\left.\begin{aligned} I_1 &\equiv \frac{c}{8\pi}|\mathbf{E}_1|^2 \\ I_2 &\equiv \frac{c}{8\pi}|\mathbf{E}_2|^2 \\ I_{12} &\equiv \frac{c}{8\pi}(\mathbf{E}_1\cdot\mathbf{E}_2^* + \mathbf{E}_1^*\cdot\mathbf{E}_2) \end{aligned}\right\} \tag{11.21}$$

* Note that it is possible to control the phase *difference* between the waves of two beams that are derived from the same source (*coherent* beams), although it is not possible to control the values of the individual phases.

Using Eqs. (11.17), we find

$$I_{12} = \frac{c}{8\pi} E_1^0 E_2^0 (e^{i\phi} + e^{-i\phi}) \tag{11.22}$$

where ϕ is the phase difference:

$$\phi \equiv \phi_1 - \phi_2 \tag{11.23}$$

Equation (11.22) simplifies to

$$I_{12} = \frac{c}{4\pi} E_1^0 E_2^0 \cos\phi \tag{11.22a}$$

Now, I_1 and I_2 are given by

$$\left.\begin{aligned} I_1 &= \frac{c}{8\pi}(E_1^0)^2 \\ I_2 &= \frac{c}{8\pi}(E_2^0)^2 \end{aligned}\right\} \tag{11.24}$$

so that the total intensity may be written as

$$I = I_1 + I_2 + 2\sqrt{I_1 I_2}\cos\phi \tag{11.25}$$

The maxima and minima of intensity are

$$\left.\begin{aligned} I_{max} &= I_1 + I_2 + 2\sqrt{I_1 I_2}, \qquad \phi = 0, \pm 2\pi, \pm 4\pi, \cdots \\ I_{min} &= I_1 + I_2 - 2\sqrt{I_1 I_2}, \qquad \phi = \pm\pi, \pm 3\pi, \cdots \end{aligned}\right\} \tag{11.26}$$

For $I_1 = I_2 \equiv I_0$, we have

$$I = 2I_0(1 + \cos\phi) = 4I_0\cos^2(\phi/2) \tag{11.27}$$

Thus, for equal intensities of the two beams, the maximum resultant intensity is $4I_0$, whereas the minimum is zero. The intensity pattern as a function of the phase difference for this case is shown in Fig. 11-3. In the event that the component intensities I_1 and I_2 are not equal, then the resultant intensity oscillates about $I_1 + I_2$, as shown in Fig. 11-4, never becoming as large as $(I_1 + I_2)^2$ nor as small as 0.

In certain experimental arrangements it is possible to convert the phase difference ϕ into a distance along a viewing screen or a photographic plate. The maxima and minima of intensity then manifest themselves as *interference fringes* which are directly observable. It is important to note that such fringes will be well defined, as in Fig. 11-3, only if the light is

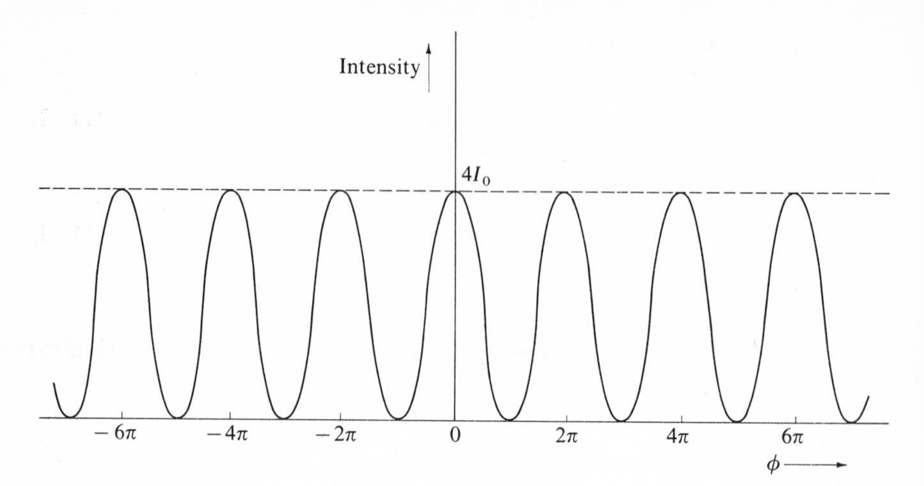

FIG. **11-3**

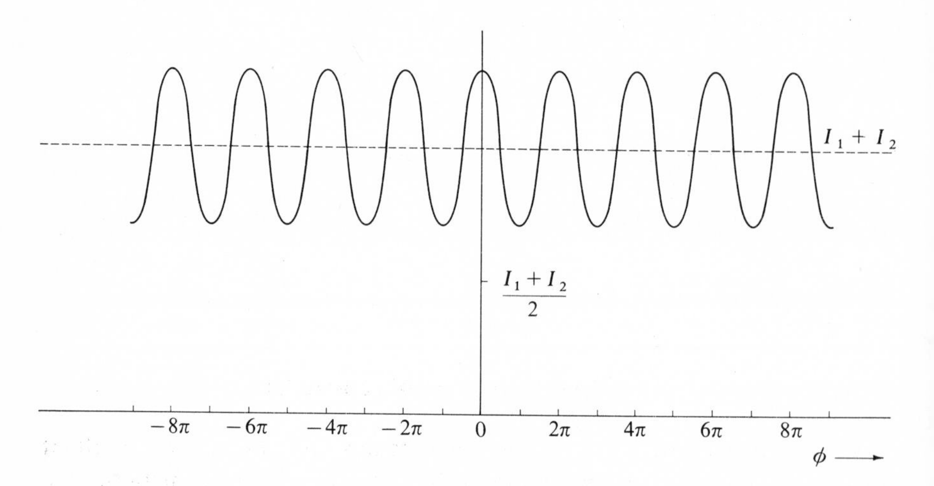

FIG. **11-4**

monochromatic (or nearly so), since the phase difference ϕ depends upon the wavelength of the radiation through the relation

$$\phi = k\Delta = \frac{2\pi}{\lambda}\Delta \tag{11.28}$$

where Δ is the difference in path lengths. Therefore, if the light is a mixture of two different frequencies, the pattern of interference fringes will appear as in Fig. 11-5, where the solid curve represents the fringes for the higher frequency (shorter wavelength) and the dashed curve represents the fringes for the lower frequency (longer wavelength). Clearly, if the radiation is *white light* (all frequencies), then only the first few fringes near zero phase difference will be visible, the remainder being obscured by the overlapping of many individual fringes.

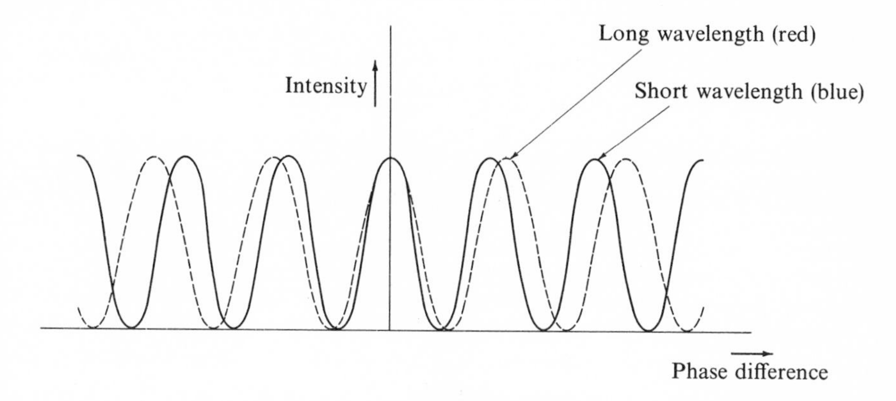

FIG. **11-5**

If we take into account the fact that the radiation is only quasi-monochromatic, then the intensity of the fringes will not remain constant as we increase the phase difference (or path length). The variation of intensity (or *visibility*) of fringes due to interference effects with quasi-monochromatic light will be discussed in Section 11.9.

11.6 Huygens' Construction

Although we shall develop a general mathematical description of the propagation of light waves in the following chapter, we mention here a clever geometrical method, known as *Huygens' construction*,* for dealing with such problems. The method is described as follows. As a light wave traverses a medium, every element of volume of the medium that is influenced by the wave may be considered the source of a secondary disturbance which propagates through the medium just as the radiation from an isolated source. In order to illustrate this construction, let us consider a pulse of radiation that is emitted by a source. If the duration of the pulse

* Developed by Christian Huygens (1629–1695) in 1678 and published in his *Treatise on Light* in 1690.

is quite short, then after a certain interval of time, the wave front associated with the pulse will be a shell whose thickness is very small and may therefore be considered to be simply a surface. If the source were spherically symmetric and if the medium were homogeneous and isotropic, then the wave front surface would be spherical. In general, however, the surface will be of some more complicated shape, such as that indicated in Fig. 11-6.

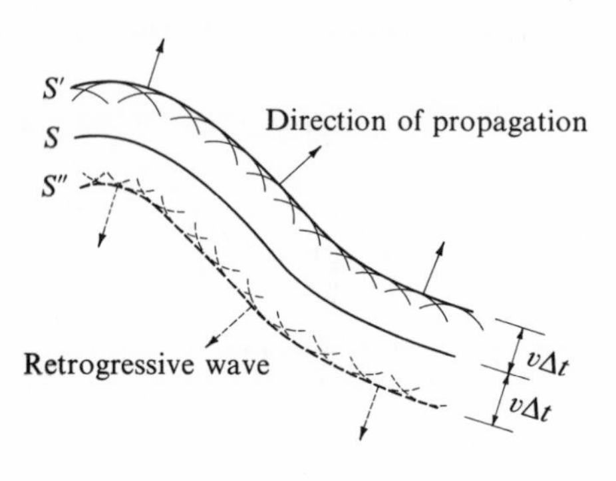

FIG. **11-6**

At a certain reference time t, the wave front is at the position of the surface S. Each element of this surface is considered to act as a source of secondary waves. A series of these secondary spherical waves is shown in the positions they would occupy at a time $t + \Delta t$, and the envelope S' of the waves constitutes the wave front of the total disturbance. The wave front S' has advanced a distance $v\Delta t$ from the position S which it occupied at the time t, a result which we know to be correct.

Huygens' construction can be used to solve a number of different types of problems. For example, the reflection and refraction of a plane wave incident on a transparent medium may be correctly determined by Huygens' construction. It is necessary only to know the velocity of propagation in each medium (i.e., the indices of refraction must be specified).

There is, however, a fundamental difficulty with the simple statement of Huygens' method given above. Referring again to Fig. 11-6, we see that if the surface S is indeed considered as a series of secondary sources, then the radiation from these sources will propagate *backward* as well as *forward* and after a time Δt will give rise to a second wave front, S''. This retrogressive wave is clearly irrelevant to the problem of the propagation of the pulse of radiation, and, since at this stage of the development we have only our intuition to tell us that this wave is unphysical, we simply eliminate it from consideration. In spite of this arbitrariness, Huygens' construction still provides a useful and uniformly successful method not only for solving problems in geometrical optics (reflection and refraction) but also for treating diffraction effects.* In the next chapter we shall see that Kirchhoff's formulation of the problem automatically eliminates the retrogressive wave and thereby obviates the necessity for its arbitrary dismissal.

11.7 Two-Beam Interference—Division of Wave Fronts

We now turn to a brief description of some of the methods for producing coherent light beams and to a discussion of the results that are obtained. The method by which interference fringes were first observed was devised by Thomas Young† in 1801 and consists of passing light from a source S through two narrow, parallel slits which are cut in a screen, as in Fig. 11-7. The source is assumed to be of small size. A spherical wave diverging from S will always have the same phase difference at the openings A and B.

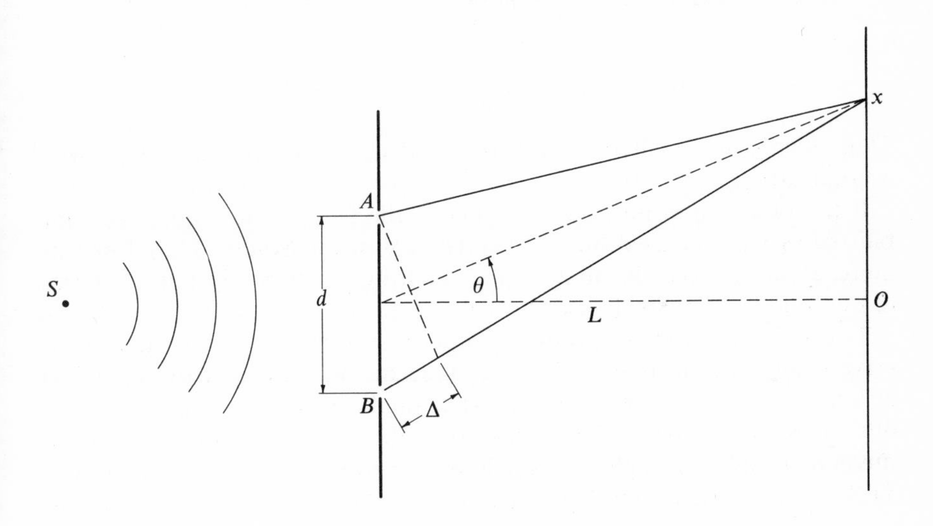

FIG. 11-7

* Fresnel's extension of the method, known as the *Huygens-Fresnel principle*, may be considered as the basic postulate of the wave theory of light. The mathematical formulation of this principle is due to Kirchhoff and is discussed in Chapter 12.

† Thomas Young (1773–1829) wrote a brilliant series of papers during 1801–1809 which advocated the wave theory of light. His ideas were supported by his interference experiments but nevertheless the theory was largely ignored. It remained for Fresnel to firmly establish the wave theory with his explanation of double refraction and of diffraction effects, 1816.

(If A and B are equidistant from S, as indicated in Fig. 11-7, this phase difference is, of course, zero.) According to Huygens' principle, the openings A and B may be considered sources of secondary waves, and because there is a constant phase difference between the waves emanating from these sources, they are coherent. This method of separating a single wave into two coherent waves is called the *division of wave fronts*. (We shall discuss the other method, *the division of amplitudes*, in Section 11.8.)

If we assume a zero phase difference between the waves radiating from A and B, when the waves reach the general point x on the observing screen, the phase difference will be

$$\phi = k\Delta \cong kd \sin \theta \cong kd \frac{x}{L} = \frac{2\pi x d}{\lambda L} \tag{11.29}$$

where we have made the approximation that θ is a small angle. If the light is monochromatic, the intensity at the observing screen will have maxima and minima at the positions

$$\text{maxima:} \qquad x = m\frac{\lambda L}{d}, \qquad m = 0, \pm 1, \pm 2, \cdots$$

$$\text{minima:} \qquad x = n\frac{\lambda L}{d}, \qquad n = \pm\tfrac{1}{2}, \pm\tfrac{3}{2}, \cdots$$

Thus, there will be alternating bright and dark interference fringes, with a bright fringe at $x = 0$.

If the radiation is not monochromatic, the fringes will tend to become blurred as x is increased (see the similar remarks in Section 11.5). Furthermore, even for monochromatic light, the fringes will be blurred if the size of the source is not small (see Problem 11-3).

Two other methods of producing interference fringes by division of the wave front were devised by Fresnel. One method involves the reflection of light from two mirrors inclined at a small angle with respect to each other (*Fresnel's mirrors*, Fig. 11-8a); the other method involves the transmission of light through two small-angle prisms (*Fresnel's bi-prism*,* Fig. 11-8b). In both cases the light that reaches the point Q on the observing

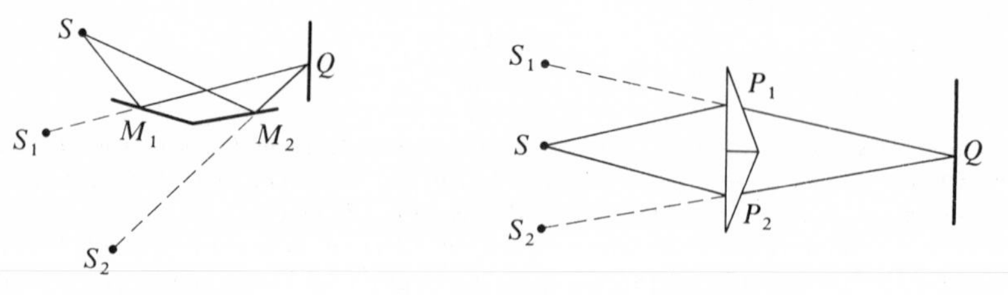

FIG. 11-8a FIG. 11-8b

* Also devised independently by Ohm (1840).

screen appears to come from two sources, S_1 and S_2, each of which is a virtual image of the real source S.

A simple variant of Fresnel's arrangement of mirrors was made by Lloyd,* who used only a single mirror, as shown in Fig. 11-9. An important result obtained with *Lloyd's mirror* is the following: At the point Q_1 on the observing screen (the point of contact of mirror and screen) there is zero path difference between the direct and reflected rays. But a *dark* fringe is found at this position. Since a dark fringe indicates *destructive* interference, this experiment demonstrates conclusively that a phase change of π occurs upon reflection.

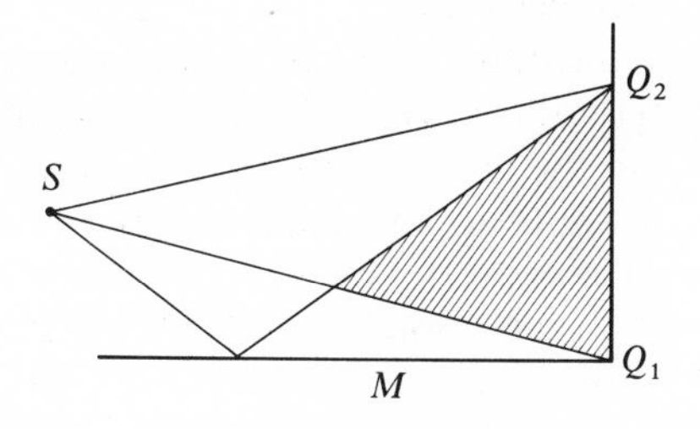

FIG. **11-9**

The method of division of wave fronts was used by Rayleigh in constructing a refractometer† for the accurate measurement of the indices of refraction of gases (and liquids). A schematic of the arrangement is shown in Fig. 11-10. Basically, the system is used to produce fringes at Q by recombining two beams which have passed through identical transmission cells, T_1 and T_2. One cell is evacuated and the other cell contains the gas under study. The difference in optical path length can be determined by observation of the fringes at Q in the following way. First, both cells are

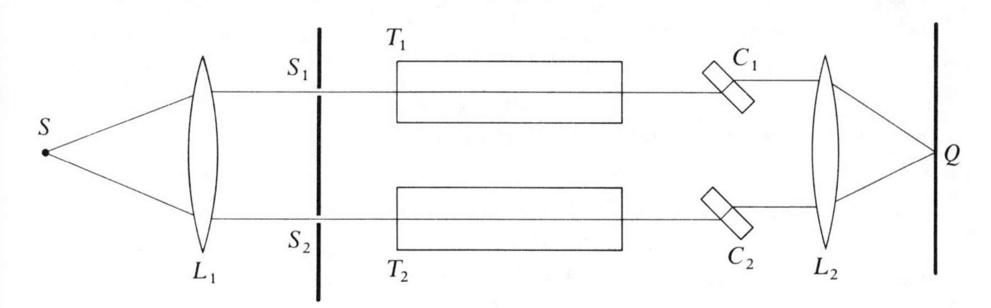

FIG. **11-10**

* Humphrey Lloyd (1800–1881), Irish physicist, 1837.

† Lord Rayleigh devised his refractometer in 1896, but a cruder form had been used much earlier by Arago. It was improved and used extensively by Haber and Löwe, 1910.

evacuated and a source of monochromatic light is placed at S. The collimating lens L_1 produces a parallel beam of light which is split into two beams by the apertures S_1 and S_2. The beams pass through the cells, the two compensating plates, C_1 and C_2, and then are recombined at Q by the lens L_2. The compensating plates can be rotated to increase or decrease the optical path length of either beam. With monochromatic light, the rotation angle can be calibrated against the observed shift of fringes.

The actual measurements are made by using *white* light, in which case only a central fringe system can be observed at Q. The gas to be measured is placed in one of the cells and the compensating plates are adjusted to reform the white-light fringes centrally at Q. The difference in the increase of optical path length introduced by the compensating plates must then just equal the path length difference in the transmission cells. By measuring the length of the cell and the temperature and pressure of the gas, the index of refraction can be computed. In actual practice, the manipulations of the system are somewhat more involved,* but the principle is the same. Under typical operating conditions of a well-designed system, a fringe displacement of $\sim 1/40$ of a fringe can be observed and a sensitivity in the measurement of $(n - 1)$ can be as great as 1 part in 10^8. (Values of $(n - 1)$ are typically about 10^{-4} for gases.)

11.8 Division of Amplitudes—The Michelson Interferometer

The second method for producing coherent beams of light is based upon the division of the *amplitude* of a single beam by means of partial reflection. Consider a single beam of monochromatic light and allow this beam to pass through a glass plate which has been given a thin reflective coating of some material (e.g., silver). Suppose for simplicity that equal amounts of light are reflected and transmitted: $R = T = \frac{1}{2}$. Therefore, two coherent beams of equal intensity are produced. These beams can again be brought together by an appropriate arrangement of mirrors, and interference will result. The degree of interference will depend on the difference of optical path length that the two beams traverse before they are brought together.

In 1881, Michelson published the design of an interferometer based on the principle of division of amplitudes. This device is shown schematically in Fig. 11-11. A single beam of light† originates at the source S and is directed toward the glass plate P_1. The surface of P_1 opposite the source is silvered so that half of the light is transmitted and half reflected. The

* See, for example, the description by Born and Wolf (Bo59, pp. 268–270).

† In practice, an extended source is usually employed, but here we treat only the simple case of a single beam.

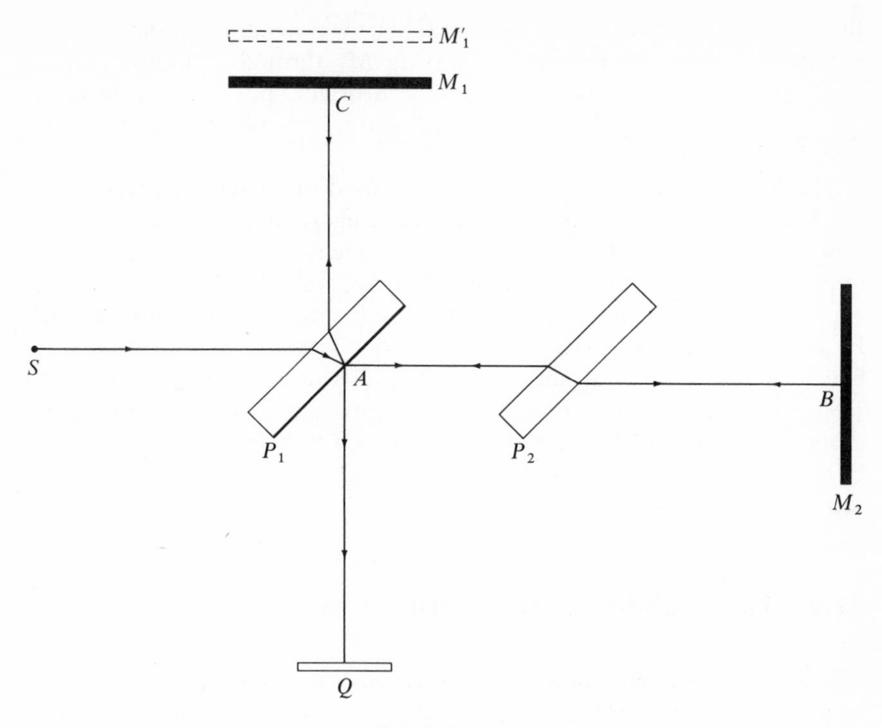

FIG. **11-11**

reflected portion travels from point A back through P_1 to point C. At C the light is reflected from the mirror M_1 and returns to P_1. A portion of this beam is then transmitted by P_1 and proceeds to the detector (or observer) at Q. The half of the original beam that is transmitted by P_1 follows the path $ABAQ$. At Q the interference of the two beams can be observed. Now, the beam that travels the path $SACAQ$, passes through P_1 three times, whereas the beam that travels the path $SABAQ$ does so only once. In order to remove this asymmetry, a compensating plate P_2, which is identical with and parallel to P_1, is introduced into the path of the latter beam.

If both of the mirrors, M_1 and M_2, are equidistant from point A, then both beams travel exactly the same distance before arriving at Q. Moreover, both beams undergo two reflections and the consequent phase changes. Therefore, at Q the beams are *in phase* and interfere constructively. Now, the mirror M_2 is fixed, but M_1 can be moved in a direction perpendicular to its surface. The movement of M_1 changes the path length traveled by the beam $SACAQ$ and thereby changes the phase difference of the beams at Q. If the phase difference is an integral multiple of 2π, then a bright spot will be observed at Q. The wavelength of monochromatic radiation can be determined by moving M_1 through a known distance and observing the number of times that a bright spot appears during the motion. In practice, using an extended source, one observes *fringes* rather than bright spots.

The Michelson interferometer is rarely used in current research since it has been superceded by more sophisticated instruments.* Before it became obsolete, however, Michelson used instruments of this design in three important experiments. The first of these was the famous ether-drift experiment, begun in 1881 and repeated several times, notably with E. W. Morley in 1887. The second was a systematic investigation of the fine structure of spectral lines, the first results of which were published in 1891. The third was a comparison of the wavelength of spectral lines with the standard meter, first reported in 1895. Of these experiments, we shall be concerned here only with the second, which is discussed in the following section.

11.9 The Visibility of Interference Fringes

If an interferometer of some sort is used to analyze monochromatic light, then as the path length traversed by one of the beams is changed, a regular sequence of bright spots (or fringes) will be observed and the brightness of each spot will be the same (as in Fig. 11-3). In the event that each of the beams has an intensity I_0, then the resulting intensity as a function of the path difference Δ is given by Eq. (11.27) with $\phi = k\Delta$:

$$I(\Delta) = 2I_0(1 + \cos k\Delta) \tag{11.30}$$

Now, if the incident beam consists of radiation with *two* different frequencies, the situation is altered in an essential way. Each component *by itself* will give rise to an intensity variation described by Eq. (11.30), but the two components will add *incoherently* and the difference between the rate at which the two variations of intensity change with Δ will produce a modulated intensity curve. For simplicity, let each frequency component have the same intensity. Therefore, we may write

$$\left.\begin{aligned} I_1 &= 2I_0(1 + \cos k_1\Delta) \\ I_2 &= 2I_0(1 + \cos k_2\Delta) \end{aligned}\right\} \tag{11.31}$$

* For details, see Born and Wolf (Bo59, Chapter 7).

Let k_0 be the mean of the two wave numbers k_1 and k_2, so that

$$\left.\begin{aligned} k_1 &= k_0 - \varepsilon \\ k_2 &= k_0 + \varepsilon \end{aligned}\right\} \tag{11.32}$$

The net intensity is then

$$\begin{aligned} I &= I_1 + I_2 \\ &= 4I_0 + 2I_0[\cos(k_0 - \varepsilon)\Delta + \cos(k_0 + \varepsilon)\Delta] \end{aligned}$$

Expanding the two cosine terms, we find

$$I = 4I_0(1 + \cos k_0\Delta \cos \varepsilon\Delta) \tag{11.33}$$

This intensity function is shown in Fig. 11-12. The rapid variation of intensity (solid curve) is determined by k_0 and the modulation (dashed curve) is determined by ε, it being assumed that $k_0 \gg \varepsilon$.*

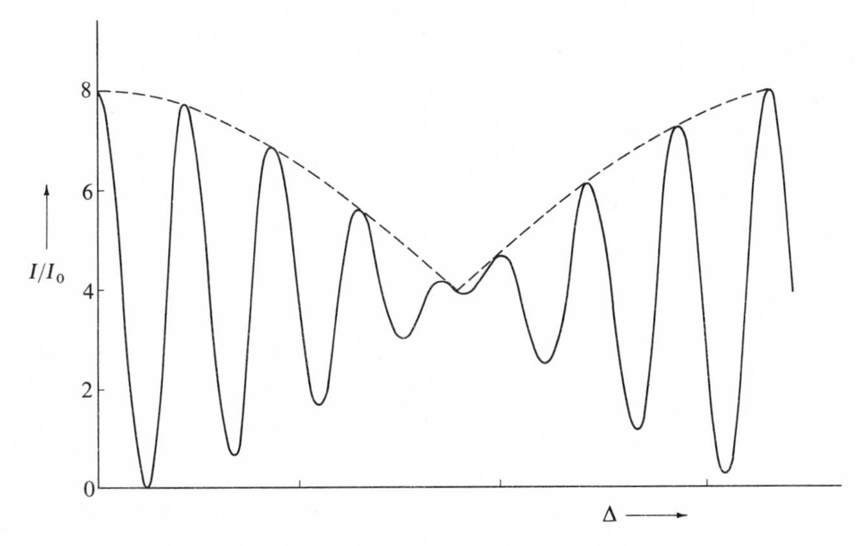

FIG. **11-12**

In the measurement of intensity curves, one is usually concerned only with the variation of the maxima of intensity. By comparing each maximum with a variable, calibrated source, it is possible to construct a curve which is the *envelope* of the intensity variation. The dashed curve in Fig. 11-12 is such an envelope, and is termed the *visibility curve.* It is clear that the shape of the visibility curve depends upon the spectral distribution of the

* In Fig. 11-12, $k_0 = 16.3\varepsilon$.

analyzed light. Indeed, by noting the manner in which the intensity of interference fringes varied in a rather crude interferometer (similar to a Newton's rings apparatus), Fizeau* was able to deduce that sodium light consists largely of radiation with two nearly equal wavelengths (the sodium D doublet). Later, Michelson systematically investigated the spectral distributions in a large number of light sources. In this work, the concern was with the *shapes* of the individual spectral lines as well as with their number. The determination of line shapes obviously requires an analysis somewhat more detailed than the simple treatment given above.

Suppose that the light incident on an interferometer has a spectral distribution described by an intensity function proportional to $I_0(k)$. If the beam is divided into two equal parts in the interferometer, the intensity of the interfering beams for wave numbers in the range k to $k + dk$ is given by

$$I(k, \Delta)\, dk = 2I_0(k)[1 + \cos k\Delta]\, dk \tag{11.34}$$

Integrating over the range of wave numbers in the distribution, the total intensity is

$$\begin{aligned} J(\Delta) &= \int I(k, \Delta)\, dk \\ &= 2\int I_0(k)[1 + \cos k\Delta]\, dk \end{aligned} \tag{11.35}$$

We may make a change of variable by writing

$$k \equiv k_0 + \xi \tag{11.36}$$

where k_0 is the wave number at some reference point; if the line is symmetric, it is convenient to let k_0 denote the center of the distribution. Then,

$$J(\Delta) = 2\int I_0(\xi)[1 + \cos(k_0 + \xi)\Delta]\, d\xi \tag{11.37}$$

If we expand the cosine term, we may write, in the customary notation,

$$J(\Delta) = P + C(\Delta)\cos k_0\Delta - S(\Delta)\sin k_0\Delta \tag{11.38}$$

where

$$\left.\begin{aligned} P &\equiv 2\int I_0(\xi)\, d\xi \\ C(\Delta) &\equiv 2\int I_0(\xi)\cos \xi\Delta\, d\xi \\ S(\Delta) &\equiv 2\int I_0(\xi)\sin \xi\Delta\, d\xi \end{aligned}\right\} \tag{11.39}$$

* These observations were made in 1862 by Armand Hippolyte Louis Fizeau (1819–1896). The conclusion that a doublet was involved was verified by Fizeau with a prism spectroscope.

If the spectral distribution lies predominantly in the vicinity of k_0 (as would be the case for a line in an optical spectrum), then ξ is always a small quantity. Therefore, $C(\Delta)$ and $S(\Delta)$ vary only slowly with Δ, and we may obtain the extrema of $J(\Delta)$ to a good approximation by neglecting the variation of $C(\Delta)$ and $S(\Delta)$ compared with the variation of $\cos k_0\Delta$ and $\sin k_0\Delta$. Hence, the extrema are approximately given by

$$\frac{\partial J}{\partial \Delta} = -k_0[C \sin k_0\Delta + S \cos k_0\Delta] = 0$$

or,

$$\tan k_0\Delta = -\frac{S}{C} \tag{11.40}$$

The maxima and minima of $J(\Delta)$ are therefore obtained by substituting Eq. (11.40) into Eq. (11.38):

$$\left.\begin{aligned} J_{\max} &= P + \sqrt{C^2 + S^2} \\ J_{\min} &= P - \sqrt{C^2 + S^2} \end{aligned}\right\} \tag{11.41}$$

The *visibility function* is defined by

$$V(\Delta) \equiv \frac{J_{\max} - J_{\min}}{J_{\max} + J_{\min}}$$

$$= \frac{\sqrt{C^2 + S^2}}{P} \tag{11.42}$$

It is easy to show that the visibility curve given by $V(\Delta)$ is indeed the envelope of the intensity curve $J(\Delta)$ (see Problem 11-5).

If the distribution function $I_0(k)$ is known, then the visibility curve may be constructed from Eq. (11.42) and the definitions, Eqs. (11.39). On the other hand, it is not in general possible to infer the distribution function from the visibility curve alone since such a process requires a knowledge of both C and S whereas $V(\Delta)$ determines only the quantity $\sqrt{C^2 + S^2}$. If the spectral distribution is symmetric, however, then $S = 0$ and the function $I_0(k)$ can be obtained from $V(\Delta) = C/P$ by a Fourier inversion.

The visibility functions for several cases of $I_0(k)$ are calculated below.

▶ **Example 11.9** *Case I.*

$$I_0(k) = \begin{cases} I_0, & \text{for} \quad |k| < \frac{1}{2}\,\delta k \\ 0, & \text{otherwise} \end{cases} \tag{1}$$

Since $I_0(k)$ is symmetric, the function S vanishes, and then

$$V(\Delta) = \frac{|C|}{P} = \frac{2\int_{-\frac{1}{2}\delta k}^{+\frac{1}{2}\delta k} I_0 \cos \xi\Delta \, d\xi}{2\int_{-\frac{1}{2}\delta k}^{+\frac{1}{2}\delta k} I_0 \, d\xi}$$

$$= \frac{|\sin(\frac{1}{2}\,\delta k\,\Delta)|}{|\frac{1}{2}\,\delta k\,\Delta|} \tag{2}$$

This visibility curve (of familiar form) is shown in Fig. 11-13b. In the event that $\delta k \to 0$ (i.e., the radiation is monochromatic), the visibility curve is just a constant (unity), as in Fig. 11-13a.

Case II.

$$I_0(k) = I_0 \exp[-(k - k_0)^2/\alpha^2] \tag{3}$$

If δk is the width of the distribution function at $I_0(k) = \frac{1}{2}I_0$, then

$$\alpha^2 = \frac{(\delta k)^2}{4 ln 2} \tag{4}$$

$$V(\Delta) = \frac{2\int_{-\infty}^{+\infty} I_0 \exp(-\xi^2/\alpha^2) \cos \xi\Delta \, d\xi}{2\int_{-\infty}^{+\infty} I_0 \exp(-\xi^2/\alpha^2) \, d\xi}$$

$$= \exp(-\alpha^2\Delta^2/4) \tag{5}$$

Therefore, if the distribution function is a Gaussian curve, then $V(\Delta)$ is also a Gaussian curve. This result is illustrated in Fig. 11-13c.

Case III. If the distribution function consists of two identical Gaussian curves whose centers are separated by $3\,\delta k$, the visibility curve is given by (see Problem 11-7)

$$V(\Delta) = \exp(-\alpha^2\Delta^2/4)|\cos(\tfrac{3}{2}\,\delta k\,\Delta)| \tag{6}$$

Figure 11-13d shows the visibility curve for this case.

11.10 Multiple-Beam Interference

In the study of antenna arrays (Section 8.9) we found that as the number of elements of the array is increased, the radiation pattern becomes more directional. If the number of elements is large, then the radiation is emitted essentially along a single line (see Fig. 8-23). A similar effect can be expected to take place for optical radiation; it remains only to devise an appropriate

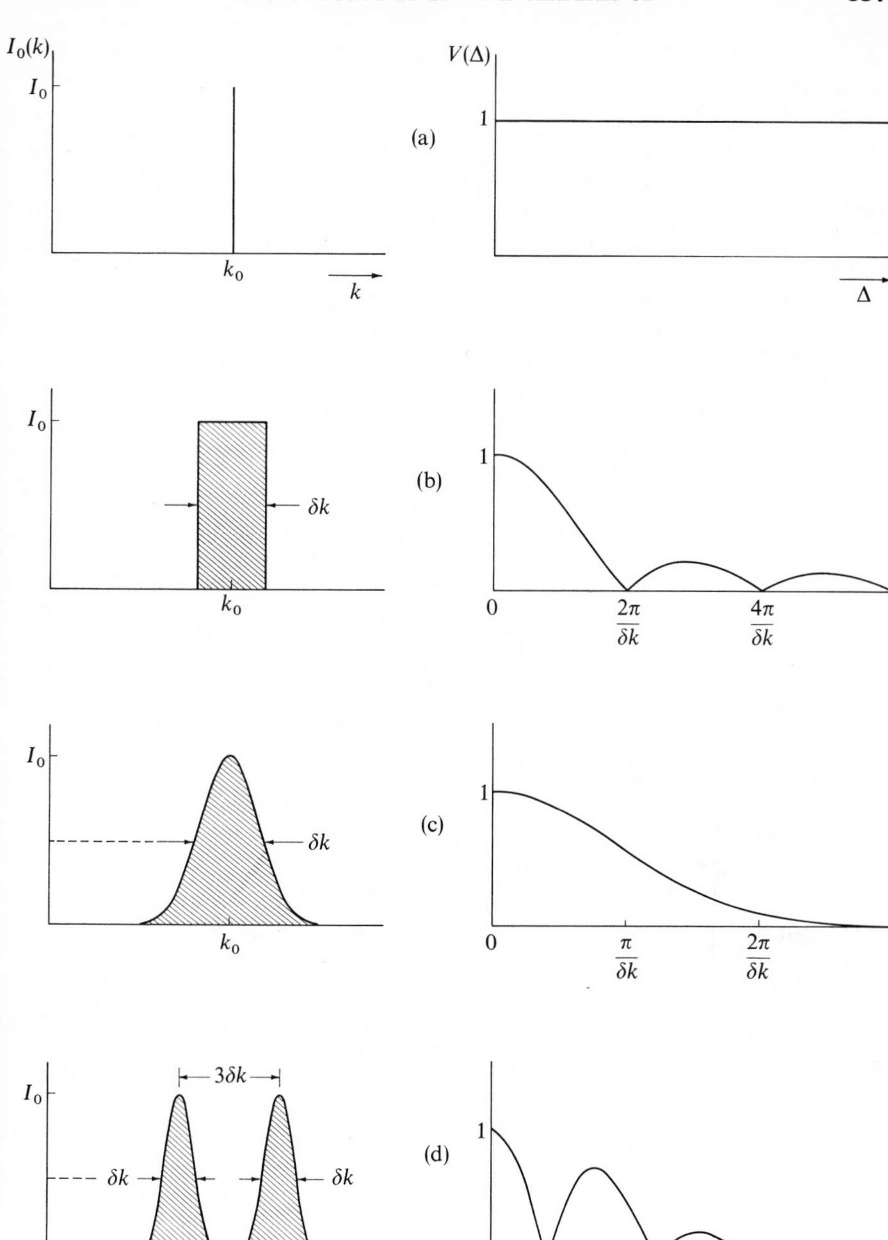

$I_0(k)$
I_0
k_0
k
(a)
$V(\Delta)$
1
Δ
I_0
δk
k_0
(b)
1
0
$\frac{2\pi}{\delta k}$
$\frac{4\pi}{\delta k}$
I_0
δk
k_0
(c)
1
0
$\frac{\pi}{\delta k}$
$\frac{2\pi}{\delta k}$
I_0
$3\delta k$
δk
δk
k_0
(d)
1
0
$\frac{\pi}{\delta k}$
$\frac{2\pi}{\delta k}$

FIG. **11-13**

source that produces a large number of beams of coherent light. Such an arrangement is shown schematically in Fig. 11-14. The essential feature is that the amplitude of a single incident beam is divided into many coherent parts by means of multiple partial reflections. The light incident on a glass plate is partially reflected and partially transmitted at each air-glass interface. The net effect is to give rise to a transmitted beam of amplitude $\mathbf{E}_2$ as well as a reflected beam of amplitude $\mathbf{E}_1$, each of which consists of a large number of coherent parts.

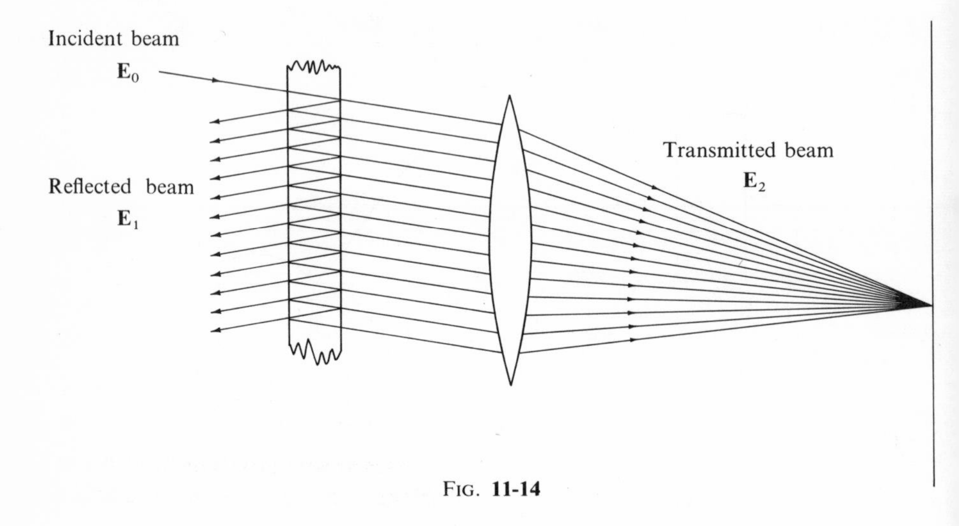

FIG. **11-14**

We may calculate the phase difference between successive beams in such a system by referring to the construction in Fig. 11-15. At any point along the common wavefront of the two transmitted beams the difference in optical path length* is

$$\Delta = 2nl - l' \tag{11.43}$$

where

$$\left.\begin{aligned} l &= \frac{d}{\cos\theta_2} \\ l' &= h\sin\theta_0 \end{aligned}\right\} \tag{11.44}$$

We also have

$$\left.\begin{aligned} h &= \frac{2d\sin\theta_2}{\cos\theta_2} \\ \sin\theta_0 &= n\sin\theta_2 \end{aligned}\right\} \tag{11.45}$$

* Recall that *optical path length* is the product of distance and index of refraction.

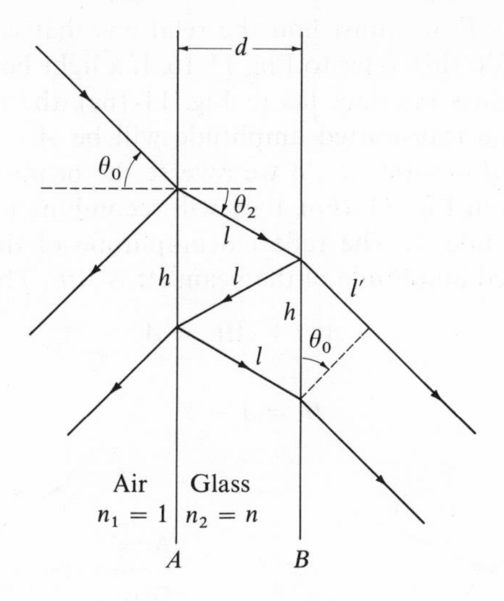

FIG. **11-15**

Therefore,

$$\begin{aligned}\Delta &= \frac{2nd}{\cos\theta_2} - h\sin\theta_0 \\ &= \frac{2nd}{\cos\theta_2} - \left(\frac{2d\sin\theta_2}{\cos\theta_2}\right)(n\sin\theta_2) \\ &= 2nd\cos\theta_2\end{aligned} \tag{11.46}$$

Hence, the phase difference between the two beams is

$$\phi = k\Delta = \frac{4\pi}{\lambda} nd\cos\theta_2 \tag{11.47}$$

Now, the incident beam may be represented by

$$\mathbf{E}_0 = \mathbf{E}_0^0 \exp[-i(\omega t - \mathbf{k}_0 \cdot \mathbf{r})] = \mathbf{E}_0^0 \exp(i\phi_0) \tag{11.48}$$

At the first surface of the glass plate which the incident beam strikes (surface A in Fig. 11-15), the reflected amplitude is $r\mathbf{E}_0$ and the transmitted amplitude is $t\mathbf{E}_0$; that is, r and t are the *amplitude* reflection and transmission coefficients, respectively, for the air-glass interface. Similarly, we may define the coefficients for the glass-air interfaces to be r' and t'. Since we wish eventually to express the results in terms of the *intensity* reflection and transmission coefficients R and T, we must find the relations that connect these quantities. In order to do this, refer to Fig. 11-16. If a light beam with amplitude A strikes an air-glass interface (as in Fig. 11-16a), the reflected amplitude will be Ar and the transmitted amplitude will be At. Now, according to Stokes' *principle of reversibility*, if we reverse the beams whose amplitudes are Ar and At (as in Fig. 11-16b), they will recombine to form the original beam with amplitude A. The reflected amplitude of the beam Ar is Ar^2 and the transmitted amplitude of the beam At is Att'. Therefore, we have

$$Ar^2 + Att' = A$$

or,

$$tt' = 1 - r^2 \tag{11.49a}$$

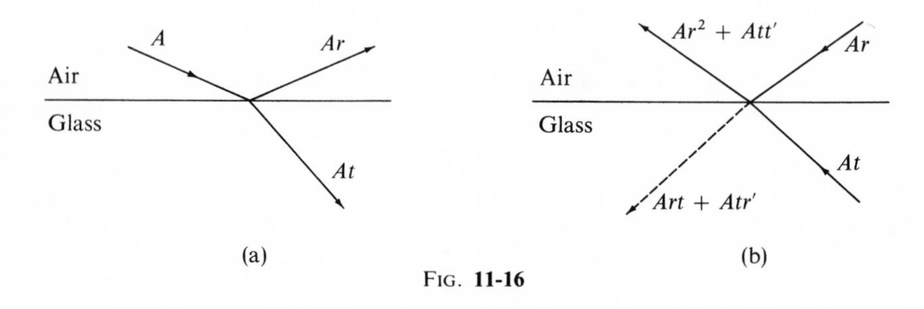

FIG. **11-16**

Similarly, the transmitted amplitude of the Ar beam (viz., Art) and the reflected amplitude of the At beam (viz., Atr') must combine to zero since the original situation had no beam at the position of the dashed line in Fig. 11-16b. Thus,

$$Art + Atr' = 0$$

or,

$$r = -r' \tag{11.49b}$$

Now, $r^2 = r'^2$ denotes the ratio of the reflected to the incident *intensity*, so that

$$r^2 = r'^2 = R \tag{11.50a}$$

and from Eq. (11.49a) we have

$$1 - R = tt' = T \tag{11.50b}$$

Therefore, we may now write for the transmitted beam,

$$\begin{aligned} \mathbf{E}_2 &= \mathbf{E}_0^0[tt'e^{i\phi_0} + tt'r'^2e^{i(\phi_0+\phi)} + tt'r'^4e^{i(\phi_0+2\phi)} + \cdots] \\ &= \mathbf{E}_0^0 T[1 + Re^{i\phi} + R^2e^{2i\phi} + \cdots]e^{i\phi_0} \end{aligned} \tag{11.51}$$

where ϕ is the phase difference between successive beams [Eq. (11.47)]. The series in the brackets is of the form

$$1 + \beta + \beta^2 + \cdots + \beta^{N-1} = \frac{\beta^N - 1}{\beta - 1} \tag{11.52}$$

where $\beta \equiv R \exp(i\phi)$. If N becomes very large, then $\beta^N \to 0$ since $R < 1$, and the series becomes simply

$$\frac{1}{1-\beta} = \frac{1}{1 - Re^{i\phi}}$$

Hence,

$$\mathbf{E}_2 = \frac{T}{1 - Re^{i\phi}} \mathbf{E}_0^0 \tag{11.53}$$

Calculating the intensity, we find

$$|\mathbf{E}_2|^2 = \frac{T^2}{(1 - Re^{i\phi})(1 - Re^{-i\phi})} (E_0^0)^2$$

$$= \frac{T^2}{1 + R^2 - 2R\cos\phi} (E_0^0)^2 \tag{11.54}$$

Now, the incident and transmitted intensities are

$$\left.\begin{aligned} \text{Incident intensity} &= I_i = |\mathbf{E}_0|^2 = (E_0^0)^2 \\ \text{Transmitted intensity} &= I_t = |\mathbf{E}_2|^2 \end{aligned}\right\} \tag{11.55}$$

Therefore, we may write Eq. (11.54) as

$$\frac{I_t}{I_i} = \frac{T^2}{1 + R^2 - 2R\cos\phi}$$

$$= \frac{T^2}{(1 - R)^2 + 4R\sin^2(\phi/2)} \tag{11.56a}$$

The reflected intensity is $I_r = I_i - I_t$, and since $T = 1 - R$, we have immediately,

$$\frac{I_r}{I_i} = \frac{4R\sin^2(\phi/2)}{(1 - R)^2 + 4R\sin^2(\phi/2)} \tag{11.56b}$$

Equations (11.56) are known as *Airy's formulae.** Clearly, the maxima of transmitted intensity will occur for phase differences of

$$\phi = \frac{4\pi}{\lambda} nd\cos\theta_2 = 2m\pi, \qquad m = 0, \pm 1, \pm 2, \cdots \tag{11.57}$$

The reflected beam is, of course, just complementary.

* Derived in 1833 by the English astronomer George Biddell Airy (1801–1892).

If we define

$$\alpha \equiv \frac{4R}{(1-R)^2} \tag{11.58}$$

then Eq. (11.56a) may be written as

$$\frac{I_t}{I_i} = \frac{1}{1 + \alpha \sin^2(\phi/2)} \tag{11.59}$$

This function is shown in Fig. 11-17 for three different values of α. It is clear that as the reflection coefficient increases, the bright transmission fringes increase in sharpness. The reflection coefficient may always be made larger by applying a thin metallic layer to the surfaces of the glass plate, but the analysis is thereby complicated somewhat by absorption in the layers (see Problem 11-9).

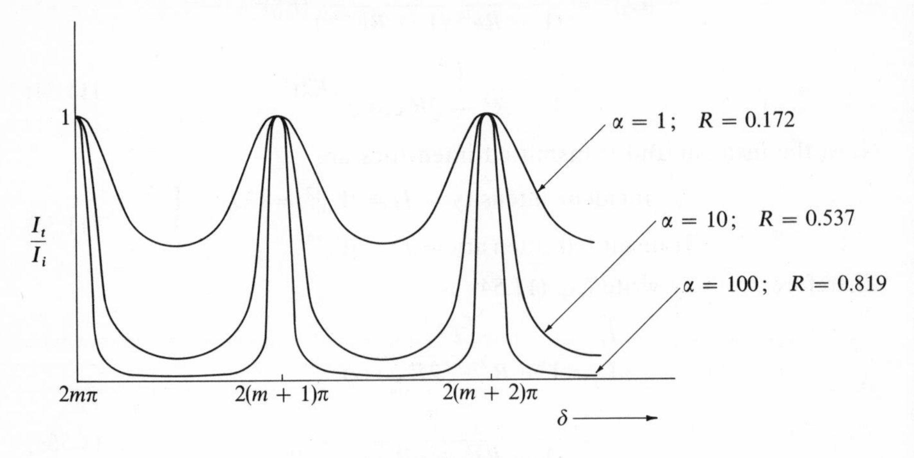

FIG. **11-17**

Several different types of interferometers are based upon the principle of fringe formation by multiple-beam interference. The most notable of these are the Fabry-Perot* and Lummer-Gehrcke† instruments; these are described in detail in most texts on physical optics. An extended source is invariably used with the Fabry-Perot interferometer; then, since the angle θ_2 is constant for a cone whose axis is normal to the plate, the fringes that are formed are the familiar circles. A set of circular fringes due to a monochromatic source is shown in Fig. 11-18.

* C. Fabry and A. Perot, 1899.

† O. Lummer, 1901; O. Lummer and E. Gehrcke, 1903.

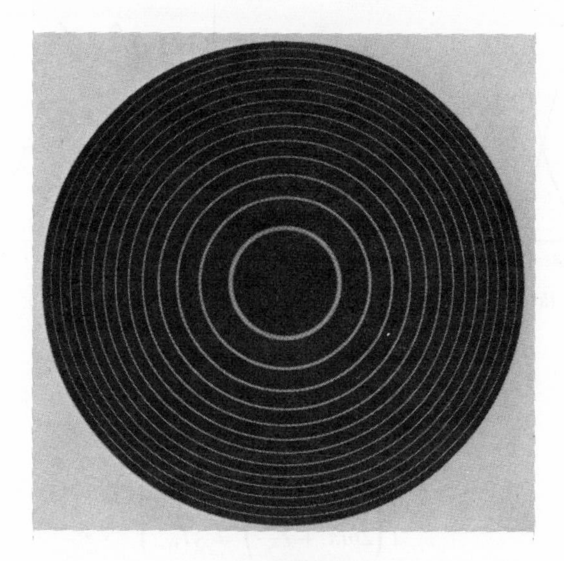

FIG. **11-18***

11.11 Resolution of Interference Fringes

If monochromatic light is incident on an interferometer that produces fringes by multiple-beam interference (as in Fig. 11-14), and if the reflection coefficients of the surfaces are high, then sharp, well-separated fringes will be formed, such as those in Fig. 11-17 for $\alpha = 100$ or those shown in Fig. 11-18. On the other hand, if the incident radiation consists of light of two well-defined but nearly equal wavelengths (e.g., the sodium D doublet), then two fringe systems will be produced. A question then arises concerning the requirements on the properties of the interferometer so that the fringes from a given doublet can be unambiguously separated (or *resolved*). There are many different criteria of resolution that may be stated; one of the simplest and most general definitions is as follows. Two fringes are said to be *just resolved* if the half-intensity points of each fringe occur at the same position. Figure 11-19a illustrates this case for two fringes of equal intensity. The total intensity of such a pair of fringes is just the incoherent sum, shown in Fig. 11-19b. Using Eq. (11.59) for the intensity as a function of ϕ, we have for the case illustrated in Fig. 11-19a,

$$I(\phi) = \frac{I_0}{1 + \alpha \sin^2(\phi/2)} \tag{11.59a}$$

* From Born and Wolf, *Principles of Optics*, Macmillan (Pergamon), New York; reprinted by permission.

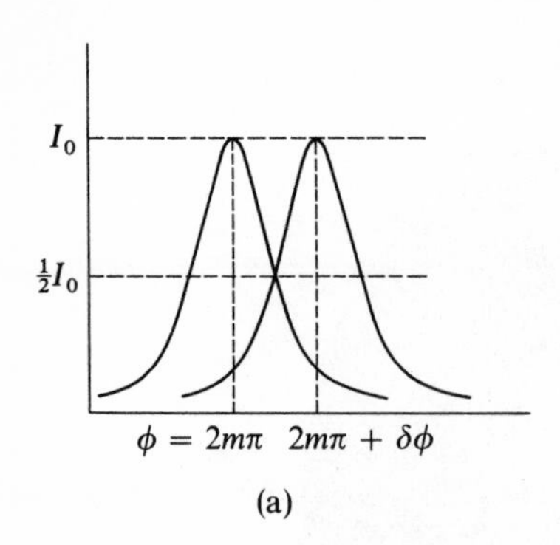

(a)

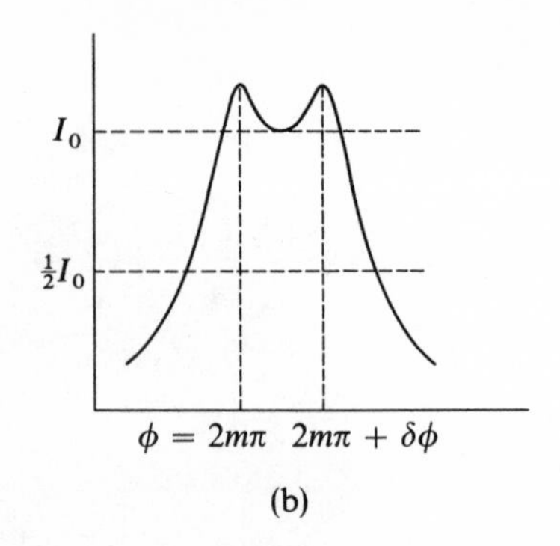

(b)

FIG. **11-19**

and,

$$\left.\begin{aligned} I(2m\pi) &= I_0 \\ I\left(2m\pi + \frac{\delta\phi}{2}\right) &= \tfrac{1}{2}I_0 \end{aligned}\right\} \tag{11.60}$$

Therefore,

$$\frac{I_0}{1 + \alpha \sin^2\left(m\pi + \dfrac{\delta\phi}{4}\right)} = \tfrac{1}{2}I_0$$

or, approximating the sine by its argument,

$$1 + \alpha\left(\frac{\delta\phi}{4}\right)^2 = 2$$

from which

$$\delta\phi = \frac{4}{\sqrt{\alpha}} \tag{11.61}$$

Now,

$$\phi = \frac{4\pi}{\lambda} nd \cos\theta_2$$

Hence,

$$|\delta\phi| = 4\pi nd\left(\frac{\delta\lambda}{\lambda^2}\right)\cos\theta_2 \tag{11.62}$$

At the maximum of order m,

$$\frac{4\pi}{\lambda} nd \cos \theta_2 = 2m\pi$$

Therefore, Eq. (11.62) may be written as

$$|\delta\phi| = 2m\pi \frac{\delta\lambda}{\lambda} \tag{11.62a}$$

and using Eq. (11.61), we have

$$\mathcal{R} \equiv \frac{\lambda}{\delta\lambda} = \frac{m\pi\sqrt{\alpha}}{2} \tag{11.63}$$

The quantity $\mathcal{R}$ is called the *resolving power* of the instrument. If we take the product $n \cos \theta_2$ to be a number approximately equal to unity, then at the maximum of order m,

$$\frac{4\pi}{\lambda} nd \cos \theta_2 \cong \frac{4\pi d}{\lambda} = 2m\pi$$

so that

$$\mathcal{R} \cong \frac{\pi d\sqrt{\alpha}}{\lambda} \tag{11.63a}$$

Thus, in order to resolve two spectral lines separated by 0.005 Å at 5000 Å with an instrument whose reflecting surfaces have $R = 0.9$, requires a resolving power of

$$\mathcal{R} = \frac{\lambda}{\delta\lambda} = 10^6$$

and a plate thickness of

$$\begin{aligned} d &= \frac{\lambda}{\pi\sqrt{\alpha}} \times 10^6 \\ &= \frac{\lambda}{\pi} \cdot \frac{1 - R}{2\sqrt{R}} \times 10^6 \\ &= \frac{5 \times 10^{-5} \times 0.1}{\pi \times 2 \times 0.95} \times 10^6 \\ &= 0.84 \text{ cm} \end{aligned}$$

Therefore, an interferometer whose reflecting surfaces are ~ 1 cm apart would (theoretically) be capable of resolving two lines separated by a wavelength interval corresponding to the width of the sharpest spectral lines.

It should be mentioned that certain types of interferometers (notably the Fabry-Perot instrument) consist of *two* glass (or quartz) plates which are parallel and separated by a distance d. The inner surfaces are lightly silvered to increase the reflectivity. The multiple reflections therefore take place in the air gap rather than in the plate, as in Fig. 11-14. In such a design the distance d which occurs in the expression for the phase [Eq. (11.57)] or in the expression for the resolving power [Eq. (11.63a)] can be easily varied by changing the plate separation. Alternatively, it is possible to vary the optical path length between the plates by controlling the pressure of a gas in the gap.

Suggested References

The subject of interference phenomena is treated in essentially every text covering physical optics. Intermediate-level accounts are given, for example, by Ditchburn (Di62, Chapter 5), Jenkins and White (Je57, Chapters 12–14), Rossi (Ro57, Chapter 3), and Valasek (Va49, Chapter 10). Andrews (An60, Chapters 5–8) also gives many interesting cases involving microwaves.

General discussions at the advanced level may be found in Born and Wolf (Bo59, Chapter 7) and Stone (St63, Chapters 13 and 16).

Huygens' principle is treated in detail by Rossi (Ro57, Chapter 1).

Interferometers are discussed by Andrews (An60, Chapter 7), Born and Wolf (Bo59, Chapter 7), Ditchburn (Di62, Chapter 8), and Jenkins and White (Je57, Chapters 13 and 14), as well as in many books devoted to optical instruments, e.g., Tolansky (To55).

Visibility curves and spectral-line analysis are discussed by Born and Wolf (Bo59, Chapter 7) and Michelson (Mi27, Chapter 4).

Problems

11-1. Investigate the appearance of interference lines in Wiener's experiment for the case of an arbitrary angle of incidence α. Obtain results for the electric vector polarized parallel to and perpendicular to the plane of incidence. Show that for $\alpha = \pi/4$ the interference lines for the two polarizations are completely different. Illustrate this result by sketching the wave fronts for $\alpha = \pi/4$.

11-2. Equation (9.99) states that the equation of motion for a bound electron which experiences radiation damping is approximately

$$m\ddot{\mathbf{r}} + l\dot{\mathbf{r}} + \gamma\mathbf{r} = 0$$

where $l = 2e^2\gamma/3mc^3$ and $\gamma = m\omega_0^2$; ω_0 is the natural frequency of oscillation. If the electron is driven, then show that the resulting resonance curve has a half-width (i.e., full width of the curve at half maximum intensity) given by $\Gamma = 2e^2\omega_0^2/3mc^3$. Use this result to show that the half-width of any spectral line is 0.000116 Å due to radiation damping and that this width is independent of the wavelength of the line. (This is the *natural width* of the line.)

11-3. Obtain a limit on the size of the source that will still permit the observation of fringes in Young's double slit experiment. (Define a reasonable criterion for this limit.) Consider a case in which $\lambda = 6000$ Å, $d = 1$ mm, and the source-to-slit distance is 1 meter. Find the maximum size of the source.

11-4. In order to produce fringes that are sharp and unblurred, one must use a small source with either Fresnel's mirrors or Fresnel's biprism. Explain why unblurred fringes can be obtained with Lloyd's mirror even if the source is extended.

11-5. Express the intensity distribution $J(\Delta)$ [Eq. (11.38)] in terms of the visibility function $V(\Delta)$:

$$\frac{J(\Delta)}{P} = 1 + V(\Delta)\cos(\theta + k_0\Delta)$$

where $\theta = \tan^{-1}(S/C)$, and thereby show that the envelope of $J(\Delta)/P$ is just $V(\Delta)$.

11-6. Derive the expression for the visibility curve given in Case III of Example 11-9.

11-7. A distribution function of radiation intensity consists of two Gaussian curves, one centered at $k = k_0$ with peak intensity I_0 and half-width equal to δk, and one centered at $k = k_0 + 2\delta k$ with peak intensity $\frac{1}{2}I_0$ and half-width equal to δk. Show that the visibility function is

$$V(\Delta) = \tfrac{1}{3}\exp(-\alpha^2\Delta^2/4)\sqrt{5 + 4\cos(2\,\delta k\,\Delta)}$$

Sketch the visibility curve.

11-8. Consider the transmission fringes observed with a plate such as that in Fig. 11-14. If the reflectivity of the plate is near unity, show that the half-width Γ (i.e., the full width at half intensity) of the bright fringes is approximately $\Gamma \cong 4/\sqrt{\alpha}$. If the incident light is not strictly monochromatic, but has a distribution of wavelengths $\Delta\lambda$ around a mean wavelength λ_0, show that the fringes will not be broadened if $2\pi m\lambda_0/\Gamma$ is small compared with the coherence length defined by Eq. (11.9).

11-9. Derive the modification in the expression for I_t/I_i [Eq. (11.59)] in the event that the plate absorbs a fraction A of the light, so that the expression of energy balance is $R + T + A = 1$.

CHAPTER 12

Scalar Diffraction Theory

12.1 Introduction

It is implicit in the development of geometrical optics that light rays travel in straight lines and therefore that opaque objects cast sharp shadows. A detailed investigation, however, reveals that even a thin, well-defined edge (such as the edge of a razor blade), in the presence of a highly localized source of light, does not produce a sharp shadow; rather, there is a significant penetration of light into the region called the *geometrical shadow*; and, moreover, in the illuminated region near the edge there is found a system of fringes.* These effects cannot be explained in terms of simple reflection and refraction; they are aspects of an entirely different phenomenon called *diffraction*.

If we attempt to formulate a theory of diffraction, we immediately discover that we are confronted with enormous mathematical difficulties. These difficulties arise because we must solve a pair of coupled vector wave

* The first detailed observations were made by the Italian physicist Francesco Maria Grimaldi (1618–1663). The results were published posthumously in 1665 and constitute the first indication that light is a wave phenomenon. Even earlier, Leonardo da Vinci (1452–1519) had observed diffraction effects.

equations (for **E** and **B**) that are subject, at the surface of the diffracting object, to the boundary conditions imposed by Maxwell's equations. The obstacles attending the vector theory are so severe that only a few simple cases have been solved completely. Typical of these is the problem of the diffraction of a plane wave by the edge of a semi-infinite plane of zero thickness and infinite conductivity.* In spite of the highly idealized nature of this case, the solution is of considerable interest since it can be given in closed form and is valid for all regions of space. The solution therefore permits the investigation of the details of the field near the edge.

Because of the limited success of the vector diffraction theory, we are led to attempt a simpler, *scalar* theory. We have no *a priori* reason to expect that such a theory will produce results that are in any way related to the real physical case of the diffraction of electromagnetic waves. The remarkable fact, however, is that scalar diffraction theory yields a quite satisfactory description of diffraction if we do not require solutions within a few wavelengths of the diffracting object. Furthermore, the scalar theory cannot be expected to yield any information regarding polarization effects, since polarization is by its nature a vector phenomenon. With these points in mind, we now set out to develop a scalar theory of diffraction.†

We shall begin with the assumption that all of the information necessary for the calculation of the intensity of light at a certain position in space is contained in the scalar wave function $\Psi(\mathbf{r}, t)$. That is, $\Psi(\mathbf{r}, t)$ specifies the amplitude and the phase of the wave, and the intensity is proportional to $|\Psi(\mathbf{r}, t)|^2$. If the light is monochromatic (or nearly so), we may write

$$\Psi(\mathbf{r}, t) = \psi(\mathbf{r})e^{-i\omega t} \tag{12.1}$$

so that the intensity may be expressed in terms of the square of the time-independent wave function:

$$\text{Intensity} \propto |\psi(\mathbf{r})|^2$$

We shall make the further assumption that $\psi(\mathbf{r})$ vanishes identically on the entire surface of any diffracting object. Finally, we assume that all sources emit radiation in an isotropic manner; i.e., the outgoing waves have only a radial variation.

On the basis of the above assumptions, we are in a position to formulate a scalar theory of diffraction. More accurately, we are now able to work out the predictions of a highly artificial theory‡ and to determine whether

* First solved in 1896 by Arnold Sommerfeld (1868–1951) for the special case that the wave is linearly polarized parallel to the edge.

† Although not explicitly mentioned, the problem of the scattering of a wave by a sphere which was solved in Chapter 10 is actually an important result of scalar diffraction theory.

‡ The theory is actually a proper one for *acoustical* (pressure) waves in a homogeneous medium.

they bear any resemblance to the physical effects that occur in the diffraction of light. There is some basis for hope in this regard since the scalar theory does contain the elements of our naïve ideas concerning the propagation of light—the "light function" satisfies the wave equation; and, since light does not penetrate even thin screens of conducting materials, the "light function" is expected to vanish on the surface. It is indeed fortunate that these crude ideas lead to a theory whose predictions so closely approximate the observations.

The applications of the theory that are presented in this chapter include only a limited number of the more important cases. No attempt is made to give extensive details regarding optical instruments that are based on diffraction effects; the reader is referred to texts specializing in physical optics for such material.

12.2 The Helmholtz-Kirchhoff Integral

In order to calculate the amplitude $\psi(P)$ of the light wave at a point P due to a number of surrounding sources (as in Fig. 12-1), it is clearly sufficient to know the amplitudes and phases of the individual waves and to evaluate the sum at the point P. Alternatively, it is possible to obtain the result from a specification of the composite wave function over a surface which encloses P but from which the sources are excluded (such as the surface indicated by the dotted line in Fig. 12-1). We will find this latter approach more amenable to the calculation of diffraction effects due to opaque screens containing apertures.

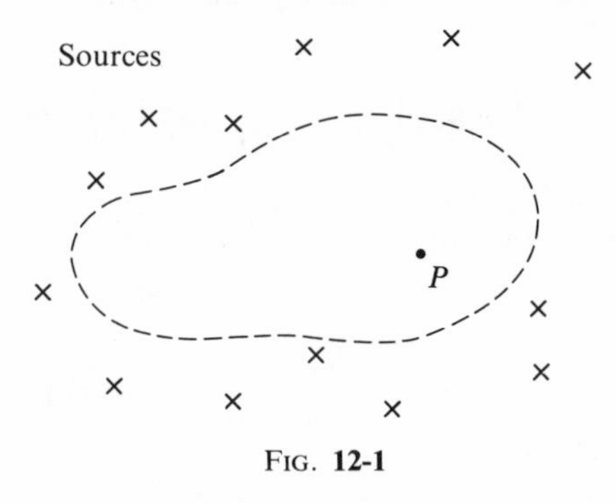

FIG. 12-1

First, we note that the wave function $\psi(\mathbf{r})$ is a solution of the time-independent wave equation [compare the development in Section 10.2]:

$$(\nabla^2 + k^2)\psi = 0 \tag{12.2a}$$

Next, consider an auxiliary function $\chi(\mathbf{r})$ to which we attach no special physical significance, but which is also a solution of the Helmholtz equation:

$$(\nabla^2 + k^2)\chi = 0 \tag{12.2b}$$

We may now use the functions ψ and χ in Green's theorem [see Eq. (A.56), Appendix A]:

$$-\oint_S (\psi \,\mathbf{grad}\, \chi - \chi \,\mathbf{grad}\, \psi) \cdot d\mathbf{a} = \int_V (\psi \nabla^2 \chi - \chi \nabla^2 \psi)\, dv \tag{12.3}$$

where the surface S bounds the volume V. A minus sign is explicitly introduced on the left-hand side of this equation since we now wish to consider the positive direction of the normal to S to be the *inward* direction (opposite to our usual convention).

Since both ψ and χ are solutions to the Helmholtz equation, the right-hand side of Eq. (12.3) vanishes. Next, we choose the function χ to be

$$\chi(\mathbf{r}) = \chi(r) = \frac{e^{ikr}}{r} \tag{12.4}$$

It is easily verified that $\chi(r)$ is indeed a solution of the Helmholtz equation and therefore satisfies the only requirement that we have placed on this function. $\chi(r)$ has a singularity at $r = 0$; we designate this point by P and divide the volume V into two regions by constructing a small sphere of radius ρ surrounding P. (We will eventually let the radius of this small sphere approach zero.*) Then, Eq. (12.3) is replaced by (refer to Fig. 12-2)

$$\oint_S \left(\psi \,\mathbf{grad}\, \frac{e^{ikr}}{r} - \frac{e^{ikr}}{r} \,\mathbf{grad}\, \psi\right) \cdot d\mathbf{a}$$

$$+ \oint_{\text{sphere}} \left(\psi \,\mathbf{grad}\, \frac{e^{ik\rho}}{\rho} - \frac{e^{ik\rho}}{\rho} \,\mathbf{grad}\, \psi\right) \cdot d\mathbf{a}' = 0 \tag{12.5}$$

(Notice that the overall sign of each integral is the same since $d\mathbf{a}$ and $d\mathbf{a}'$

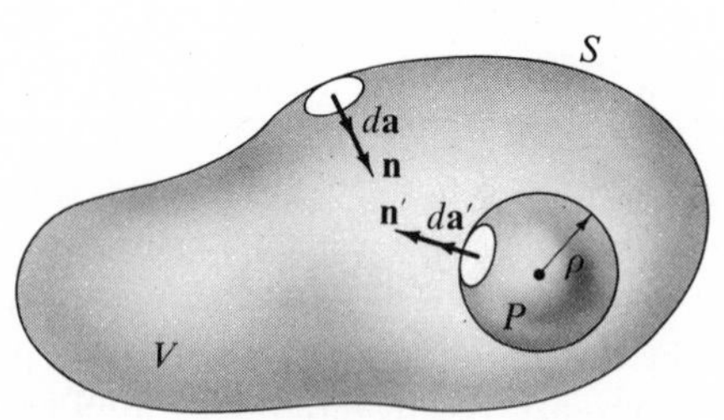

FIG. 12-2

* Compare this development with that in Section 7.2.

are both directed *inward* relative to the volume V. Upon expanding $\mathbf{grad}(e^{ik\rho}/\rho)$, the integral over the small sphere becomes

$$\oint_{\text{sphere}} (\,)\cdot d\mathbf{a}' = \oint_{\text{sphere}} \left\{ \psi\left(\frac{ik}{\rho} - \frac{1}{\rho^2}\right) e^{ik\rho}\mathbf{n}' - \frac{1}{\rho} e^{ik\rho}\,\mathbf{grad}\,\psi \right\}\cdot \mathbf{n}'\,\rho^2\,d\Omega \qquad (12.6)$$

where

$$d\mathbf{a}' = \mathbf{n}'\rho^2 \sin\theta\,d\theta\,d\varphi = \mathbf{n}'\rho^2\,d\Omega$$

with $d\Omega$ equal to the element of solid angle. The terms proportional to ρ will vanish as ρ shrinks to zero. Therefore, in the limit $\rho \to 0$, there remains

$$\oint_{\text{sphere}} (\,)\cdot d\mathbf{a}' = -\int_{\text{sphere}} \psi\,d\Omega$$

As ρ approaches zero, we have $\psi \to \psi(P)$. Then, removing $\psi(P)$ from the integral, the integral of $d\Omega$ just yields 4π. Thus,

$$\oint_{\text{sphere}} (\,)\cdot d\mathbf{a}' = -4\pi\psi(P) \qquad (12.7)$$

Returning to Eq. (12.5), we may now write

$$\boxed{\psi(P) = \frac{1}{4\pi}\oint_S \left(\psi\,\mathbf{grad}\,\frac{e^{ikr}}{r} - \frac{e^{ikr}}{r}\,\mathbf{grad}\,\psi\right)\cdot\mathbf{n}\,da} \qquad (12.8)$$

This is the *Helmholtz-Kirchhoff integral**, and it will form the basis for our further discussion of diffraction.

12.3 The Kirchhoff Diffraction Theory

In the study of diffraction phenomena we are usually concerned with the passage of light through an aperture (or various apertures) in an opaque screen. We may consider as typical the situation shown in Fig. 12-3 in which an aperture of arbitrary shape is cut in an otherwise infinite plane opaque screen. Around the point P at which we wish to calculate the amplitude of light $\psi(P)$ we construct the surface S referred to in Eq. (12.8). The specification of this surface is arbitrary, subject only to the requirements that the point P be in the interior and that all sources are exterior to the

* First derived in 1859 for the case of monochromatic acoustical waves by Hermann von Helmholtz. Gustav Kirchhoff extended the treatment to the diffraction of light in 1882.

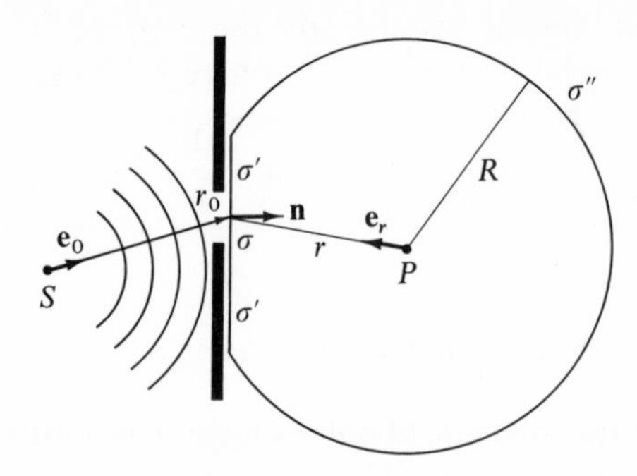

FIG. **12-3**

surface. Clearly, it is desirable to construct S in such a way that the evaluation of the integral in Eq. (12.8) is as easy as possible. We may accomplish this in the following manner. First, we let a portion of S coincide with the aperture in the screen; call this part σ (see Fig. 12-3). (In the event that we are dealing with a *plane* screen, then σ may be chosen to be the plane that fills the aperture. Actually, *any* open surface bounded by the curve which defines the aperture will serve equally well. If the screen is not plane, then we choose the simplest surface over which the integral can be carried out.) Next, we allow a portion of S to lie along the side of the screen opposite the source; this part is σ'. Finally, we complete the surface with a portion of a sphere of radius R; this part is σ''.

In order to evaluate the integral appearing in Eq. (12.8), it is necessary that we know ψ and $(\mathbf{grad}\,\psi)\cdot\mathbf{n} \equiv \partial\psi/\partial n$ on σ, σ', and σ''. In general, these functions are not known *a priori*, and we must therefore resort to some approximation procedure. Kirchhoff's solution to the diffraction problem makes use of the following set of boundary conditions:

(a) On σ it is assumed that ψ and $\partial\psi/\partial n$ have the values possessed by the incident wave in the absence of the screen. That is, the assumption is made that the presence of the screen does not appreciably perturb the initial wave in the vicinity of the aperture. If we limit the consideration to apertures whose dimensions are large compared to a wavelength of the radiation, it seems reasonable that this assumption is approximately correct, except, of course, near the boundary of the aperture.

(b) On σ', it is assumed that ψ and $\partial\psi/\partial n$ vanish. This assumption is consistent with the hypothesis that the screen is perfectly opaque. Again, we expect the assumption to lose its validity near the boundary of the aperture.

(c) On σ'', we can force ψ and $\partial\psi/\partial n$ to become arbitrarily small by allowing $R \to \infty$. But this is not sufficient to insure that the integral over σ'' will vanish, since the area of the surface becomes infinitely large as $R \to \infty$. We may overcome this difficulty by making the additional assumption that the radiation emitted from the source has not existed for all time, but that it originated at some instant in the past. We then make R sufficiently large that the radiation field cannot have propagated to this distance by the time at which we are concerned with calculating $\psi(P)$. Therefore, the value of ψ is identically zero over σ'', and the integral vanishes. Of course, by this procedure we forego the possibility of considering truly monochromatic waves (which must exist for all time), but we understand that such waves are only idealizations anyway. Besides, we expect that almost-monochromatic waves can be quite satisfactorily represented for these purposes by a time variation of the usual form, $\exp(-i\omega t)$, and this is all that we require in our theory of diffraction.*

Actually, if we use the Kirchhoff boundary conditions to evaluate the diffraction integral, then the function $\psi(P)$ so derived will not satisfy the boundary conditions. This is another aspect of the fact that we have constructed a theory that is not rigorous. The sole justification for the use of these boundary conditions is that the results agree well with experiment in spite of the gross approximations that are made.

With the boundary conditions specified above, Eq. (12.8) becomes

$$\psi(P) = \frac{1}{4\pi}\int_\sigma \left(\psi_{\text{inc}}\,\textbf{grad}\,\frac{e^{ikr}}{r} - \frac{e^{ikr}}{r}\,\textbf{grad}\,\psi_{\text{inc}}\right)\cdot \mathbf{n}\,da \tag{12.9}$$

If we take the incident wave to be a spherical wave with amplitude A originating at a distance r_0 from the aperture,

$$\psi_{\text{inc}} = A\frac{e^{ikr_0}}{r_0} \tag{12.10}$$

then we have

$$\psi(P) = \frac{1}{4\pi}\int_\sigma \left\{\left(A\frac{e^{ikr_0}}{r_0}\right)\left(\frac{ik}{r} - \frac{1}{r^2}\right)e^{ikr}\mathbf{e}_r - \left(\frac{e^{ikr}}{r}\right)\left(\frac{ik}{r_0} - \frac{1}{r_0^2}\right)Ae^{ikr_0}\mathbf{e}_0\right\}\cdot \mathbf{n}\,da$$

If we consider only distances r and r_0 that are large compared with the wavelength of the radiation, the terms containing $1/r^2$ and $1/r_0^2$ make

* For the added complication of explicitly treating the polychromatic nature of the light, see, for example, Born and Wolf (Bo59, Chapter 10).

only negligible contributions to the integral. In this limit, Eq. (12.9) becomes approximately

$$\psi(P) = i\frac{Ak}{4\pi}\int_{\sigma}\frac{e^{ik(r+r_0)}}{rr_0}(\mathbf{e}_r - \mathbf{e}_0)\cdot\mathbf{n}\,da \tag{12.11}$$

This result is known as the *Fresnel-Kirchhoff diffraction integral.*

In most diffraction problems we deal with incident radiation in the form of plane waves. For situations similar to that illustrated in Fig. 12-4,

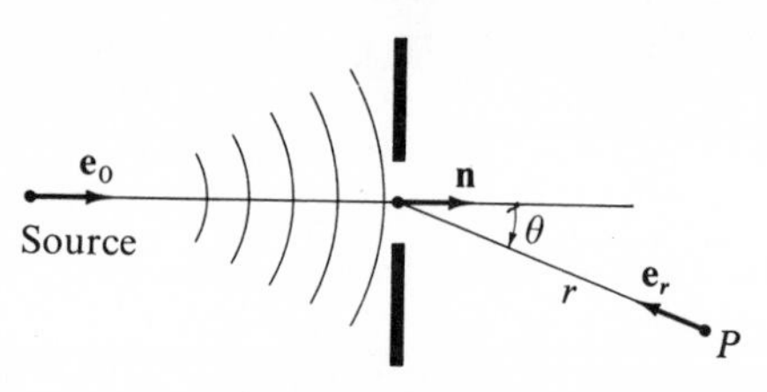

FIG. 12-4

the wave fronts incident on the aperture may be viewed as plane waves if the source is removed a sufficiently large distance. In practice such a procedure would reduce the incident intensity to the point that measurements would become extremely tedious. Therefore, it is preferable to use a lens system to transform the light rays from a nearby source into a parallel beam (plane waves*). Knowledge of the details of the method is unnecessary in discussing the consequences.

If the incident radiation is in the form of plane waves, $\psi_{\text{inc}} = (A/r_0)\exp ikr_0$ may be replaced by a constant amplitude ψ_0. Furthermore, if the wave fronts are parallel to the screen, $\mathbf{e}_0\cdot\mathbf{n} = 1$. Then, since $\mathbf{e}_r\cdot\mathbf{n} = -\cos\theta$ (see Fig. 12-4), Eq. (12.11) may be expressed as

$$\psi(P) = -i\frac{\psi_0}{2\lambda}\int_{\sigma}\frac{e^{ikr}}{r}(1 + \cos\theta)\,da \tag{12.12}$$

The integrand in Eq. (12.12) consists of a term representing an outgoing spherical wave ($r^{-1}\exp ikr$) multiplied by the so-called *Stokes' inclination factor* $(1 + \cos\theta)$. It is just this inclination factor that allows us to justify the remarks made in Section 11.6 regarding the retrogressive wave in Huygens' principle. The function $1 + \cos\theta$ is shown in Fig. 12-5; it is evident that there is no propagation of the radiation in the backward direction ($\theta = 180°$). Therefore, Huygens' retrogressive wave is automatically eliminated in the Kirchhoff theory.

* Again, such waves are only approximately plane over dimensions corresponding to those of the aperture.

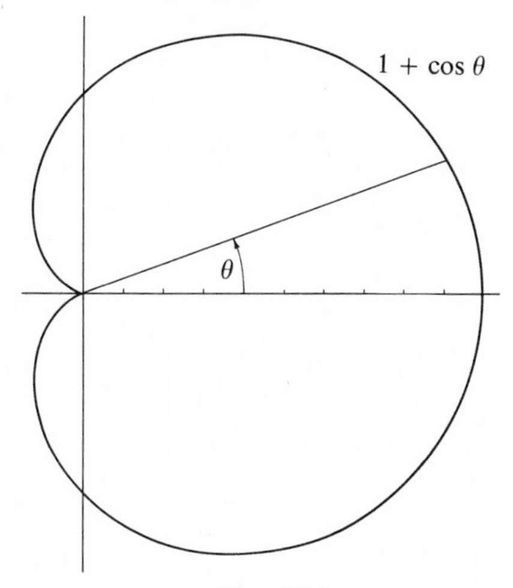

FIG. **12-5**

12.4 Babinet's Principle

According to Eq. (12.11) or (12.12), the calculation of the amplitude of the radiation at a point P is accomplished by performing an integral over the aperture in a screen; call this amplitude ψ_1. If the aperture and screen are interchanged (so that the screen becomes a disk and the aperture becomes the remainder of the space), we may calculate another amplitude, ψ_2. Clearly, the calculation of the amplitude at P in the absence of any screen whatsoever is just the sum of these two integrals. If this latter amplitude is ψ_0, then

$$\psi_0 = \psi_1 + \psi_2 \tag{12.13}$$

This result regarding the amplitudes due to complementary apertures is known as *Babinet's principle.** For example, behind a screen containing an aperture there are certain positions at which the radiation amplitude is zero: $\psi_1 = 0$. Babinet's principle then states that $\psi_0 = \psi_2$. That is, if the screen is removed and a disk placed at the previous position of the aperture, the amplitude (or intensity) at P will be the same whether the disk is present or not.

Another interesting example is the following. Suppose that a source and lens are arranged as in Fig. 12-6. Since the light is focused by the lens, the amplitude (or intensity) at point P in the upper diagram will be zero.

* First obtained in 1837 by Jacques Babinet (1794–1872) for the case of scalar waves. An equivalent result for electromagnetic waves and perfectly conducting screens was derived by H. G. Booker in 1946; see, for example, Born and Wolf (Bo59, pp. 556–557).

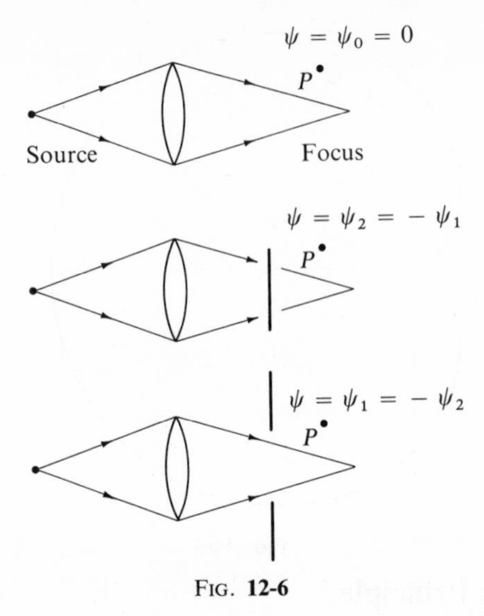

FIG. **12-6**

Therefore $\psi_1 = -\psi_2$, $|\psi_1|^2 = |\psi_2|^2$; that is, there are equal intensities of light at the points P in the complementary situations illustrated in the lower two diagrams of Fig. 12-6. The fact that the amplitudes ψ_1 and ψ_2 have opposite signs in this case means that the waves differ in phase by π.

12.5 Diffraction by a Circular Disk

We now apply the Kirchhoff diffraction formula to the calculation of the intensity of light behind a circular disk. This is an historically important problem since it materially contributed to the establishment of the wave theory of light at the expense of the corpuscular theory. We shall consider in this section only the calculation of the intensity of the light *on the axis* behind the disk.

In order to simplify the derivation we require the source and the field point to be located symmetrically with respect to the disk (see Fig. 12-7).

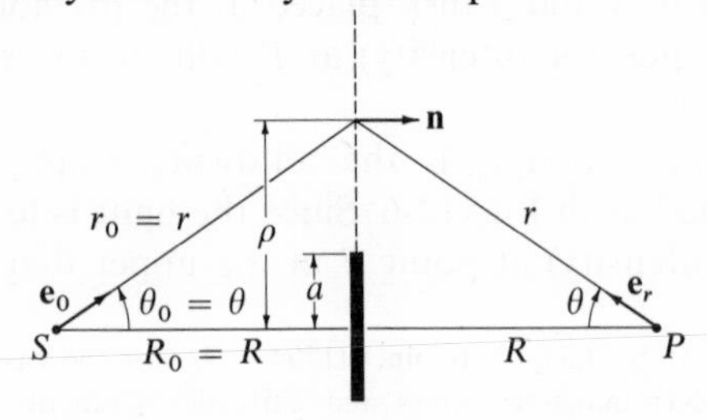

FIG. **12-7**

The diffraction integral is given by Eq. (12.11), and since $\mathbf{e}_0 \cdot \mathbf{n} = \cos\theta = -\mathbf{e}_r \cdot \mathbf{n}$ and $r = r_0$, we have

$$\psi(P) = -i\frac{A}{\lambda}\int_\sigma \frac{e^{2ikr}}{r^2}\cos\theta\, da \tag{12.14}$$

Expressing the element of area in polar coordinates ρ, φ, we find

$$\psi(P) = -i\frac{A}{\lambda}\int_0^{2\pi} d\varphi \int_a^\infty \frac{e^{2ikr}}{r^2}\cos\theta \rho\, d\rho$$

The integral over the angle φ may be performed at once; then, since $r^2 = R^2 + \rho^2$ and $\cos\theta = R/r$, we may write

$$\psi(P) = -i\frac{2\pi AR}{\lambda}\int_{\sqrt{R^2+a^2}}^\infty \frac{e^{2ikr}}{r^2}\, dr \tag{12.15}$$

This integral may be approximated by carrying out successive integrations by parts:

$$\psi(P) = -ikAR\left\{\frac{1}{2ik}\frac{e^{2ikr}}{r^2}\Bigg|_{\sqrt{R^2+a^2}}^\infty + \frac{1}{ik}\int_{\sqrt{R^2+a^2}}^\infty \frac{e^{ikr}}{r^3}\, dr\right\}$$

$$= -ikAR\left\{-\frac{1}{2ik}\frac{\exp[2ik\sqrt{R^2+a^2}]}{R^2+a^2} + \frac{1}{2k^2}\frac{\exp[2ik\sqrt{R^2+a^2}]}{(R^2+a^2)^{\frac{3}{2}}} - \frac{3}{2k^2}\int_{\sqrt{R^2+a^2}}^\infty \frac{e^{2ikr}}{r^4}\, dr\right\}$$

$$= \frac{AR}{2}\frac{\exp[2ik\sqrt{R^2+a^2}]}{R^2+a^2}\left\{1 - \frac{i}{k}\frac{1}{\sqrt{R^2+a^2}} + \cdots\right\} \tag{12.16}$$

The magnitude of the second term in the brackets is of the order of $(kR)^{-1} = \lambda/2\pi R$. If we consider only distances R that are large compared with the wavelength λ, only the first term in the expansion is significant. The intensity is therefore given approximately by

$$I(P) = |\psi(P)|^2 = \frac{A^2R^2}{4(R^2+a^2)^2} \tag{12.17}$$

Now, the incident amplitude ψ_{inc} at the edge of the disk is

$$\psi_{\text{inc}} = A\frac{\exp[ik\sqrt{R^2 + a^2}]}{\sqrt{R^2 + a^2}} \tag{12.18}$$

and

$$I_{\text{inc}} = |\psi_{\text{inc}}|^2 = \frac{A^2}{R^2 + a^2} \tag{12.19}$$

Hence, $I(P)$ may be expressed as

$$I(P) = \tfrac{1}{4} I_{\text{inc}} \frac{R^2}{R^2 + a^2} \tag{12.20}$$

This result is illustrated in Fig. 12-8. (The solution obtained is not valid close to the disk, i.e., for $R \cong 0$.) We arrive at the remarkable conclusion that the axial region behind the disk is nowhere dark. The verification of this prediction was one of the early outstanding successes of the wave theory of light.* We may explain this result in an elementary way by noting

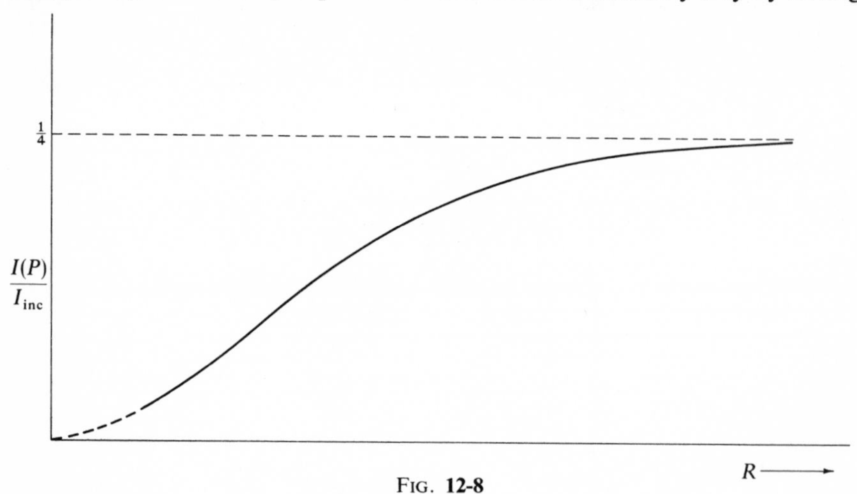

FIG. **12-8**

* In 1818 Fresnel presented an essay to the Paris Academy in competition for a prize to be awarded for the best paper on diffraction. Poisson was a member of the judging commission (along with Laplace, Biot, and Arago), and he noticed that Fresnel's theory predicted that a bright spot would be observed on the axis behind an illuminated disk. Poisson (who was an advocate of the corpuscular theory) believed that this result refuted Fresnel's theory. The prediction was experimentally tested and verified by Arago and Fresnel, thereby contributing to the overthrow of the corpuscular theory. (The bright spot behind a disk is therefore (?) known as *Poisson's bright spot*.) By 1826 the corpuscular theory was completely dead, due largely to a series of papers by Fresnel concerning diffraction phenomena and double refraction effects.

that due to the symmetry of the arrangement, the light which passes near a point on the edge of the disk will arrive at the axis *in phase* with light passing near any other point on the edge of the disk. Constructive interference will therefore result in the appearance of a bright spot at any position on the axis. (Off the axis, the phases will no longer be equal, and destructive interference will occur, giving rise to a set of circular fringes.*)

12.6 Diffraction by a Circular Aperture

We next examine the situation complementary to that discussed in the preceding section. We wish to calculate the on-axis intensity of the light diffracted by a circular aperture. Again, we choose a symmetrical situation in which the source and field point are equidistant from the aperture (see Fig. 12-9).

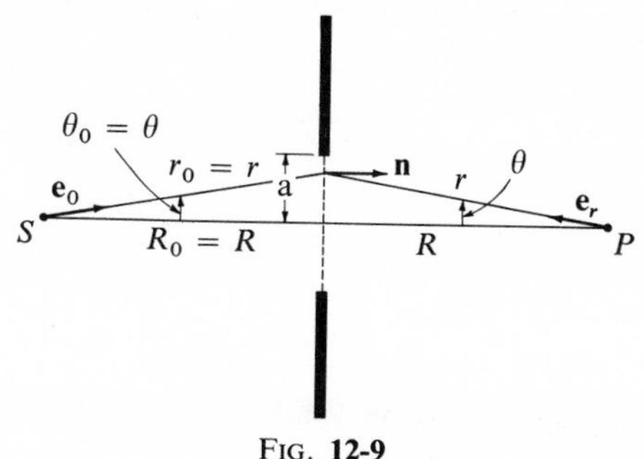

FIG. 12-9

The amplitude is given by Eq. (12.14); only the limits of integration are different:

$$\psi(P) = -i\frac{2\pi AR}{\lambda}\int_R^{\sqrt{R^2+a^2}} \frac{e^{2ikr}}{r^2}\,dr \tag{12.21}$$

Integrating by parts, we obtain

$$\psi(P) = -ikAR\left\{\frac{1}{2ik}\frac{e^{2ikr}}{r^2}\bigg|_R^{\sqrt{R^2+a^2}} + \text{(terms of order } \frac{1}{kR} \text{ and higher)}\right\} \tag{12.22}$$

If $R \gg \lambda$, only the integrated term is important, and we have, approximately,

$$\psi(P) = -\frac{AR}{2}\left\{\frac{\exp[2ik\sqrt{R^2+a^2}]}{R^2+a^2} - \frac{e^{2ikR}}{R^2}\right\} \tag{12.23}$$

* These circular fringes may be observed, for example, by focusing the eye on a dust particle on the surface of the lens of a pair of glasses in bright sunlight. There is always a central bright spot.

If we further require that $R \gg a$, we may neglect a^2 in the denominator of the first term. But since k is a large number for optical radiation, we may not simply neglect a^2 in the phase. Rather, the approximation must be based on expanding the radical:

$$\psi(P) = -\frac{A}{2R}\left\{\exp[2ikR\sqrt{1 + (a^2/R^2)}] - \exp[2ikR]\right\}$$

$$= -\frac{A}{2R}\left\{\exp[2ikR(1 + (a^2/2R^2) + \cdots)] - \exp[2ikR]\right\}$$

Neglecting the terms in the exponential of order higher than those shown, we have, approximately,

$$\psi(P) = -\frac{A}{2R}\exp[2ikR]\left\{\exp[ika^2/R] - 1\right\}$$

$$= -\frac{A}{2R}\exp[2ikR]\exp[ika^2/2R]\left(2i\sin\frac{ka^2}{2R}\right) \tag{12.24}$$

The intensity is therefore given by

$$I(P) = |\psi(P)|^2 = \frac{A^2}{R^2}\sin^2\frac{ka^2}{2R} \tag{12.25}$$

or in terms of I_{inc} [see Eq. (12.19)], we obtain

$$I(P) = I_{\text{inc}}\sin^2\frac{ka^2}{2R} \tag{12.26}$$

This result, shown in Fig. 12-10, is fundamentally different from that for the circular disk. The symmetry with respect to light passing near the edge of the aperture is the same as before, but now there is the additional light which comes directly from the source. These two components, as a function of R, are sometimes in phase and sometimes out of phase. Therefore, the intensity pattern alternates between bright and dark spots.* No simple relationship exists between the *intensities* in these two cases, but the *amplitudes* sum to the incident amplitude, as required by Babinet's principle (see Problem 12-1).

12.7 Fraunhofer Diffraction

The two examples which were worked out in the preceding sections are rather special problems in diffraction theory. We now wish to treat more general cases in which we examine the radiation intensity at off-axis

* Again, off-axis the phases differ, giving rise to circular fringes. But the central spot will be bright or dark, depending on the distance from the aperture. A series of photographs demonstrating the effect is given by Stone (St63, p. 203).

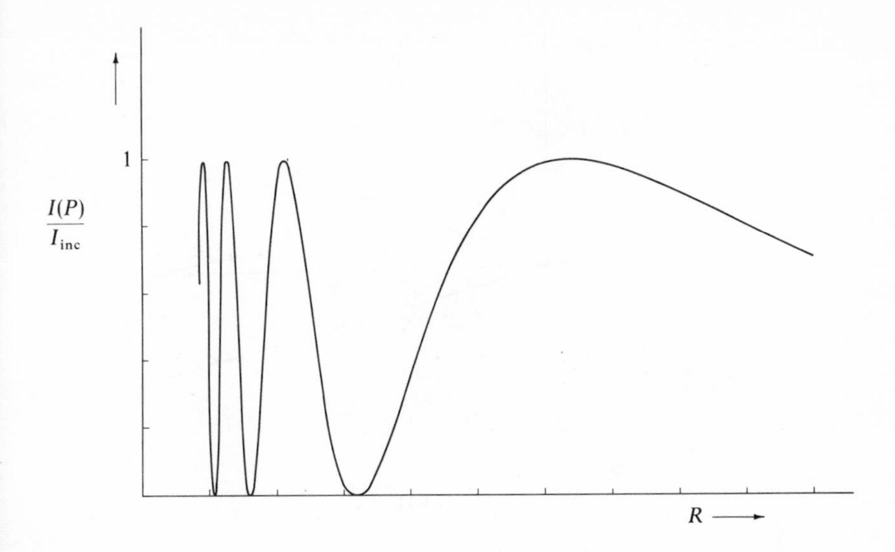

FIG. 12-10

positions due to diffraction by apertures of various shapes. We begin with the general expression for the diffraction of an incident plane wave [Eq. (12.12)]:

$$\psi(P) = -i\frac{\psi_0}{2\lambda}\int_\sigma \frac{e^{ikr}}{r}(1 + \cos\theta)\, da \tag{12.27}$$

If we confine our attention to the angular region in the vicinity of the normal to the aperture, then $\cos\theta \cong 1$, so that $\psi(P)$ becomes approximately

$$\psi(P) = -i\frac{\psi_0}{\lambda}\int_\sigma \frac{e^{ikr}}{r}\, da \tag{12.28}$$

Consider the situation shown in Fig. 12-11 in which a plane wave is incident normally on an aperture of arbitrary shape cut in an otherwise infinite plane opaque screen. We choose a coordinate system with an origin located at some point within the aperture. The field point P has the rectangular coordinates (x, y, z). The variables for the integration over the aperture are chosen to be ξ, η, so that $da = d\xi\, d\eta$. The distance from the variable point of integration (ξ, η) to the field point (x, y, z) is r:

$$r^2 = (x - \xi)^2 + (y - \eta)^2 + z^2 \tag{12.29}$$

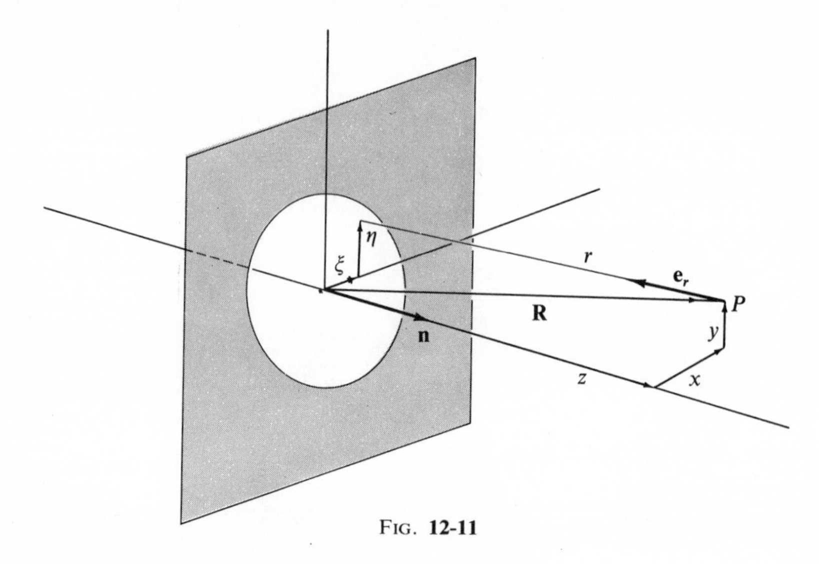

FIG. **12-11**

Now, the distance from the origin to P is R, where

$$R^2 = x^2 + y^2 + z^2 \tag{12.30}$$

Therefore,

$$\begin{aligned} r^2 &= R^2 - 2(x\xi + y\eta) + (\xi^2 + \eta^2) \\ &= R^2\left[1 - \frac{2(x\xi + y\eta)}{R^2} + \frac{\xi^2 + \eta^2}{R^2}\right] \end{aligned} \tag{12.31}$$

It will be convenient to use the direction cosines of the vector **R**:

$$\alpha \equiv \frac{x}{R}; \qquad \beta \equiv \frac{y}{R} \tag{12.32}$$

Then, the square root of Eq. (12.31) becomes

$$r = R\left[1 - \frac{2(\alpha\xi + \beta\eta)}{R} + \frac{\xi^2 + \eta^2}{R^2}\right]^{\frac{1}{2}} \tag{12.33}$$

Now, since the distance R to the observation point is assumed to be large, the second and third terms in this equation may be considered small. Expanding the radical we obtain an expression for r that can be used in the diffraction integral [Eq. (12.28)]:

$$\begin{aligned} r &\cong R\left[1 - \frac{\alpha\xi + \beta\eta}{R} + \frac{\xi^2 + \eta^2}{2R^2} + \cdots\right] \\ &\cong R - (\alpha\xi + \beta\eta) + \frac{\xi^2 + \eta^2}{2R} + \cdots \end{aligned} \tag{12.34}$$

When R is large compared to the dimensions of the aperture, $R \gg (\xi^2 + \eta^2)$, the third term in this equation may be neglected. The value of $\psi(P)$ will then depend only on α and β; i.e., the intensity at the observation point depends only on the *angle* of deviation that the wave undergoes at the aperture. This type of diffraction is called *Fraunhofer diffraction** and is a reasonably accurate description of the effects that take place at large distances from the aperture. Fraunhofer diffraction is usually observed in practice by means of a lens system which removes the observation point to optical infinity. In this case the higher-order terms all vanish identically (see Problem 12-2). If the observation point is close to the aperture, it is no longer permissible to neglect the term $(\xi^2 + \eta^2)/2R$. Diffraction under this condition is called *Fresnel diffraction* and will be discussed in Sections 12.12 and 12.13.

For the case of Fraunhofer diffraction, we have, approximately,

$$r = R - (\alpha\xi + \beta\eta) \tag{12.34a}$$

and the Fraunhofer diffraction integral is

$$\boxed{\psi(P) = -i\frac{\psi_0 e^{ikR}}{\lambda R}\int_\sigma e^{-ik(\alpha\xi + \beta\eta)}\, d\xi\, d\eta} \tag{12.35}$$

In the next sections we will use this equation to investigate several cases of particular interest.

12.8 Fraunhofer Diffraction by an Infinite Slit

If the aperture σ is an infinitely long slit of width $2a$ in the ξ-direction (as in Fig. 12-12), then the diffraction integral is

$$\psi(P) = C\int_{-a}^{+a} e^{-ik\alpha\xi}\, d\xi \tag{12.36}$$

where the constant C includes the coefficient of the integral in Eq. (12.35) and also the constant contribution of the integral over η.

$$\psi(P) = C \cdot \frac{i}{k\alpha} e^{-ik\alpha\xi}\Big|_{-a}^{+a}$$

$$= i\frac{C}{k\alpha}(e^{-ik\alpha a} - e^{ik\alpha a})$$

$$= \frac{2C}{k\alpha}\sin k\alpha a \tag{12.37}$$

* After the German optician and physicist Joseph von Fraunhofer (1787–1826), an accomplished lens maker and inventor of optical instruments, among which was a diffraction grating for the accurate measurement of wavelengths.

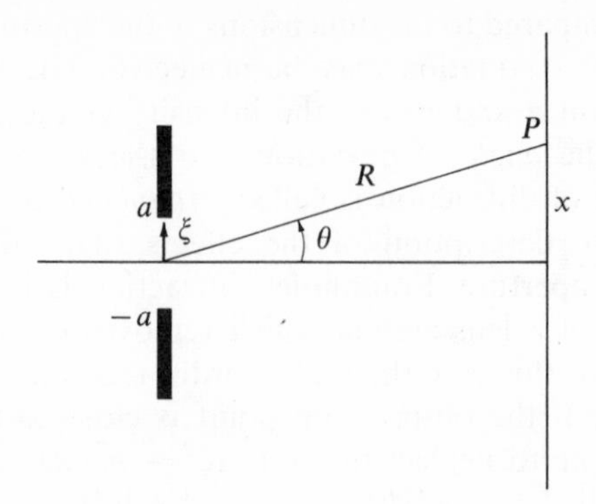

FIG. **12-12**

The intensity is therefore given by

$$I(P) = |\psi(P)|^2 = 4C^2a^2\left(\frac{\sin\gamma}{\gamma}\right)^2 \tag{12.38}$$

where $\gamma \equiv k\alpha a$. Figure 12-13 shows the magnitude of the amplitude, $|\psi(P)|$, and the intensity, $I(P)$, as functions of γ.

Notice that the variable γ is

$$\gamma = k\alpha a = 2\pi \frac{a}{\lambda} \sin\theta \tag{12.39}$$

where θ is the angle between the normal to the aperture and the line connecting the mid-point of the aperture with the observation point, as shown in Fig. 12-12. Most of the intensity of the diffracted beam is contained within the central maximum. The angular spread between the minima on either side of the central maximum is

$$\Delta\theta = 2\sin^{-1}\left(\frac{\lambda}{2a}\right) \cong \frac{\lambda}{a} \tag{12.40}$$

Thus, the pattern will become more diffuse if the wavelength is increased or if the slit width is decreased.

It is apparent from Fig. 12-13 that the intensities of the secondary maxima decrease rapidly with increasing θ. The values of the intensities in the first few maxima are (in per cent of the central maximum) 4.72%, 1.69%, 0.83%, 0.50%. (See also Table 12.1 in Section 12.11.)

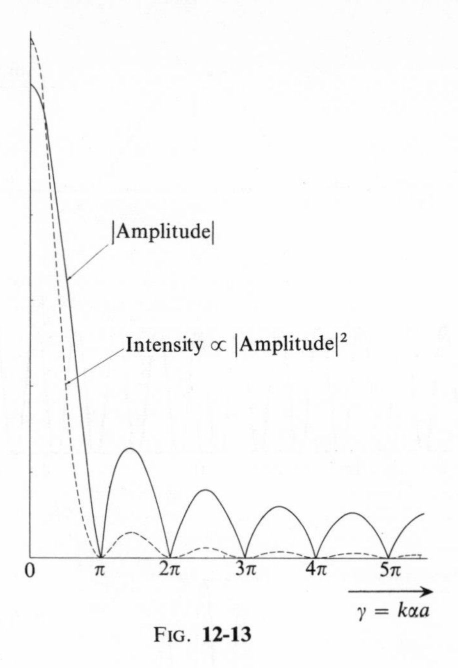

FIG. 12-13

12.9 Fraunhofer Diffraction by a Double Slit

We next increase the complexity of the situation by adding a second slit to the system, as in Fig. 12-14. The diffraction integral [Eq. (12.36)] now becomes the sum of two terms:

$$\psi(P) = C\int_{-d-a}^{-d+a} e^{-ik\alpha\xi}\, d\xi + C\int_{d-a}^{d+a} e^{-ik\alpha\xi}\, d\xi \tag{12.41}$$

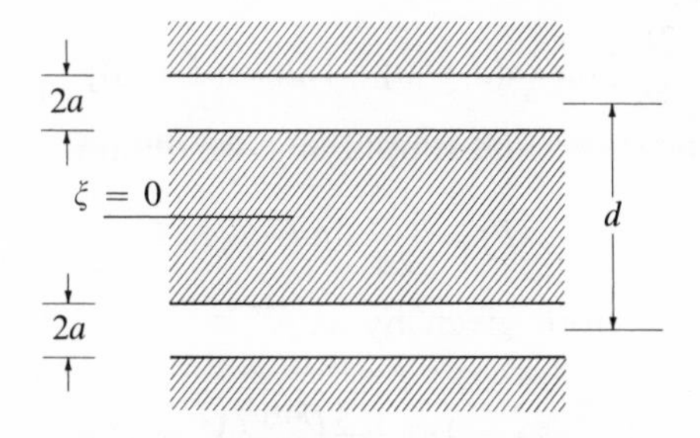

FIG. 12-14

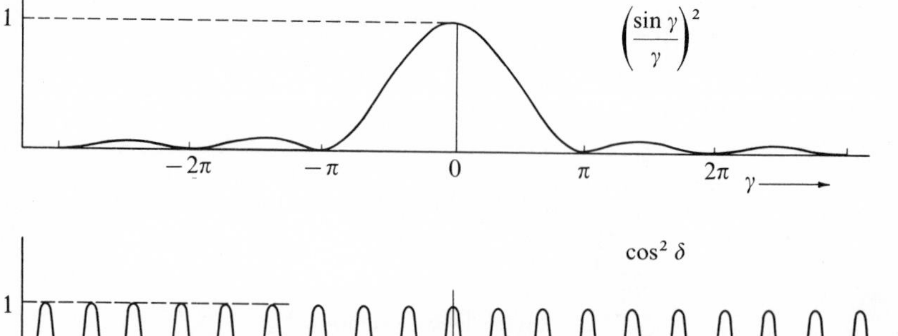

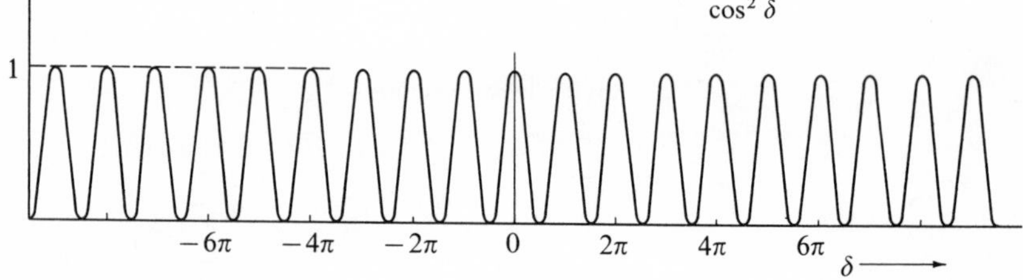

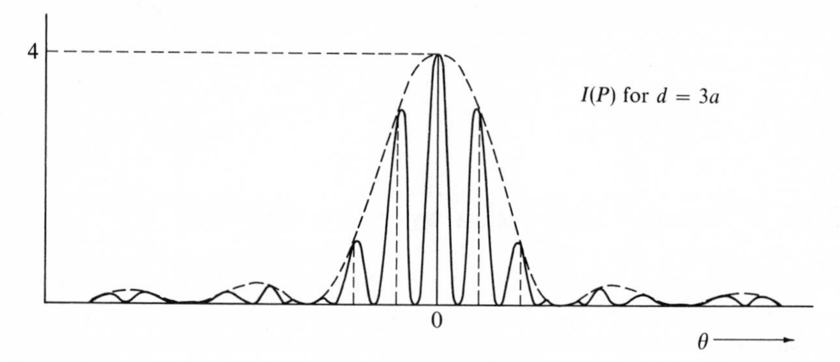

FIG. **12-15**

The integrated terms may be grouped in the following way:

$$\psi(P) = i\frac{C}{k\alpha}[(e^{ik\alpha(d-a)} - e^{-ik\alpha(d-a)}) - (e^{ik\alpha(d+a)} - e^{-ik\alpha(d+a)})]$$

$$= -\frac{2C}{k\alpha}[\sin k\alpha(d-a) - \sin k\alpha(d+a)]$$

Expanding the sine terms and simplifying, we obtain

$$\psi(P) = \frac{4C}{k\alpha}\sin k\alpha a \cos k\alpha d \tag{12.42}$$

The intensity is therefore given by

$$\boxed{I(P) = 16C^2a^2\left(\frac{\sin \gamma}{\gamma}\right)^2 \cos^2 \delta} \tag{12.43}$$

where $\gamma \equiv k\alpha a$ and $\delta \equiv k\alpha d$. The diffraction pattern is seen to be the same as that for the single slit, but multiplied by a factor of 4* and modulated by the term $\cos^2 \delta$. That is, the *envelope* of the double-slit pattern is just the single-slit pattern. Figure 12-15 shows the functions $(\sin \gamma/\gamma)^2$ and $\cos^2 \delta$ as well as the intensity $I(P)$ for the case $d = 3a$.

Notice that if a becomes very small compared with d, the term $(\sin \gamma/\gamma)^2$ will remain essentially constant for many oscillations of the term $\cos^2 \delta$. Such a situation is just the case for Young's experiment, discussed in Section 11.7.

12.10 Fraunhofer Diffraction by a Rectangular Aperture

If the infinite slit of Section 12.8 is replaced by a rectangular aperture as in Fig. 12-16, the integral over η must also be performed. If the width in the η-direction is $2b$, the diffraction integral is [cf. Eq. (12.36)]

$$\psi(P) = C\int_{-a}^{+a} e^{-ik\alpha\xi}\, d\xi \int_{-b}^{+b} e^{-ik\beta\eta}\, d\eta$$

$$= 4Cab\,\frac{\sin k\alpha a}{k\alpha a}\,\frac{\sin k\beta b}{k\beta b} \tag{12.44}$$

We define

$$\gamma_a \equiv k\alpha a; \qquad \gamma_b \equiv k\beta b \tag{12.45}$$

so that the intensity becomes

$$I(P) = 16C^2a^2b^2\left(\frac{\sin \gamma_a}{\gamma_a}\right)^2\left(\frac{\sin \gamma_b}{\gamma_b}\right)^2 \tag{12.46}$$

The radiation intensity along either the x-direction or the y-direction is therefore the same as for the infinite slit. A typical diffraction pattern

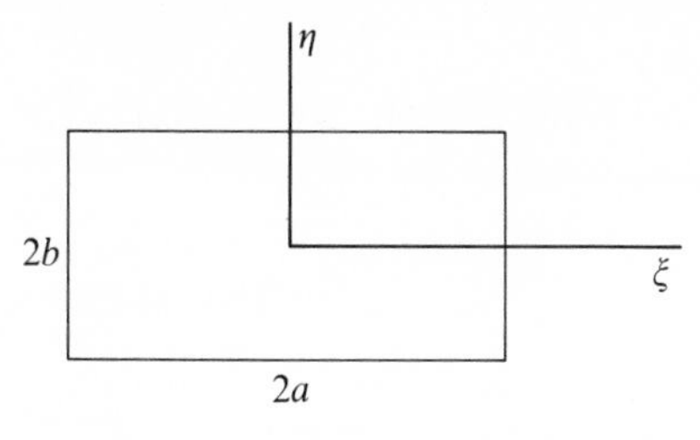

FIG. **12-16**

* For a system of N equally spaced slits, the central maximum is enhanced by a factor of N^2 over that for a single slit.

is shown in Fig. 12-17. Notice that the pattern exhibits a greater lateral extent in the direction corresponding to the narrow dimension of the slit.

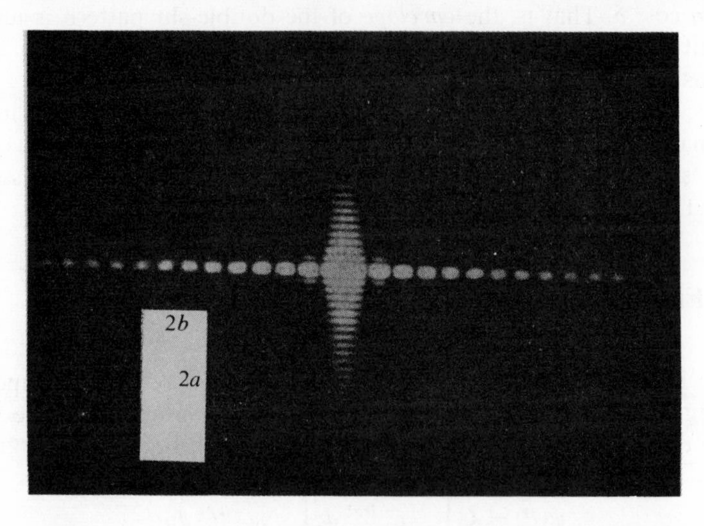

FIG. 12-17*

The intensity of the maxima are given by

$$k\alpha a = (m + \tfrac{1}{2})\pi; \qquad k\beta b = (n + \tfrac{1}{2})\pi, \qquad m, n = 0, \pm 1, \pm 2, \cdots \quad (12.47a)$$

or,

$$\alpha = \frac{(m + \frac{1}{2})\lambda}{2a}; \qquad \beta = \frac{(n + \frac{1}{2})\lambda}{2b}, \qquad m, n = 0, \pm 1, \pm 2, \cdots \quad (12.47b)$$

The maxima that occur along the x- and y-axes are those for which $n = 0$, $m = 0, \pm 1, \pm 2, \cdots$ or $m = 0$, $n = 0 \pm 1, \pm 2, \cdots$. In addition there are off-axis maxima ($m \neq 0$, $n \neq 0$) that are of considerably smaller intensity. A few of these bright spots are barely visible in Fig. 12-17.

12.11 Fraunhofer Diffraction by a Circular Aperture

The case of diffraction by a circular aperture is of considerable importance since the ultimate limitation on the resolving power of telescopic and microscopic instruments is due to diffraction effects. We consider a plane wave to be incident normally on a circular aperture of radius a, as seen in Fig. 12-18, and we wish to calculate the radiation intensity on the x-y plane

* From F. A. Jenkins and H. E. White, "Fundamentals of Optics," 3rd Ed. McGraw-Hill, New York, 1957. (Reprinted by permission.)

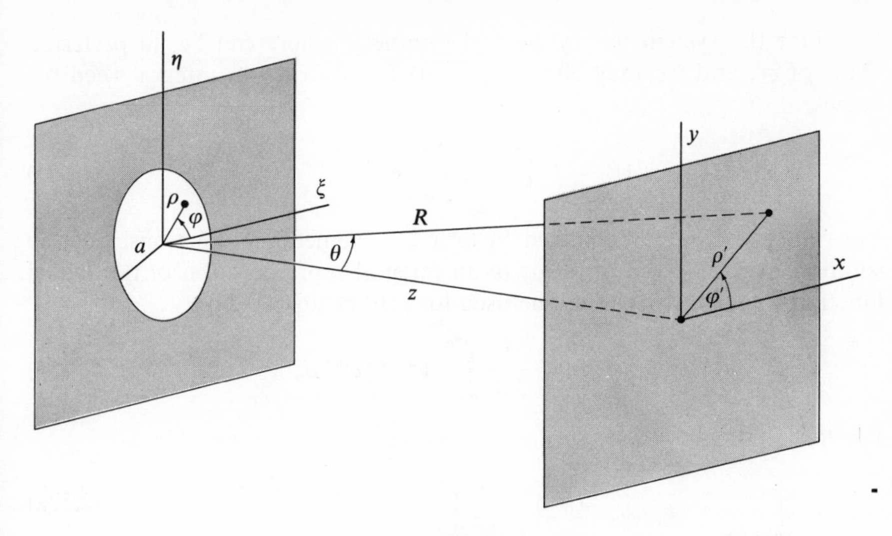

FIG. **12-18**

at a distance z. The radiation amplitude is

$$\psi(P) = C \int_{\sigma} e^{-ik(\alpha\xi + \beta\eta)} \, d\xi \, d\eta \tag{12.48}$$

The integration over σ will be simplified if polar coordinates are used:

$$\xi = \rho \cos \varphi; \qquad \eta = \rho \sin \varphi \tag{12.49a}$$

Similarly, on the observation plane we specify a point by

$$x = \rho' \cos \varphi'; \qquad y = \rho' \sin \varphi' \tag{12.49b}$$

The direction cosines then become

$$\alpha = \frac{x}{R} = \frac{\rho'}{R} \cos \varphi'; \qquad \beta = \frac{y}{R} = \frac{\rho'}{R} \sin \varphi' \tag{12.49c}$$

Furthermore, if θ is restricted to be a small angle,

$$\frac{\rho'}{R} = \sin \theta \cong \theta \tag{12.49d}$$

The phase factor in the diffraction integral may now be expressed as

$$\begin{aligned} \alpha\xi + \beta\eta &= \frac{\rho\rho'}{R} (\cos \varphi \cos \varphi' + \sin \varphi \sin \varphi') \\ &= \rho\theta \cos(\varphi - \varphi') \end{aligned} \tag{12.50}$$

But since the system has cylindrical symmetry, there can be no preferred value of φ', and we may choose $\varphi' = 0$. The diffraction integral then becomes

$$\psi(P) = C\int_0^a \rho\, d\rho \int_0^{2\pi} e^{-ik\rho\theta\cos\varphi}\, d\varphi \tag{12.51}$$

This integral cannot be solved in terms of elementary functions, but the solution may be given in terms of an integral representation of the Bessel function $J_n(u)$ similar to the one used for $j_n(u)$ in Eq. (10.24)*:

$$J_n(u) = \frac{1}{2\pi i^n}\int_0^{2\pi} e^{iu\cos\varphi} e^{in\varphi}\, d\varphi \tag{12.52}$$

For $n = 0$, this becomes

$$J_0(u) = \frac{1}{2\pi}\int_0^{2\pi} e^{iu\cos\varphi}\, d\varphi \tag{12.52a}$$

which is the general expression corresponding to Eq. (3.11a). We identify

$$J_0(u) = J_0(-k\rho\theta) = J_0(k\rho\theta) \tag{12.53}$$

Hence, Eq. (12.51) reduces to

$$\psi(P) = 2\pi C\int_0^a J_0(k\rho\theta)\rho\, d\rho \tag{12.54}$$

This integral may be evaluated by using Eq. (3.107d):

$$\int uJ_0(u)\, du = uJ_1(u)$$

Therefore,

$$\psi(P) = 2\pi Ca^2 \frac{J_1(k\theta a)}{k\theta a} \tag{12.55}$$

and the intensity is†

$$\boxed{I(P) = \pi^2 C^2 a^4 \left(\frac{2J_1(k\theta a)}{k\theta a}\right)^2} \tag{12.56}$$

* See, for example, Jahnke and Emde (Ja45, p. 149).

† This result was first obtained in 1835 by Sir George Biddell Airy (1801–1892), the English Astronomer Royal. Before the expression for the diffraction integral was known in terms of Bessel functions, the diffraction pattern for the circular aperture was approximated by replacing the circle with a regular polygon of many sides. The most ambitious such effort was a calculation with a polygon of 180 sides performed by F. M. Schwerd, a German *hochschule* teacher. His results appeared almost simultaneously with Airy's solution.

(The factor of 2 is included with J_1 in order to normalize the term in parentheses to unity at $\theta = 0$.) The diffraction pattern is shown in Fig. 12-19. It is apparent that the result is quite similar to the pattern derived for the

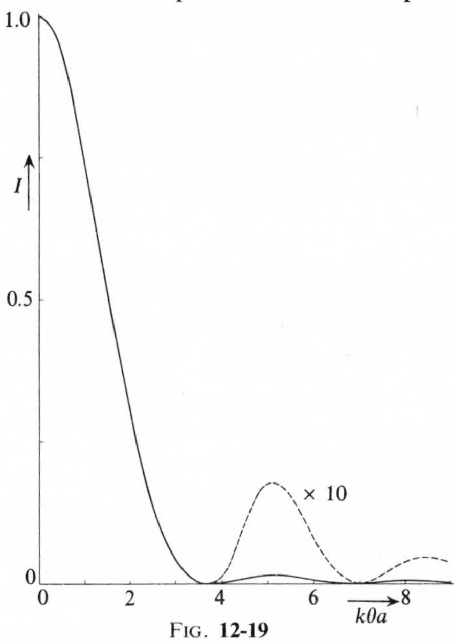

FIG. **12-19**

infinite slit (Fig. 12-13). The secondary maxima in this case, however, are somewhat smaller, as indicated in Table 12.1. We also see that the maxima and minima lie at approximately the same positions, with those for the circle always at slightly larger angles.

The dark rings for the circular aperture occur for $k\theta a = 2\pi a\theta/\lambda = 3.83$, $7.02, \cdots$, i.e., for the angles

$$\theta = 0.61\frac{\lambda}{a}, \quad 1.12\frac{\lambda}{a}, \cdots \qquad \text{(dark rings)} \tag{12.57}$$

The question of the resolution of interference fringes was discussed in Section 11.11. If we view two point sources of light with a telescope, then the minimum separation at which the sources can still be resolved is limited by the diffraction of the light in the lens system. The *Rayleigh criterion* for resolution in this case is as follows: two point sources of monochromatic light of the same wavelength are said to be just resolved if the maximum intensity of one source occurs at the position of the first diffraction minimum of the other source. This situation is illustrated in Fig. 12-20a which shows two diffraction patterns of equal intensity that are just resolved. Figure 12-20b shows the net intensity (incoherent sum) due to the two individual

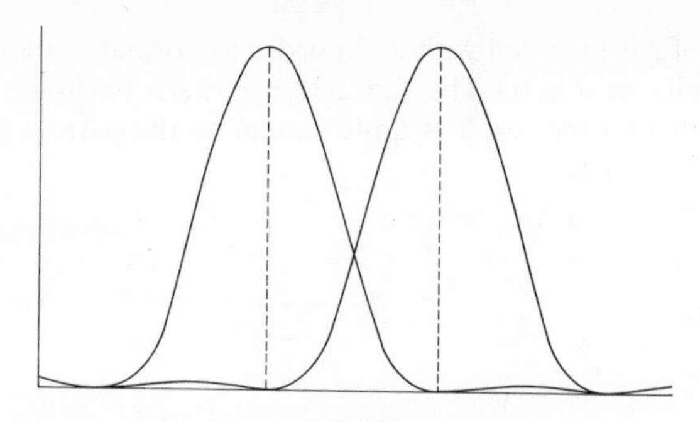

FIG. 12-20a

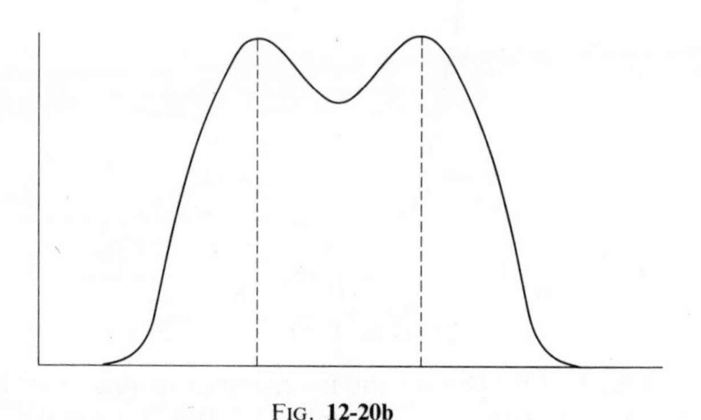

FIG. 12-20b

sources. The *angular resolution* $\mathscr{R}$ is therefore expressed by

$$\mathscr{R} = 0.61 \frac{\lambda}{a} \tag{12.58}$$

It is evident that telescopes of large aperture are necessary in order to resolve objects that have small angular separation.

12.12 Fresnel Diffraction by a Straight Edge—Approximate Solution

The problem of the radiation field near an aperture is called *Fresnel diffraction.* If the distance from the aperture to the observation point cannot be considered large compared to the dimensions of the aperture, then the quadratic terms in the expansion of r [see Eq. (12.34)] cannot be neglected.

Table 12.1

Salient Points of the Diffraction Patterns for the Infinite Slit and for the Circular Aperture

	Slit		Circular aperture	
	$k\alpha a$	$\left(\frac{\sin k\alpha a}{k\alpha a}\right)^2$	$k\theta a$	$\left(\frac{2J_1(k\theta a)}{k\theta a}\right)^2$
First maximum	0	1	0	1
First minimum	$\pi = 3.14$	0	$1.22\pi = 3.83$	0
Second maximum	$1.43\pi = 4.49$	0.0472	$1.64\pi = 5.14$	0.0175
Second minimum	$2\pi = 6.28$	0	$2.23\pi = 7.02$	0
Third maximum	$2.46\pi = 7.72$	0.0169	$2.68\pi = 8.42$	0.0042
Third minimum	$3\pi = 9.42$	0	$3.24\pi = 10.17$	0
Fourth maximum	$3.47\pi = 10.90$	0.0083	$3.67\pi = 11.62$	0.0016

The inclusion of these terms makes it impossible to evaluate the diffraction integral by means of simple functions; numerical values of the functions must in general be obtained from tables or graphs. It is not our intent to give here a comprehensive discussion of Fresnel diffraction. Rather, we shall treat one problem—the diffraction by a straight edge—which illustrates the mathematical complications involved and yields an interesting result. Two methods of solution are given: an approximate solution using a series expansion and an "exact" solution which involves the so-called *Fresnel integrals*.

We choose a coordinate system as indicated in Fig. 12-21. The straight edge extends infinitely far in the y-direction and in the direction of negative x. The distance r from the integration point (ξ, η) to the observation point

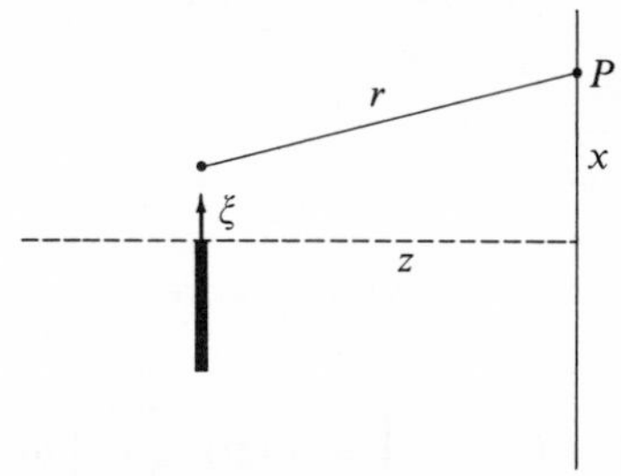

Fig. 12-21

(x, y, z) is given by

$$r^2 = (x - \xi)^2 + (y - \eta)^2 + z^2 \tag{12.59}$$

Therefore,

$$r = z\left[1 + \frac{(x - \xi)^2}{z^2} + \frac{(y - \eta)^2}{z^2}\right]^{\frac{1}{2}}$$

$$\cong z\left[1 + \frac{(x - \xi)^2}{2z^2} + \frac{(y - \eta)^2}{2z^2} + \cdots\right]$$

Neglecting terms higher than quadratic, we have, approximately,

$$r \cong z + \frac{(x - \xi)^2}{2z} + \frac{(y - \eta)^2}{2z} \tag{12.60}$$

The diffraction integral then becomes

$$\psi(P) = -i\frac{\psi_0}{\lambda}\int_\sigma \frac{e^{ikr}}{r}\,da$$

$$= -i\frac{\psi_0 e^{ikz}}{\lambda z}\int_\sigma \exp\left[i\frac{k}{2z}[(x - \xi)^2 + (y - \eta)^2]\right] d\xi\, d\eta \tag{12.61}$$

The integration over η yields a constant contribution; we may combine this constant with the coefficient of the integral and write

$$\psi(P) = C\int_0^\infty \exp\left[i\frac{k}{2z}(x - \xi)^2\right] d\xi \tag{12.62}$$

Define a new variable u such that

$$\frac{k}{2z}(x - \xi)^2 \equiv \frac{\pi}{2}u^2 \tag{12.63}$$

Then,

$$x - \xi = \sqrt{\frac{\pi z}{k}}\,u \tag{12.64}$$

and

$$d\xi = -\sqrt{\frac{\pi z}{k}}\,du \tag{12.65}$$

The value of u at $\xi = 0$ is

$$u(\xi = 0) = \sqrt{\frac{k}{\pi z}}\,x \equiv u_0 \tag{12.66}$$

Therefore, the diffraction integral may be expressed as

$$\psi(P) = C\sqrt{\frac{\pi z}{k}}\int_{-\infty}^{+u_0} \exp\left[i\frac{\pi}{2}u^2\right] du \tag{12.67}$$

Now, at distances far removed from the straight edge (i.e., $x \to \infty$ or $u_0 \to \infty$), the amplitude must approach the value for the incident wave; that is, $\psi(P)|_{x\to\infty} = \psi_0$. Thus,

$$\psi_0 = C\sqrt{\frac{\pi z}{k}}\int_{-\infty}^{+\infty} \exp\left[i\frac{\pi}{2}u^2\right] du \tag{12.68}$$

This is a standard definite integral and may be evaluated by the following nonrigorous argument.* The integral of the *Gaussian error function* is†

$$\int_{-\infty}^{+\infty} \exp[-\alpha v^2]\, dv = \sqrt{\frac{\pi}{\alpha}} \tag{12.69}$$

If we compare this integral with that in Eq. (12.68) and identify α with $-i\pi/2$, then

$$\int_{-\infty}^{+u_0} \exp\left[i\frac{\pi}{2}u^2\right] du = \sqrt{\frac{2}{-i}} = 1 + i \tag{12.70}$$

Therefore,

$$\psi_0 = C\sqrt{\frac{\pi z}{k}}(1 + i) \tag{12.71}$$

Now, the intensity of the incident wave is

$$I_0 = |\psi_0|^2 = C^2 \cdot \frac{\pi z}{k} \cdot |1 + i|^2$$

$$= 2C^2 \frac{\pi z}{k} \tag{12.72}$$

This expression allows us to substitute for C^2 when we square $\psi(P)$ to obtain the intensity $I(P)$. We find

$$\boxed{I(P) = |\psi(P)|^2 = \tfrac{1}{2}I_0\left|\int_{-\infty}^{+u_0} \exp\left[i\frac{\pi}{2}u^2\right] du\right|^2} \tag{12.73}$$

This equation gives the general form of the intensity for the Fresnel diffraction by a straight edge. The remainder of this section will be devoted to an approximate evaluation of $I(P)$; in the following section we will discuss an exact method.

* "Nonrigorous" because Eq. (12.68) involves a *complex* exponential whereas we use a *real* exponential in the evaluation. Nevertheless, the result is correct.

† See, for example, Dwight (Dw61, item 860.11).

We may expand the diffraction integral in Eq. (12.73) in a power series in $1/u_0$ by performing successive integrations by parts:

$$\int_{-\infty}^{+u_0} \exp\left[i\frac{\pi}{2}u^2\right] du = \int_{-\infty}^{+u_0} \frac{d}{du}\left(\exp\left[i\frac{\pi}{2}u^2\right]\right)\frac{du}{i\pi u}$$

$$= \frac{1}{i\pi}\int_{-\infty}^{+u_0} \frac{1}{u}\, d\left(\exp\left[i\frac{\pi}{2}u^2\right]\right)$$

$$= \frac{1}{i\pi}\left[\frac{\exp[i(\pi/2)u^2]}{u}\Bigg|_{-\infty}^{+u_0} + \int_{-\infty}^{+u_0} \frac{\exp[i(\pi/2)u^2]}{u^2}\, du\right]$$

Carrying out a second integration by parts in the same manner, we find

$$\int_{-\infty}^{+u_0} \exp\left[i\frac{\pi}{2}u^2\right] du = -i\frac{\exp[i(\pi/2)u_0^2]}{\pi u_0}\left[1 + \frac{1}{i\pi u_0^2} + \cdots\right] \tag{12.74}$$

If we confine our attention to large values of u_0, then only the first term in the expansion is important. The intensity at P is therefore the absolute square of the coefficient of the brackets in Eq. (12.74) multiplied by $I_0/2$:

$$I(P) = \frac{I_0}{2}\cdot\frac{1}{\pi^2 u_0^2}, \qquad u_0 < 0 \tag{12.75}$$

or, in terms of x,

$$I(P) = I_0\cdot\frac{z}{2\pi k}\cdot\frac{1}{x^2}, \qquad x < 0 \tag{12.75a}$$

These results are clearly valid only for $u_0 < 0$ or $x < 0$, since the intensity must approach zero within the geometrical shadow; in the illuminated region (u_0, $x > 0$) the intensity must approach I_0 as u_0 or x is increased. We must therefore in addition seek an expression for $I(P)$ which is applicable to the illuminated region.

The diffraction integral can be rewritten in the following way:

$$\int_{-\infty}^{+u_0} \exp\left[i\frac{\pi}{2}u^2\right] du = \int_{-\infty}^{+\infty} \exp\left[i\frac{\pi}{2}u^2\right] du - \int_{u_0}^{+\infty} \exp\left[i\frac{\pi}{2}u^2\right] du$$

$$= (1 + i) - \int_{u_0}^{+\infty} \exp\left[i\frac{\pi}{2}u^2\right] du$$

The integral remaining on the right-hand side can be evaluated through use of the result given in Eq. (12.74) which is independent of the sign of the infinite limit. Then,

$$\int_{-\infty}^{+u_0} \exp[i(\pi/2)u^2]\, du = (1 + i) - i\frac{\exp[i(\pi/2)u_0^2]}{\pi u_0} \tag{12.76}$$

where we have again neglected all terms of order higher than the first. The intensity therefore becomes

$$I(P) = \frac{I_0}{2}\left|(1 + i) - i\frac{\exp[i(\pi/2)u_0^2]}{\pi u_0}\right|^2$$

$$= \frac{I_0}{2}\left|\left(1 + \frac{\sin(\pi u_0^2/2)}{\pi u_0}\right) + i\left(1 - \frac{\cos(\pi u_0^2/2)}{\pi u_0}\right)\right|^2$$

$$= \frac{I_0}{2}\left[2 + \frac{1}{\pi^2 u_0^2} + \frac{2}{\pi u_0}\left(\sin\frac{\pi}{2}u_0^2 - \cos\frac{\pi}{2}u_0^2\right)\right] \tag{12.77}$$

In keeping with the previously established degree of approximation, we neglect the term $1/\pi^2 u_0^2$. If we then multiply and divide the term in parenthesis by $\sin(\pi/4) = \cos(\pi/4) = \sqrt{2}/2$, we have

$$I(P) = I_0\left[1 + \frac{\sqrt{2}}{\pi u_0}\left(\sin\frac{\pi}{2}u_0^2\cos\frac{\pi}{4} - \cos\frac{\pi}{2}u_0^2\sin\frac{\pi}{4}\right)\right]$$

$$= I_0\left[1 + \frac{\sqrt{2}}{\pi u_0}\sin\left(\frac{\pi}{2}u_0^2 - \frac{\pi}{4}\right)\right] \tag{12.78}$$

or, in terms of x,

$$I(P) = I_0\left[1 + \sqrt{\frac{2z}{\pi k}}\,\frac{\sin\left(\dfrac{k}{2z}x^2 - \dfrac{\pi}{4}\right)}{x}\right] \tag{12.78a}$$

These results are clearly valid only for $u_0 > 0$ or $x > 0$ since they indicate that $I(P) \to I_0$ as u_0 or x becomes very large; this can be true only for the illuminated region.

We may easily obtain one more point on the intensity curve, viz., the point at which $u_0 = 0$ or $x = 0$:

$$I(P)|_{u_0=0} = \frac{I_0}{2}\left|\int_0^{-\infty}\exp\left[i\frac{\pi}{2}u^2\right]du\right|^2$$

$$= \frac{I_0}{2}\left|\frac{1}{2}\int_{-\infty}^{+\infty}\exp\left[i\frac{\pi}{2}u^2\right]du\right|^2$$

$$= \frac{I_0}{2}\left|\frac{1+i}{2}\right|^2$$

$$= \frac{I_0}{4} \tag{12.79}$$

We may summarize our approximate results as follows:

Illuminated region ($u_0 \gg 0$):

$$I(P) = I_0\left[1 + \frac{\sqrt{2}}{\pi u_0}\sin\left(\frac{\pi}{2}u_0^2 - \frac{\pi}{4}\right)\right] \tag{12.80a}$$

In line with straight edge ($u_0 = 0$):

$$I(P) = \frac{I_0}{4} \tag{12.80b}$$

Shadow region ($u_0 \ll 0$):

$$I(P) = \frac{I_0}{2\pi^2 u_0^2} \tag{12.80c}$$

These results are illustrated in Fig. 12-22 in which the dashed portions of the curves indicate the regions where the results are not valid. Evidently there is a penetration of the light into the region of geometrical shadow and there is a set of bright and dark fringes in the illuminated region. The solution presented in the following section is valid even in the vicinity of $u_0 = 0$.

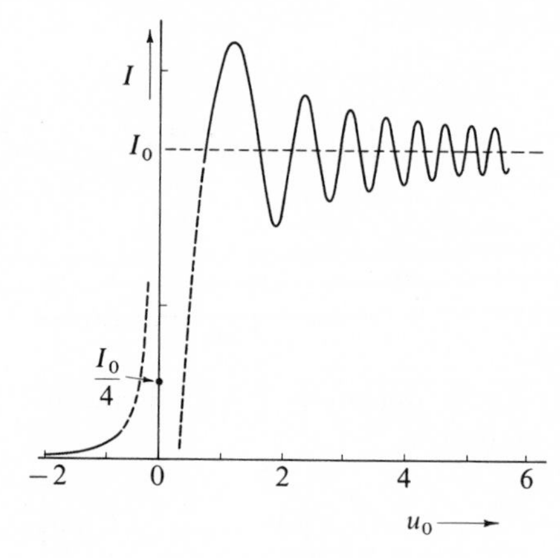

FIG. **12-22**

12.13 Fresnel Diffraction by a Straight Edge—Solution in Terms of Fresnel Integrals

Having obtained an approximate solution to the problem of the Fresnel diffraction by a straight edge in terms of simple functions, we now seek an "exact" solution to the problem. The solution will be "exact" in the sense that the diffraction integral can be computed to any desired degree of accuracy, but, of course, the entire formulation of the problem is subject to the limitations of the Kirchhoff theory. The expression for the intensity is [Eq. (12.73)]

$$I(P) = \frac{I_0}{2}\left|\int_{-\infty}^{+u_0} \exp\left[i\frac{\pi}{2}u^2\right] du\right|^2 \tag{12.81}$$

We may write the complex exponential in terms of a sine and cosine, so that

$$\begin{aligned} I(P) &= \frac{I_0}{2}\left|\int_{-\infty}^{+u_0} \cos\frac{\pi}{2}u^2\, du + i\int_{-\infty}^{+u_0} \sin\frac{\pi}{2}u^2\, du\right|^2 \\ &= \frac{I_0}{2}\left\{\left[\int_{-\infty}^{+u_0} \cos\frac{\pi}{2}u^2\, du\right]^2 + \left[\int_{-\infty}^{+u_0} \sin\frac{\pi}{2}u^2\, du\right]^2\right\} \end{aligned} \tag{12.82}$$

These integrals cannot, of course, be evaluated in terms of simple functions; numerical methods involving series expansions must be used. In fact, one possible series is that developed in the preceding section where only the leading terms were retained. (See also Problems 12-12 and 12-13.)

An elegant description of the problem may be made in the following way. Define the integrals

$$C(u) \equiv \int_0^u \cos\frac{\pi}{2}u^2\, du \tag{12.83a}$$

$$S(u) \equiv \int_0^u \sin\frac{\pi}{2}u^2\, du \tag{12.83b}$$

These integrals (called *Fresnel's integrals*) may be evaluated at once for certain values of u:

$$C(0) = 0; \qquad S(0) = 0 \tag{12.84a}$$

$$C(-u) = -C(u); \qquad S(-u) = -S(u) \tag{12.84b}$$

We may compute $C(\infty)$ and $S(\infty)$ by using Eq. (12.70):

$$\int_{-\infty}^{+\infty} \exp\left[i\frac{\pi}{2}u^2\right] du = 1 + i$$

The integrand is an even function of u, so

$$\int_0^{+\infty} \exp\left[i\frac{\pi}{2}u^2\right] du = \frac{1+i}{2}$$

Writing the exponential as a sine and cosine, we have

$$\int_0^{+\infty} \cos\frac{\pi}{2}u^2\,du + i\int_0^{+\infty} \sin\frac{\pi}{2}u^2\,du = \frac{1+i}{2}$$

Finally, equating real and imaginary parts, we obtain

$$\begin{aligned}\int_0^{+\infty} \cos\frac{\pi}{2}u^2\,du &= C(\infty) = \tfrac{1}{2}\\ \int_0^{+\infty} \sin\frac{\pi}{2}u^2\,du &= S(\infty) = \tfrac{1}{2}\end{aligned} \tag{12.84c}$$

Then, using Eqs. (12.84b), we also have

$$C(-\infty) = -\tfrac{1}{2}; \qquad S(-\infty) = -\tfrac{1}{2} \tag{12.84d}$$

If we let $C(u)$ and $S(u)$ be the rectangular coordinates of a point $Q(u)$, then as u takes on all possible values ($-\infty < u < \infty$), the locus of the points $Q(u)$ defines a certain curve, known as *Cornu's spiral.** According to Eqs. (12.84a), this curve passes through the origin; Eqs. (12.84b) show that the curve is symmetric with respect to the origin; and Eqs. (12.84c) and (12.84d) specify the asymptotic points. In order to locate other points on the curve, it is necessary to calculate numerically the integrals in Eq. (12.83). The resulting Cornu spiral is shown in Fig. 12-23.†

The length L of the straight line from any point $Q(u_1)$ on the Cornu spiral to any other point $Q(u_2)$ is given by

$$L^2 = [C(u_2) - C(u_1)]^2 + [S(u_2) - S(u_1)]^2 \tag{12.85}$$

Now, according to Eq. (12.82), the intensity $I(P)$ may be expressed as

$$I(P) = \frac{I_0}{2}\left\{[C(u_0) - C(-\infty)]^2 + [S(u_0) - S(-\infty)]^2\right\} \tag{12.86}$$

Comparing Eqs. (12.85) and (12.86), we see that the intensity at any point P specified by u_0 is proportional to the square of the length of the straight line drawn from the point $Q(u_0)$ on the Cornu spiral to the point $Q(-\infty)$. That is, if $u_0 = 0$, then

$$\begin{aligned} I(P)\big|_{u_0=0} &= \frac{I_0}{2}\left\{(-\tfrac{1}{2})^2 + (-\tfrac{1}{2})^2\right\}\\ &= \frac{I_0}{4}\end{aligned}$$

* This geometrical construction was first used in 1874 by M. Alfred Cornu (1841–1902).

† Tabulated values of the Fresnel integrals are usually more satisfactory than Cornu's spiral for quantitative work. Short tables will be found in Jahnke and Emde (Ja45, p.35) and in Jenkins and White (Je57, p. 367); an extensive tabulation is that of Pearcey (Pe56).

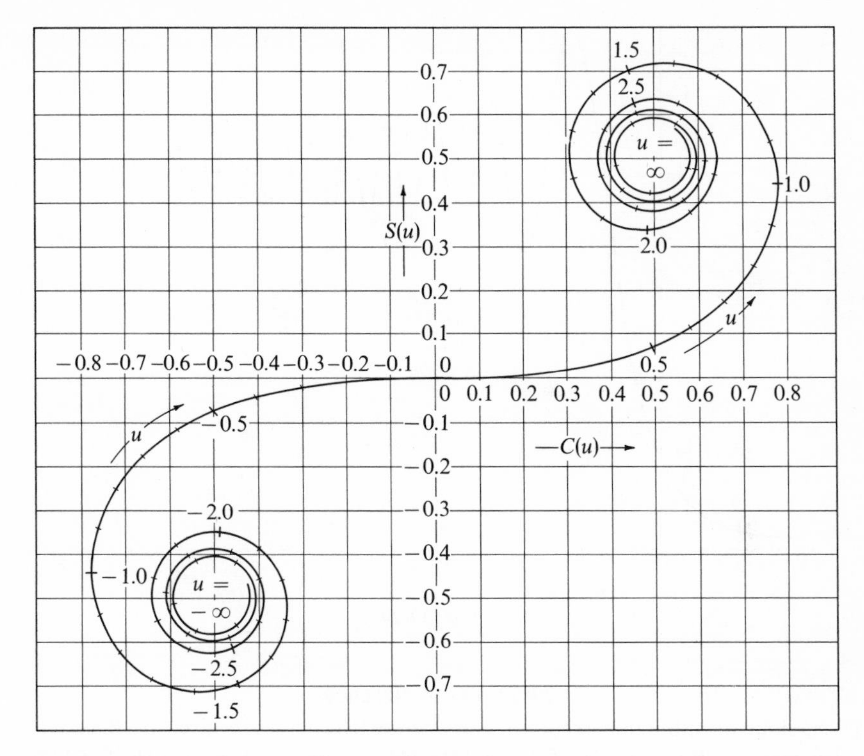

FIG. **12-23**

as before [Eq. (12.79)]. If u_0 decreases from $u_0 = 0$, then the distance from $Q(u_0)$ to $Q(-\infty)$ decreases monotonically toward zero. Thus, the intensity in the shadow region falls off smoothly with increasing penetration into the shadow and vanishes for $u_0 \to -\infty$. In the illuminated region u_0 increases; and, as the point $Q(u_0)$ passes around the upper spiral, the intensity oscillates between maxima and minima with decreasing amplitude, reaching an asymptotic value of I_0. Therefore, these results duplicate those of the preceding section for $u_0 \ll 0$ and $u_0 \gg 0$. With the present method we find in addition the behavior of the intensity in the vicinity of $u_0 = 0$. The complete intensity pattern is shown in Fig. 12-24. In spite of the approximate nature of the Kirchhoff theory, the predictions of the Fresnel diffraction pattern for the straight edge are in excellent agreement with experiment. By comparing Figs. 12-22 and 12-24, it is apparent that the approximate solution obtained in the preceding section is reasonably accurate for $|u_0| \gtrsim 1$.

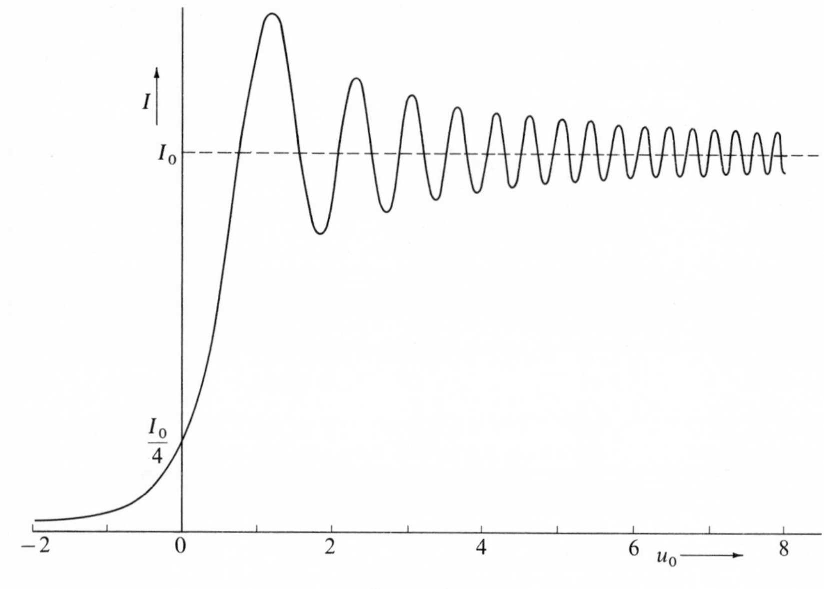

FIG. **12-24**

Suggested References

Discussions of diffraction theory at the intermediate level are given by Blass (Bl62, Chapter 32), Born and Wolf (Bo59, Chapter 8), Joos and Freeman (Jo50, Chapter 20), Slater and Frank (Sl47, Chapters 14 and 15), Sommerfeld (So54, Chapter 5), and Wangsness (Wa63, Chapters 35–37). One of the most comprehensive treatments at this level is that of Stone (St63, Chapters 6–10).

More advanced topics are to be found in Born and Wolf (Bo59, Chapters 8, 10, and 11) and Sommerfeld (So54, Section 38 and Chapter 6).

There are many books on optics which treat the applications of diffraction theory; see, for example, Ditchburn (Di62, Chapter 6), Jenkins and White (Je57), Rossi (Ro57), or Strong (St58).

A beautiful collection of photographs of various types of diffraction phenomena has been assembled by Cagnet, Francon, and Thrier (Ca62).

Problems

12-1. Refer to the calculation of the amplitudes of light diffracted by a circular disk and a circular aperture (Sections 12.5 and 12.6). Show that, at a point on the axis, the sum of the two amplitudes is equal to the amplitude that would result in the absence of any screen. Thus, verify Babinet's principle for this case.

12-2. A plane wave is incident normally on an aperture in an opaque screen. A lens is used to focus the diffracted light on a screen located at the focal point of the lens. Use a geometrical construction to obtain an expression for the quantity r that occurs in the diffraction integral [cf. Eq. (12.34)]. Show that under these conditions the Fresnel (and higher-order) terms vanish identically, and the diffraction pattern is a pure Fraunhofer pattern.

12-3. Calculate the Fraunhofer diffraction pattern for the case of N identical infinite slits of width $2a$ with separations $2d$. Sketch the results for $N = 6$. How would the diffraction pattern appear if the incident radiation consisted of two components with wavelengths λ_0 and $\frac{3}{2}\lambda_0$ and with equal intensities?

12-4. A rectangular aperture is illuminated by a plane wave. Integrate the power passing through the aperture and compare with the integrated power in the Fraunhofer diffraction pattern. Examine carefully and discuss the way in which the various approximations enter, especially in view of the fact that the results for the integrated power are exactly the same.

12-5. Consider the Fraunhofer diffraction pattern for a circular aperture. Show that if the circle is enlarged by a factor b along a certain direction (i.e., the circle is deformed into an ellipse), then the diffraction pattern *contracts* by a factor b in the same direction. Show further that the intensity at any point along the line of deformation is a factor b^2 greater than at the corresponding point of the original pattern. (These results are valid for an aperture of *any* shape, not just a circle.)

12-6. Integrate the light intensity from diffraction by a circular aperture and show that the intensity contained within the angle θ_0 is proportional to

$$1 - J_0^2(ka\theta_0) - J_1^2(ka\theta_0)$$

Therefore, show that approximately 84% of the intensity lies within the first dark ring and that 91% lies within the second dark ring.* Sketch the integrated light intensity as a function of $ka\theta_0$.

12-7. How many times would it be possible (in principle) to write the Lord's Prayer on the head of a pin and still be able to read the letters with the aid of a good microscrope?†

12-8. A diffracting aperture is in the form of an annulus with inner radius b and outer radius a. Obtain the expression for the intensity in the Fraunhofer diffraction pattern. Calculate the position of the first dark ring and the position and intensity of the secondary maximum for the case $b = a/2$

* This result was first obtained by Lord Rayleigh, 1881.

† From A. B. Pippard, ed., *Cavendish Problems in Classical Physics*, Cambridge University Press, 1962.

and compare with the result for the circular aperture. Thus, show that the resolution is *increased* by adding the central disk, but the contrast is reduced because the intensity of the secondary maximum is increased.

12-9. Continue the analysis of the previous problem and investigate the limiting case $b \to a$. Discuss the resolution and the contrast compared with the circular aperture. Sketch the intensity pattern for $b \to a$ and $b = 0$ (circular aperture).

12-10. Compare the theoretical angular resolutions of the human eye (dilated in dim light) and the Mount Palomar 200 in. telescope for light in the middle of the optical spectrum. If a double star system consisted of two identical stars the size of the Sun with a separation equal to the Earth-Sun separation, at what distance could they still be resolved by (a) the human eye; and (b) the Palomar instrument?

12-11. Show that the length of the Cornu spiral from $u = 0$ to $u = u_1$ is just u_1.

12-12. In section 12.12 the Fresnel diffraction integral was expanded in a series of inverse powers of u_0. Apply the same procedure of successive integrations by parts to show that the Fresnel integrals [Eqs. (12.83)] may be expressed as

$$C(u) = C(\infty) - \frac{1}{\pi u}\left[P(u) \cos\frac{\pi}{2}u^2 - Q(u) \sin\frac{\pi}{2}u^2\right]$$

$$S(u) = S(\infty) - \frac{1}{\pi u}\left[P(u) \sin\frac{\pi}{2}u^2 + Q(u) \cos\frac{\pi}{2}u^2\right]$$

where

$$P(u) = \frac{1}{\pi u^2} - \frac{1 \cdot 3 \cdot 5}{(\pi u^2)^3} + \frac{1 \cdot 3 \cdot 5 \cdot 7 \cdot 9}{(\pi u^2)^5} - \cdots$$

$$Q(u) = 1 - \frac{1 \cdot 3}{(\pi u^2)^2} + \frac{1 \cdot 3 \cdot 5 \cdot 7}{(\pi u^2)^4} - \cdots$$

These series expansions are useful if u is large.

12-13. If u is small, the Fresnel integrals [Eqs. (12.83)] may be evaluated by expanding the sine and cosine terms in a power series and then performing the integrations. Show that

$$C(u) = u\left[1 - \frac{1}{2!5}\left(\frac{\pi}{2}u^2\right)^2 + \frac{1}{4!9}\left(\frac{\pi}{2}u^2\right)^4 - \cdots\right]$$

$$S(u) = u\left[\frac{1}{1!3}\left(\frac{\pi}{2}u^2\right) - \frac{1}{3!7}\left(\frac{\pi}{2}u^2\right)^3 + \frac{1}{5!11}\left(\frac{\pi}{2}u^2\right)^5 - \cdots\right]$$

These series actually converge for all values of u (show this), but they are useful for computations only when u is small.

12-14. Use the Cornu spiral and construct the intensity pattern for diffraction by an infinitely long slit. Assume incident plane waves. Let the slit width be 1 mm and let the distance to the observing screen be 1 meter. Consider light with $\lambda = 5000$ Å.

CHAPTER 13

Relativistic Electrodynamics

13.1 Introduction

In the development of a classical description of mechanical systems, it is customary to justify, in some way, the Newtonian equation of motion, $\mathbf{F} = m\mathbf{a}$, and to proceed by working out various consequences. As the discussion becomes more detailed in an attempt to describe effects that take place at high velocities, it is necessary to take into account the fundamental modifications that are required by relativity theory. That is, the basic equation of Newtonian mechanics, $\mathbf{F} = m\mathbf{a}$, is only approximately correct. If an exact description of mechanics (excluding quantum effects) is desired, explicit use of relativistic formalism is required.

In several of the derivations in the preceding chapters a statement was made to the effect that the results were valid only for $v \ll c$. But in each case, the statement applied to the neglect of an *existing* term in the equation (for example, the term $(e/c)\mathbf{u} \times \mathbf{B}$ in the Lorentz force), and was not used to indicate that the original equation was in any way approximate. Maxwell's equations and the Lorentz force equation are, in fact, correct (*relativistically* correct); it is only certain methods of solution that are approximate.

The remarkable fact that classical electrodynamics is relativistically correct is indeed a fortunate circumstance in that the many consequences worked out by Maxwell and his followers require no modification to be consistent with relativity theory. Maxwell's equations were formulated in order to represent the results of certain experiments. The equations were repeatedly checked in the laboratory and found always to be correct. In the latter part of the nineteenth century several experiments were performed to examine the accuracy of Maxwell's equations in moving reference frames. The most famous of these was the Michelson-Morley experiment which indicated that there is no preferred reference frame in which Maxwell's equations are valid.* It was then necessary to conclude that Maxwell's equations are valid in *all* inertial reference frames. The special theory of relativity was developed specifically to account for this conclusion.

Although the formalism of special relativity had been set up earlier by Poincaré, Lorentz, and others (but with many *ad hoc* hypotheses), it was Einstein who in 1905 made a bold step forward by basing a unified description of mechanics and electrodynamics on only two postulates. Einstein asserted (a) that all physical laws are the same in all inertial systems and (b) that the velocity of light (in free space) is a universal constant, independent of the motion of the source. Using these postulates as a foundation, Einstein was able to construct a beautiful theory which is a model of logical precision. We will investigate in this chapter some of the consequences of relativity theory in electrodynamics. We will find that it is possible to simplify and unify the equations of electrodynamics in a most elegant way.

This elegant unification comes only at the cost of considerable mathematical complexity. It becomes necessary, for example, to use the methods of vector analysis in *four*-dimensional space; various tensor operations are required to obtain results regarding the electromagnetic field equations; and variational calculus is used to derive the field equations from a Lagrangian formulation of the field. This chapter is by no means a complete discussion of relativistic electrodynamics; rather, the attempt is made to show how some of the more important results can be obtained in a straightforward manner from relativity theory. The reader should not be misled by the apparent simplicity of some of the equations; if one defines enough quantities, even the most complex result can be expressed in a simple form. That Maxwellian electrodynamics is correct from a relativistic standpoint and that relativity theory provides a means of deriving many of the results

* The first results were published by Michelson in 1881. More precise experiments were later carried out in collaboration with the chemist E. W. Morley; these results appeared in 1887. Further refinements of the experiments have been made by other workers on numerous occasions, even in recent years.

are facts of fundamental significance. This chapter can serve only as an introduction to this important subject.

13.2 Galilean Transformations

In Newtonian mechanics the concepts of space and time are supposed to be completely separable, and it is further assumed that time is an absolute quantity, susceptible of precise definition independent of the reference frame. It is also implicit in Newtonian mechanics that "action-at-a-distance" forces (gravitational, electromagnetic) are capable of transmitting effects with infinite velocity. These assumptions lead to the invariance of the laws of mechanics under coordinate transformations of the following type. Consider two inertial reference frames* K and K' which move along their x_3- and x_3'-axes with a uniform relative velocity v, as in Fig. 13-1. The transformation of the coordinates of a point from one system to the other is clearly of the form

$$\left.\begin{aligned} x_1' &= x_1 \\ x_2' &= x_2 \\ x_3' &= x_3 - vt \end{aligned}\right\} \tag{13.1a}$$

In addition we have

$$t' = t \tag{13.1b}$$

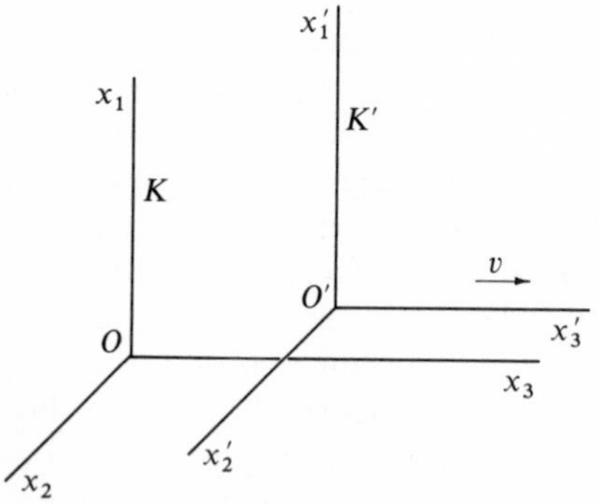

FIG. 13-1

* An *inertial reference frame* is defined to be a frame in which a particle subject to no external force moves with uniform velocity. A precise and logical discussion of reference frames can be given only within the framework of *general relativity*. In relativity theory, the term *Lorentz frame* is frequently used instead of *inertial frame*.

Equations (13.1) define a *Galilean transformation.* Furthermore, the element of length in the two systems is the same and is given by

$$\begin{aligned} ds^2 &= \sum_j dx_j^2 \\ &= \sum_j dx_j'^2 = ds'^2 \end{aligned} \tag{13.2}$$

The fact that Newton's laws are invariant with respect to Galilean transformations is termed *the principle of Newtonian relativity* or *Galilean invariance.* Newton's equations of motion in the two systems are

$$\begin{aligned} F_j &= m\ddot{x}_j \\ &= m\ddot{x}'_j = F'_j, \qquad j = 1, 2, 3 \end{aligned} \tag{13.3}$$

Thus, the form of the law of motion is *invariant* to a Galilean transformation. The individual terms are not invariant, however, but they transform according to the same scheme and are said to be *covariant.*

Although Newton's equations are covariant with respect to Galilean transformations, Maxwell's equations are not. For example, consider the scalar wave equation which is derivable from Maxwell's equations:

$$\nabla^2\Psi - \frac{1}{c^2}\frac{\partial^2\Psi}{\partial t^2} = 0 \tag{13.4}$$

Under a Galilean transformation, we have

$$\frac{\partial^2}{\partial x_1^2} = \frac{\partial^2}{\partial x_1'^2}; \qquad \frac{\partial^2}{\partial x_2^2} = \frac{\partial^2}{\partial x_2'^2}; \qquad \frac{\partial^2}{\partial t^2} = \frac{\partial^2}{\partial t'^2} \tag{13.5a}$$

but

$$\begin{aligned} \frac{\partial}{\partial x_3} &= \frac{\partial}{\partial x'_3} + \frac{1}{v}\frac{\partial}{\partial t'} \\ \frac{\partial^2}{\partial x_3^2} &= \frac{\partial^2}{\partial x_3'^2} + \frac{1}{v^2}\frac{\partial^2}{\partial t'^2} + \frac{2}{v}\frac{\partial^2}{\partial t'\,\partial x'_3} \end{aligned} \tag{13.5b}$$

so that Eq. (13.4) transforms to

$$\nabla'^2\Psi - \frac{1}{c^2}\frac{\partial^2\Psi}{\partial t'^2} + \frac{1}{v^2}\frac{\partial^2\Psi}{\partial t'^2} + \frac{2}{v}\frac{\partial^2\Psi}{\partial t'\,\partial x'_3} = 0 \tag{13.6}$$

This equation does not describe the propagation of electromagnetic waves in the manner prescribed by the second of Einstein's postulates. Electrodynamics cannot therefore be consistent both with the assumption of

Galilean invariance and Einstein's postulate. In fact, Maxwell's equations (and other equations based on them, such as the wave equation) are covariant only under a particular type of transformation called a *Lorentz transformation.* Since the Lorentz transformation can be derived from Einstein's postulates, *Maxwellian electrodynamics is relativistically correct.*

13.3 The Lorentz Transformation

Historically, the so-called Lorentz transformation equations were introduced prior to the development of Einsteinian relativity theory, but in an *ad hoc* manner without rigorous justification.* The equations can be obtained, however, solely on the basis of the two fundamental postulates of relativity.

If a light pulse is emitted from the common origin of the moving systems K and K' (see Fig. 13-1) when they are coincident, then according to the second postulate, the wavefronts observed in the two systems must be described by

$$\left.\begin{aligned} \sum_{j=1}^{3} x_j^2 - c^2t^2 &= 0 \\ \sum_{j=1}^{3} x_j'^2 - c^2t'^2 &= 0 \end{aligned}\right\} \tag{13.7}$$

If we define a new coordinate in each system, $x_4 \equiv ict$ and $x_4' \equiv ict'$, then we may write Eq. (13.7) as†

$$\left.\begin{aligned} \sum_{\mu=1}^{4} x_\mu^2 &= 0 \\ \sum_{\mu=1}^{4} x_\mu'^2 &= 0 \end{aligned}\right\} \tag{13.8}$$

From these equations it is clear that the two sums must be proportional, and since the motion is symmetric between the systems, the proportionality

* This transformation was originally postulated by Hendrik Anton Lorentz (1853–1928) in 1904 in order to explain certain electromagnetic phenomena, but the formulae had been set up as early as 1900 by J. J. Larmor. The complete generality of the transformation was not realized until Einstein *derived* the result. W. Voigt was actually the first to use a set of similar equations in a discussion of oscillatory phenomena in 1887.

† In accordance with standard convention we use Greek indices to indicate summations that run from 1 to 4; in relativity theory Latin indices are usually reserved for summations that run from 1 to 3.

constant is unity.* Thus,

$$\sum_{\mu} x_{\mu}^2 = \sum_{\mu} x_{\mu}'^2 \tag{13.9}$$

This relation is analogous to a three-dimensional, distance-preserving, orthogonal rotation and indicates that the transformation which we are now seeking corresponds to a rotation in a *four-dimensional* space (called *world space* or *Minkowski space*†). Therefore, the *Lorentz transformations are orthogonal transformations in Minkowski space.* That is,

$$\boxed{x_{\mu}' = \sum_{\nu} \lambda_{\mu\nu} x_{\nu}} \tag{13.10}$$

where the $\lambda_{\mu\nu}$ are the elements of the Lorentz transformation matrix and obey the orthogonality relation

$$\sum_{\nu} \lambda_{\mu\nu} \lambda_{\sigma\nu} = \delta_{\mu\sigma} \tag{13.11}$$

In discussions of relativity theory it is customary and convenient to employ the *Einstein summation convention.* According to this convention, a summation over *repeated indices* is automatically implied (unless otherwise stated). Therefore, we may write Eqs. (13.9), (13.10), and (13.11) as

$$x_{\mu} x_{\mu} = x_{\mu}' x_{\mu}' \tag{13.9a}$$

$$x_{\mu}' = \lambda_{\mu\nu} x_{\nu} \tag{13.10a}$$

$$\lambda_{\mu\nu} \lambda_{\sigma\nu} = \delta_{\mu\sigma} \tag{13.11a}$$

If the K' system moves at a uniform velocity v with respect to K along the x_3-direction, then $x_1 = x_1'$ and $x_2 = x_2'$ so that the transformation matrix is of the form

$$\lambda = \begin{pmatrix} 1 & 0 & 0 & 0 \\ 0 & 1 & 0 & 0 \\ 0 & 0 & \lambda_{33} & \lambda_{34} \\ 0 & 0 & \lambda_{43} & \lambda_{44} \end{pmatrix} \tag{13.12}$$

* A "proof" is given in Appendix F; see also Landau and Lifshitz (La62, p. 6) and Pauli (Pa58, p. 10).

† After Herman Minkowski (1864–1909) who introduced the use of *ict* and treated the four quantities x_{μ} as the components of a four-dimensional vector (1907).

Since the orthogonality relations $\lambda_{\mu\nu}\lambda_{\sigma\nu} = \delta_{\mu\sigma}$ and $\lambda_{\nu\mu}\lambda_{\nu\sigma} = \delta_{\mu\sigma}$ are equivalent, we can write these relations explicitly as

$$\lambda_{33}^2 + \lambda_{34}^2 = \lambda_{33}^2 + \lambda_{43}^2 = \lambda_{43}^2 + \lambda_{44}^2 = \lambda_{34}^2 + \lambda_{44}^2 = 1 \tag{13.13a}$$

and

$$\lambda_{33}\lambda_{34} + \lambda_{43}\lambda_{44} = \lambda_{33}\lambda_{43} + \lambda_{34}\lambda_{44} = 0 \tag{13.13b}$$

If we apply the transformation matrix $\boldsymbol{\lambda}$ to the matrix $\mathbf{x}$, we find for x_3',

$$\begin{aligned} x_3' &= \lambda_{33}x_3 + \lambda_{34}x_4 \\ &= \lambda_{33}\left(x_3 + ic\frac{\lambda_{34}}{\lambda_{33}}t\right) \end{aligned} \tag{13.14}$$

Now, when $x_3' = 0$, we must have $x_3 = vt$; i.e., the origin of the K' system moves with a uniform velocity along the x_3-axis. Therefore, Eq. (13.14) yields

$$v = -ic\frac{\lambda_{34}}{\lambda_{33}}$$

or,

$$\frac{\lambda_{34}}{\lambda_{33}} = i\beta \tag{13.15}$$

where

$$\beta \equiv \frac{v}{c} \tag{13.16}$$

From the equations in (13.13a) we may also write

$$\lambda_{33}^2 + \lambda_{34}^2 = 1$$

or, using Eq. (13.15),

$$\begin{aligned} \lambda_{33}^2 &= \frac{1}{1 + (\lambda_{34}^2/\lambda_{33}^2)} \\ &= \frac{1}{1 - \beta^2} \end{aligned}$$

Therefore,

$$\lambda_{33} = \frac{1}{\sqrt{1 - \beta^2}} \tag{13.17}$$

where the positive square root must be chosen in order that Eq. (13.14) reduce to $x_3' = x_3$ when $v = 0$.

Next, from the relations in Eqs. (13.13a), we have

$$\lambda_{34} = \pm \lambda_{43} \tag{13.18}$$

and from Eq. (13.13b),

$$\lambda_{44} = -\frac{\lambda_{33}\lambda_{43}}{\lambda_{34}} = \pm \lambda_{33}$$

$$= \pm \frac{1}{\sqrt{1 - \beta^2}}$$

We may choose the sign of λ_{44} by writing the expression for x_4':

$$x_4' = \lambda_{43}x_3 + \lambda_{44}x_4$$

or,

$$ict' = \lambda_{43}x_3 + ic\lambda_{44}t \tag{13.19}$$

Now, when $v = 0$, then $\lambda_{44} \rightarrow \pm 1$. But we must have $t = t'$ at the common origin ($x_1 = x_1' = 0$) in such a case. Therefore, in this limit λ_{44} must reduce to $+1$:

$$\lambda_{44} = \frac{1}{\sqrt{1 - \beta^2}} \tag{13.20}$$

Since both λ_{33} and λ_{44} are positive numbers, Eq. (13.13b) requires that λ_{34} and λ_{43} be of opposite sign. Therefore, Eq. (13.18) becomes

$$\lambda_{34} = -\lambda_{43} \tag{13.21}$$

Combining this result with Eqs. (13.15) and (13.17), we have finally

$$\lambda_{34} = i\beta\lambda_{33} = \frac{i\beta}{\sqrt{1 - \beta^2}} = -\lambda_{43} \tag{13.22}$$

Using Eqs. (13.17), (13.20), and (13.22), the Lorentz transformation matrix is

$$\boxed{\lambda = \begin{pmatrix} 1 & 0 & 0 & 0 \\ 0 & 1 & 0 & 0 \\ 0 & 0 & \gamma & i\beta\gamma \\ 0 & 0 & -i\beta\gamma & \gamma \end{pmatrix}} \tag{13.23}$$

where, in the customary notation,

$$\gamma \equiv \frac{1}{\sqrt{1-\beta^2}} \tag{13.24}$$

Therefore, the space-time coordinates in the K' system are

$$\boxed{\begin{aligned} x'_1 &= x_1 \\ x'_2 &= x_2 \\ x'_3 &= \gamma(x_3 - vt) \\ t' &= \gamma\left(t - \frac{\beta}{c}x_3\right) \end{aligned}} \tag{13.25}$$

As required, these equations reduce to the Galilean equations (13.1) when $v \to 0$ (or when $c \to \infty$).

If the motion of K' with respect to K is specified by the velocity vector $\mathbf{v}$, then the vector $\mathbf{x}'$ that represents a point in K' is related to a similar vector $\mathbf{x}$ in K by (see Problem 13-4)

$$\left.\begin{aligned} \mathbf{x}' &= \mathbf{x} + \mathbf{v}\left[\frac{\mathbf{x}\cdot\mathbf{v}}{v^2}(\gamma - 1) - \gamma t\right] \\ t' &= \gamma\left[t - \frac{\mathbf{x}\cdot\mathbf{v}}{c^2}\right] \end{aligned}\right\} \tag{13.26}$$

These general transformation equations reduce to Eq. (13.25) in the event that $\mathbf{v} = (0, 0, v)$.

13.4 Velocity, Momentum, and Energy in Relativity

In four-dimensional space, a quantity $\mathbb{M}$ is called a vector (a *four-vector**) if it consists of four components M_μ, each of which transform according to the relation

$$\boxed{M'_\mu = \lambda_{\mu\nu} M_\nu} \tag{13.27}$$

The position vector of a point in Minkowski space† is such a vector:

$$\mathbb{X} = (x_1, x_2, x_3, ict)$$

* Open-faced capitals are used exclusively to denote four-vectors.

† A "point" in Minkowsky space is actually an "event" since the *time* is explicitly included in the specification of the coordinates.

or,

$$\boxed{\mathbb{X} = (\mathbf{x}, ict)} \tag{13.28}$$

where the notation of the last line means that the first three (space) components of $\mathbb{X}$ define the ordinary three-dimensional position vector $\mathbf{x}$ and that the fourth component is ict. Similarly, the differential of $\mathbb{X}$ is a four vector:

$$d\mathbb{X} = (d\mathbf{x}, ic\, dt) \tag{13.29}$$

Now, in Minkowski space the four-dimensional element of length is an *invariant* (i.e., the magnitude is unaffected by a Lorentz transformation):

$$ds = \sqrt{dx_\mu\, dx_\mu} = \sqrt{dx_j\, dx_j - c^2\, dt^2} \tag{13.30}$$

Further, the quantity

$$\begin{aligned} d\tau &= \sqrt{dt^2 - \frac{1}{c^2}\, dx_j\, dx_j} \\ &= \frac{i}{c}\sqrt{dx_\mu\, dx_\mu} \end{aligned} \tag{13.31}$$

is an invariant since it is simply i/c times the element of length ds. The quantity $d\tau$ is called the element of *proper time* in Minkowski space. The ratio of the four-vector $d\mathbb{X}$ to the invariant $d\tau$ is therefore also a four-vector, called the *four-vector velocity* $\mathbb{U}$:

$$\begin{aligned} \mathbb{U} &= \frac{d\mathbb{X}}{d\tau} \\ &= \left(\frac{d\mathbf{x}}{d\tau},\ ic\frac{dt}{d\tau}\right) \end{aligned} \tag{13.32}$$

Now, the components of the ordinary velocity* $\mathbf{u}$ of a particle are

$$u_j = \frac{dx_j}{dt} \tag{13.33}$$

* The symbol $\mathbf{v}$ is in general used to indicate the relative velocity of *coordinate systems*; $\mathbf{u}$ is reserved for *particle* velocities. Sometimes the two quantities will be equal; that is, we sometimes attach the K' system to the particle.

so that $d\tau$ may be expressed as

$$d\tau = dt\sqrt{1 - \frac{1}{c^2}\frac{dx_j dx_j}{dt^2}}$$

$$= dt\sqrt{1 - \frac{u^2}{c^2}} \tag{13.34}$$

Therefore,

$$\boxed{\mathbb{U} = \left(\frac{\mathbf{u}}{\sqrt{1 - \dfrac{u^2}{c^2}}}, \frac{ic}{\sqrt{1 - \dfrac{u^2}{c^2}}}\right)} \tag{13.35}$$

That is, the components of the four-vector velocity are

$$U_j = \frac{u_j}{\sqrt{1 - \dfrac{u^2}{c^2}}}, \qquad U_4 = \frac{ic}{\sqrt{1 - \dfrac{u^2}{c^2}}} \tag{13.35a}$$

In Newtonian mechanics the momentum of a particle is obtained by taking the product of its mass and its velocity. We may do the same in relativistic mechanics, but in order that the "mass" of the particle be truly a characteristic of the *particle* and not of its velocity in some arbitrary reference frame, the "mass" must be that measured in the frame of reference in which the particle is at rest, i.e., the particle's *rest frame* (or *proper frame*). We call this mass the *rest mass* (or *proper mass*) of the particle and denote it by m_0. The four-vector momentum is therefore

$$\mathbb{P} = \left(\frac{m_0\mathbf{u}}{\sqrt{1 - \dfrac{u^2}{c^2}}}, \frac{im_0 c}{\sqrt{1 - \dfrac{u^2}{c^2}}}\right) \tag{13.36}$$

If we define

$$m \equiv \frac{m_0}{\sqrt{1 - \dfrac{u^2}{c^2}}} \tag{13.37}$$

then the space components of $\mathbb{P}$ are just those of ordinary momentum $\mathbf{p}$:

$$P_j = mu_j = p_j; \qquad P_4 = imc \tag{13.38}$$

Therefore, if we wish to interpret the momentum of a particle in the customary sense, the mass is no longer an invariant but depends upon its velocity in the particular reference frame.* Thus, the covariant formulation of momentum leads immediately to the variation of mass with velocity [Eq. (13.37)]. It should be emphasized that it is the *inertial mass m* which is a function of the velocity.

Next, by taking the time derivative of the three space components of the momentum, we obtain the equations of motion from $F_j = \dot{p}_j$. Thus,

$$\boxed{\mathbf{F} = \frac{d}{dt}\left(\frac{m_0\mathbf{u}}{\sqrt{1 - \frac{u^2}{c^2}}}\right)} \tag{13.39}$$

where $\mathbf{F}$ is the three-dimensional force vector.

The relativistic relation for energy may be derived by noting that $\mathbf{F}\cdot\mathbf{u}$ is just the work done on the particle by the force per unit time and is equal to the time rate of change of the kinetic energy T. Using Eq. (13.39),

$$\mathbf{F}\cdot\mathbf{u} = \frac{dT}{dt} = \mathbf{u}\cdot\frac{d}{dt}\left(\frac{m_0\mathbf{u}}{\sqrt{1 - \frac{u^2}{c^2}}}\right) \tag{13.40}$$

It is easily verified by direct calculation that this expression is equivalent to

$$\frac{dT}{dt} = m_0c^2\frac{d}{dt}\left(\frac{1}{\sqrt{1 - \frac{u^2}{c^2}}}\right) \tag{13.40a}$$

If we integrate this equation with respect to time, we obtain

$$\begin{aligned}\int_{t_1}^{t_2}\frac{dT}{dt}\,dt &= T_2 - T_1\\ &= \left.\frac{m_0c^2}{\sqrt{1 - \frac{u^2}{c^2}}}\right|_{t_1}^{t_2}\end{aligned} \tag{13.41}$$

If we take t_1 to correspond to the time at which the particle was at rest, the kinetic energy T may be written in general form as

$$T = \frac{m_0c^2}{\sqrt{1 - \frac{u^2}{c^2}}} - m_0c^2 \tag{13.42}$$

* This result was first obtained by Lorentz in 1904, but under very special assumptions that are not necessary in Einsteinian relativity theory.

The first term in this expression is just c^2 times the mass m defined by Eq. (13.37) so that

$$\boxed{T = mc^2 - m_0c^2} \tag{13.42a}$$

That is, the kinetic energy T is the difference between mc^2 and the *rest energy* m_0c^2. Hence, the quantity mc^2 is interpreted as the total energy W of the particle:

$$W(\text{total energy}) = mc^2 = T(\text{kinetic energy}) + m_0c^2(\text{rest energy}) \tag{13.43}$$

This is the simplest example of the equivalence of mass and energy, a result which is of paramount importance in all theories and applications of nuclear physics.*

If, in Eq. (13.42), we have $u \ll c$, we may expand the radical and obtain

$$\begin{aligned} T &= m_0c^2\left[1 + \frac{1}{2}\left(\frac{u}{c}\right)^2 + \frac{3}{8}\left(\frac{u}{c}\right)^4 + \cdots\right] - m_0c^2 \\ &= \frac{1}{2}m_0u^2 + \frac{3}{8}m_0\frac{u^4}{c^2} + \cdots \end{aligned} \tag{13.44}$$

For sufficiently small velocities, only the first term is significant, and the relation becomes the same as the Newtonian result $T = \frac{1}{2}m_0u^2$ to a high degree of accuracy.

According to Eq. (13.43), the fourth component of the momentum may be expressed as

$$P_4 = \frac{im_0c}{\sqrt{1 - \dfrac{u^2}{c^2}}} = imc = i\frac{W}{c} \tag{13.45}$$

Therefore, the four-vector momentum may be written as

$$\begin{aligned} \mathbb{P} &= m_0\mathbb{U} \\ &= \left(\mathbf{p}, i\frac{W}{c}\right) \end{aligned} \tag{13.46}$$

Thus, in relativity theory, momentum and energy are linked in a manner similar to that which joins the concepts of space and time.

As far as applications of the Lorentz transformation are concerned, we shall confine our attention in this chapter to electromagnetic effects. Some examples in mechanics are contained in Marion (Ma65a, Chapters 4, 9, and 11) and in the Suggested References.

* The mass-energy relation was first obtained by Einstein in 1905.

13.5 Four-Vectors in Electrodynamics

Having established some of the basic formalism of relativity theory, we now turn our attention exclusively to electromagnetic matters.

In ordinary three-dimensional space the gradient operator is

$$\mathbf{grad} \equiv \mathbf{e}_j \frac{\partial}{\partial x_j} \tag{13.47}$$

We may also define a four-dimensional gradient operator according to*

$$\begin{aligned} \mathbf{Grad} &\equiv \mathbf{e}_j \frac{\partial}{\partial x_j} - \frac{i}{c}\mathbf{e}_4 \frac{\partial}{\partial t} \\ &= \mathbf{e}_\mu \frac{\partial}{\partial x_\mu} \end{aligned} \tag{13.47a}$$

By forming the scalar product of **Grad** with itself, we obtain the four-dimensional version of the Laplacian operator, the so-called *d'Alembertian operator*, denoted by $\Box^2$:

$$\begin{aligned} \Box^2 &= \frac{\partial^2}{\partial x_\mu \partial x_\mu} \\ &= \frac{\partial^2}{\partial x_j \partial x_j} - \frac{1}{c^2}\frac{\partial^2}{\partial t^2} \\ &= \nabla^2 - \frac{1}{c^2}\frac{\partial^2}{\partial t^2} \end{aligned} \tag{13.48}$$

Therefore, the wave equation

$$\nabla^2 \Psi - \frac{1}{c^2}\frac{\partial^2 \Psi}{\partial t^2} = 0 \tag{13.49}$$

may be expressed as

$$\Box^2 \Psi = 0 \tag{13.49a}$$

Clearly, $\Box^2$ is a Lorentz-invariant operator.

The mathematical statement of the experimental fact that charge is conserved is contained in the continuity equation [Eq. (4.4)]:

$$\operatorname{div} \mathbf{J} + \frac{\partial \rho}{\partial t} = 0 \tag{13.50}$$

* Capitalized differential operators indicate four-dimensional quantities.

In relativity theory it is clear that current density and charge density cannot be distinct and completely separable entities since a charge distribution that is static in one reference frame will appear to be a current distribution in a moving reference frame. Therefore, we group together the current density **J** and the charge density ρ according to

$$\boxed{\mathbb{J} = (\mathbf{J}, ic\rho)} \tag{13.51}$$

Then the scalar product of the four-dimensional gradient operator and $\mathbb{J}$ is

$$\frac{\partial J_\mu}{\partial x_\mu} = \frac{\partial J_j}{\partial x_j} + \frac{\partial(ic\rho)}{\partial(ict)}$$

$$= \operatorname{div}\mathbf{J} + \frac{\partial\rho}{\partial t} = 0$$

Therefore, the continuity equation may be expressed in four-dimensional form as

$$\boxed{\mathrm{Div}\,\mathbb{J} = 0} \tag{13.52}$$

where Div is the four-dimensional divergence operator.*

In writing Eq. (13.51) there is the implicit assumption that $\mathbb{J}$ is a four-vector as defined in Section 13.4. We shall now show that this is actually the case. In the reference system K, in which the charge is all at rest, an element of charge dq is given by the product of the charge density ρ_0 and an element of volume dV:

$$dq = \rho_0\, dV, \qquad \text{in } K$$

If charge is to be conserved, then the charge dq, when viewed from a moving system K', will remain unchanged; that is,

$$dq = \rho_0\, dV = \rho\, dV' = dq'$$

where ρ_0 and ρ are the charge densities in K and in K', respectively, and where

$$dV = dx_1\, dx_2\, dx_3, \qquad \text{in } K$$

$$dV' = dx_1'\, dx_2'\, dx_3', \qquad \text{in } K'$$

* The four-dimensional gradient operator is frequently represented by $\square$ (in analogy with ∇ for the three-dimensional case); therefore, the divergence operator is $\mathrm{Div} = \square\cdot$, and $\square^2 = \square\cdot\square$.

Now, if K' moves along the x_3-axis of K with a velocity $\mathbf{v} = (0, 0, v)$, then $dx'_1 = dx_1$ and $dx'_2 = dx_2$; but, as may be seen from Eq. (13.25), $dx'_3 = dx_3\sqrt{1-\beta^2}$. (This is the so-called *FitzGerald–Lorentz contraction of length* in the direction of motion.*) Therefore,

$$\begin{aligned}\rho_0\, dV &= \rho\, dV' = \rho\, dx'_1\, dx'_2\, dx'_3 \\ &= \rho\, dx_1\, dx_2\, dx_3\sqrt{1-\beta^2} \\ &= \rho\, dV\sqrt{1-\beta^2}\end{aligned}$$

Hence,

$$\rho = \frac{\rho_0}{\sqrt{1-\beta^2}} \tag{13.53}$$

Thus, the charge density ρ in a moving system is related to the proper charge density in the same way that mass and proper mass are related. The conservation law therefore applies to *total charge*, but not to *charge density*. Since the ordinary current density is given by $\mathbf{J} = \rho\mathbf{u}$, the quantity $\mathbb{J}$ may be expressed as

$$\begin{aligned}\mathbb{J} &= (\mathbf{J}, ic\rho) \\ &= (\rho\mathbf{u}, ic\rho) \\ &= \rho_0\left(\frac{\mathbf{u}}{\sqrt{1-\beta^2}}, \frac{ic}{\sqrt{1-\beta^2}}\right)\end{aligned}$$

That is,

$$\boxed{\mathbb{J} = \rho_0\mathbb{U}} \tag{13.54}$$

Since ρ_0 is a scalar invariant and $\mathbb{U}$ is a four-vector, $\mathbb{J}$ must possess the transformation properties of $\mathbb{U}$ and must therefore be a four-vector.

We have previously found it convenient to represent the magnetic field vector $\mathbf{B}$ as the curl of the vector potential $\mathbf{A}$. Since $\mathbf{A}$ is not completely determined by the specification of its curl alone, we are at liberty to choose the divergence of $\mathbf{A}$; that is, we choose a *gauge* for the potential. A particularly useful choice is the Lorentz gauge [Eq. (4.26)] in which

$$\operatorname{div}\mathbf{A} + \frac{1}{c}\frac{\partial\Phi}{dt} = 0 \tag{13.55}$$

* Consider a length increment $\Delta x'_3$ and transform the end points to the K system. Then in the limit $\Delta x'_3 \to 0$, one finds $dx'_3 = dx_3\sqrt{1-\beta^2}$. See Marion [Ma65a, Example 4.5(a)].

If we define

$$\boxed{\mathbb{A} = (\mathbf{A}, i\Phi)} \tag{13.56}$$

the Lorentz condition is expressed as

$$\boxed{\operatorname{Div} \mathbb{A} = 0} \tag{13.57}$$

In free space the potentials **A** and **Φ** satisfy inhomogeneous wave equations [see Eqs. (4.34) and (4.35)]:

$$\nabla^2 \mathbf{A} - \frac{1}{c^2}\frac{\partial^2 \mathbf{A}}{\partial t^2} = -\frac{4\pi}{c}\mathbf{J} \tag{13.58a}$$

$$\nabla^2 \Phi - \frac{1}{c^2}\frac{\partial^2 \Phi}{\partial t^2} = -4\pi\rho \tag{13.58b}$$

By using the four-vector potential $\mathbb{A}$ and the four-vector current density $\mathbb{J}$, these two equations may be expressed simply as

$$\boxed{\Box^2 \mathbb{A} = -\frac{4\pi}{c}\mathbb{J}} \tag{13.59}$$

The space portion of this equation is just Eq. (13.58a) and the fourth component is Eq. (13.58b). From Eq. (13.59) it is clear that $\mathbb{A}$ is indeed a four-vector since $\mathbb{J}$ is a four-vector and the operator $\Box^2$ is Lorentz invariant.

13.6 The Electromagnetic Field Tensor

The electromagnetic field vectors **E** and **B** may be written in terms of the potentials as

$$\mathbf{E} = -\mathbf{grad}\,\Phi - \frac{1}{c}\frac{\partial \mathbf{A}}{\partial t} \tag{13.60a}$$

$$\mathbf{B} = \mathbf{curl}\,\mathbf{A} \tag{13.60b}$$

The vectors **E** and **B** are not four-vectors, but the six components, E_1, E_2, E_3, B_1, B_2, B_3, may be used to define an antisymmetrical tensor (called the *electromagnetic field tensor*) in the following way. Consider

$$E_1 = -\frac{\partial \Phi}{\partial x_1} - \frac{1}{c}\frac{\partial A_1}{\partial t}$$

$$= -\frac{1}{i}\frac{\partial A_4}{\partial x_1} + \frac{1}{i}\frac{\partial A_1}{\partial x_4}$$

or,

$$iE_1 = \frac{\partial A_1}{\partial x_4} - \frac{\partial A_4}{\partial x_1}$$

and similarly for E_2 and E_3. The components of **B** are

$$B_1 = \frac{\partial A_3}{\partial x_2} - \frac{\partial A_2}{\partial x_3}$$

and similarly for B_2 and B_3. Now define a set of quantities

$$\boxed{F_{\mu\nu} \equiv \frac{\partial A_\nu}{\partial x_\mu} - \frac{\partial A_\mu}{\partial x_\nu}} \tag{13.61}$$

so that

$$\left.\begin{aligned} iE_1 &= F_{41} \\ B_1 &= F_{23}, \qquad \text{etc.} \end{aligned}\right\}$$

Calculating all of the components, the tensor $\{\mathbf{F}\}$ whose elements are $F_{\mu\nu}$ becomes

$$\{\mathbf{F}\} = \begin{Bmatrix} 0 & B_3 & -B_2 & -iE_1 \\ -B_3 & 0 & B_1 & -iE_2 \\ B_2 & -B_1 & 0 & -iE_3 \\ iE_1 & iE_2 & iE_3 & 0 \end{Bmatrix} \tag{13.62}$$

According to its definition [Eq. (13.61)], the field tensor must be antisymmetric since

$$F_{\mu\nu} = -F_{\nu\mu} \qquad \text{and} \qquad F_{\mu\mu} = 0 \qquad \text{(no summation)}$$

By using the electromagnetic field tensor, Maxwell's equations may be expressed in a particularly simple and elegant way. Consider the equation

$$\boxed{\frac{\partial F_{\lambda\mu}}{\partial x_\nu} + \frac{\partial F_{\mu\nu}}{\partial x_\lambda} + \frac{\partial F_{\nu\lambda}}{\partial x_\mu} = 0} \tag{13.63}$$

If we choose λ, μ, ν to be any combination of 1, 2, 3, then Eq. (13.63) always reduces to

$$\frac{\partial F_{12}}{\partial x_3} + \frac{\partial F_{23}}{\partial x_1} + \frac{\partial F_{31}}{\partial x_2} = 0$$

or,

$$\frac{\partial B_3}{\partial x_3} + \frac{\partial B_1}{\partial x_1} + \frac{\partial B_2}{\partial x_2} = 0$$

which is the Maxwell equation

$$\operatorname{div} \mathbf{B} = 0$$

Similarly, if we set one of the indices λ, μ, ν equal to 4, then we obtain one component of

$$\mathbf{curl}\, \mathbf{E} + \frac{1}{c}\frac{\partial \mathbf{B}}{\partial t} = 0$$

For example, let $\lambda = 1$, $\mu = 2$, $\nu = 4$. Then, Eq. (13.63) becomes

$$\frac{\partial F_{12}}{\partial x_4} + \frac{\partial F_{24}}{\partial x_1} + \frac{\partial F_{41}}{\partial x_2} = 0$$

$$\frac{\partial B_3}{\partial (ict)} + \frac{\partial (-iE_2)}{\partial x_1} + \frac{\partial (iE_1)}{\partial x_2} = 0$$

$$\frac{1}{c}\frac{\partial B_3}{\partial t} + \frac{\partial E_2}{\partial x_1} - \frac{\partial F_1}{\partial x_2} = 0$$

or,

$$(\mathbf{curl}\, \mathbf{E})_3 + \frac{1}{c}\frac{\partial B_3}{\partial t} = 0$$

Therefore, we find that the two homogeneous Maxwell equations are represented by Eq. (13.63). The two inhomogeneous equations may be obtained from

$$\boxed{\frac{\partial F_{\mu\nu}}{\partial x_\nu} = \frac{4\pi}{c} J_\mu} \tag{13.64}$$

Consider $\mu = 1$:

$$\frac{\partial F_{1\nu}}{\partial x_\nu} = \frac{4\pi}{c} J_1$$

$$\frac{\partial F_{11}}{\partial x_1} + \frac{\partial F_{12}}{\partial x_2} + \frac{\partial F_{13}}{\partial x_3} + \frac{\partial F_{14}}{\partial (ict)} = \frac{4\pi}{c} J_1$$

$$0 + \frac{\partial B_3}{\partial x_2} - \frac{\partial B_2}{\partial x_3} - \frac{1}{c}\frac{\partial E_1}{\partial t} = \frac{4\pi}{c} J_1$$

or,

$$(\mathbf{curl\,B})_1 - \frac{1}{c}\frac{\partial E_1}{\partial t} = \frac{4\pi}{c} J_1$$

so that in general we have

$$\mathbf{curl\,B} - \frac{1}{c}\frac{\partial \mathbf{E}}{\partial t} = \frac{4\pi}{c}\mathbf{J}$$

For $\mu = 4$, we find in a similar way,

$$\text{div}\,\mathbf{E} = 4\pi\rho$$

Thus, the four Maxwell equations are represented by only two equations involving operations on the components of the field tensor.

We may take the divergence of Eq. (13.64) by differentiating with respect to x_μ and summing over μ:

$$\frac{\partial^2 F_{\mu\nu}}{\partial x_\mu \partial x_\nu} = \frac{4\pi}{c}\frac{\partial J_\mu}{\partial x_\mu}$$

Since $\{\mathbf{F}\}$ is antisymmetric, the left-hand side of this equation may be written as

$$\frac{\partial^2 F_{\mu\nu}}{\partial x_\mu \partial x_\nu} = -\frac{\partial^2 F_{\nu\mu}}{\partial x_\mu \partial x_\nu}$$

and by interchanging the dummy indices μ and ν on the right-hand side of this expression, we have

$$\frac{\partial^2 F_{\mu\nu}}{\partial x_\mu \partial x_\nu} = -\frac{\partial^2 F_{\mu\nu}}{\partial x_\mu \partial x_\nu}$$

The only condition under which a quantity may equal the negative of itself is for the quantity to vanish identically. We therefore conclude that

$$\frac{\partial J_\mu}{\partial x_\mu} = 0$$

or,

$$\text{Div } \mathbb{J} = 0$$

Thus, the continuity equation is recovered from the field equations. (Compare the similar calculation in Section 4.4.)

In this section we simply asserted Eq. (13.64) and then showed that it represented two of the Maxwell equations. In Section 13.12 we will demonstrate that Eq. (13.64) can be derived from a Lagrangian formulation of the electromagnetic field problem.

13.7 Transformation Properties of the Field Tensor

If the field equations are to be covariant with respect to Lorentz transformations, it is, of course, necessary that the field tensor components $F_{\mu\nu}$ have the same form in all Lorentz reference frames. That is, if

$$F_{\mu\nu} = \frac{\partial A_\nu}{\partial x_\mu} - \frac{\partial A_\mu}{\partial x_\nu} \quad \text{in } K \tag{13.65a}$$

then we must also have

$$F'_{\mu\nu} = \frac{\partial A'_\nu}{\partial x'_\mu} - \frac{\partial A'_\mu}{\partial x'_\nu} \quad \text{in } K' \tag{13.65b}$$

This requirement specifies the manner in which the $F_{\mu\nu}$ behave under a Lorentz transformation, as may be shown as follows.

First, we recall the way in which $\mathbb{X}$ and $\mathbb{A}$ transform:

$$\left.\begin{aligned} x'_\mu &= \lambda_{\mu\sigma} x_\sigma \\ A'_\nu &= \lambda_{\nu\rho} A_\rho \end{aligned}\right\} \tag{13.66}$$

The inverse transformation of $\mathbb{X}$ is

$$x_\sigma = \lambda_{\mu\sigma} x'_\mu \tag{13.66a}$$

so that

$$\frac{\partial x_\sigma}{\partial x'_\mu} = \lambda_{\mu\sigma} \tag{13.67}$$

Therefore,

$$\begin{aligned} F'_{\mu\nu} &= \frac{\partial A'_\nu}{\partial x'_\mu} - \frac{\partial A'_\mu}{\partial x'_\nu} \\ &= \lambda_{\nu\rho} \frac{\partial A_\rho}{\partial x_\sigma} \frac{\partial x_\sigma}{\partial x'_\mu} - \lambda_{\mu\sigma} \frac{\partial A_\sigma}{\partial x_\rho} \frac{\partial x_\rho}{\partial x'_\nu} \end{aligned}$$

Using Eq. (13.67), this equation becomes

$$F'_{\mu\nu} = \lambda_{\mu\sigma}\lambda_{\nu\rho}\frac{\partial A_\rho}{\partial x_\sigma} - \lambda_{\mu\sigma}\lambda_{\nu\rho}\frac{\partial A_\sigma}{\partial x_\rho}$$

$$= \lambda_{\mu\sigma}\lambda_{\nu\rho}\left(\frac{\partial A_\rho}{\partial x_\sigma} - \frac{\partial A_\sigma}{\partial x_\rho}\right)$$

or,

$$\boxed{F'_{\mu\nu} = \lambda_{\mu\sigma}\lambda_{\nu\rho}F_{\sigma\rho}} \qquad (13.68)$$

components under a Lorentz transformation.* We may alternatively express the result in terms of the transposed Lorentz matrix:

$$F'_{\mu\nu} = \lambda_{\mu\sigma}F_{\sigma\rho}\lambda^t_{\rho\nu} \qquad (13.68a)$$

If F represents the matrix composed of the elements of the tensor $\{\mathbf{F}\}$, then Eq. (13.68a) may be expressed as a matrix equation:

$$\mathsf{F}' = \boldsymbol{\lambda}\mathsf{F}\boldsymbol{\lambda}^t \qquad (13.69)$$

Equation (13.68) may be used to compute the field vector components in moving reference systems. For example, the component B'_1 in K' is

$$B'_1 = F'_{23} = \lambda_{2\sigma}\lambda_{3\rho}F_{\sigma\rho}$$

Using Eq. (13.23) for the elements of $\boldsymbol{\lambda}$, we find that the only nonvanishing terms in the summation are

$$B'_1 = \lambda_{22}\lambda_{33}F_{23} + \lambda_{22}\lambda_{34}F_{24}$$

$$= \gamma B_1 + \beta\gamma E_2$$

The other components of $\mathbf{E}'$ and $\mathbf{B}'$ may be calculated in the same manner.

It is instructive to obtain all of the individual results simultaneously by computing the matrix F' from Eq. (13.69):

$$\mathsf{F}' = \begin{pmatrix} 1 & 0 & 0 & 0 \\ 0 & 1 & 0 & 0 \\ 0 & 0 & \gamma & i\beta\gamma \\ 0 & 0 & -i\beta\gamma & \gamma \end{pmatrix} \begin{pmatrix} 0 & B_3 & -B_2 & -iE_1 \\ -B_3 & 0 & B_1 & -iE_2 \\ B_2 & -B_1 & 0 & -iE_3 \\ iE_1 & iE_2 & iE_3 & 0 \end{pmatrix} \begin{pmatrix} 1 & 0 & 0 & 0 \\ 0 & 1 & 0 & 0 \\ 0 & 0 & \gamma & -i\beta\gamma \\ 0 & 0 & i\beta\gamma & \gamma \end{pmatrix}$$

* The field tensor $\{\mathbf{F}\}$ follows, of course, the general tensor transformation equation; see Section A.6, Appendix A.

Carrying out the matrix multiplication, we find

$$
\mathsf{F}' = \begin{pmatrix} 0 & B_3 & -\gamma(B_2 - \beta E_1) & -i\gamma(E_1 - \beta B_2) \\ -B_3 & 0 & \gamma(B_1 + \beta E_2) & -i\gamma(E_2 + \beta B_1) \\ \gamma(B_2 - \beta E_1) & -\gamma(B_1 + \beta E_2) & 0 & -iE_3 \\ i\gamma(E_1 - \beta B_2) & i\gamma(E_2 + \beta B_1) & iE_3 & 0 \end{pmatrix}
$$

$$
= \begin{pmatrix} 0 & B_3' & -B_2' & -iE_1' \\ -B_3' & 0 & B_1' & -iE_2' \\ B_2' & -B_1' & 0 & -iE_3' \\ iE_1' & iE_3' & iE_3' & 0 \end{pmatrix} \tag{13.70}
$$

These results may be summarized by

$$
\boxed{\begin{array}{ll} E_1' = \gamma(E_1 - \beta E_2) & B_1' = \gamma(B_1 + \beta E_2) \\ E_2' = \gamma(E_2 + \beta B_1) & B_2' = \gamma(B_2 - \beta E_1) \\ E_3' = E_3 & B_3' = B_3 \end{array}} \tag{13.71}
$$

We may condense these equations even further if we decompose the field vectors into components parallel to and perpendicular to the direction of motion. If the motion of the K' system with respect to the K system is described by a velocity vector $\mathbf{v}$, then (see Problem 13-9)

$$
\left.\begin{array}{ll} \mathbf{E}_\perp' = \gamma\left(\mathbf{E}_\perp + \dfrac{1}{c}\mathbf{v} \times \mathbf{B}_\perp\right); & \mathbf{E}_\parallel' = \mathbf{E}_\parallel \\[2ex] \mathbf{B}_\perp' = \gamma\left(\mathbf{B}_\perp - \dfrac{1}{c}\mathbf{v} \times \mathbf{E}_\perp\right); & \mathbf{B}_\parallel' = \mathbf{B}_\parallel \end{array}\right\} \tag{13.72}
$$

It is apparent from these results that electric and magnetic fields have no independent existence. A pure $\mathbf{E}$ field in K transforms into $\mathbf{E}$ and $\mathbf{B}$ fields in K'. But no velocity $v < c$ allows a pure $\mathbf{B}$ field in K'; i.e., if a Lorentz frame exists in which the field is entirely electric, it is impossible to find another Lorentz frame in which the field is entirely magnetic.

13.8 Electric Field of a Point Charge in Uniform Motion

If a charge q is at rest at the origin of system K, in that system the electric field vector is

$$\mathbf{E} = q\frac{\mathbf{r}}{r^3} \tag{13.73}$$

We wish to calculate the electric field as it appears to an observer in another system K' which moves with uniform velocity v along the x_3-axis of K. For convenience we consider the field observed in K' at the instant the two origins coincide; call this instant $t = 0$. Since $\mathbf{B} = 0$ in K, Eqs. (13.71) shows that in K' we have

$$E_1' = \gamma E_1; \qquad E_2' = \gamma E_2; \qquad E_3' = E_3 \tag{13.74}$$

At $t = 0$, the coordinates are (by the inverse transformation)

$$x_1 = x_1'; \qquad x_2 = x_2'; \qquad x_3 = \gamma x_3' \tag{13.75}$$

Therefore, the distance r from the origin to the observation point P (see Fig. 13-2) is

$$r = \sqrt{x_j x_j} = \sqrt{x_1'^2 + x_2'^2 + \gamma^2 x_3'^2} \tag{13.76}$$

so that the components of the electric field vector $\mathbf{E}'$ in K' are

$$E_j' = q\gamma \frac{x_j'}{(x_1'^2 + x_2'^2 + \gamma^2 x_3'^2)^{\frac{3}{2}}}$$

or,

$$\mathbf{E}' = q\gamma \frac{\mathbf{r}'}{(x_1'^2 + x_2'^2 + \gamma^2 x_3'^2)^{\frac{3}{2}}} \tag{13.77}$$

Now, the projection of the vector $\mathbf{r}'$ onto the x_3'-axis is (see Fig. 13-2)

$$x_3' = r' \cos\theta$$

and also

$$x_1'^2 + x_2'^2 + x_3'^2 = r'^2$$

Hence,

$$x_1'^2 + x_2'^2 = r'^2 \sin^2\theta$$

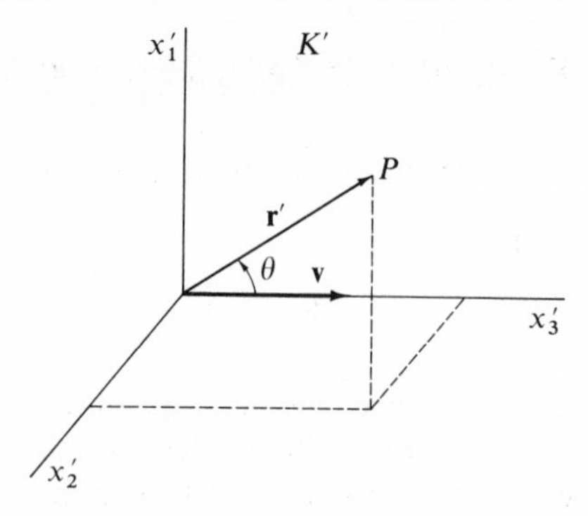

FIG. 13-2

Therefore,

$$x_1'^2 + x_2'^2 + \gamma^2 x_3'^2 = r'^2 \sin^2\theta + \gamma^2 r'^2 \cos^2\theta$$

$$= r'^2\left(\sin^2\theta + \frac{1}{1-\beta^2}\cos^2\theta\right)$$

$$= \gamma^2 r'^2(1-\beta^2\sin^2\theta) \tag{13.78}$$

and the field vector becomes

$$\mathbf{E}' = q\frac{(1-\beta^2)\mathbf{r}'}{r'^3(1-\beta^2\sin^2\theta)^{\frac{3}{2}}} \tag{13.79}$$

which is identical with the result obtained from considerations of the Liénard-Wiechert potentials [Eq. (7.55)]. The field patterns of Fig. 7-3 therefore apply to the present case as well.

This problem is just one illustration of the fact that Maxwellian electrodynamics, as developed without regard to relativistic concepts, is relativistically correct. The expression for the electric field of a moving charge which was obtained so laboriously by the Liénard-Wiechert method, follows simply and elegantly from relativity theory.

13.9 Magnetic Field due to an Infinitely Long Wire Carrying a Uniform Current

Consider an infinite linear array of charges arranged along the x_3-axis of system K in which all of the charges are at rest. If there is a uniform linear charge density ρ_l in K, then in any element of length dx_3 there is a charge $\rho_l\,dx_3$. According to the law of charge conservation there is an equal amount of charge contained in the interval dx'_3 in a system K' which is in uniform motion (along the x_3-axis) with respect to K:

$$\rho_l \, dx_3 = \rho'_l \, dx'_3$$

In K, there is no magnetic field, so that in K' we have, according to Eqs. (13.71),

$$B'_1 = \gamma\beta E_2; \qquad B'_2 = -\gamma\beta E_1; \qquad B'_3 = 0 \tag{13.80}$$

Therefore, the magnetic field due to the element of moving charge $\rho'_l \, dx'_3$ in K' is

$$\begin{aligned} dB' &= \sqrt{dB'^2_1 + dB'^2_2} \\ &= \gamma\beta\sqrt{dE_1^2 + dE_2^2} \end{aligned} \tag{13.81}$$

Using the results of the preceding section, we have

$$\begin{aligned} dB' &= \gamma\beta\rho'_l \, dx'_3 \frac{\sqrt{x_1^2 + x_2^2}}{r^3} \\ &= \gamma\beta\rho'_l \, dx'_3 \frac{\sqrt{x'^2_1 + x'^2_2}}{(x'^2_1 + x'^2_2 + \gamma^2 x'^2_3)^{\frac{3}{2}}} \end{aligned} \tag{13.82}$$

The total field B' is obtained by integrating Eq. (13.82) over the entire (infinite) length of the charge distribution:

$$\begin{aligned} B' &= \gamma\beta\rho'_l\sqrt{x'^2_1 + x'^2_2}\int_{-\infty}^{+\infty} \frac{dx'_3}{(x'^2_1 + x'^2_2 + \gamma^2 x'^2_3)^{\frac{3}{2}}} \\ &= \frac{2\beta\rho'_l}{\sqrt{x'^2_1 + x'^2_2}} \end{aligned} \tag{13.83}$$

Now, in K' the magnitude of the total current is

$$I' = \rho'_l u \tag{13.84}$$

The perpendicular distance from the line of moving charge (the x'_3-axis) to a point at a distance r'_0 is

$$r'_0 = \sqrt{x'^2_1 + x'^2_2} \tag{13.85}$$

Using Eqs. (13.84) and (13.85) in the expression for B', we have, finally,

$$B' = \frac{2I'}{cr'_0} \tag{13.86}$$

This is the familiar result that may be obtained from Ampère's law or the Biot-Savart law. The prediction of these laws is therefore relativistically exact and requires no approximation regarding the magnitude of velocity of the charges (see also Problem 7-4).

13.10 Radiation by an Accelerated Charge

In Chapter 7 we investigated the radiation produced by moving charges, and we were able to conclude that only charges undergoing acceleration could produce radiation. In particular, we found that the rate of radiation by slow-moving charges ($u \ll c$) is proportional to the square of the acceleration. This result is embodied in the Larmor formula for the radiated power [Eq. (7.68)]:

$$P = \frac{2e^2a^2}{3c^3} \tag{13.87}$$

This formula is valid only in the event that the relative velocity of the charge and the observer is small. The formula is *exact*, however, in the reference frame that is instantaneously at rest with respect to the charge. Since the charge is accelerating, a reference frame at rest with respect to the charge is not a Lorentz frame. But, *at any given instant*, a Lorentz frame can be found that corresponds to the rest frame. Therefore, an exact expression for the radiation observed in any reference frame K may be obtained by calculating the radiation in the instantaneous rest frame K' according to the Larmor formula and then transforming the result from K' to K by means of the standard relativistic equations. This procedure necessitates finding the transformation equations for acceleration, which we may accomplish as follows.

According to Eq. (13.35), the four-vector velocity is

$$\mathbb{U} = \left(\frac{\mathbf{u}}{\sqrt{1-\dfrac{u^2}{c^2}}}, \frac{ic}{\sqrt{1-\dfrac{u^2}{c^2}}}\right) \tag{13.88}$$

We may define a new four-vector by

$$\mathbb{D} \equiv d\mathbb{U}/d\tau \tag{13.89}$$

(A physical interpretation of $\mathbb{D}$ is unnecessary in this calculation, but it is clearly the four-vector acceleration.) Carrying out the differentiation, we find

$$\mathbb{D} = \left(\frac{\dot{\mathbf{u}}}{1-\dfrac{u^2}{c^2}} + \frac{\mathbf{u}(\mathbf{u}\cdot\dot{\mathbf{u}})}{c^2\left(1-\dfrac{u^2}{c^2}\right)^2}, \frac{i(\mathbf{u}\cdot\dot{\mathbf{u}})}{c\left(1-\dfrac{u^2}{c^2}\right)^2}\right) \tag{13.90}$$

where $\dot{\mathbf{u}} = d\mathbf{u}/dt$. Since

$$D_4 = \frac{i(\mathbf{u} \cdot \dot{\mathbf{u}})}{c\left(1 - \frac{u^2}{c^2}\right)^2}$$

$\mathbb{D}$ can be written as

$$\mathbb{D} = \left(\frac{\dot{\mathbf{u}}}{1 - \frac{u^2}{c^2}} - i\frac{\mathbf{u}}{c} D_4, \quad D_4 \right) \tag{13.91}$$

This expression for $\mathbb{D}$ is valid in the observer's system K. In the instantaneous rest frame K' the velocity $\mathbf{u}'$ vanishes, so that

$$\mathbb{D}' = (\dot{\mathbf{u}}', 0) \tag{13.92}$$

Now, $\mathbf{u}$ is the velocity of the charge in K and, according to the definition of the instantaneous rest frame, it is also the velocity of K' relative to K. We may orient the axes so that $\mathbf{u} = (0, 0, u)$, and for convenience, we carry out the calculation at the instant designated $t = 0$.

The transformation from K' to K is the inverse of Eq. (13.27), namely,

$$D_\nu = \lambda_{\mu\nu} D'_\mu \tag{13.93}$$

Therefore, using Eqs. (13.92) and (13.93), the components of $\mathbb{D}$ are

$$\left.\begin{aligned} D_1 &= D'_1 = \dot{u}'_1 \\ D_2 &= D'_2 = \dot{u}'_2 \\ D_3 &= \frac{D'_3}{\sqrt{1 - \beta^2}} = \frac{\dot{u}'_3}{\sqrt{1 - \beta^2}} \\ D_4 &= i\beta \frac{D'_3}{\sqrt{1 - \beta^2}} \end{aligned}\right\} \tag{13.94}$$

where $\beta = u/c$. Identifying the components of $\mathbb{D}$ from Eqs. (13.90) and (13.94), we have

$$\left.\begin{aligned} \dot{u}_1 &= \dot{u}'_1(1 - \beta^2) \\ \dot{u}_2 &= \dot{u}'_2(1 - \beta^2) \\ \dot{u}_3 &= \dot{u}'_3(1 - \beta^2)^{3/2} \end{aligned}\right\} \tag{13.95}$$

The square of the acceleration in K' is

$$a'^2 = \dot{u}'_j \dot{u}'_j$$
$$= \frac{\dot{u}_1^2 + \dot{u}_2^2}{(1-\beta^2)^2} + \frac{\dot{u}_3^2}{(1-\beta^2)^3} \tag{13.96}$$

Recalling that $\mathbf{u}$ was chosen to be $(0, 0, u)$, it is easy to verify that a'^2 may be written in general as

$$a'^2 = \frac{1}{(1-\beta^2)^2}\left[\dot{\mathbf{u}}\cdot\dot{\mathbf{u}} + \frac{(\mathbf{u}\cdot\dot{\mathbf{u}})^2}{c^2(1-\beta^2)}\right] \tag{13.97}$$

The radiated power P is given by the rate of energy loss, $-dW/dt$, as observed in K. Similarly, in K' we have $P' = -dW'/dt'$. But W and t are each proportional to the fourth component of a four-vector (momentum $\mathbb{P}$ and position $\mathbb{X}$, respectively) and, therefore, they transform in the same way. It follows that the ratio dW/dt is Lorentz invariant. Thus,

$$P = -\frac{dW}{dt} = -\frac{dW'}{dt'} = P' = \frac{2e^2a'^2}{3c^3} \tag{13.98}$$

Hence, the radiated power observed in K is*

$$P = \frac{2e^2}{3c^3}\cdot\frac{1}{(1-\beta^2)^2}\left[\dot{\mathbf{u}}\cdot\dot{\mathbf{u}} + \frac{(\mathbf{u}\cdot\dot{\mathbf{u}})^2}{c^2(1-\beta^2)}\right] \tag{13.99}$$

This expression for P may be compared with the results obtained in Chapter 7, Sections 7.7 and 7.8:

(a) CO-LINEAR VELOCITY AND ACCELERATION. In this case $(\mathbf{u}\cdot\dot{\mathbf{u}})^2 = \mathrm{u}^2\mathrm{a}^2$, so that Eq. (13.99) reduces to

$$P = \frac{2e^2}{3c^3}\cdot\frac{1}{(1-\beta^2)^2}\left[a^2 + \frac{u^2a^2}{c^2(1-\beta^2)}\right]$$
$$= \frac{2e^2a^2}{3c^3}\cdot\frac{1}{(1-\beta^2)^3}$$

A short calculation shows that this is just the integral over all space of $dP/d\Omega$ given by Eq. (7.78).

(b) PERPENDICULAR VELOCITY AND ACCELERATION. In this case $\mathbf{u}\cdot\dot{\mathbf{u}} = 0$, so that Eq. (13.99) reduces to

$$P = \frac{2e^2a^2}{3c^3}\cdot\frac{1}{(1-\beta^2)^2}$$

* This result was first obtained by Liénard in 1898.

which is just Eq. (7.89) for the power radiated by a charge moving in a circular orbit.

13.11 Motion of a Charged Particle in an Electromagnetic Field—Lagrangian Formulation

In Section 4.10 we found that the Lorentz force equation could be obtained from the Lagrange equations of motion if we use a (nonrelativistic) Lagrangian of the form

$$L = \tfrac{1}{2}m_0 u^2 + \frac{e}{c}\mathbf{u}\cdot\mathbf{A} - e\Phi$$

Now, if there are no forces acting on the particle (i.e., if $\mathbf{A}$ and Φ are zero), then it is easy to verify that the relativistically correct equation of motion can be obtained by using the Lagrangian

$$L = -m_0 c^2\sqrt{1-\beta^2} = -\frac{m_0 c^2}{\gamma}$$

where $\beta^2 = u^2/c^2$. Therefore, we are led to expect that for a relativistic particle in an electromagnetic field the correct Lagrangian is

$$L = -\frac{m_0 c^2}{\gamma} + \frac{e}{c}\mathbf{u}\cdot\mathbf{A} - e\Phi \tag{13.100}$$

Using

$$\mathbb{A} = (\mathbf{A}, i\Phi)$$

and

$$\mathbb{U} = (\gamma\mathbf{u}, i\gamma c)$$

Eq. (13.100) may be expressed as

$$L = \frac{1}{\gamma}\left(-m_0 c^2 + \frac{e}{c}\mathbb{U}\cdot\mathbb{A}\right)$$

$$= \frac{1}{\gamma}\left(-m_0 c^2 + \frac{e}{c}U_\mu A_\mu\right) \tag{13.101}$$

According to Hamilton's Principle of dynamics (or the principle of *least action*), the equations of motion can be obtained from the variational equation*

$$\delta\int_{t_1}^{t_2} L\,dt = 0 \tag{13.102}$$

* The reader unfamiliar with variational methods in dynamics should consult an advanced text on classical mechanics; see, for example, Marion (Ma65a, Chapters 8 and 9).

Since it is desired to find the motion of a particle in a given field described by $\mathbb{A}$, the variation which is indicated by δ is to be a variation only of the coordinates of the particle. That is, the variations δx_μ are independent, but the variations δA_ν are dependent functions of the δx_μ:

$$\delta A_\nu = \frac{\partial A_\nu}{\partial x_\mu}\delta x_\mu \tag{13.103}$$

Now, $dt = \gamma\, d\tau$, so that the variational equation becomes

$$\delta \int_{\tau_1}^{\tau_2} \left(-m_0 c^2 + \frac{e}{c} U_\mu A_\mu\right) d\tau = 0 \tag{13.104}$$

or, using $U_\mu = dx_\mu/d\tau$,

$$\delta \int \left(-m_0 c^2\, d\tau + \frac{e}{c} A_\mu\, dx_\mu\right) = 0 \tag{13.105}$$

Performing the variation, we have

$$\int \left[-m_0 c^2 \delta(d\tau) + \frac{e}{c}\delta A_\nu\, dx_\nu + \frac{e}{c} A_\mu \delta(dx_\mu)\right] = 0 \tag{13.106}$$

Equation (13.31) states that

$$d\tau = \frac{i}{c}\sqrt{dx_\mu\, dx_\mu}$$

from which we calculate the variation

$$\begin{aligned}
\delta(d\tau) &= \frac{\partial \tau}{\partial x_\mu}\delta(dx_\mu) = \frac{\partial \tau}{\partial x_\mu} d(\delta x_\mu) \\
&= \frac{i}{c}\frac{dx_\mu}{\sqrt{dx_\nu\, dx_\nu}} d(\delta x_\mu) \\
&= -\frac{1}{c^2}\frac{dx_\mu}{d\tau} d(\delta x_\mu) \\
&= -\frac{1}{c^2} U_\mu\, d(\delta x_\mu)
\end{aligned} \tag{13.107}$$

Using Eqs. (13.103) and (13.107) in Eq. (13.106), we obtain

$$\int \left\{\left[m_0 U_\mu + \frac{e}{c} A_\mu\right] d(\delta x_\mu) + \frac{e}{c}\frac{\partial A_\nu}{\partial x_\mu}\delta x_\mu\, dx_\nu\right\} = 0 \tag{13.108}$$

The first term may be integrated by parts; the integrated portion is proportional to δx_μ and, since the variation of the coordinates must vanish at the end points of the integral, this term vanishes. There remains

$$\int \left[-\frac{\partial}{\partial x_\nu}\left(m_0 U_\mu + \frac{e}{c} A_\mu \right) + \frac{e}{c}\frac{\partial A_\nu}{\partial x_\mu} \right] \delta x_\mu \, dx_\nu = 0$$

$$\int \left[m_0 \frac{\partial U_\mu}{\partial x_\nu} - \frac{e}{c}\left(\frac{\partial A_\nu}{\partial x_\mu} - \frac{\partial A_\mu}{\partial x_\nu} \right) \right] \delta x_\mu \, dx_\nu = 0$$

$$\int \left[m_0 \frac{\partial U_\mu}{\partial x_\nu} - \frac{e}{c} F_{\mu\nu} \right] \delta x_\mu \, dx_\nu = 0 \qquad (13.109)$$

We may use

$$dx_\nu = U_\nu \, d\tau$$

and

$$\frac{\partial U_\mu}{\partial x_\nu} dx_\nu = dU_\mu = \frac{dU_\mu}{d\tau} d\tau$$

to write Eq. (13.109) as

$$\int_{\tau_1}^{\tau_2} \left[m_0 \frac{dU_\mu}{d\tau} - \frac{e}{c} F_{\mu\nu} U_\nu \right] \delta x_\mu \, d\tau = 0 \qquad (13.110)$$

The variations δx_μ are independent and arbitrary; therefore, the integrand is required to vanish:

$$\boxed{m_0 \frac{dU_\mu}{d\tau} = \frac{e}{c} F_{\mu\nu} U_\nu} \qquad (13.111)$$

which is the desired expression of the equations of motion. We may readily calculate the space portion (i.e., $\mu = 1, 2, 3$) of this equation:

$$\frac{d\mathbf{p}}{dt} = e\left(\mathbf{E} + \frac{1}{c}\mathbf{u} \times \mathbf{B} \right) \qquad (13.112a)$$

where $\mathbf{p} = m_0 \gamma \mathbf{u}$. The fourth component is

$$\frac{dW}{dt} = e\mathbf{E} \cdot \mathbf{u} \qquad (13.112b)$$

where $W = m_0 c^2 \gamma$ is the total energy of the particle [Eq. (13.43)].

We therefore conclude that Eq. (13.111) represents not only the Lorentz force equation (13.112a) but also the fact that the rate of change of energy of the particle is equal to the power supplied the particle by the field (13.112b).

The result given by Eq. (13.111) may also be expressed in a four-vector manner as follows. Consider the four-vector $\mathbb{K}$ that results from the scalar product of $\{\mathsf{F}\}$ and $\mathbb{J}/c$:

$$\mathbb{K} = \frac{1}{c}\{\mathsf{F}\} \cdot \mathbb{J} \tag{13.113}$$

That is,

$$K_\mu = \frac{1}{c} F_{\mu\nu} J_\nu$$

or,

$$\boxed{K_\mu = \frac{1}{4\pi} F_{\mu\nu} \frac{\partial F_{\nu\sigma}}{\partial x_\sigma}} \tag{13.114}$$

where Eq. (13.64) for J_μ has been used. Calculating the components of $\mathbb{K} = (\mathbf{K}, K_4)$, we find

$$\mathbf{K} = \rho\left(\mathbf{E} + \frac{1}{c}\mathbf{u} \times \mathbf{B}\right) \tag{13.115a}$$

$$K_4 = \frac{i}{c}\mathbf{E} \cdot \mathbf{J} \tag{13.115b}$$

The quantity $\mathbb{K}$ is seen to be a four-vector *force density** whose space part represents the rate of change of mechanical momentum per unit volume, and whose time part represents the rate of change of mechanical energy per unit volume (i.e., the rate at which the field does work on the charges per unit volume).

13.12 Lagrangian Formulation of the Field Equations

In the preceding section we assumed the existence of a certain electromagnetic field and calculated the motion of a charged particle in that field. The variation of the so-called *action integral*, $\int L\,dt$, was therefore performed with respect to the *coordinates of the particle* and the equations of motion resulted. If we wish to obtain the *field equations* by varying the action integral, we must adopt the view that the particle trajectories are given and vary only the *electromagnetic potentials*.

* Also called the *Minkowski force*.

Since the electromagnetic field is considered to exist in a certain arbitrary volume V and since the field in general varies from point to point, it is necessary to define the Lagrangian for the field as the volume integral of a *Lagrangian density* $\mathscr{L}$:

$$L = \int_V \mathscr{L}\, dv \tag{13.116}$$

The function $\mathscr{L}$ must describe (a) the charged particle or particles, (b) the electromagnetic field, and (c) the interaction of the charge(s) and the field. The Lagrangian used in the previous section [Eq. (13.101)] contained terms for the particle and for the interaction; the field term was absent since we were considering a fixed field and a constant term can always be dropped from the Lagrangian. In the Lagrangian we now require, the term for the particle will be the same as before. Therefore, we may write

$$L = -\frac{m_0 c^2}{\gamma} + \int_V \mathscr{L}'\, dv \tag{13.116a}$$

We again use the variation principle*

$$\delta \int L\, dt = 0$$

but, now, only the field quantities are allowed to vary, so the variation of the term $m_0 c^2/\gamma$ vanishes; there remains

$$\delta \int \mathscr{L}'\, dv\, dt = 0 \tag{13.117}$$

The portion of $\mathscr{L}'$ that describes the charge-field interaction must be the density version of the previous result; i.e., this term is proportional to $J_\nu A_\nu$. Now, the variation process reduces by one power any varied term in the integrand. Since the field equations must be *linear* equations,† the field term in $\mathscr{L}'$ is required to be *quadratic* in the field quantities; i.e., this term is proportional to $F_{\mu\nu}F_{\mu\nu}$. Therefore, supplying the appropriate constants, we assert that a proper Lagrangian density is

$$\mathscr{L}' = \frac{1}{\gamma}\left[\frac{1}{c}J_\nu A_\nu - \frac{1}{16\pi}F_{\mu\nu}F_{\mu\nu}\right] \tag{13.118}$$

so that the variation of the action integral becomes

$$\delta \int \left[\frac{1}{c}J_\nu A_\nu - \frac{1}{16\pi}F_{\mu\nu}F_{\mu\nu}\right] dv\, d\tau = 0 \tag{13.119}$$

* The variational principle for the electromagnetic field was established by J. J. Larmor prior to Einsteinian relativity theory (1900).

† Experiment shows that the *principle of superposition* applies to the field quantities.

In performing the variation, only the potentials are allowed to vary; the current J_ν remains unaltered since this quantity describes the motion of charges, and the trajectories are assumed fixed. Hence, the varied integral is

$$\int\left[\frac{1}{c}J_\nu\,\delta A_\nu - \frac{1}{8\pi}F_{\mu\nu}\,\delta F_{\mu\nu}\right]dv\,d\tau = 0$$

Substituting for $F_{\mu\nu}$ in terms of the potential $\mathbb{A}$,

$$\int\left[\frac{1}{c}J_\nu\,\delta A_\nu - \frac{1}{8\pi}F_{\mu\nu}\,\delta\left(\frac{\partial A_\nu}{\partial x_\mu} - \frac{\partial A_\mu}{\partial x_\nu}\right)\right]dv\,d\tau = 0$$

$$\int\left[\frac{1}{c}J_\nu\,\delta A_\nu - \frac{1}{8\pi}F_{\mu\nu}\frac{\partial(\delta A_\nu)}{\partial x_\mu} + \frac{1}{8\pi}F_{\mu\nu}\frac{\partial(\delta A_\mu)}{\partial x_\nu}\right]dv\,d\tau = 0 \qquad (13.120)$$

The middle term of the integrand may be written as

$$-\frac{1}{8\pi}F_{\mu\nu}\frac{\partial(\delta A_\nu)}{\partial x_\mu} = \frac{1}{8\pi}F_{\nu\mu}\frac{\partial(\delta A_\nu)}{\partial x_\mu} = \frac{1}{8\pi}F_{\mu\nu}\frac{\partial(\delta A_\mu)}{\partial x_\nu}$$

where the first equality makes use of the antisymmetry of the $F_{\mu\nu}$ and where the last expression results from the interchange of the dummy indices μ and ν. Therefore, Eq. (13.120) becomes

$$\int\left[\frac{1}{c}J_\nu\,\delta A_\nu + \frac{1}{4\pi}F_{\mu\nu}\frac{\partial(\delta A_\mu)}{\partial x_\nu}\right]dv\,d\tau = 0 \qquad (13.121)$$

If we integrate the second term by parts, the integrated portion will be proportional to δA_μ. Since the potential is assumed given at the initial and final times, $\delta A_\mu = 0$ at these points and the integrated term vanishes. We then have

$$\int\left[\frac{1}{c}J_\nu - \frac{1}{4\pi}\frac{\partial F_{\mu\nu}}{\partial x_\nu}\right]\delta A_\mu\,dv\,d\tau = 0 \qquad (13.122)$$

The variations δA_μ are independent and arbitrary, so that the integrand must vanish. Hence, the field obeys the equation

$$\frac{\partial F_{\mu\nu}}{\partial x_\nu} = \frac{4\pi}{c}J_\nu \qquad (13.123)$$

which is just the expression of the two inhomogeneous Maxwell equations discussed previously [Eq. (13.64)].

13.13 The Energy-Momentum Tensor of the Electromagnetic Field

In a general system consisting of charged particles moving in an electromagnetic field, a portion of the energy of the system may be identified as kinetic energy of the particles, and the remainder may be viewed as a potential energy or *field energy*.* In Section 4.7 an argument was presented whereby the field energy could be represented as the volume integral of an electromagnetic field energy density $\mathscr{E}$ [see Eq. (4.51)]:

$$\mathscr{E} = \frac{1}{8\pi}(\mathbf{E}\cdot\mathbf{E} + \mathbf{B}\cdot\mathbf{B}) \tag{13.124}$$

where we continue to consider only the free-space situation in which $\mathbf{D} = \mathbf{E}$ and $\mathbf{H} = \mathbf{B}$. We also found in Section 4.7 that the relation connecting energy density and energy flow is

$$\frac{\partial\mathscr{E}}{\partial t} + \operatorname{div}\mathbf{S} = -\mathbf{J}\cdot\mathbf{E} \tag{13.125}$$

where $\mathbf{S} = c(\mathbf{E}\times\mathbf{B})/4\pi$ is the Poynting vector in free space and where $-\mathbf{J}\cdot\mathbf{E}$ represents the energy lost to the charged particles by the field. We will now show that these results follow in an elegant way from considerations of the so-called *electromagnetic energy-momentum tensor*, $\{\mathbf{T}\}$.

The tensor $\{\mathbf{T}\}$ is defined in terms of the field tensor $\{\mathbf{F}\}$ according to

$$\boxed{T_{\mu\nu} = \frac{1}{4\pi}\left[F_{\mu\sigma}F_{\sigma\nu} + \tfrac{1}{4}\delta_{\mu\nu}F_{\lambda\rho}F_{\lambda\rho}\right]} \tag{13.126}$$

By calculating the individual tensor elements, we readily verify that

$$\left.\begin{aligned} T_{jk} &= \frac{1}{4\pi}\left[E_jE_k + B_jB_k - \tfrac{1}{2}\delta_{jk}(E^2 + B^2)\right] \\ T_{4k} &= T_{k4} = -\frac{i}{4\pi}(\mathbf{E}\times\mathbf{B})_k \\ T_{44} &= \frac{1}{8\pi}(E^2 + B^2) \end{aligned}\right\} \tag{13.127}$$

* There is also, of course, the *rest energy* of the particles.

Using the expressions for the energy density $\mathscr{E}$ and the Poynting vector **S**, we have

$$\left.\begin{aligned} T_{jk} &= \frac{1}{4\pi}(E_j E_k + B_j B_k) - \delta_{jk}\mathscr{E} \\ T_{4k} &= T_{k4} = -\frac{i}{c}S_k \\ T_{44} &= \mathscr{E} \end{aligned}\right\} \tag{13.128}$$

The energy-momentum tensor $\{\mathbf{T}\}$ can therefore be represented as*

$$\{\mathbf{T}\} = \begin{Bmatrix} \{\mathbf{T}^M\} & \left(-\frac{i}{c}\mathbf{S}\right) \\ \left(-\frac{i}{c}\mathbf{S}\right) & \mathscr{E} \end{Bmatrix} \tag{13.129}$$

This notation means that the "space portion" of $\{\mathbf{T}\}$ consists of a three-dimensional tensor $\{\mathbf{T}^M\}$, the so-called *Maxwell stress tensor.* The stress tensor itself is not a meaningful physical quantity in the relativistic sense and becomes one only with the addition of the vector $i\mathbf{S}/c$ and the energy density $\mathscr{E}$ in the fourth row and fourth column.

Evidently, $\{\mathbf{T}\}$ is a symmetrical tensor with a vanishing trace:

$$T_{\mu\nu} = T_{\nu\mu} \tag{13.130a}$$

and,

$$\begin{aligned} \mathrm{tr}\{\mathbf{T}\} &= T_{\mu\mu} \\ &= T_{kk} + \mathscr{E} \\ &= \frac{1}{4\pi}\left[(E^2 + B^2) - 3\cdot\tfrac{1}{2}(E^2 + B^2)\right] + \frac{1}{8\pi}(E^2 + B^2) \\ &= 0 \end{aligned} \tag{13.130b}$$

We will now show that the four-vector Lorentz force equation (13.114) can be obtained by calculating the four-dimensional divergence of the tensor $\{\mathbf{T}\}$. Using the definition of the elements of $\{\mathbf{T}\}$ [Eq. (13.126)], we have

$$\begin{aligned} \frac{\partial T_{\mu\nu}}{\partial x_\nu} &= \frac{1}{4\pi}\frac{\partial}{\partial x_\nu}\left[F_{\mu\sigma}F_{\sigma\nu} + \tfrac{1}{4}\delta_{\mu\nu}F_{\lambda\rho}F_{\lambda\rho}\right] \\ &= \frac{1}{4\pi}\left[\frac{\partial F_{\mu\sigma}}{\partial x_\nu}F_{\sigma\nu} + F_{\mu\sigma}\frac{\partial F_{\sigma\nu}}{\partial x_\nu} + \frac{1}{4}\frac{\partial(F_{\lambda\rho}F_{\lambda\rho})}{\partial x_\mu}\right] \end{aligned} \tag{13.131}$$

* The *momentum* aspect will become apparent shortly.

Consider the first term in this expression. Making use of the antisymmetry of the $F_{\mu\nu}$, we can write

$$\frac{\partial F_{\mu\sigma}}{\partial x_\nu} F_{\sigma\nu} = \frac{\partial F_{\sigma\mu}}{\partial x_\nu} F_{\nu\sigma}$$

Interchanging the dummy indices ν and σ, we have

$$\frac{\partial F_{\mu\sigma}}{\partial x_\nu} F_{\sigma\nu} = \frac{\partial F_{\nu\sigma}}{\partial x_\sigma} F_{\sigma\nu}$$

$$= \frac{1}{2}\left(\frac{\partial F_{\mu\sigma}}{\partial x_\nu} + \frac{\partial F_{\nu\sigma}}{\partial x_\sigma}\right) F_{\sigma\nu} \tag{13.132}$$

Now, Eq. (13.63) can be expressed in the form

$$\frac{\partial F_{\mu\sigma}}{\partial x_\nu} + \frac{\partial F_{\nu\mu}}{\partial x_\sigma} + \frac{\partial F_{\sigma\nu}}{\partial x_\mu} = 0$$

Using this equation to substitute for the terms in parentheses in Eq. (13.132), we obtain

$$\frac{\partial F_{\mu\sigma}}{\partial x_\nu} F_{\sigma\nu} = -\frac{1}{2}\frac{\partial F_{\sigma\nu}}{\partial x_\mu} F_{\sigma\nu}$$

$$= -\frac{1}{4}\frac{\partial(F_{\sigma\nu}F_{\sigma\nu})}{\partial x_\mu} \tag{13.133}$$

If we substitute this result into Eq. (13.131), the last term will just be canceled (because σ, ν and λ, ρ are dummy indices). Then,

$$\frac{\partial T_{\mu\nu}}{\partial x_\nu} = \frac{1}{4\pi} F_{\mu\sigma} \frac{\partial F_{\sigma\nu}}{\partial x_\nu}$$

or, interchanging σ and ν on the right-hand side, we finally obtain

$$\frac{\partial T_{\mu\nu}}{\partial x_\nu} = \frac{1}{4\pi} F_{\mu\nu} \frac{\partial F_{\nu\sigma}}{\partial x_\sigma} \tag{13.134}$$

which is just the expression of the Lorentz force density [Eq. (13.114)]:

$$\boxed{\frac{\partial T_{\mu\nu}}{\partial x_\nu} = K_\mu} \tag{13.135}$$

or, in tensor notation,*

$$\mathbf{Div}\,\{\mathbf{T}\} = \mathbb{K} \tag{13.135a}$$

* **Div** is written in bold face since the divergence of a tensor yields a *vector*.

The fourth component of Eq. (13.135) is

$$K_4 = \frac{\partial T_{4\nu}}{\partial x_\nu} = \frac{\partial T_{4k}}{\partial x_k} + \frac{\partial T_{44}}{\partial x_4} \tag{13.136}$$

Using Eqs. (13.115b) and (13.128) for K_4, T_{4k}, and T_{44}, respectively, we obtain,

$$\frac{i}{c}\mathbf{E}\cdot\mathbf{J} = -\frac{i}{c}\frac{\partial S_k}{\partial x_k} + \frac{\partial \mathscr{E}}{\partial(ict)}$$

or,

$$\operatorname{div}\mathbf{S} + \frac{\partial \mathscr{E}}{\partial t} = -\,\mathbf{E}\cdot\mathbf{J} \tag{13.137}$$

which is the equation of energy flow previously derived.

The equation that expresses momentum conservation may be obtained from the space portion of Eq. (13.135):

$$K_j = \frac{\partial T_{j\nu}}{\partial x_\nu} = \frac{\partial T_{jk}}{\partial x_k} + \frac{\partial T_{j4}}{\partial(ict)} \tag{13.138}$$

Now, $\partial T_{jk}/\partial x_k$ is just the (three-dimensional) divergence of the Maxwell stress tensor $\{\mathbf{T}^M\}$ and $T_{j4} = -(i/c)S_j$. Therefore in vector notation, Eq. (13.138) becomes

$$\mathbf{K} = \mathbf{div}\{\mathbf{T}^M\} - \frac{1}{c^2}\frac{\partial \mathbf{S}}{\partial t} \tag{13.139}$$

If we consider a volume V in which all of the charged particles are contained and outside of which the field vanishes, then, integrating Eq. (13.139) over this volume yields

$$\int_V \left(\mathbf{K} + \frac{1}{c^2}\frac{\partial \mathbf{S}}{\partial t}\right) dv = \int_V \mathbf{div}\{\mathbf{T}^M\}\, dv \tag{13.140}$$

The integral of the force density $\mathbf{K}$ gives the total force, i.e., the time derivative of the mechanical momentum $\mathbf{p}$. Also we define

$$\frac{1}{c^2}\mathbf{S} \equiv \mathbf{g} \tag{13.141a}$$

and

$$\int_V \mathbf{g}\, dv \equiv \mathbf{G} \tag{13.141b}$$

so that Eq. (13.140) becomes*

$$\frac{d}{dt}(\mathbf{p} + \mathbf{G}) = \int_V \mathbf{div}\{\mathbf{T}^M\}\, dv \tag{13.142}$$

The volume integral may be converted to a surface integral by means of the divergence theorem. There results

$$\frac{d}{dt}(\mathbf{p} + \mathbf{G}) = \int_S \{\mathbf{T}^M\} \cdot \mathbf{n}\, da \tag{13.142a}$$

If the field vanishes outside of V, it must do so also on the boundary surface S. Hence,

$$\frac{d}{dt}(\mathbf{p} + \mathbf{G}) = 0 \tag{13.143}$$

The result states that it is not the mechanical momentum $\mathbf{p}$ alone that is conserved, but the mechanical momentum plus the quantity $\mathbf{G}$. If we wish to use the momentum conservation law for a system of charged particles in an electromagnetic field, then it is necessary to interpret $\mathbf{G}$ as the *momentum of the field.* Similarly,

$$\mathbf{g} = \frac{1}{c^2}\mathbf{S} = \frac{1}{4\pi c}(\mathbf{E} \times \mathbf{B}) \tag{13.144}$$

is the momentum *density* of the field.

If the field does not vanish on the surface S, it is necessary to take account of the integral appearing in Eq. (13.142a). Clearly, $-\{\mathbf{T}^M\} \cdot \mathbf{n}$ must represent the normal *outward* flow of momentum per unit area from the volume V through the surface S. As an example of such a case, consider a plane electromagnetic wave incident normally on a perfectly absorbing surface. Let the direction of propagation of the wave be along x_1 and let the electric vector be polarized in the x_2-direction; then, $\mathbf{B}$ has a component only along x_3. Thus,

$$\begin{aligned} -\{\mathbf{T}^M\} \cdot \mathbf{n} &= -T_{11}\mathbf{e}_1 \\ &= -\frac{1}{4\pi}[E_1^2 + B_1^2 - \tfrac{1}{2}(E^2 + B^2)] \end{aligned}$$

* Note that

$$\frac{d\mathbf{G}}{dt} = \frac{d}{dt}\int_V \mathbf{g}\, dv = \int_V \frac{\partial \mathbf{g}}{\partial t}\, dv$$

since we hold fixed the boundary surface of the volume V.

But $\mathbf{E} = \mathbf{e}_2 E$ and $\mathbf{B} = \mathbf{e}_3 B$, and in a plane wave, $|\mathbf{E}| = |\mathbf{B}|$; therefore,

$$-\{\mathbf{T}^M\} \cdot \mathbf{n} = \frac{1}{4\pi} E^2 \mathbf{e}_1 \tag{13.145}$$

which is the energy density in the wave at the surface multiplied by the unit vector in the direction of propagation. Integrating over unit area of the surface and averaging over one complete oscillation of the wave, we obtain the average force per unit area or the *pressure* of the radiation*:

$$\langle \text{Radiation pressure} \rangle = \frac{1}{8\pi} E^2 = \frac{1}{c} \langle |\mathbf{S}| \rangle \tag{13.146}$$

One of the most striking phenomena resulting directly from the effects of radiation pressure is to be found in comets. The tails of these objects are always directed *away* from the Sun. Because the material of which comets are composed is extremely tenuous and because the effects take place over long periods of time, the radiation pressure from the Sun is sufficient to elongate and direct the tails.

Suggested References

Discussions of relativity theory at the intermediate level tend to emphasize relativistic mechanics. See, for example, Goldstein (Go50, Chapter 6), a brief but particularly good treatment. Leighton (Le59, Chapter 1), Ney (Ne62), and Richtmyer, Kennard, and Lauritsen (Ri55, Chapter 2) are also useful.

Somewhat more extensive in applications to electrodynamics are the discussions of Landau and Lifshitz (La62, Chapter 2–4) and, at a less demanding level, Schwarz (Sc64, Chapter 13).

An extensive discussion of relativity theory at the intermediate level is given by Rosser (Ro64); considerable material on electrodynamics is included in this excellent book (Chapters 7–10).

The advanced accounts of relativity theory by Møller (Mø52) and by Pauli (Pa58) contain several sections on electrodynamics.

Books devoted to electrodynamics but which contain extensive material on relativistic considerations include Jackson (Ja62, Chapters 11 and 12), Panofsky and Phillips (Pa62, Chapters 15–18), and Sommerfeld (So52, Sections 26–37).

* The unequivocal observation of the effect of radiation pressure was first made in 1899 by the Russian physicist Pëtr Nikolajevich Lebedev (1866–1912). Several earlier measurements which purported to demonstrate the effect were in fact not valid due to the occurrence of systematic errors (mainly, convection currents due to heating effects).

Problems

13-1. Show that the transformation equations connecting the K and K' systems may be expressed as

$$x_1' = x_1; \qquad x_2' = x_2$$

$$x_3' = x_3 \cosh \alpha - ct \sinh \alpha$$

$$t' = t \cosh \alpha - \frac{x_3}{c} \sinh \alpha$$

where $\tanh \alpha = v/c$. Show that the Lorentz transformation corresponds to a rotation through an angle $i\alpha$ in four-dimensional space.

13-2. Two clocks, located at the origins of the K and K' systems, are synchronized when the origins coincide. After a time t, an observer at the origin of the K system observes the K' clock by means of a telescope. What does the K' clock read?

13-3. The energy of a light quantum (or *photon*) is expressed by $W = h\nu$, where h is Planck's constant and ν is the frequency of the photon. The momentum of the photon is $h\nu/c$. Show that if the photon scatters from a free electron (of mass m_e), the scattered photon will have an energy

$$W' = W\left[1 + \frac{W}{m_e c^2}(1 - \cos \theta)\right]^{-1}$$

where θ is the angle through which the photon scatters. Show also that the electron acquires a kinetic energy

$$T = \frac{W^2}{m_e c^2}\left[\frac{1 - \cos \theta}{1 + \dfrac{W}{m_e c^2}(1 - \cos \theta)}\right]$$

13-4. The position of a particle in a system K is given by the (three-dimensional) vector $\mathbf{x}$; in K' the position is given by $\mathbf{x}'$. If the motion of K' relative to K is described by the velocity vector $\mathbf{v}$ show that the general Lorentz transformation is

$$\mathbf{x}' = \mathbf{x} + \mathbf{v}\left[\frac{\mathbf{x} \cdot \mathbf{v}}{v^2}(\gamma - 1) - \gamma t\right]$$

$$t' = \gamma\left[t - \frac{\mathbf{x} \cdot \mathbf{v}}{c^2}\right]$$

where $\gamma = (1 - v^2/c^2)^{-\frac{1}{2}}$. If the velocity of the particle relative to K is $\dot{\mathbf{u}} = d\mathbf{x}/dt$ and if the velocity relative to K' is $\mathbf{u}' = d\mathbf{x}'/dt'$, show that the general velocity transformation law is

$$\mathbf{u}' = \frac{\mathbf{u}\sqrt{1-\beta^2} + \mathbf{v}\left[\dfrac{\mathbf{u}\cdot\mathbf{v}}{v^2}(1 - \sqrt{1-\beta^2}) - 1\right]}{1 - \dfrac{\mathbf{u}\cdot\mathbf{v}}{c^2}}$$

where $\beta = |\mathbf{v}|/c$, as usual. Test these expressions in various ways and demonstrate that they reduce to the well-known formulae in special cases.

13-5. Use the fact that a plane wave in system K will also appear as a plane wave in system K' (why?) to define a four-dimensional propagation vector. Show that the space components are just those of $\mathbf{k}$ and that the fourth component is $i\omega/c$. Obtain the equations that transform $(\mathbf{k}, i\omega/c)$ from K to K'. If the velocity of K' relative to K is $\mathbf{v}$ and if the angle between $\mathbf{k}$ and $\mathbf{v}$ is θ, show that the frequency as measured in K' is

$$\omega' = \frac{[1 - (v/c)\cos\theta]\omega}{\sqrt{1 - v^2/c^2}}$$

This is the familiar expression for the *Doppler shift*, but modified by the presence of the radical in the denominator. It is just this difference from the nonrelativistic result that gives rise to an effect even for $\theta = \pi/2$, the so-called *transverse* Doppler shift.

13-6. Show that the four-dimensional gradient of a scalar in Minkowski space (called a *Lorentz scalar*) is a four-vector.

13-7. Show by an explicit calculation involving the transformation properties of the $F_{\mu\nu}$ that Eqs. (13.63) and (13.64) are covariant under a Lorentz transformation.

13-8. Show that if $\mathbf{E} \perp \mathbf{B}$ in K, then $\mathbf{E}' \perp \mathbf{B}'$ in any other Lorentz frame K'.

13-9. In a Lorentz reference frame K the electromagnetic field vectors are $\mathbf{E}, \mathbf{B}$. Show that in a system K' which moves with a uniform velocity $\mathbf{v}$ with respect to K the field vectors are

$$\mathbf{E}' = \gamma\mathbf{E} + \frac{\mathbf{v}}{v^2}(\mathbf{v}\cdot\mathbf{E})(1 - \gamma) + \frac{\gamma}{c}(\mathbf{v}\times\mathbf{B})$$

$$\mathbf{B}' = \gamma\mathbf{B} + \frac{\mathbf{v}}{v^2}(\mathbf{v}\cdot\mathbf{B})(1 - \gamma) - \frac{\gamma}{c}(\mathbf{v}\times\mathbf{E})$$

where $\gamma = (1 - v^2/c^2)^{-\frac{1}{2}}$. Show further that if the field vectors are decomposed into components parallel to and perpendicular to the direction of motion, then

$$\mathbf{E}'_{\perp} = \gamma\left(\mathbf{E}_{\perp} + \frac{1}{c}\,\mathbf{v} \times \mathbf{B}_{\perp}\right); \quad \mathbf{E}'_{\parallel} = \mathbf{E}_{\parallel}$$

$$\mathbf{B}'_{\perp} = \gamma\left(\mathbf{B}_{\perp} - \frac{1}{c}\,\mathbf{v} \times \mathbf{E}_{\perp}\right); \quad \mathbf{B}'_{\parallel} = \mathbf{B}_{\parallel}$$

13-10. Show that the relativistic form of the three-dimensional acceleration vector for a charged particle in an electromagnetic field is

$$\mathbf{a} = \dot{\mathbf{u}} = \frac{e}{m\gamma}\left[\mathbf{E} + \frac{1}{c}\mathbf{u} \times \mathbf{B} - \frac{1}{c^2}(\mathbf{u} \cdot \mathbf{E})\mathbf{u}\right]$$

13-11. A charged particle enters a uniform magnetic field with a nonvanishing velocity component parallel to the field. Show that a relativistic calculation of the trajectory yields a helix, just as does a nonrelativistic calculation.

13-12. A spherical shell of radius a carries a total charge q uniformly distributed over the surface. If the sphere moves with a velocity u along the x_3-axis, calculate the total electric and total magnetic energy in the space exterior to the sphere. Show that in the limit $u \ll c$ the result reduces to the static value $q^2/2a$ (see Section 4.9).

13-13. Show that Eq. (13.99) can also be expressed as

$$P = \frac{2e^2}{3c^3} \cdot \frac{1}{(1 - \beta^2)^3}\left[\dot{\mathbf{u}} \cdot \dot{\mathbf{u}} - \frac{1}{c^2}(\mathbf{u} \times \dot{\mathbf{u}})^2\right]$$

Verify that identical results are obtained from the two formulae for the cases $\mathbf{u} \parallel \dot{\mathbf{u}}$ and $\mathbf{u} \perp \dot{\mathbf{u}}$. For the case $\mathbf{u} \parallel \dot{\mathbf{u}}$, show that P may be written as

$$P = \frac{2e^2}{3m_0^2c^3}\left(\frac{dT}{dx}\right)^2$$

where dT/dx is the rate of change of kinetic energy with distance. In electrostatic charged-particle accelerators the rate of gain in energy is about 3 MeV/meter. Show that under such conditions the radiation losses are completely negligible.

13-14. The covariant form of the Lagrange equations of motion (which can be obtained by a variational calculation similar to that in Section 13.11) is

$$\frac{d}{d\tau}\frac{\partial L}{\partial u_\nu} - \frac{\partial L}{\partial x_\nu} = 0$$

Show that the proper equations of motion for a particle in an electromagnetic field result from this equation.

13-15. Show that the total energy of a particle moving in an electromagnetic field is

$$W = \sqrt{\left(\mathbf{p} - \frac{e}{c}\mathbf{A}\right)^2 c^2 + m_0^2 c^4} + e\Phi$$

13-16. Show that $\mathbb{K} \cdot \mathbb{U} = 0$. Interpret this result.

13-17. Set up the variational problem for the electromagnetic field by using the field vectors directly instead of the $F_{\mu\nu}$:

$$\mathscr{L}' = \tfrac{1}{2}(\mathbf{E} \cdot \mathbf{E} - \mathbf{B} \cdot \mathbf{B}) - 4\pi\rho\Phi + \frac{4\pi}{c}\mathbf{J} \cdot \mathbf{A}$$

Perform the variation

$$\delta \int \mathscr{L}' \, dv \, dt = 0$$

and by making use of the fact that $\delta\Phi$ and $\delta\mathbf{A}$ are independent variations, obtain the two inhomogeneous Maxwell equations.

13-18. An energy flux of ϕ ergs/cm^2-sec is incident on a plane, totally reflecting surface at an angle θ. Calculate the radiation pressure (a) normal to the surface, and (b) along the direction of the incident radiation. Find the total radiation pressure on a perfectly *reflecting* sphere produced by incident plane radiation. What is the result for a perfectly *absorbing* sphere?

13-19. The average solar energy incident on the Earth is about 1.4×10^6 ergs/cm^2-sec. Calculate the power radiated by the Sun and the electric field intensity at the surface of the Sun. (Radius of the Sun $\cong 7 \times 10^{10}$ cm; distance from the Sun to Earth $\cong 1.5 \times 10^{13}$ cm.) Consider the Earth to be a perfectly reflecting sphere and calculate the radiation pressure on the Earth.

13-20. A spherical, totally reflecting particle has a radius R and a density 5 g/cm^3. If such a particle is in space in the solar system, what is the limit on R such that the total radiation force due to the Sun exceeds the Sun's gravitational attraction? The particle would then be accelerated *away* from the Sun.

APPENDIX A

*Vector and Tensor Analysis**

A.1 Definition of a Vector

A vector may be defined in terms of the manner in which its components transform under a coordinate rotation. If a set of rectangular axes x_i ($i = 1, 2, 3$) are rotated to a new orientation specified by axes x'_i, the rotation may be described by giving the angles between each of the axes x'_i and each of the axes x_i. The quantity λ_{ij} is defined to be the cosine of the angle between the x'_i-axis and the x_j-axis:

$$\lambda_{ij} \equiv \cos(x'_i, x_j) \tag{A.1}$$

There are nine quantities λ_{ij}, and they may be arranged in matrix form:

$$\boldsymbol{\lambda} = \begin{pmatrix} \lambda_{11} & \lambda_{12} & \lambda_{13} \\ \lambda_{21} & \lambda_{22} & \lambda_{23} \\ \lambda_{31} & \lambda_{32} & \lambda_{33} \end{pmatrix} \tag{A.2}$$

* For a detailed account of vector analysis see Marion (Ma65b); tensors are discussed in Ma65a, Chapters 13 and 14.

The λ_{ij} are not all independent since they are connected by six equations which may be summarized by the *orthogonality relation*

$$\sum_j \lambda_{ij}\lambda_{kj} = \delta_{ik} \tag{A.3}$$

Three of these six equations express the fact that the coordinate axes in both the original and the rotated systems are mutually perpendicular (or *orthogonal*), and the other three equations express the fact that the sum of the squares of the direction cosines of a line equals unity.

For example, if the rotation takes place about the x_3-axis and if the rotation angle is θ (see Fig. A-1), the rotation matrix is

$$\boldsymbol{\lambda} = \begin{pmatrix} \cos\theta & \sin\theta & 0 \\ -\sin\theta & \cos\theta & 0 \\ 0 & 0 & 1 \end{pmatrix}$$

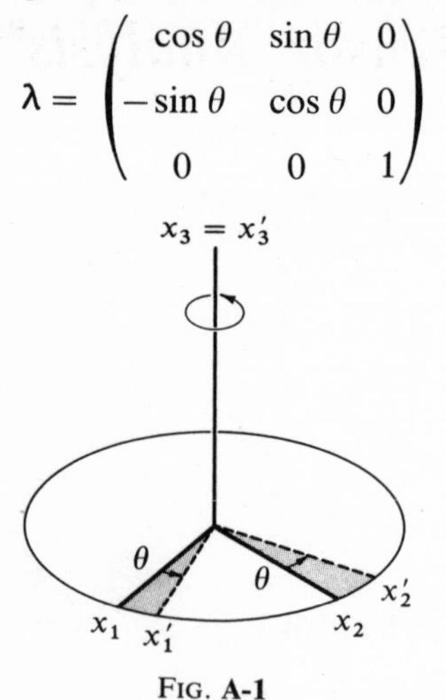

FIG. A-1

If the coordinates of a point are given in the original coordinate system by (x_1, x_2, x_3), then in the rotated system they are given by

$$x_i' = \sum_j \lambda_{ij} x_j \tag{A.4}$$

Expanded, this set of equations becomes

$$\left.\begin{aligned} x_1' &= \lambda_{11}x_1 + \lambda_{12}x_2 + \lambda_{13}x_3 \\ x_2' &= \lambda_{21}x_1 + \lambda_{22}x_2 + \lambda_{23}x_3 \\ x_3' &= \lambda_{31}x_1 + \lambda_{32}x_2 + \lambda_{33}x_3 \end{aligned}\right\} \tag{A.5}$$

In matrix notation we may write

$$\begin{pmatrix} x_1' \\ x_2' \\ x_3' \end{pmatrix} = \begin{pmatrix} \lambda_{11} & \lambda_{12} & \lambda_{13} \\ \lambda_{21} & \lambda_{22} & \lambda_{23} \\ \lambda_{31} & \lambda_{32} & \lambda_{33} \end{pmatrix} \begin{pmatrix} x_1 \\ x_2 \\ x_3 \end{pmatrix} \tag{A.6}$$

or, simply,

$$\mathsf{x}' = \boldsymbol{\lambda}\mathsf{x} \tag{A.7}$$

where x' and x are *column* matrices.

The inverse transformation is given by

$$\begin{aligned} x_i &= \sum_j \lambda_{ji} x'_j \\ &= \sum_j \lambda^t_{ij} x'_j \end{aligned} \tag{A.8}$$

where $\lambda^t_{ij} \equiv \lambda_{ji}$ is an element of the *transpose* of the matrix $\boldsymbol{\lambda}$. In matrix notation we have

$$\mathsf{x} = \boldsymbol{\lambda}^t \mathsf{x}' \tag{A.9}$$

The *identity matrix* I is defined by

$$\mathsf{IA} = \mathsf{A}; \qquad \mathsf{BI} = \mathsf{B} \tag{A.10}$$

The *inverse* $\boldsymbol{\lambda}^{-1}$ of the matrix $\boldsymbol{\lambda}$ is defined by

$$\boldsymbol{\lambda\lambda}^{-1} = \boldsymbol{\lambda}^{-1}\boldsymbol{\lambda} = \mathsf{I} \tag{A.11}$$

If $\boldsymbol{\lambda}$ is an orthogonal matrix, then the transpose is equal to the inverse:

$$\boldsymbol{\lambda}^t = \boldsymbol{\lambda}^{-1}, \qquad \text{for orthogonal matrices} \tag{A.12}$$

A *vector* is defined to be a set of quantities $\mathbf{A} = (A_1, A_2, A_3)$ which transform as do the coordinates of a point:

$$A'_i = \sum_j \lambda_{ij} A_j \tag{A.13}$$

A *scalar* is a quantity which is *invariant* under a coordinate transformation.

A.2 Vector Algebra Operations

The *scalar* or *dot product* (or *inner* product) of two vectors **A** and **B** is defined as

$$\begin{aligned} \mathbf{A} \cdot \mathbf{B} &= \sum_i A_i B_i \\ &= |\mathbf{A}|\,|\mathbf{B}| \cos(\mathbf{A}, \mathbf{B}) \end{aligned} \tag{A.14}$$

The *vector* or *cross product* (or *outer* product) of **A** and **B** is defined as

$$\mathbf{A} \times \mathbf{B} = \sum_{i,j,k} \varepsilon_{ijk} \mathbf{e}_i A_j B_k \tag{A.15}$$

where ε_{ijk} is the *permutation symbol:*

$$\varepsilon_{ijk} = \begin{cases} 0, & \text{if any two indices are equal} \\ +1, & \text{if } i, j, k \text{ are cyclic} \\ -1, & \text{if } i, j, k \text{ are not cyclic} \end{cases}$$

The quantity $\mathbf{e}_i$ is the *unit vector* along the x_i-axis.

We also have for the magnitude of the vector product,

$$|\mathbf{A} \times \mathbf{B}| = |\mathbf{A}|\,|\mathbf{B}| \sin(\mathbf{A}, \mathbf{B}) \tag{A.16}$$

The unit vectors obey the relations:

$$\mathbf{e}_i \cdot \mathbf{e}_j = \delta_{ij}; \qquad \mathbf{e}_i \times \mathbf{e}_j = \mathbf{e}_k \varepsilon_{ijk} \tag{A.17}$$

Some useful identities are

$$\mathbf{A} \cdot (\mathbf{B} \times \mathbf{C}) = \mathbf{B} \cdot (\mathbf{C} \times \mathbf{A}) = \mathbf{C} \cdot (\mathbf{A} \times \mathbf{B}) \equiv \mathbf{ABC} \tag{A.18}$$

$$\mathbf{A} \times (\mathbf{B} \times \mathbf{C}) = (\mathbf{A} \cdot \mathbf{C})\mathbf{B} - (\mathbf{A} \cdot \mathbf{B})\mathbf{C} \tag{A.19}$$

$$\left.\begin{aligned} (\mathbf{A} \times \mathbf{B}) \cdot (\mathbf{C} \times \mathbf{D}) &= \mathbf{A} \cdot [\mathbf{B} \times (\mathbf{C} \times \mathbf{D})] \\ &= \mathbf{A} \cdot [(\mathbf{B} \cdot \mathbf{D})\mathbf{C} - (\mathbf{B} \cdot \mathbf{C})\mathbf{D}] \\ &= (\mathbf{A} \cdot \mathbf{C})(\mathbf{B} \cdot \mathbf{D}) - (\mathbf{A} \cdot \mathbf{D})(\mathbf{B} \cdot \mathbf{C}) \end{aligned}\right\} \tag{A.20}$$

$$\left.\begin{aligned} (\mathbf{A} \times \mathbf{B}) \times (\mathbf{C} \times \mathbf{D}) &= [(\mathbf{A} \times \mathbf{B}) \cdot \mathbf{D}]\mathbf{C} - [(\mathbf{A} \times \mathbf{B}) \cdot \mathbf{C}]\mathbf{D} \\ &= (\mathbf{ABD})\mathbf{C} - (\mathbf{ABC})\mathbf{D} \end{aligned}\right\} \tag{A.21}$$

$$\mathbf{A} \times [\mathbf{B} \times (\mathbf{C} \times \mathbf{D})] = (\mathbf{B} \cdot \mathbf{D})(\mathbf{A} \times \mathbf{C}) - (\mathbf{B} \cdot \mathbf{C})(\mathbf{A} \times \mathbf{D}) \tag{A.22}$$

$$(\mathbf{A} \times \mathbf{B}) \cdot [(\mathbf{B} \times \mathbf{C}) \times (\mathbf{C} \times \mathbf{A})] = [\mathbf{A} \cdot (\mathbf{B} \times \mathbf{C})]^2 \tag{A.23}$$

A.3 Vector Differential Operators

The gradient of a scalar function $\Phi(x_i)$ is defined by

$$\mathbf{grad}\,\Phi = \nabla\Phi = \sum_i \mathbf{e}_i \frac{\partial \Phi}{\partial x_i} \tag{A.24}$$

The rate of change of Φ in the direction defined by the unit vector $\mathbf{n}$ is called the *normal derivative* of Φ and is given by

$$\mathbf{n} \cdot \mathbf{grad}\,\Phi \equiv \frac{\partial \Phi}{\partial n} \tag{A.25}$$

The operator $\mathbf{A} \cdot \mathbf{grad}$, where $\mathbf{A}$ is a vector, may be applied to either scalar or vector functions. In rectangular coordinates, we have

$$(\mathbf{A} \cdot \mathbf{grad})\psi = \sum_i \left(A_i \frac{\partial}{\partial x_i} \right) \psi$$

$$= \mathbf{A} \cdot \mathbf{grad}\, \psi \tag{A.26a}$$

$$(\mathbf{A} \cdot \mathbf{grad})\mathbf{B} = \sum_i \left(A_i \frac{\partial}{\partial x_i} \right) \mathbf{B}$$

$$= \left(\sum_i A_i \frac{\partial B_1}{\partial x_i}, \ \sum_i A_i \frac{\partial B_2}{\partial x_i}, \ \sum_i A_i \frac{\partial B_3}{\partial x_i} \right) \tag{A.26b}$$

The *divergence* of a vector $\mathbf{A}$ is defined by

$$\operatorname{div} \mathbf{A} = \nabla \cdot \mathbf{A} = \sum_i \frac{\partial A_i}{\partial x_i} \tag{A.27}$$

The *curl* of a vector $\mathbf{A}$ is defined by

$$\mathbf{curl}\, \mathbf{A} = \nabla \times \mathbf{A} = \sum_{i,j,k} \varepsilon_{ijk} \mathbf{e}_i \frac{\partial A_k}{\partial x_j} \tag{A.28}$$

The *Laplacian* of a scalar function Φ is defined by

$$\nabla^2 \Phi = \operatorname{div} \mathbf{grad}\, \Phi = \nabla \cdot \nabla \Phi = \sum_i \frac{\partial^2 \Phi}{\partial x_i^2} \tag{A.29}$$

In rectangular coordinates we may define the Laplacian of a vector $\mathbf{A}$ as

$$\nabla^2 \mathbf{A} = (\operatorname{div} \mathbf{grad})\mathbf{A}$$

$$= (\nabla^2 A_1, \nabla^2 A_2, \nabla^2 A_3) \tag{A.30}$$

Some important differential operations are

$$\mathbf{grad}(\varphi + \psi) = \mathbf{grad}\, \varphi + \mathbf{grad}\, \psi \tag{A.31}$$

$$\mathbf{grad}(\varphi\psi) = \varphi\, \mathbf{grad}\, \psi + \psi\, \mathbf{grad}\, \varphi \tag{A.32}$$

$$\operatorname{div}(\mathbf{A} + \mathbf{B}) = \operatorname{div} \mathbf{A} + \operatorname{div} \mathbf{B} \tag{A.33}$$

$$\mathbf{curl}(\mathbf{A} + \mathbf{B}) = \mathbf{curl}\, \mathbf{A} + \mathbf{curl}\, \mathbf{B} \tag{A.34}$$

$$\operatorname{div}(\varphi \mathbf{A}) = \mathbf{A} \cdot \mathbf{grad}\, \varphi + \varphi \operatorname{div} \mathbf{A} \tag{A.35}$$

$$\mathbf{curl}(\varphi \mathbf{A}) = \varphi\, \mathbf{curl}\, \mathbf{A} - \mathbf{A} \times \mathbf{grad}\, \varphi \tag{A.36}$$

$$\mathbf{grad}(\mathbf{A} \cdot \mathbf{B}) = (\mathbf{A} \cdot \mathbf{grad})\mathbf{B} + (\mathbf{B} \cdot \mathbf{grad})\mathbf{A}$$

$$+ \mathbf{A} \times \mathbf{curl}\, \mathbf{B} + \mathbf{B} \times \mathbf{curl}\, \mathbf{A} \tag{A.37}$$

$$\operatorname{div}(\mathbf{A} \times \mathbf{B}) = \mathbf{B} \cdot \mathbf{curl}\,\mathbf{A} - \mathbf{A} \cdot \mathbf{curl}\,\mathbf{B} \tag{A.38}$$

$$\mathbf{curl}(\mathbf{A} \times \mathbf{B}) = \mathbf{A}\operatorname{div}\mathbf{B} - \mathbf{B}\operatorname{div}\mathbf{A} + (\mathbf{B} \cdot \mathbf{grad})\mathbf{A} - (\mathbf{A} \cdot \mathbf{grad})\mathbf{B} \tag{A.39}$$

$$\mathbf{curl}\,\mathbf{curl}\,\mathbf{A} = \mathbf{grad}\operatorname{div}\mathbf{A} - \nabla^2\mathbf{A} \tag{A.40}$$

$$\mathbf{curl}\,\mathbf{grad}\,\varphi \equiv 0 \tag{A.41}$$

$$\operatorname{div}\mathbf{curl}\,\mathbf{A} \equiv 0 \tag{A.42}$$

A.4 Differential Operations in Curvilinear Coordinates

The geometry of *cylindrical coordinates* is shown in Fig. A-2. The relations connecting cylindrical and rectangular coordinates are

$$\begin{aligned} r &= \sqrt{x_1^2 + x_2^2} & x_1 &= r\cos\theta \\ \theta &= \tan^{-1}(x_2/x_1) & x_2 &= r\sin\theta \\ z &= x_3 & x_3 &= z \end{aligned} \tag{A.43}$$

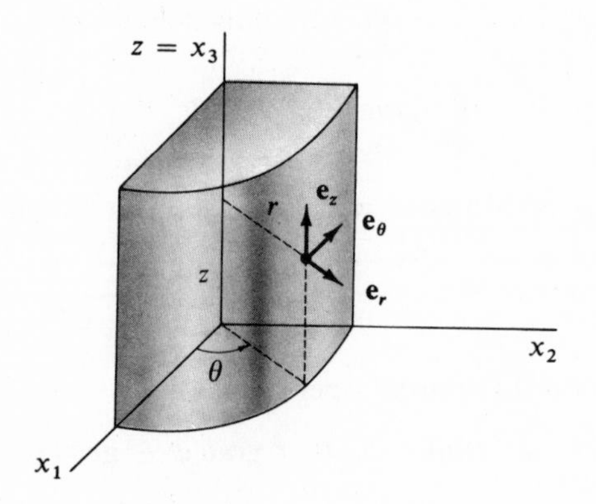

FIG. A-2

The element of volume in cylindrical coordinates is shown in Fig. A-3. Differential operations in cylindrical coordinates are

$$\mathbf{grad}\,\psi = \mathbf{e}_r\frac{\partial\psi}{\partial r} + \mathbf{e}_\theta\frac{1}{r}\frac{\partial\psi}{\partial\theta} + \mathbf{e}_z\frac{\partial\psi}{\partial z} \tag{A.44}$$

$$\operatorname{div}\mathbf{A} = \frac{1}{r}\frac{\partial}{\partial r}(rA_r) + \frac{1}{r}\frac{\partial A_\theta}{\partial\theta} + \frac{\partial A_z}{\partial z} \tag{A.45}$$

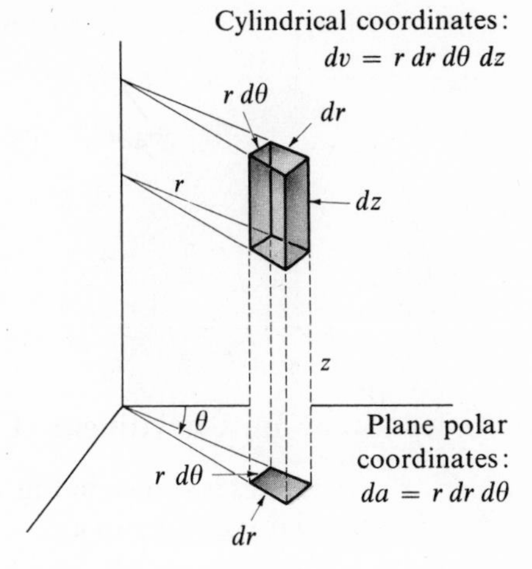

FIG. A-3

$$\textbf{curl}\,\mathbf{A} = \mathbf{e}_r\left(\frac{1}{r}\frac{\partial A_z}{\partial \theta} - \frac{\partial A_\theta}{\partial z}\right) + \mathbf{e}_\theta\left(\frac{\partial A_r}{\partial z} - \frac{\partial A_z}{\partial r}\right)$$

$$+ \mathbf{e}_z\left(\frac{1}{r}\frac{\partial}{\partial r}(rA_\theta) - \frac{1}{r}\frac{\partial A_r}{\partial \theta}\right) \tag{A.46}$$

$$\nabla^2\psi = \frac{1}{r}\frac{\partial}{\partial r}\left(r\frac{\partial \psi}{\partial r}\right) + \frac{1}{r^2}\frac{\partial^2\psi}{\partial \theta^2} + \frac{\partial^2\psi}{\partial z^2} \tag{A.47}$$

The geometry of *spherical coordinates* is shown in Fig. A-4. The relations connecting spherical and rectangular coordinates are

$$\begin{aligned} r &= \sqrt{x_1^2 + x_2^2 + x_3^2} \qquad & x_1 &= r \sin\theta \cos\varphi \\ \theta &= \cos^{-1}(x_3/r) & x_2 &= r\sin\theta\sin\varphi \\ \varphi &= \tan^{-1}(x_2/x_1) & x_3 &= r\cos\theta \end{aligned} \tag{A.48}$$

The element of volume in spherical coordinates is shown in Fig. A-5. Differential operations in spherical coordinates are

$$\textbf{grad}\,\psi = \mathbf{e}_r\frac{\partial \psi}{\partial r} + \mathbf{e}_\theta\frac{1}{r}\frac{\partial \psi}{\partial \theta} + \mathbf{e}_\varphi\frac{1}{r\sin\theta}\frac{\partial \psi}{\partial \varphi} \tag{A.49}$$

$$\text{div}\,\mathbf{A} = \frac{1}{r^2}\frac{\partial}{\partial r}(r^2 A_r) + \frac{1}{r\sin\theta}\frac{\partial}{\partial \theta}(A_\theta \sin\theta)$$

$$+ \frac{1}{r\sin\theta}\frac{\partial A_\varphi}{\partial \varphi} \tag{A.50}$$

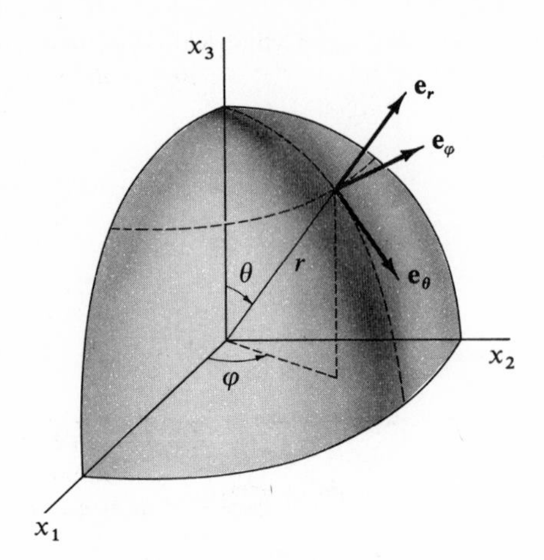

FIG. A-4

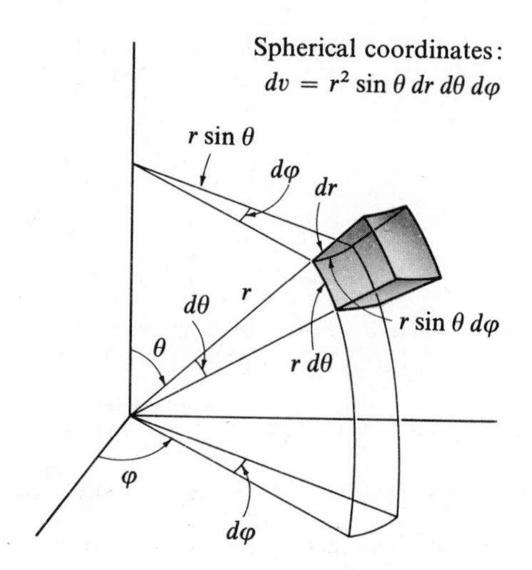

FIG. A-5

$$\begin{aligned}
\mathbf{curl\ A} = {} & \mathbf{e}_r \frac{1}{r \sin\theta}\left(\frac{\partial}{\partial\theta}(A_\varphi \sin\theta) - \frac{\partial A_\theta}{\partial\varphi}\right) \\
& + \mathbf{e}_\theta \frac{1}{r \sin\theta}\left(\frac{\partial A_r}{\partial\varphi} - \sin\theta \frac{\partial}{\partial r}(r A_\varphi)\right) \\
& + \mathbf{e}_\varphi \frac{1}{r}\left(\frac{\partial}{\partial r}(r A_\theta) - \frac{\partial A_r}{\partial\theta}\right)
\end{aligned} \tag{A.51}$$

$$\nabla^2\psi = \frac{1}{r^2}\frac{\partial}{\partial r}\left(r^2\frac{\partial\psi}{\partial r}\right) + \frac{1}{r^2\sin\theta}\frac{\partial}{\partial\theta}\left(\sin\theta\frac{\partial\psi}{\partial\theta}\right) + \frac{1}{r^2\sin^2\theta}\frac{\partial^2\psi}{\partial\varphi^2} \tag{A.52}$$

A.5 Integral Theorems

The *divergence theorem* (or *Gauss' theorem*) states that

$$\int_V \operatorname{div}\mathbf{A}\,dv = \oint_S \mathbf{A}\cdot\mathbf{n}\,da \tag{A.53}$$

where the closed surface S bounds the volume V; $\mathbf{n}$ is the unit vector in the direction of the outward normal.

Stokes' theorem states that

$$\int_S \mathbf{curl}\,\mathbf{A}\cdot\mathbf{n}\,da = \oint_\Gamma \mathbf{A}\cdot d\mathbf{s} \tag{A.54}$$

where the line Γ bounds the open surface S; the positive sense of traversing Γ is such that the right-hand screw direction is *into* S.

Several forms of *Green's theorem* may be stated. The basic equation is obtained by substituting $\mathbf{A} = \psi\,\mathbf{grad}\,\varphi$ into the divergence theorem:

$$\oint_S \psi\frac{\partial\varphi}{\partial n}\,da = \int_V [\psi\nabla^2\varphi + (\mathbf{grad}\,\varphi)\cdot(\mathbf{grad}\,\psi)]\,dv \tag{A.55}$$

Next, by interchanging ψ and φ and subtracting, we find

$$\oint_S\left(\psi\frac{\partial\varphi}{\partial n} - \varphi\frac{\partial\psi}{\partial n}\right)da = \int_V (\psi\nabla^2\varphi - \varphi\nabla^2\psi)\,dv \tag{A.56}$$

Finally, by setting $\psi = 1$, we have

$$\oint_S \frac{\partial\varphi}{\partial n}\,da = \int_V \nabla^2\varphi\,dv \tag{A.57}$$

Some useful related theorems are

$$\int_V \mathbf{grad}\,\varphi\,dv = \oint_S \varphi\,\mathbf{n}\,da \tag{A.58}$$

$$\int_V \mathbf{curl}\,\mathbf{A}\,dv = \oint_S \mathbf{n}\times\mathbf{A}\,da \tag{A.59}$$

$$\oint_\Gamma \mathbf{r}\times d\mathbf{s} = 2\int_S \mathbf{n}\,da \tag{A.60}$$

The necessary and sufficient condition that a vector **A** be represented as the gradient of a scalar function Φ is that the curl of **A** vanish identically:

$$\mathbf{curl\ A} \equiv 0 \leftrightarrow \mathbf{A} = \mathbf{grad}\ \Phi \tag{A.61}$$

Gauss' law may be stated as follows. If a vector **A** obeys a radial inverse-square law,

$$\mathbf{A} = \frac{m}{r^2}\mathbf{e}_r \tag{A.62}$$

then

$$\oint_S \mathbf{A}\cdot\mathbf{n}\,da = 4\pi m \tag{A.63}$$

where S is any closed surface that contains the *source* whose strength is m. Since **A** has a vanishing curl, we may use Eq. (A.61) to write

$$\oint_S \mathbf{grad}\ \Phi\cdot\mathbf{n}\,da = \int_V \nabla^2\Phi\,dv = 4\pi m \tag{A.64}$$

where the divergence theorem has been used. If the source m has a volume distribution with a density ρ, then

$$m = \int_V \rho\,dv \tag{A.65}$$

Combining Eqs. (A.64) and (A.65), and equating the integrands, *Poisson's equation* results:

$$\nabla^2\Phi = 4\pi\rho \tag{A.66}$$

(In electrostatics, a minus sign occurs in this equation since it is customary to write $\mathbf{A} = -\mathbf{grad}\ \Phi$ if **A** represents the electric field vector and Φ the scalar potential.)

A.6 Definition of a Tensor

In n-dimensional space, a tensor of the mth rank is a set of n^m quantities which transform under a coordinate rotation in the following way:

$$T'_{abcd\cdots} = \sum_{i,j,k,l,\cdots} \lambda_{ai}\lambda_{bj}\lambda_{ck}\lambda_{dl}\cdots T_{ijkl\cdots} \tag{A.67}$$

For the purposes of this book we need to consider only tensors of the second rank in three- and four-dimensional spaces. Therefore, it is sufficient to discuss quantities which transform according to

$$T'_{ij} = \sum_{k,l} \lambda_{ik}\lambda_{jl}T_{kl} \tag{A.68}$$

where each index can assume the values 1, 2, 3 or 1, 2, 3, 4, depending on the dimensionality of the space. For simplicity, we consider only three-dimensional space in this appendix; the extension to four dimensions (as required in Chapter 13) is obvious. The general form of such a tensor is a set of nine quantities:

$$\{\mathbf{T}\} = \begin{Bmatrix} T_{11} & T_{12} & T_{13} \\ T_{21} & T_{22} & T_{23} \\ T_{31} & T_{32} & T_{33} \end{Bmatrix} \tag{A.69}$$

The transformation equation (A.68) may also be written as

$$T'_{ij} = \sum_{k,l} \lambda_{ik} T_{kl} \lambda^t_{lj} \tag{A.70}$$

If we understand T to be the matrix which consists of the elements of the tensor $\{\mathbf{T}\}$, then Eq. (A.70) is equivalent to the matrix equation

$$\mathsf{T}' = \boldsymbol{\lambda}\mathsf{T}\boldsymbol{\lambda}^t = \boldsymbol{\lambda}\mathsf{T}\boldsymbol{\lambda}^{-1} \tag{A.70a}$$

An orthogonal transformation of this type is called a *similarity transformation* (T' is *similar* to T).

A tensor is said to be *symmetric* if $T_{ij} = T_{ji}$. A tensor is said to be *antisymmetric* if $T_{ij} = -T_{ji}$; each diagonal element of an antisymmetrical tensor necessarily vanishes. A symmetrical tensor can have at most six independent elements; an antisymmetrical tensor can have at most three independent elements. In general, a tensor is neither symmetric nor antisymmetric, but a separation into two tensors, one symmetric and one antisymmetric, is always possible.

The *trace* of a tensor is the sum of the diagonal elements:

$$\mathrm{tr}\{\mathbf{T}\} = \sum_j T_{jj} \tag{A.71}$$

The trace of a tensor is unaffected by an orthogonal coordinate transformation and is therefore an *invariant* quantity. The trace of an antisymmetrical tensor is, of course, zero.

A.7 Diagonalization of a Tensor

It is always possible to render a symmetrical tensor *diagonal* by a suitable coordinate rotation. A tensor in *diagonal form* has nonvanishing elements only along the diagonal, and these elements are called the *principal values* of the tensor. We therefore seek the general specification of a rotation that takes a tensor $\{\mathbf{T}\}$ into a diagonal tensor $\{\mathbf{T}'\}$, where

$$T'_{ij} = T_i\delta_{ij} \tag{A.72}$$

that is,

$$\{\mathbf{T}'\} = \begin{Bmatrix} T_1 & 0 & 0 \\ 0 & T_2 & 0 \\ 0 & 0 & T_3 \end{Bmatrix} \tag{A.73}$$

Combining Eqs. (A.68) and (A.72), we can write

$$T_i\delta_{ij} = \sum_{k,l} \lambda_{ik}\lambda_{jl}T_{kl} \tag{A.74}$$

If we multiply both sides of this equation by λ_{im} and sum over i, we obtain

$$\sum_i T_i\lambda_{im}\delta_{ij} = \sum_{k,l}\left(\sum_i \lambda_{im}\lambda_{ik}\right)\lambda_{jl}T_{kl} \tag{A.75}$$

The term in parentheses is just δ_{mk}, so that performing the summation over k on the right-hand side and over i on the left-hand side yields

$$T_j\lambda_{jm} = \sum_l \lambda_{jl}T_{ml} \tag{A.76}$$

Now, the left-hand side of this equation can be expressed as

$$T_j\lambda_{jm} = \sum_l T_j\lambda_{jl}\delta_{ml} \tag{A.77}$$

so that Eq. (A.76) becomes

$$\sum_l T_j\lambda_{jl}\delta_{ml} = \sum_l \lambda_{kl}T_{ml} \tag{A.78}$$

or,

$$\sum_l (T_{ml} - T_j\delta_{ml})\lambda_{jl} = 0 \tag{A.78a}$$

This is a set of simultaneous, linear algebraic equations; for each value of j there are three such equations, one for each of the three possible values of m. In order for a nontrivial solution to exist, the determinant of the coefficients must vanish, so that the principal values T_1, T_2, and T_3 are obtained as the roots of the so-called *secular determinant*:

$$|T_{ml} - T\delta_{ml}| = 0 \tag{A.79}$$

The process of diagonalizing a tensor is called a *principal-axis transformation* in analogy with the principal moments of inertia and the principal axes of a rigid body.*

* See for example, Chapter 13 of Ma65a.

A.8 Tensor Operations

The inner product of a vector **A** and a tensor $\{\mathbf{T}\}$ is a *vector*:

$$\sum_j T_{ij} A_j = B_i \tag{A.80}$$

or,

$$\{\mathbf{T}\} \cdot \mathbf{A} = \mathbf{B} \tag{A.80a}$$

For example, the product of the inertia tensor $\{\mathbf{I}\}$ and the angular velocity vector $\boldsymbol{\omega}$ produces the angular momentum vector, $\mathbf{L} = \{\mathbf{I}\} \cdot \boldsymbol{\omega}$.

Since the inner product of two vectors produces a scalar, it follows that the inner product of a tensor with two vectors produces a scalar:

$$\sum_{i,j} A_i T_{ij} B_j = C \tag{A.81}$$

or,

$$\mathbf{A} \cdot \{\mathbf{T}\} \cdot \mathbf{B} = C \tag{A.81a}$$

For example, the product of angular velocity and angular momentum yields the kinetic energy, $T = \frac{1}{2}\boldsymbol{\omega} \cdot \mathbf{L} = \frac{1}{2}\boldsymbol{\omega} \cdot \{\mathbf{I}\} \cdot \boldsymbol{\omega}$.

APPENDIX B

Fourier Series and Integrals

B.1 Fourier Series

If a function $f(x)$ has only a finite number of finite discontinuities within the interval $-\pi < x < \pi$ but is arbitrary otherwise, then $f(x)$ may be expanded in a trigonometric series:

$$f(x) = \frac{a_0}{2} + \sum_{r=1}^{\infty} (a_r \cos rx + b_r \sin rx) \tag{B.1}$$

The Fourier coefficients are given by

$$\left.\begin{aligned} a_r &= \frac{1}{\pi}\int_{-\pi}^{+\pi} f(x) \cos rx \, dx \\ b_r &= \frac{1}{\pi}\int_{-\pi}^{+\pi} f(x) \sin rx \, dx \end{aligned}\right\} \tag{B.2}$$

If $f(x)$ is an *even* function, $f(x) = f(-x)$, then all of the b_r vanish. If $f(x)$ is an *odd* function, $f(x) = -f(-x)$, then all of the a_r (including a_0) vanish.

If $f(x)$ is discontinuous at the point x_0, the series converges to the mean value:

$$f(x_0) = \tfrac{1}{2} \lim_{\delta \to 0} [f(x_0 + \delta) + f(x_0 - \delta)] \tag{B.3}$$

The function $f(x)$ may alternatively be expanded in a series of complex exponentials:

$$f(x) = \sum_{r=-\infty}^{\infty} c_r e^{-irx} \tag{B.4}$$

Then,

$$c_r = \frac{1}{2\pi} \int_{-\pi}^{+\pi} f(x) e^{irx} \, dx, \qquad r = 0, \pm 1, \pm 2, \cdots \tag{B.5}$$

The size of the interval may be changed from $\pm\pi$ to $\pm L$ by making the change of variable $x \to \pi u/L$. Then,

$$c_r = \frac{1}{2L} \int_{-L}^{+L} f(u) \exp\left(i \frac{r\pi u}{L}\right) du \tag{B.6}$$

so that

$$f(x) = \frac{1}{2L} \sum_{r=-\infty}^{\infty} \int_{-L}^{+L} f(u) \exp\left(-i \frac{r\pi}{L}(x - u)\right) du \tag{B.7}$$

B.2 Fourier Integrals

In Eq. (B.7) we may further increase the interval from $\pm L$ to $\pm\infty$ by suitably passing to the limit. We obtain

$$f(x) = \frac{1}{2\pi} \int_{-\infty}^{+\infty} e^{-ikx} \, dk \int_{-\infty}^{+\infty} f(u) e^{iku} \, du \tag{B.8}$$

We may therefore write

$$\left.\begin{aligned} f(x) &= \frac{1}{\sqrt{2\pi}} \int_{-\infty}^{+\infty} A(k) e^{-ikx} \, dk \\ A(k) &= \frac{1}{\sqrt{2\pi}} \int_{-\infty}^{+\infty} f(x) e^{ikx} \, dx \end{aligned}\right\} \tag{B.9}$$

The quantities $f(x)$ and $A(k)$ are therefore reciprocally related and are called *Fourier transforms.* In studies of wave propagation, these equations allow transformations between wave number (k) and spatial (x) representations of the wave. Similarly, we may also write transforms which allow frequency (ω) and time (t) representations:

$$\left.\begin{aligned} f(t) &= \frac{1}{\sqrt{2\pi}} \int_{-\infty}^{+\infty} A(\omega) e^{-i\omega t}\, d\omega \\ A(\omega) &= \frac{1}{\sqrt{2\pi}} \int_{-\infty}^{+\infty} f(t) e^{i\omega t}\, dt \end{aligned}\right\} \tag{B.10}$$

$A(\omega)$ is the *frequency spectrum* of the wave.

APPENDIX C

Fundamental Constants

Velocity of light	$c = 2.9979 \times 10^{10}$ cm/sec
Electronic charge	$e = 4.8029 \times 10^{-10}$ statcoulombs
1 eV = energy acquired by an electron in falling through a potential difference of 1 volt	$= 1.6021 \times 10^{-12}$ ergs
1 keV = 10^3 eV	
1 MeV = 10^6 eV	
1 BeV = 10^9 eV	
	$e^2 = 1.440 \times 10^{-13}$ MeV-cm
Electron mass	$m_e = 9.1083 \times 10^{-28}$ gm
	$m_e c^2 = 0.5110$ MeV
Classical electron radius	$r_0 = e^2/m_e c^2 = 2.818 \times 10^{-13}$ cm
Thomson cross section	$(8/3)\,\pi r_0^2 = 0.6652 \times 10^{-24}$ cm^2
Avogadro's number	$N = 6.023 \times 10^{23}$ mol^{-1}

APPENDIX D

*Conversion of Electric and Magnetic Units**

Unit	Rationalized MKS	Gaussian†
Charge, q, e	1 coulomb	3×10^9 statcoulombs
Charge density, ρ	1 coulomb/m^3	3×10^3 statcoulombs/cm^3
Current, I	1 ampere = 1 coulomb/sec	3×10^9 statamperes
Current density, J	1 ampere/m^2	3×10^5 statamperes/cm^2
Potential, Φ	1 volt	$1/300$ statvolt
Electric intensity, E	1 volt/m	$(1/3) \times 10^4$ statvolts/cm
Electric displacement, D	1 coulomb/m^2	$3 \times 4\pi \times 10^5$ {statvolts/cm; statcoulombs/cm^2}
Polarization, P	1 coulomb/m^2	3×10^5 {statvolts/cm; statcoulombs/cm^2}
Resistance, R	1 ohm	$(1/3)^2 \times 10^{-11}$ statohms
Conductivity, σ	1 mho/m	$(3)^2 \times 10^9$ sec^{-1}
Capacitance, C	1 farad	$(3)^2 \times 10^{11}$ statfarads
Magnetic induction, B	1 weber/m^2	10^4 gauss
Magnetic intensity, H	1 ampere/m	$4\pi \times 10^{-3}$ oersteds
Magnetic flux, F	1 weber	10^8 {gauss-cm^2; maxwells}
Magnetization, M	1 weber/m^2	$(1/4\pi) \times 10^4$ gauss
Inductance, L	1 henry	$(1/3)^2 \times 10^{-11}$ stathenry
Energy, T, U, W	1 joule	10^7 ergs
Power, P	1 watt	10^7 ergs/sec

* In the column of Gaussian units, the numbers indicated *3* result from the value of the velocity of light; therefore, if greater accuracy is desired, the value 2.99793 should be substituted.

† Electric quantities in *esu*, magnetic quantities in *emu*.

APPENDIX E

Equivalence of Electric and Magnetic Quantities in the MKS and Gaussian Systems

Quantity	Rationalized MKS	Gaussian
$\mathbf{D} =$	$\varepsilon_0 \mathbf{E} + \mathbf{P}$	$\mathbf{E} + 4\pi\mathbf{P}$
$\mathbf{H} =$	$\frac{1}{\mu_0}\mathbf{B} - \mathbf{M}$	$\mathbf{B} - 4\pi\mathbf{M}$
$\text{div}\,\mathbf{D} =$	ρ	$4\pi\rho$
$\text{div}\,\mathbf{B} =$	0	0
$\textbf{curl}\,\mathbf{E} =$	$-\frac{\partial \mathbf{B}}{\partial t}$	$-\frac{1}{c}\frac{\partial \mathbf{B}}{dt}$
$\textbf{curl}\,\mathbf{H} =$	$\mathbf{J} + \frac{\partial \mathbf{D}}{\partial t}$	$\frac{1}{c}\left(4\pi\mathbf{J} + \frac{\partial \mathbf{D}}{\partial t}\right)$
$\mathbf{F} =$	$q(\mathbf{E} + \mathbf{u} \times \mathbf{B})$	$q\left(\mathbf{E} + \frac{1}{c}\mathbf{u} \times \mathbf{B}\right)$
$\mathbf{S} =$	$\mathbf{E} \times \mathbf{H}$	$\frac{c}{4\pi}\mathbf{E} \times \mathbf{H}$

APPENDIX F

A "Proof" of the Relation $x_\mu x_\mu = x'_\mu x'_\mu$

Consider the two inertial systems K and K' which are moving relative to one another with a velocity v. At the instant when the two origins coincide ($t = 0$, $t' = 0$), let a light pulse be emitted from the common origin. The equations that describe the propagation of the wavefronts are required, by the second Einstein postulate, to be of the same form in the two systems:

$$x_j x_j - c^2 t^2 = x_\mu x_\mu \equiv s^2 = 0, \quad \text{in } K \tag{F.1a}$$

$$x'_j x'_j - c^2 t'^2 = x'_\mu x'_\mu \equiv s'^2 = 0, \quad \text{in } K' \tag{F.1b}$$

These equations state that the vanishing of the four-dimensional interval between two events in one Lorentz frame implies the vanishing of the interval between the same two events in any other Lorentz frame. But we need more than this; we must show, in fact, that $s^2 = s'^2$.

If we require that the motion of a particle, observed to be *linear* in the system K, also be linear in the system K', then the equations of transformation that connect the x_μ and the x'_μ must themselves be linear. In such a case, the quadratic forms s^2 and s'^2 can be connected by, at most, a proportionality factor:

$$s'^2 = \kappa s^2 \tag{F.2}$$

The factor κ could conceivably depend on the coordinates, the time, and the relative velocity of the two systems.

Now, the space and time associated with an inertial reference frame are *homogeneous*,* so that the relation between s^2 and s'^2 cannot be different at different points in space nor at different instants of time. Therefore, the factor κ cannot depend on either the coordinates or the time. A dependence on v is still allowed, however, but the *isotropy* of space forbids a dependence on the *direction* of v. We have therefore reduced the possible dependence of s'^2 on s^2 to a factor which involves at most the magnitude of the velocity v. That is, we have

$$s'^2 = \kappa(v)s^2 \tag{F.2a}$$

If we make the transformation from K' back to K, we have the result

$$s^2 = \kappa(-v)s'^2$$

where $-v$ occurs since the velocity of K relative to K' is the negative of the velocity of K' relative to K. But we have already argued that the factor κ can depend only on the *magnitude* of v. Therefore, we have the two equations

$$s'^2 = \kappa(v)s^2; \qquad s^2 = \kappa(v)s'^2 \tag{F.3}$$

combining these equations, we conclude that $\kappa^2 = 1$, or $\kappa(v) = \pm 1$. Now, the value of $\kappa(v)$ must not be a discontinuous function of v. That is, if we change v at some rate, κ cannot suddenly jump from $+1$ to -1. Clearly, in the limit of zero velocity, the systems K and K' become identical, so that $\kappa(v = 0) = +1$. Hence,

$$\kappa = +1 \tag{F.4}$$

for all values of the velocity, and we have, finally,

$$s^2 = s'^2 \tag{F.5}$$

This important result states that the four-dimensional interval between two events is the same in all Lorentz reference frames.

* See, for example, Section 3.3 of Ma65a.

REFERENCES

Ab50 M. Abraham and R. Becker, *The Classical Theory of Electricity and Magnetism*, 14th German ed. transl. Hafner, New York, 1950. (See also Be64.)

Ah46 J. Aharoni, *Antennae*. Oxford Univ. Press, London and New York, 1946.

An60 C. L. Andrews, *Optics of the Electromagnetic Spectrum*. Prentice-Hall, Englewood Cliffs, New Jersey, 1960.

Ba59 W. Band, *Introduction to Mathematical Physics*. Van Nostrand, Princeton, New Jersey, 1959.

Be64 R. Becker and F. Sauter, *Electromagnetic Fields and Interactions*, Vol. 1, *Electromagnetic Theory and Relativity*. Blaisdell, New York, 1964. This volume is a revision of and replaces Ab50.

Bl62 G. A. Blass, *Theoretical Physics*. Appleton-Century-Crofts, New York, 1962.

Bo59 M. Born and E. Wolf, *Principles of Optics*. Macmillan (Pergamon), New York, 1959.

By93 W. E. Byerly, *Fourier's Series and Spherical Harmonics*. Ginn, Boston, 1893; reprinted by Dover, New York.

Ca62 M. Cagnet, M. Francon, and J. C. Thrier, *Atlas of Optical Phenomena*. Springer, Berlin; Prentice-Hall, Englewood Cliffs, New Jersey, 1962.

Ch41 R. V. Churchill, *Fourier Series and Boundary Value Problems*. McGraw-Hill, New York, 1941.

Co58 F. W. Constant, *Theoretical Physics: Thermodynamics, Electromagnetism, Waves, and Particles*. Addison-Wesley, Reading, Massachusetts, 1958.

Co62 D. R. Corson and P. Lorrain, *Introduction to Electromagnetic Fields and Waves*. Freeman, San Francisco, 1962.

Da63 H. F. Davis, *Fourier Series and Orthogonal Functions*. Allyn & Bacon, Boston, 1963.

Di62 R. W. Ditchburn, *Light*, 2nd edition Wiley (Interscience), New York, 1953.

Dw61 H. B. Dwight, *Tables of Integrals and other Mathematical Data*, 4th ed. Macmillan, New York, 1961.

Fa60 R. M. Fano, Lan Jen Chu, and R. B. Adler, *Electromagnetic Fields, Energy, and Forces*. Wiley, New York, 1960.

Fe61 N. Feather, *An Introduction to the Physics of Vibrations and Waves*. Univ. of Edinburgh Press, Edinburgh, 1961.

Go50 H. Goldstein, *Classical Mechanics*. Addison-Wesley, Reading, Massachusetts, 1950.

Ha49 G. P. Harnwell, *Principles of Electricity and Electromagnetism*, 2nd ed. McGraw-Hill, New York, 1949.

He93 H. Hertz, *Electric Waves*, English transl. Macmillan, London, 1893; reprinted by Dover, New York, 1962.

Ho48 W. V. Houston, *Principles of Mathematical Physics,* 2nd ed. McGraw-Hill, New York, 1948.

Ho51 W. V. Houston, *Principles of Quantum Mechanics*. McGraw-Hill, New York, 1951; reprinted by Dover, New York.

Ho61 H. Hochstadt, *Special Functions of Mathematical Physics.* Holt, Rinehart, and Winston, New York, 1961.

Ho63 C. A. Holt, *Introduction to Electromagnetic Fields and Waves*. Wiley, New York, 1963.

Ja45 E. Jahnke and F. Emde, *Tables of Functions with Formulae and Curves,* 4th ed. Dover, New York, 1945.

Ja62 J. D. Jackson, *Classical Electrodynamics*. Wiley, New York, 1962.

Je25 Sir James Jeans, *The Mathematical Theory of Electricity and Magnetism,* 5th ed. Cambridge Univ. Press, London and New York, 1925.

Je46 H. Jeffreys and B. S. Jeffreys, *Mathematical Physics*. Cambridge Univ. Press, London and New York, 1946.

Je57 F. A. Jenkins and H. E. White, *Fundamentals of Optics,* 3rd ed. McGraw-Hill, New York, 1957.

Je58 J. V. Jelley, *Cherenkov Radiation and Its Applications*. MacMillan (Pergamon), New York, 1958.

Jo50 G. Joos and I. M. Freeman, *Theoretical Physics*. Hafner, New York, 1950.

Ke29 O. D. Kellogg, *Foundations of Potential Theory*. Springer, Berlin, 1929; reprinted by Dover, New York, 1953.

Ki56 C. Kittel, *Introduction to Solid State Physics*, 2nd ed. Wiley, New York, 1956.

Ki62 A. F. Kip, *Fundamentals of Electricity and Magnetism*. McGraw-Hill, New York, 1962.

Ko62 A. S. Kompaneyets, *Theoretical Physics*. Dover, New York, 1962.

Kr50 J. D. Kraus, *Antennas*. McGraw-Hill, New York, 1950.

La32 Sir Horace Lamb, *Hydrodynamics*, 6th ed. Cambridge Univ. Press, London and New York, 1932; reprinted by Dover, New York, 1945.

La60 L. D. Landau and E. M. Lifshitz, *Electrodynamics of Continuous Media*. Addison-Wesley, Reading, Massachusetts, 1960.

La61 R. V. Langmuir, *Electromagnetic Fields and Waves*. McGraw-Hill, New York, 1961.

La62 L. D. Landau and E. M. Lifshitz, *The Classical Theory of Fields*, 2nd ed. Addison-Wesley, Reading, Massachusetts, 1962.

Le59 R. B. Leighton, *Principles of Modern Physics*. McGraw-Hill, New York, 1959.

Le62 B. A. Lengyel, *Lasers*. Wiley, New York, 1962.

Lo09 H. A. Lorentz, *The Theory of Electrons*. Teubner, Leipzig, 1909 (2nd ed. 1915); reprinted by Dover, New York, 1952.

Ma04 J. C. Maxwell, *Treatise on Electricity and Magnetism*, 3rd ed. 2 vols., 1904; reprinted by Dover, New York, 1954.

Ma29 M. Mason and W. Weaver, *The Electromagnetic Field*. Dover, New York, 1929.

Ma43 H. Margenau and G. M. Murphy, *The Mathematics of Physics and Chemistry*. Van Nostrand, Princeton, New Jersey, 1943.

Ma65a J. B. Marion, *Classical Dynamics of Particles and Systems*. Academic Press, New York, 1965.

Ma65b J. B. Marion, *Principles of Vector Analysis*. Academic Press, New York, 1965.

Me61 E. Merzbacher, *Quantum Mechanics*. Wiley, New York, 1961.

Me53 D. H. Menzel, *Mathematical Physics*. Prentice-Hall, Englewood Cliffs, New Jersey, 1953.

Mi27 A. A. Michelson, *Studies in Optics*. Univ. of Chicago Press, Chicago, Illinois, 1927.

Mø52 C. Møller, *The Theory of Relativity*. Oxford Univ. Press, London and New York, 1952.

Mo53 P. M. Morse and H. Feshbach, *Methods of Theoretical Physics,* 2 Vols. McGraw-Hill, New York, 1953.

Ne62 E. P. Ney, *Electromagnetism and Relativity.* Harper and Row, New York, 1962.

Ow63 G. E. Owen, *Introduction to Electromagnetic Theory*. Allyn & Bacon, Boston, 1963.

Pa52 L. Page, *Introduction to Theoretical Physics,* 3rd ed. Van Nostrand, Princeton, New Jersey, 1952.

Pa58 W. Pauli, *Theory of Relativity.* Macmillan (Pergamon Press), New York, 1958 (translated from the original publication in *Handbuch der Physik*, Springer, Berlin, 1921).

Pa62 W. K. H. Panofsky and M. Phillips, *Classical Electricity and Magnetism,* 2nd ed. Addison-Wesley, Reading, Massachusetts, 1962.

Pe53 E. R. Peck, *Electricity and Magnetism*. McGraw-Hill, New York, 1953.

Pe56 T. Pearcey, *Tables of Fresnel Integrals to Six Decimal Places*. Cambridge Univ. Press, London and New York, 1956.

Pi46 L. A. Pipes, *Applied Mathematics for Engineers and Physicists*. McGraw-Hill, New York, 1946.

Pl61 R. Plonsey and R. E. Collin, *Principles and Applications of Electromagnetic Fields*. McGraw-Hill, New York, 1961.

Pu60 E. M. Pugh and E. W. Pugh, *Principles of Electricity and Magnetism*. Addison-Wesley, Reading, Massachusetts, 1960.

Ra44 S. Ramo and J. R. Whinnery, *Fields and Waves in Modern Radio*. Wiley, New York, 1944.

Re60 J. R. Reitz and F. J. Milford, *Foundations of Electromagnetic Theory*. Addison-Wesley, Reading, Massachusetts, 1960.

Ri55 F. K. Richtmyer, E. H. Kennard, and T. Lauritsen, *Introduction to Modern Physics,* 5th ed. McGraw-Hill, New York, 1955.

Ro51 L. Rosenfeld, *Theory of Electrons*. North-Holland Publ., Amsterdam, 1951.

Ro57 B. Rossi, Optics. Addison-Wesley, Reading, Massachusetts, 1957.

Ro64 W. G. V. Rosser, *An Introduction to the Theory of Relativity.* Butterworths, London, 1964.

Sc52 S. A. Schelkunoff, *Advanced Antenna Theory*. Wiley, New York, 1952.

Sc52a S. A. Schelkunoff and H. T. Friis, *Antennas: Theory and Practice*. Wiley, New York, 1952.

Sc55 L. I. Schiff, *Quantum Mechanics,* 2nd ed. McGraw-Hill, New York, 1955.

Sc59 W. T. Scott, *The Physics of Electricity and Magnetism*. Wiley, New York, 1959.

Sc64 W. M. Schwartz, *Intermediate Electromagnetic Theory*. Wiley, New York, 1964.

Se40 F. Seitz, *The Modern Theory of Solids*. McGraw-Hill, New York, 1940.

Sh59 M. H. Shamos, *Great Experiments of Physics*. Holt, New York, 1959.

Sk48 H. H. Skilling, *Fundamentals of Electric Waves*. Wiley, New York, 1948.

Sl42 J. C. Slater, *Microwave Transmission*. McGraw-Hill, New York, 1942; reprinted by Dover, New York, 1959.

Sl47 J. C. Slater and N. H. Frank, *Electromagnetism*. McGraw-Hill, New York, 1947.

Sm50 W. R. Smythe, *Static and Dynamic Electricity,* 2nd ed. McGraw-Hill, New York, 1950.

So50 G. C. Southworth, *Principles and Applications of Waveguide Transmission*. Van Nostrand, Princeton, New Jersey, 1950.

So52 A. Sommerfeld, *Electrodynamics*. Academic Press, New York, 1952.

So54 A. Sommerfeld, *Optics*. Academic Press, New York, 1954.

So62 G. C. Southworth, *Forty Years of Radio Research*. Gordon & Breach, New York, 1962.

Sp56 L. Spitzer, *Physics of Fully Ionized Gases*. Wiley (Interscience), New York, 1956.

St41 J. A. Stratton, *Electromagnetic Theory*. McGraw-Hill, New York, 1941.

St58 J. Strong, *Concepts of Classical Optics*. Freeman, San Francisco, 1958.

St63 J. M. Stone, *Radiation and Optics*. McGraw-Hill, New York, 1963.

Te55 F. E. Terman, *Electronic and Radio Engineering*. McGraw-Hill, New York, 1955.

To55 S. Tolansky, *An Introduction to Interferometry*. Longmans, Green, New York, 1955.

Tr63 N. Tralli, *Classical Electromagnetic Theory*. McGraw-Hill, New York, 1963.

Va49 J. Valasek, *Introduction to Theoretical and Experimental Optics*. Wiley, New York, 1949.

Va60 A. Vašíček, *Optics of Thin Films*. North Holland Publ., Amsterdam, 1960.

Va64 J. Van Bladel, *Electromagnetic Fields*. McGraw-Hill, New York, 1964.

Wa63 R. K. Wangsness, *Introduction to Theoretical Physics*. Wiley, New York, 1963.

Wh51 Sir Edmund Whittaker, *A History of the Theories of Aether and Electricity: Vol. I: The Classical Theories*. Nelson, London, 1951; reprinted by Harper, New York, 1960.

Wh52 Sir Edmund Whittaker and G. N. Watson, *A Course of Modern Analysis*, 4th ed. Cambridge Univ. Press, London and New York, 1952.

Wh62 R. M. Whitmer, *Electromagnetics,* 2nd ed. Prentice-Hall, Englewood Cliffs, New Jersey, 1962.

Wi53 A. H. Watson, *Theory of Metals*. Cambridge Univ. Press, London and New York, 1953.

Wu62 T.-Y. Wu and T. Ohmura, *Quantum Theory of Scattering*. Prentice-Hall, Englewood Cliffs, New Jersey, 1962.

Index